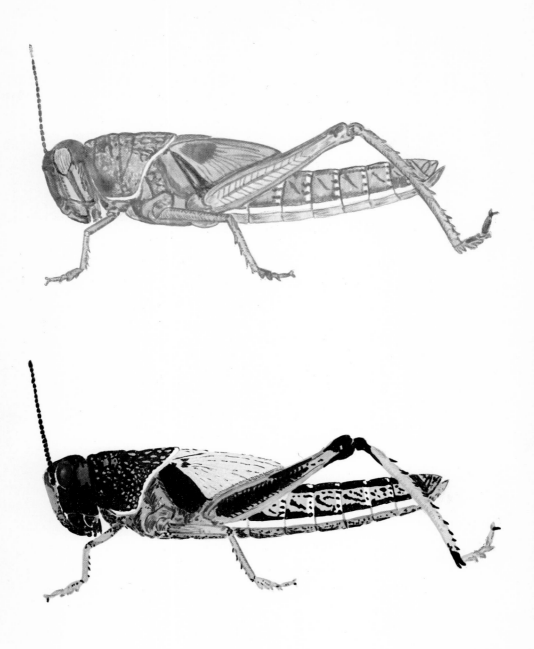

Extreme colour types of Desert Locust hoppers: solitarious above, gregarious below (original by Dr W. Stower). × 2·5

GRASSHOPPERS AND LOCUSTS

GRASSHOPPERS AND LOCUSTS

A HANDBOOK OF GENERAL ACRIDOLOGY

BY

SIR BORIS UVAROV

K.C.M.G., D.Sc., F.R.S.

Formerly Director of the Anti-Locust Research Centre

VOLUME 1

ANATOMY, PHYSIOLOGY, DEVELOPMENT
PHASE POLYMORPHISM
INTRODUCTION TO TAXONOMY

CAMBRIDGE

PUBLISHED FOR THE
ANTI-LOCUST RESEARCH CENTRE

AT THE UNIVERSITY PRESS

1966

PUBLISHED BY
THE SYNDICS OF THE CAMBRIDGE UNIVERSITY PRESS

Bentley House, 200 Euston Road, London, N.W. 1
American Branch: 32 East 57th Street, New York 10022, N.Y.
West African Office: PMB 5181 Ibadan, Nigeria

©

ANTI–LOCUST RESEARCH CENTRE
1966

Printed in Great Britain by
Spottiswoode, Ballantyne and Co. Ltd.,
London and Colchester

LIBRARY OF CONGRESS CATALOGUE
CARD NUMBER: 64–21575

CONTENTS

CONTENTS

PREFACE

In spite of a similar title, the present book is not merely a revised edition of my *Locusts and Grasshoppers* published in 1928. The change in the title is deliberate and is intended to stress the idea that a knowledge of the general characteristics of members of the large superfamily Acridoidea, commonly called grass-hoppers, is essential for understanding the nature of the specialisations which result in only a few of them acquiring the status of locusts. The distinction is essentially based on the gregarious habits of the latter, which make them particularly notorious as pests, and it is useful in practice, although it is neither sharp nor permanent. Moreover, past and more recent experience shows that non-gregarious grasshoppers are even more serious enemies of agriculture in many countries than locusts. It is also significant that, out of a vast number of grasshopper species, only a relatively small proportion are of serious economic importance, though the numbers of the latter are continually increasing, particularly in the newly developing countries. An essential problem facing an economic acridologist is to be able to understand what are the properties of those species that have already become, or may become, important pests, as compared with the others; and a wider knowledge of the whole group should help in this connection.

Studies of these insects have recently made and are making remarkably rapid advances on a very wide front. In addition to practical investigations, aiming at the solution of the economic problems involved, they have become popular objects for general ecological studies, as well as for anatomical and physiological research. A notable and most welcome development was the introduction of locusts, mainly through the initiative of the Anti-Locust Research Centre (Hunter-Jones 1961), into many university laboratories where they became accepted as very convenient experimental animals for a variety of fundamental investigations. Although a general research worker may use a locust as only one of the several animals studied from a special point of view, the results usually include some data which add to the sum of our knowledge and help in a better understanding of locust biology.

An outcome of the present interest in locusts and grasshoppers is a great number of publications, often dealing with narrowly specialised topics, and scattered through many periodicals, conference reports and general books, many of which are not easily accessible to acridologists, particularly those working in the field. Since this book is intended mainly for them, I have attempted to select such data and ideas as may help them in the study of living insects in relation to their environment. This has made it necessary to try to interpret the findings and views of specialist research workers in terms that would be understood by a person with only a general biological background. While I hope to have succeeded reasonably in the latter objective, I am aware that some specialists will find my treatment of their themes somewhat superficial and, possibly, inaccurate. Fundamental research, for example, in physiology and biochemistry, has now become so narrowly specialised that no one can cover all of its results relating to an animal group in a way that would satisfy a specialist and be understood by a general biologist. Moreover, there are many points on which the present evidence is incomplete, or contradictory, and specialist opinions differ. In such cases, a compiler can either merely record the differences or take the risk of expressing his own tentative views. Such risks have been taken by me in some cases in the hope of stimulating a fresh approach. Some purely theoretical aspects and far-reaching hypotheses, particularly those based on the evidence from other insects, have been omitted, but appropriate references to them are given. Another deliberate omission is that of descriptions of specialised experimental techniques, not because they are unimportant, but because their detailed presentation would have considerably increased the book, while abbreviated accounts would be useless; again, full references are made to the original sources.

In spite of the great flood of publications concerning these insects, there are many important gaps in our knowledge of them. One could be strictly factual and review only what is known, glossing over the gaps, but it appeared more useful to point them out and sometimes to suggest how they might be filled, in the hope of stimulating investigations of certain neglected problems. Some of them can be dealt with only by specialists, but an acridologist, whether he is working in a laboratory or in the field, will find in the book many suggestions for useful work. It is also hoped that a comprehensive treatment of this group of insects may serve the purpose of attracting to it the attention of general entomologists, who would certainly find that it offers a host of interesting problems for study. Much can be done to increase our knowledge of these insects, particularly of their biology, behaviour and ecology, by relatively simple observations and experiments—provided they are concentrated on well-formulated questions and carefully planned, and the results critically examined.

The scope of the present work differs in one important aspect, from that of the previous one. The latter was intended as a handbook for the study and control of locusts and grasshoppers, and an attempt was then made to cover the whole field as fully as possible, including the problems presented by individual species and by the conditions in particular countries. The amount of such factual material has now grown to an extent making such an approach impracticable. The present work is, therefore, intended to be no more than an introduction to general acridology, providing the basic knowledge necessary for investigating individual species and regional and local problems. Accordingly, the data relating to species are used only as illustrations of general points, or in the course of a discussion. It should be stressed also that any quantitative data need not be regarded as established values; they are often the only ones available and usually serve merely for comparisons between species and sets of conditions. The same reservation applies even to much of the morphological and anatomical data, where the most suitable (or, again, the only available) examples are described and illustrated. As will be seen, there is much variation in the same structures within the whole group and this is discussed whenever possible; but when it is not, this is usually due to lack of information.

The original intention was to cover the whole subject of acridology in a single volume, but this has proved to be undesirable, because of the time factor. If the preparation of the book had been too long delayed its earlier parts would have required a thorough revision when the whole was completed, owing to the incessant flow of new publications. It was therefore decided to divide the book into two volumes, and the first (dealing mainly with structure, physiology and development) is being presented now, so that acridologists can have at their disposal, without delay, an up-to-date review of available information on these aspects. A special chapter is devoted to phase polymorphism, earlier views on which have undergone great changes. Since this volume covers the whole of Acridoidea, and the next will also do so, a brief outline of the taxonomy of this superfamily is added in order to acquaint acridologists with the modern approach and to help them to understand the present classification within the group: this is essential because references are made throughout the text to the various families and subfamilies.

With regard to the nomenclature, special care was taken, when quoting examples, to ascertain the actual species to which the information refers. This was essential because some specialist research workers are apt to disregard taxonomy and consider it sufficient to say that the work has been done on a locust, or a grasshopper. Also, unreliable identifications and obsolete generic and specific names are frequently used. Wherever possible, the names now accepted as valid are used to replace outdated, ambiguous, or clearly incorrect designations, and the more frequent synonyms under which the species have been recorded in the past will be found in the taxonomic chapter.

Much of the available information of general value is derived from only a few species and, to avoid repetition of their full names, they are referred to throughout the text by their generic names only, as follows:

Anacridium	means	*A. aegyptium*
Dociostaurus		*D. maroccanus* (Moroccan Locust)
Locusta		*L. migratoria migratorioides* (African Migratory Locust)
Melanoplus		*M. differentialis* (Differential grasshopper)
Nomadacris		*N. septemfasciata* (Red Locust)
Schistocerca		*S. gregaria* (Desert Locust)

Other species and subspecies of these genera are given full names.

The decision to publish the work in two volumes was taken, as stated above, for practical reasons and should not be regarded as support for the views of some acridologists that fundamental knowledge of the kind summarised in the present volume bears little relation to the field biology of the insects and the practice of their control. While it is true that some laboratory findings are not directly applicable to field conditions, it is my firm belief that the two approaches must be complementary. Throughout the present volume, I have endeavoured to focus attention on such data and conclusions as may help either to interpret field observations, or to plan field experiments designed to follow laboratory work, as well as to define further problems which can be investigated only in the laboratory. The second volume, now in preparation, will deal with the behaviour, ecology, biogeography, population dynamics, economics and principles of rational control of grasshoppers and locusts, and these aspects will be reviewed against the background provided by the first volume. I can only hope that this ambitious attempt to bridge the gap between the two approaches will be reasonably successful and that the two volumes will present a synthesis of present-day knowledge of the theory and the practice of acridology. There is no doubt that, with the present rate of progress continuing, much of the information reviewed and of the ideas put forward will soon become outdated, but this is inevitable in any viable field of study.

The first volume is based on the published (and some unpublished) information available up to the end of the year 1961, and at least references to some papers dated 1962, 1963 and 1964 have also been included. The information is believed to be reasonably complete, because of the library facilities of the Anti-Locust Research Centre, where current publications are traced and assembled as soon as they appear and are added to the collection of earlier acridological works, giving a unique coverage. I regard it as my first and pleasant duty to offer my sincere thanks to the library personnel, particularly to Miss J. E. R. Salter, Mrs E. Blaxter and Miss J. Burchett for invaluable help in tracing and obtaining the necessary papers, and to Mrs Blaxter and Miss G. Tilbury for compiling the bibliography. To the Director of the Centre I am grateful for providing facilities for the preparation of the work, and to Dr T. H. C. Taylor for editing it. I am particularly grateful to the following friends and colleagues, at the Centre and elsewhere, who helped me with their advice and, in many cases, generously placed at my disposal their unpublished data and illustrations: Dr F. O. Albrecht, Mr A. Antoniou, Dr D. B. Carlisle, Dr S. Clare, Mr D. E. Davies, Mr F. Delphin, Dr V. M. Dirsh, Dr A. B. C. Dudley, Dr Peggy E. Ellis, Dr G. E. Gregory, Dr A. G. Hamilton, Dr P. T. Haskell, Dr K. C. Highnam, Mr P. Hunter-Jones, Dr. K. M. L. Key, Dr B. Linzen, Dr W. Loher, Dr. G. A. Mazokhin, Miss J. Mason, Mr. J. E. Moorhouse, Dr Maud Norris (Mrs O. W. Richards), Miss J. M. Roscow, Professor A. Shulov, Dr G. B. Staal, Dr W. Stower, Dr.

M. P. Pener, Mme M. Tchelebi-Papillon, Dr Joan Thomas, M. M. Verdier and Miss Z. Waloff.

With regard to the illustrations, my particular thanks are due to Professor Giuseppe Jannone who most generously presented to the Anti-Locust Research Centre an almost complete set of the original drawings in his classical monograph of *Dociostaurus maroccanus*, enabling me to reproduce a number of his excellent figures. I am grateful to Dr W. Stower for the coloured frontispiece plate of Desert Locust hoppers. I wish also to thank the Governors of the Athlone Press of the University of London for permission to reproduce some illustrations from Dr Albrecht's well-known book on the anatomy of the Migratory Locust, and the Councils of the Royal Society and the Royal Entomological Society of London, and the Director of the Commonwealth Institute of Entomology, for permission to copy a number of illustrations in their respective publications. The source of illustrations is indicated in every case. For the careful copying and re-drawing of many illustrations I am grateful to Mrs A Walpole and Miss E. Hawkins. The typing from my most difficult manuscript has been done by Mrs D. Taylor and I am grateful for her great care in doing it.

BORIS UVAROV

GENERAL MORPHOLOGY

The best and most detailed treatment of the morphology, anatomy and histology of an acridoid is that of *Dociostaurus maroccanus* by Jannone (1939*b*). Other comprehensive descriptions of the morphology and anatomy are available for *Locusta* (Albrecht 1953*a*, J. Thomas 1963) and *Nomadacris* (Albrecht 1956) and of morphology only for *Schistocerca* (Karandikar 1939, 1942), *Poekilocerus pictus* (Latif, Haque & Khan 1959), *Marellia remipes* (Carbonell 1959) and *Chrotogonus trachypterus* (Arora & Singh 1958); papers dealing with parts of the body and systems of organs will be mentioned where appropriate.

The main features of the body are shown in fig. 1.

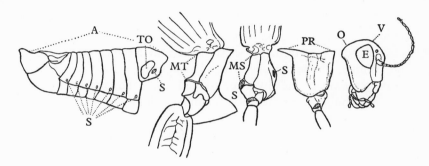

Fig. 1. Main features of acridoid body.
   V, vertex; O, occiput; E, compound eye; PR, prothorax; MS, mesothorax; MT, metathorax; S, spiracle; A, abdomen; TO, tympanal organ (Uvarov 1928).

SHAPE

The majority of acridoids can be described as approximately spindle-shaped, that is, more or less cylindrical but narrowing both anteriorly and posteriorly. There are, however, many modifications of the shape. The whole body may be compressed laterally, or dorso-ventrally, and the proportions of its length, width and height, which can be used to define the general shape, vary greatly, as can be seen from a few examples in table 1.

Further modifications of general shape are brought about by the development of large excrescences (tubercles, ridges, crests, spines), particularly on the pronotum. In most cases, there can be observed a correlation of body shape with the type of habitat and with the habits of the species, and this will be more appropriately discussed in relation to ecology.

1   I

Table 1. *Variations in the general body shape as defined by three measurements and their proportions*

	Length	Width of sternum		Height at metathorax	
	mm	mm	Percentage of length	mm	Percentage of length
Catantops axillaris	43·6	8·9	20·41	9·1	20·87
Poekilocerus pictus	62·3	11·0	17·66	15·0	24·08
Acrida bicolor	55·2	8·0	14·49	8·1	14·67
Acanthoxia gladiator	97·7	6·6	6·76	8·5	8·70
Mesopsera filum	44·4	2·8	6·31	3·6	8·11
Chrotogonus homalodemus	21·3	9·8	46·01	6·1	28·64
Stibarosterna serrata	26·7	12·5	46·82	7·0	26·22

SIZE

As a group, acridoids are relatively large insects. The smallest known grass-hopper is the South African *Lithidium pusillum*, the apterous male of which is about 7 mm long; the largest is the South American *Tropidacris latreillei*, the female being 120 mm long, with a wing-span of 230 mm. The length of body, from the frons to the tip of the abdomen, may however be due to the body being slender (see table 1), so that the real measure of size should be either the volume, or the surface area. The volume, which can be measured by the displacement of water by a submerged insect, has not been determined for any species, but several methods for measuring or estimating the surface area have been proposed.

Slifer (1954 c) has found empirically that the body of a grasshopper (without legs and wings), which just fits into a rectangular box, has the surface area equal to one-half of that of the box. The area of the box is obtained by adding two lateral, two terminal, one dorsal and one ventral areas; therefore, the surface area of a grasshopper can be expressed by the formula $LW + LH + WH$, where L is length (frons to tip of abdomen), W is width (of metasternum just anterior to the coxa), and H is height (at metathorax). Areas calculated in this way were compared with the values actually observed by dissecting the whole body wall into convenient small pieces and measuring them. The mean percentage difference between observed and calculated values in a number of species was $\pm 9.56\%$, which could reasonably be expected. Surface areas were determined in this way for a large number of species (Slifer 1953 a, 1953 b) and some figures are given in table 2.

The figures in the table give some idea of the range of surface areas in different species and some comparison of species with differently shaped bodies is of interest. Thus, females of both *Xiphoceriana* and *Acrida* measure about 75 mm in length, but the surface area of the plump *Xiphoceriana* is nearly twice that of the very slender *Acrida*, and the heavily built female of *Brachystola* with the body length some 50–60 mm has relatively an even larger surface area. This means that the surface area, which takes into account the shape of the insect, is a better measure of size than mere body length.

Table 2. *Surface areas (in sq.cm) of some grasshoppers and locusts (Slifer 1953a, 1953b)*

	Male	Female
PAMPHAGIDAE		
Xiphoceriana atrox	10·48	23·78
PYRGOMORPHIDAE		
Pyrgomorpha sp.	1·30	2·61
ROMALEINAE		
Romalea microptera	14·22	27·17
Brachystola magna	22·13	30·52
CATANTOPINAE		
Catantops axillaris	6·45	10·60
Melanoplus differentialis	6·92	8·27
„ *sanguinipes*	3·38	3·93
Phaulacridium nanum	0·83	1·23
CYRTACANTHACRIDINAE		
Schistocerca gregaria, solitarious	12·19	20·03
„ „ gregarious	12·85	15·82
Nomadacris septemfasciata	13·76	18·65
OEDIPODINAE		
Austroicetes pusilla	1·04	2·82
Locustana pardalina, solitarious	7·47	5·79
„ „ gregarious	10·10	10·00
Locusta m. migratorioides, solitarious	7·59	15·68
„ „ „ gregarious	10·18	12·74
ACRIDINAE		
Acrida bicolor	4·23	12·49
Duronia tricolor	3·11	6·49

Weis-Fogh (1952) estimated the surface area and the volume of gregarious *Schistocerca* from only two measurements, length of tegmen (E) and of posterior femur (F). He found that the surface area is very close to E multiplied by F, while the volume nearly equals $(E \times F)^{\frac{3}{2}}$. His results are shown in table 3.

Table 3. *Size indices of* Schistocerca gregaria *(Weis-Fogh 1952)*

	Surface area sq.cm	Volume cu.cm
Male	11·9–13·9 (mean 12·9)	41·2–51·7 (mean 46·3)
Female	14·6–16·6 (mean 15·7)	55·8–68·9 (mean 61·9)

As can be seen, Weis-Fogh's values of the surface area are in agreement with those of Slifer for the same species and phase.

Chefurka & Pepper (1955a) based their determinations of surface area on the, so called, Meeh's formula (originally developed for the human body) which expresses the surface area as a function of the weight, provided a constant factor for the species is determined empirically. According to these authors, in *Melanoplus bivittatus* hoppers the relationship between surface area (S) in square millimetres and weight (W) in milligrams is expressed by the formula: $S = 10 \cdot 27 \; W^{0 \cdot 72}$.

Since the weight of both adults and hoppers is subject to much individual variation connected with internal growth and maturation (pp. 274, 302), empirical formulae of this kind will need to be worked out not only for each species, but also for development stages.

It would appear, on present evidence, that Weis-Fogh's method, which is the simplest, is also sufficiently exact, at least for the species with the somewhat standard body shape (as in the Desert Locust), but its applicability to differently shaped species needs to be tested. It certainly cannot be applied to brachypterous species or to hoppers, and there is obvious need for developing reasonably reliable methods of calculating the surface area and the volume from the minimum number of measurements. Such data are essential for qualitative studies, for example, on metabolism, evaluation of dosages of contact insecticides, and so on.

HEAD

Head capsule

In its typical form, the head is more or less oval in shape and of the orthognathous type, that is, its face is approximately vertical in profile, with the mouth directed downwards; but it varies greatly from almost prognathous to strongly hypognathous (fig. 2).

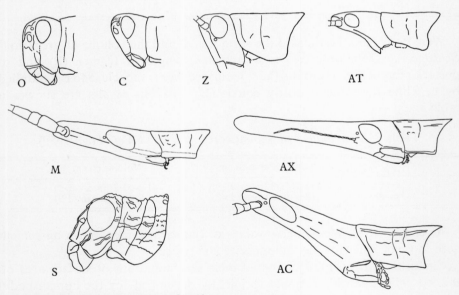

Fig. 2. Variations in the shape of head.
Orthognathous head: O, *Oedipoda*. Hypognathous heads: C, *Chorthippus*; Z, *Zonocerus*; AT, *Atractomorpha*; M, *Mesopsis*; AX, *Acanthoxia*; AC, *Acrida* (Salfi 1935). Prognathous head: S, *Shelfordites* (Dirsh 1956 b).

4

The head capsule consists of several sclerites, but they are largely fused and the sutures separating them may be barely visible externally as furrows; internally, there are ridges, corresponding to the furrows, which serve for the attachment of muscles (fig. 3).

The anterior surface of the head is the *frons*, delimited laterally by vertical *subocular furrows*, behind which lie the *genae*. The middle portion of the

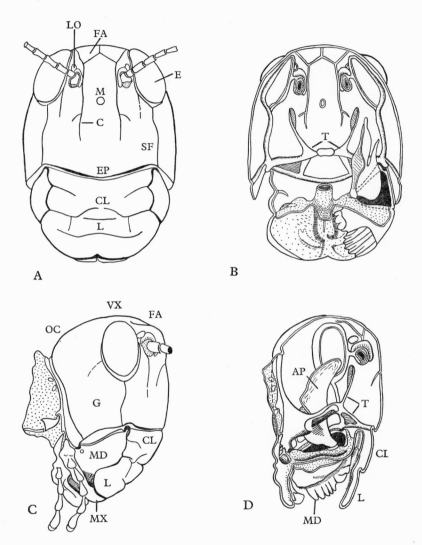

Fig. 3. *Locusta*, head. A, frontal part, outside; B, ditto, inside; C, lateral part, outside; D, ditto, inside (after Albrecht 1953 *a*).

E, compound eye; FA, fastigium; C, frontal costa; M, median ocellus; LO, lateral ocellus; SF, subocular furrow; EP, epistomal suture; CL, clypeus; L, labrum; T, tentorium; VX, vertex; OC, occiput; G, gena; MD, mandible; MX, maxilla; AP, apodeme of mandibular adductor muscle.

frons is usually raised, forming a *frontal costa* (or ridge) which may be convex, flat, or grooved. In the middle of the costa lies the *median ocellus*. Below, the frons is clearly separated from the *clypeo-labrum* by the *epistomal suture*. On the sides of the upper part of the head there are large *compound eyes*; between the eyes and the frontal costa are the bases of the antennae, above which lie the *lateral ocelli*.

The frontal costa may be more or less clearly separated above by the *frontal suture* from the upper surface of the head, the *vertex*, which extends behind, usually without any division, into the *occiput*. The part of the vertex

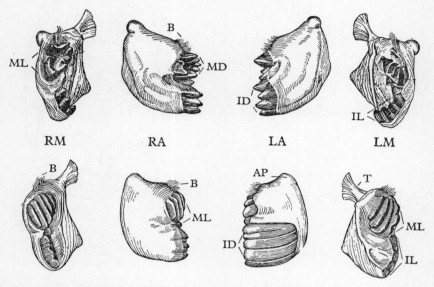

Fig. 4. Upper row, herbivorous mandibles of *Brachystola magna*; lower row, graminivorous mandibles of *Mermiria maculipennis* (Isely 1944).
RM, right mandible, inner view; RA, ditto, anterior view; LA, left mandible, anterior view; LM, ditto, inner view; ML, molar lobe; MD, molar dents; IL, incisor lobe; ID, incisor dents; B, brush (brustia); AP, apodeme; T, muscle.

anterior to the imaginary shortest line between the eyes is the *fastigium*. The surface of the fastigium may be convex, or flat, or with a median concavity, in which some of the sensitive hairs of the aerodynamic organ (p. 162) may be found. The sides of the fastigium often bear a pair of *fastigial foveolae*, but their fine structure has never been studied, although their high degree of development in the most advanced subfamily Gomphocerinae suggests some important function. The fastigium may also have a *median furrow*, possibly representing the coronal suture; in some groups (Pyrgomorphidae, Pamphagidae) the furrow dissects the fastigium (fig. 223) and is continuous with the furrow of the frontal costa. The edges of the furrow on the fastigium may be raised forming a ridge, sometimes continuing backwards on to the occiput.

The *clypeus* is less strongly sclerotised than the frons and separated from it by a well defined *epistomal suture* (represented internally by a strong ridge). The somewhat asymmetrical *labrum* (fig. 5, C) is still less sclerotised, imperfectly separated from the clypeus, and movable. The inner surface of the clypeo-labrum is membranous and forms a part of the epipharyngeal surface of the preoral cavity (p. 70) which is concave and fits over the surface of the mandibles; this surface bears numerous sensilla and bands of long hairs.

Mouth parts. The paired *mandibles* (fig. 4) are strongly sclerotised, but hollow, structures, articulated to the cranium. Each has two apodemes, extending into the head and serving for the attachment of powerful abductor and adductor muscles (p. 60).

Notable features of the mandibles are their asymmetry and the structure of their biting surfaces (Petrov 1905; Isely 1944; L. H. Williams 1954; Gangwere 1960a, 1961). The asymmetry enables the left mandible to overlap the right when mandibles are closed.

The biting surface of a mandible has two lobes with different armament. The lobe nearer to the base is the molar lobe, usually bearing short and blunt dents; the dents on the other, incisor, lobe are higher and more acute. In this respect, however, there are significant differences between species with different food habits. Those species that feed exclusively, or mainly, on grasses of tough texture, have the mandibles of *graminivorous* type and those feeding on softer broad-leaved plants have *herbivorous* mandibles. The differences between the two types can be summarised as follows:

	Herbivorous	*Graminivorous*
Mandibles	Overlap and interlock	Overlap slightly
Incisor dents	Pointed; left dents not longer than right	Relatively blunt; left dents longer than right
Molar lobe	With several subconical dents	With series of ridges

Between these two extreme types there are transitional ones, found in species with mixed food habits.

At the inner edge of each mandible there is a brush of fine hairs (*brustia*); when the mandibles are closed, the two brushes form a screen through which the food is, presumably, filtered.

The *maxillae* lie behind the mandibles. A maxilla (fig. 5, A) consists of a basal part divided into cardo and stipes, and an apical comprising lacinia and galea. The lacinia bears at its apex some pointed and heavily sclerotised dents, which take part in the mastication of food; it appears that the number (2 in *Locusta*, 3 in *Nomadacris*) and the shape of the dents may vary specifically, possibly in relation to food habits, but no such comparative studies as for mandibles have been made. Each maxilla has a five-segmented palp, inserted at the base of the galea on a small sclerite, the palpifer; the palps bear numerous sensilla, particularly abundant near the tip of the apical segment (Jannone 1939b). In some cases (*Stenobothrus maroccanus, Pseudoarcyptera palpalis*)

7

the apical segment is flattened, dilated and black in colour (fig. 5, D); comparative studies of the maxillary palps, including their sensilla, would be of interest.

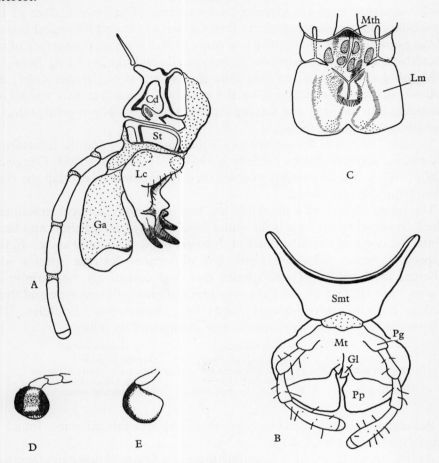

Fig. 5. *Nomadacris.* A, right maxilla, anterior view.
  Cd, cardo; St, stipes; Lc, lacinia; Ga, galea.
B. Labium.
  Smt, submentum; Mt, mentum; Gl, galea; Pp, paraglossa; Pg, palpiger.
C. Epipharyngeal surface of clypeus and labrum.
  Mth, mouth; Lm, labrum (Albrecht 1956).
D. *Pseudoarcyptera palpalis,* tip of maxillary palp; E, ditto, of labial palp (Uvarov 1929).

The hindmost part of the mouth parts is the *labium* (Fig. 5, B), which consists of the basal portion or submentum, the middle-mentum, and two broad, not quite symmetrical lobes (paraglossae) separated by a deep cleft, at the base of which there are two small, strongly asymmetrical galeae. The mentum bears a pair of labial palps, which have three segments, not counting the basal, which is fused with the mentum and is called the palpiger. The

8

apical segment of the labial palp may be flattened and dilated, as in the case of the maxillary one (fig. 5, E).

All the mouth parts, particularly on their inner surfaces, are abundantly supplied with the various sensilla, which have been studied, however, only in *Dociostaurus* (Jannone 1939*b*).

Antennae. The base of each antenna (fig. 6) is surrounded by elastic membrane (antacorium), ringed by the hard *antennal sclerite*; above it lies the *antennal crescent* (Slifer 1951) which is poorly sclerotised, soft in the live insect and pale-cream in colour, and has some specialised sensilla. The basal segment of the antenna is a thickened *scape*, which is articulated with the antennal sclerite by a small process. The next segment is the *pedicel*,

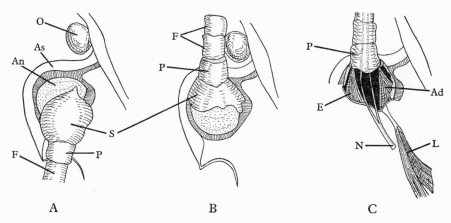

A   B   C

Fig. 6. *Schistocerca*, antennal base. A, dorsal view; B, ventral view; C, muscles (Misra 1946).
    O, lateral ocellus; As, antennal sclerite; An, antacorium; S, scape; P, pedicel; F, flagellum; E, extensor; Ad, adductor; L, levator; N, nerve.

which is followed by the *flagellum* consisting of many segments. The total length of an antenna in acridoids is shorter than that of the whole insect. The number of antennal segments (Mason 1954; Katiyar 1953) is sometimes not easy to determine, since an antenna grows in the hopper by a series of divisions of the proximal flagellar segments (p. 276) and the division sometimes remains incomplete in the adult. The total number of segments (counting the scape and the pedicel) varies from seven to thirty-three and, in this respect, the Acridoidea can be divided into two main groups: one, comprising Pyrgomorphidae, Pamphagidae, Charilaidae, Lathiceridae and Trigonopterygidae, with the mean segment number sixteen to eighteen; and the other comprising Acrididae, Lentulidae and Pauliniidae, with twenty-two to twenty-four. The number in females is often greater than in the smaller males of the same species; this reflects the number of hopper instars (p. 276) and a similar difference occurs between individuals of the same sex if the number of instars is variable. There is also some correlation between the segment number and the

9

development of wings, the apterous, or micropterous, species often having a lower number of segments than related macropterous species.

While most acridoids have simple filiform (thread-like) antennae, with segments of the flagellum circular or oval in section, there are many modifications (fig. 7). The most common is flattening and dilation of segments which may become triangular in section; this is usually more pronounced in the proximal part of the flagellum, resulting in an ensiform antenna. Another less common variation is the enlargement or merely fusion of several apical segments to form a clavate antenna.

Antennae bear very numerous and varied sensilla (p. 171) on their surfaces and complicated chordotonal organs inside their bases (p. 168).

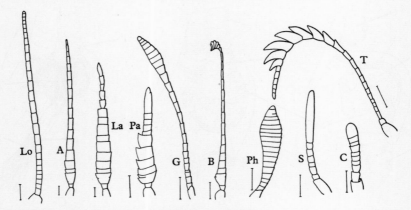

Fig. 7. Variations of antenna (original by J. B. Mason).
Lo, *Locusta*; A, *Acrida*; La, *Lamarckiana*; Pa, *Parga*; G, *Gomphocerippus*; B, *Baidoceracris*; Ph, *Phlocerus*; S, *Stibarosterna*; C, *Crypsiceracris*; T, *Taramassus*. Line = 1 mm.

The muscular mechanism of the antenna is confined to the scape and the pedicel (p. 60); the flagellum is devoid of muscles and moves only as a whole, but its flexibility may be controlled by the presence of blood pumped into it by the antennal ampulla (p. 106).

THORAX

The neck (fig. 8) (Jannone 1939*b*; Misra 1947; Goodman 1959)

The head is connected with the prothorax by *cervical membrane* which is not visible, except ventrally, when the insect is at rest, but can be stretched by blood pressure (p. 106) and contracted by muscles originating in the thorax and attached to the membrane and to the head (p. 61). The membrane bears fine spinules and is usually whitish in colour, but in some species (particularly amongst Pamphagidae) it may be very brightly coloured. Thus in *Eremopeza gibbera* there are two mid-dorsal 'eye-spots', with white centres ringed with purple and surrounded by orange colour, which are exposed when the head is bent down (Porchinskiĭ 1886). Burr (1927–30) thought these spots to be special organs of some kind, but the structure of the membrane in this area has never been studied. Laterally on the membrane there are two small *dorsal cervical sclerites* and, lower down, two larger and articulated *lateral sclerites*. The anterior lateral sclerite is articulated with a tubercle on the edge of the occiput; its anterior part is swollen and bears numerous sensory hairs, which participate, together with other sensitive hairs on the anterior edge of the pronotum, in controlling head movements (p. 61); internally this sclerite has two hollow processes to which muscles are attached.

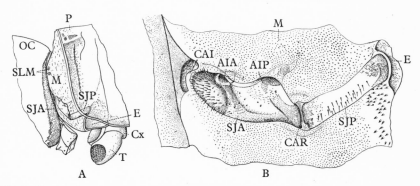

Fig. 8. *Dociostaurus*, neck. A, general view; B, cervical membrane, enlarged (Jannone 1939 *b*).

OC, occiput; P, pronotum; M, cervical membrane; SLM, dorsal cervical sclerites; SJA, SJP, lateral cervical sclerites; E, episternum; Cx, coxa; T, trochanter; AIA, AIP, hollow processes; CAI, CAR, articulations.

The prothorax (fig. 9)

The largest and most conspicuous part of the prothorax is the *pronotum* which covers it dorsally and laterally. The shape of the pronotum is extremely variable: cylindrical, subconical (narrowing anteriorly), box-like, or even triangular in section (Trigonopterygidae only). Its upper surface may be flat or somewhat convex transversely, without, or with, a linear *median carina*. The latter may be more or less raised, sometimes becoming a high crest, which may be entire or dissected by transverse furrows into several prominent dents; along its middle there is sometimes a fine furrow, along which the pronotum of a hopper splits during moulting (p. 284). The side parts, or *lateral lobes*, of the pronotum may form a rounded, or a very distinct, angle with its dorsum; in the latter case, they are separated from the dorsum by the *lateral carinae*, which may be straight and parallel, or variously incurved, or outcurved. The anterior edge of the dorsum is usually broadly convex, but may be either notched or projecting forward in the middle. The posterior edge is either more or less convex, or angular, overlapping the mesonotum; but in brachypterous species it tends to become straight, and in the apterous even excised. The lateral lobes are approximately pentagonal, with the lower margin more or less sinuate.

Conspicuous external features of the pronotum are a series of *transverse furrows*, partly connected on the lateral lobes by short longitudinal ones; they correspond to ridges on the inner surface, from which originate various muscles moving the head, the first pair of legs, and the prothorax in relation to

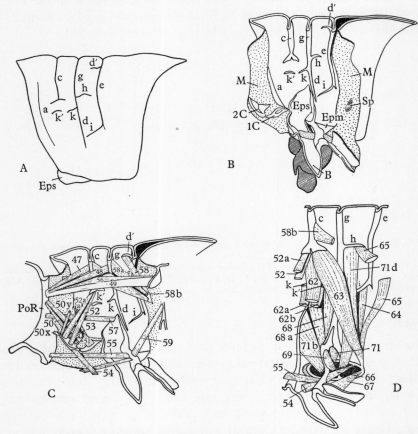

Fig. 9. *Nomadacris*, thorax and its muscles. A, external view; B, internal view; C, D, muscles (Albrecht 1956).

a, c, d, e, g, h, i, k, furrows; M, cervical membrane; 1C, 2C, cervical sclerites; Eps, episternum; Epm, epimeron; Sp, spiracle; PoR, postoccipital ridge; B, prosternal process; muscles numbered.

the mesothorax. There is great variation in the number and the degree of development of the pronotal furrows, some of which may intersect the dorsal carina, while often nearly all become obsolete; the relation of such externally visible variations to the corresponding internal ridges (and, possibly, to the musculature) has not been investigated. The lateral (pleural) sclerite of the prothorax is mostly concealed under the pronotum, but one part of it, the *episternum*, is visible as a triangular piece just below the anterior part of the lower edge of the lateral lobe.

The ventral part of the prothorax is the *prosternum* (fig. 10) which consists of two sclerites, the basisternum and, behind it, the spinasternum, separated

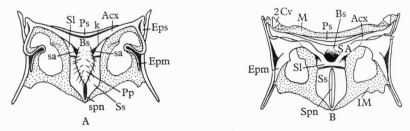

Fig. 10. *Nomadacris*, prosternum. A, external view; B, internal view (Albrecht 1956).
   Bs, basisternum; Ss, spinasternum; k, furcal suture; Ps, presternum; Acx, precoxal bridge; Eps, episternum; Epm, epimeron; Sl, sternellum; SA, sternal apophysis; sa, pit; spn, spina; Pp, prosternal process; IM, intersegmental membrane.

by a furcal suture, which internally corresponds to a ridge; at each end of the furrow there is a pit, which is a cavity of an internal process (apophysis), from which ventral longitudinal muscle arises. The basisternum in many species (Catantopinae, Cyrtacanthacridinae, etc.) often bears a *prosternal process* of various shapes; it may be a simple conical tubercle, a finger-like projection, a

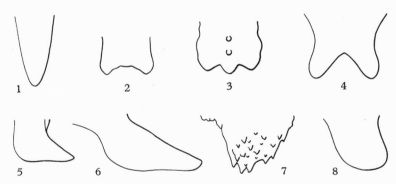

Fig. 11. Variations of the prosternal process. Upper row, frontal view; lower row, lateral view (original by J. B. Mason).
   1, *Tropidauchen marginatum*; 2, *Spathosternum prasinferum*; 3, *Pagopedilum bradyana*; 4, *Tropidauchen nizvai*; 5, *Tristria pallida*; 6. *Cyrtacanthacris tatarica*; 7, *Xiphoceriana brunneriana*; 8, *Catantops melanostictus*.

straight or curved spine, a thin transverse plate, almost a cube with flat or depressed top, and so on (fig. 11). This process has considerable taxonomic value, and its probable function is discussed below (p. 164). The spinasternum has a narrow longitudinal pit in its middle, leading into the cavity of the *spina*, an apophysis to which are attached muscles connecting prothorax and mesothorax.

The pterothorax (fig. 12, A, B)

The mesothorax and metathorax are two distinct segments, but they are closely integrated and are unable to move in relation to each other.

Dorsally, these two segments are represented by the moderately sclerotised *mesonotum* (mesotergum) and *metanotum* (metatergum), with which the

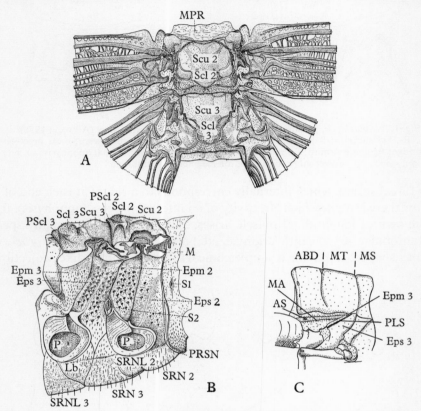

Fig. 12. *Dociostaurus*, pterothorax. A, from above; B, lateral view (Jannone 1939 *b*).
MPR, M, membrane between pronotum and mesonotum; Scu, scutum; Scl, scutellum; PScl, postscutellum; Epm, epimeron; Eps, episternum; S, spiracle; PRSN, presternum; SRN, sternum; SRNL, sternellum; Lb, metasternal lobe; P, base of leg.
C, *Lentula callani*, lateral view of pterothorax (Ewer 1958).
ABD, first abdominal tergite; MT, metathorax; MS, mesothorax; AS, first abdominal spiracle; MA, membranous area; PLS, pleural suture.

tegmina and the wings are articulated by means of a very complicated system of small sclerites (La Greca 1947). The dorsal surfaces of the mesonotum and metanotum bear several convexities (scutum, scutellum, postscutellum) and are abundantly supplied with hairs, which may have a sensory function, probably related to the closing and opening of wings.

In fully-winged species the mesonotum and at least part of the metanotum are covered by the posterior projection of the pronotum, but in those with wings reduced or absent they are exposed and their surface is as strongly sclerotised as that of the abdominal tergites, and not hairy. Also, while the pterothorax of fully-winged species is larger than two-thirds of the whole thorax, in the brachypterous ones it is relatively much shorter (Atzinger 1957).

The lateral parts of the pterothoracic segments, or *pleurae*, are strongly sclerotised and each is divided by an oblique furrow into two sclerites, the *episternum* and *epimeron*; their lower ends adjoin the rims of the coxal cavities of the second and third legs. In representatives of the family Lentulidae, which lack not only all wings, but also all the indirect wing muscles, the metaepimeron (Epm 3) is greatly reduced and the pleural suture (PLS) separating it from the metaepisternum (Eps 3) runs almost horizontally, instead of obliquely downwards (fig. 12, C).

Sternal plate (fig. 13, A)

The mesosternum, metasternum and first abdominal sternite are closely fused and form one well sclerotised plate, more or less clearly divided by

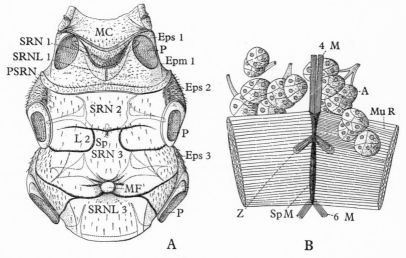

A   B

Fig. 13. *Dociostaurus*. A, sternum from below; B, mesosternal bodies (Jannone 1939 *b*). MC, cervical membrane; Eps, episternum; Epm, epimeron; P, base of leg; SRN 1, prosternum; SRNL 1, prosternellum (spinasternum); PSRN, presternal ridge; SRN 2, mesosternum; L2, mesosternal lobe; Sp, spina; SRN 3, metasternum; MF, metasternal interspace; SRNL 3, first abdominal sternite. A, salivary glands; 4 M, 6M, ventral abdominal muscles; MuR, rotator of coxa; SpM, sclerotised spiniform process; Z, mesosternal body.

sutures (corresponding to ridges internally) into component parts. The *mesosternum* is separated anteriorly by a *presternal ridge* from the prosternum, and posteriorly it is limited by the transverse *mesofurcal suture*, in which lie three pits corresponding to internal apophyses, the middle one (the *spina*) being the largest and bearing a pair of *mesosternal bodies* (fig. 13, B). They were regarded by Jannone (1939 *b*) as glandular organs, but J. Thomas (1962) found them to consist of sclerotised lamellae and to lack any ducts; they are not likely to be sensory either, and their function, if any, remains problematic. Behind the mesofurcal suture lie a pair of *mesosternal lobes*, separated by the *mesosternal interspace*, which is merely a projecting part of the metasternum. The latter is separated from the first abdominal sternite by the *metafurcal suture*, which is curved and bears two pits, again corresponding to apophyses; the two lateral *metasternal lobes* are separated by the *metasternal interspace*. Considerable variation in the relative size and shape of the component parts of the sternal plate is observed between species (fig. 14). Thus, in the subfamily

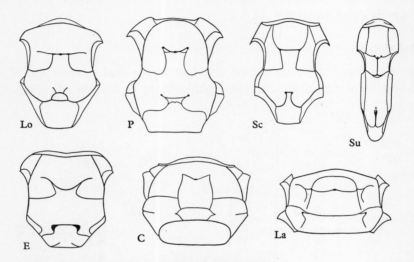

Fig. 14. Variations in sternal plate (original by J. B. Mason).
Lo, *Locusta*; P, *Phymateus*; Sc, *Schistocerca*; Su, *Sudanacris*; E, *Egnatius*; C, *Chrotogonus*; La, *Lathicerus*.

Egnatiinae (fig. 14, E) the mesofurcal suture, strongly bent backwards in the middle, constitutes a reliable taxonomic character. The subfamily Cyrtacanthacridinae (fig. 14, Sc) is characterised by angular mesosternal lobes, whereas these are always rounded in other subfamilies, but vary greatly in shape. The mesosternal and metasternal interspaces also vary greatly, from being broad and transverse to completely disappearing when the lateral lobes become separated only by a suture (fig. 14, Su): this happens particularly in species of very narrow build and with climbing habits. In species with strongly depressed body the whole sternal plate is very broad and its subdivisions distorted and partly obliterated externally (fig. 14, C, La). Since all these external features of the sternum merely reflect the internal details of the skeleton serving for muscle attachment, detailed comparative anatomical studies of these various types would be of great interest.

ABDOMEN

General structure

The abdomen (fig. 15, A, B, C) consists of eleven segments, though some of the posterior ones are either somewhat transformed, or not visible externally. Each segment is divided into two parts, the *tergite* and the *sternite*, joined by membranes, and the segments are separated from each other by intersegmental

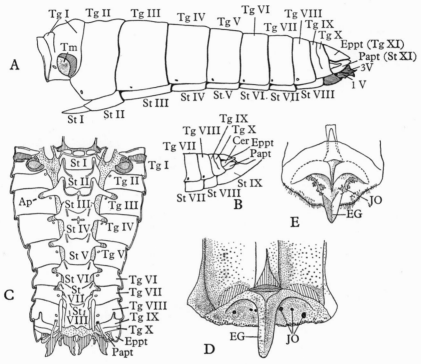

Fig. 15. A, *Nomadacris*, female abdomen; B, ditto, end of male abdomen (Albrecht 1956); C, *Locusta*, female abdomen opened along median line, internal view (Albrecht 1953 a); D, *Locusta*, dorsal (inner) surface of subgenital plate; E, *Locustana*, ditto (Agarwala 1952-4).

Tg, tergites; St, sternites; Tm, tympanal organ; Eppt, epiproct; Ap, apodeme; Papt, paraproct; Cer, cercus; EG, egg-guide; JO, Jannone's organ.

membranes; all membranes are extensible (p. 33) and this permits expansion and contraction of the abdomen during respiratory movements (p. 128) and oviposition (p. 323). The sternites have large internal apodemes to which the lateral muscles (p. 63) are attached.

The first abdominal segment differs in its structure from the others, its large tergite being separated by the membrane in which the posterior coxa is inserted from the sternite which is practically fused with the sternal plate. It also bears the tympanal organ (p. 188). Segments II to VIII are similar to each other; their tergites sometimes have a median longitudinal ridge and the integument on both sides of it has irregular paired areas of different histological structure (Slifer's patches, p. 33); at the lower anterior angle of each tergite lies a spiracle. Tergites IX and X are dorsally very short in both sexes. The last externally visible sternite is VIII in the female and IX in the male; it is called the subgenital plate and is discussed below as a component part of the external genitalia with which tergite XI (epiproct) is also included for convenience.

External genitalia: male (fig. 15, B)

The posterior edge of tergite X is more or less incurved; sometimes it is incised in the middle and the incision may divide it into two lateral parts,

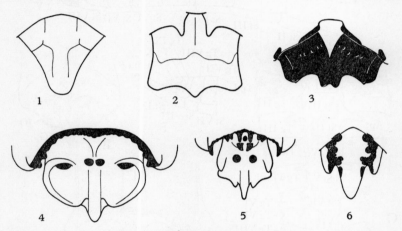

Fig. 16. Variations in the male epiproct (supra-anal plate) (original by J. B. Mason).
1, *Locusta*; 2, *Conophyma comtulum*; 3, *Anischnansis burtti*; 4, *Plegmapterus splendens*;
5, *Plegmapteropsis gracilis*; 6, *Lentula obtusifrons*.

which sometimes bear on their inner corners small projections forming a *furcula*. Tergite XI is the *epiproct* (supra-anal plate of taxonomists); in its simplest form it is triangular, but it may be semi-elliptical, rectangular, pentagonal, etc.; its surface is somewhat uneven, and there may be on it either a furrow, or a ridge, along the middle, as well as some tubercles (fig. 16).

Half-concealed under the epiproct are the paired *paraprocts*, representing the XIth sternite, and with the membrane between them and the epiproct are articulated the *cerci*. A cercus consists of two sclerotised parts: the main body and a small basal lobe usually concealed under the epiproct, although in the subfamily Euryphyminae it is large and conspicuous. The lobe has a well defined dense patch of hairs called *brustia* (fig. 99), possibly sensory (Jannone 1939 *b*). The cercus itself is usually conical, but there is much variation (fig. 17).

The males of *Calliptamus* and allied genera have a special clasper-like type of cercus, very long, compressed and incurved, with the apex divided into two to three lobes, some of which bear strongly sclerotised incurved points;

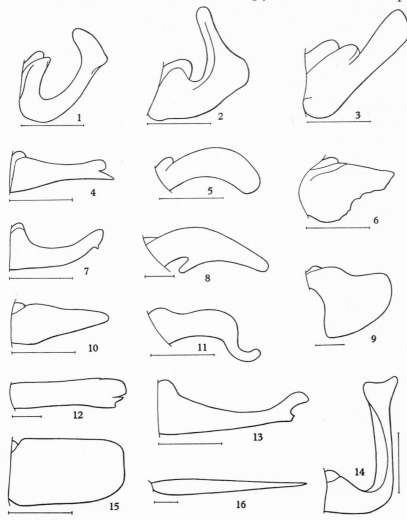

Fig. 17. Variations in the male cercus (original by J. B. Mason).
1, *Anabibia thoracica*; 2, *Platacanthoides bituberculatus*; 3, *Acrophymus cuspidatus*; 4, *Crobylostenus indecisus*; 5, *Heteracris adspersa*; 6, *Aneuryphymus rhodesianus*; 7, *Pezocatantops impotens*; 8, *Tropidiopsis haasi*; 9, *Phyllocercus bicoloripes*; 10, *Locusta migratoria*; 11, *Cyphocerastis laeta*; 12, *Calliptamus italicus*; 13, *Afroxyrrhepes procera*; 14, *Anischnansis burtti*; 15, *Schistocerca gregaria*; 16, *Mesopsilla roseoviridis*. Line = 1 mm.

the inner surface bears, before the apex, a membranous area, under which there is a layer of large hypodermal cells, and the whole may be a special dermal organ of unknown function (La Greca 1950; Pichler 1952). The cercus is abundantly supplied with sensory bristles of special structure, probably tactile in function (p. 163); Sihler (1924) recorded also some sensilla, apparently of campaniform type (p. 165).

The greatly enlarged IXth sternite is fully, or partly, subdivided by a transverse furrow into two parts which are more or less movable on each other; when the division is complete, the basal portion is regarded as the true IXth sternite and the apical as the *subgenital plate* (Snodgrass 1935 a). This plate, which envelops the phallic complex (p. 141), is generally conical, but there is much variation in its shape.

External genitalia: female (fig. 15, A, C, D, E)

The Xth tergite, the epiproct and the cercus in females are always of simple structure, even in the species where these parts are highly specialised in the male sex. The *subgenital plate* of the female is the VIIIth sternite and is therefore not homologous with that of the male. It is usually much longer than it is wide; its surface is smooth and its visible posterior margin straight. In some species, however, the posterior margin is excised, or projecting, and sometimes serrate, bearing spinules. In *Oxya* the ventral surface of the plate also bears spines or serrate ridges. The posterior margin merely represents an edge of the plate folding up on itself, so that its concealed dorsal surface is actually a less sclerotised continuation of the ventral. In the middle this surface has a finger-like process, the egg-guide (fig. 15, D) which extends beyond the posterior margin of the plate between the bases of the lower ovipositor valves and is often concealed by them. On each side of the egg-guide there are sometimes found brown sclerotised patches, briefly mentioned and figured by Jannone (1939 b) who regarded them as sensory. Agarwala (1952–4) found them in several groups of acridoids, but not in Pamphagidae; he called them *Jannone's organs* and also thought them to be sensory. Their shape and number are variable and in some cases (e.g. in *Locustana*, fig. 15, E) they are very complicated. Karandikar (1942), however, regarded them in *Schistocerca* as sclerotised supporting structures and this view is shared by Randell (1963) who suggested that their possible function during copulation is as parts of a locking system, corresponding to the structures on the epiphallus (p. 142), and by J. Thomas (1965), who gave a detailed description of female genitalia.

The ovipositor (Snodgrass 1935 a; Agarwala 1952–4; Makhotin 1953) consists of three pairs of valves, two of them large and conspicuous and the third (inner) concealed between them (fig. 18). The ventral valve is articulated with the subgenital plate and ends in a strongly sclerotised hook. The dorsal valve is also strongly sclerotised and with a hook-like tip. The inner valve is a small, moderately sclerotised lobe. Basally, the valves are articulated with a pair of long, parallel sclerotised apodemes, extending well into the body cavity, to which are attached the main muscles of the ovipositor. In the membrane between the base of the ventral valve and the apodeme there is a small sclerotised area with peculiar spinules, from the base of which fine canals run into

20

the membrane; their sensory function was presumed by Jannone and Agarwala, but details of their structure are not known. There are also abundant hair sensilla on the valves and membranes, but they remain unstudied.

There is considerable specific variation in the structure of the ovipositor, in relation to egg-laying habits, but this can best be discussed in relation to ecology.

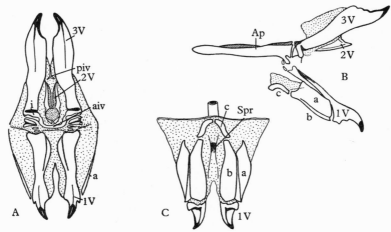

Fig. 18. *Nomadacris*, ovipositor. A, posterior view, with the valves wide open; B, lateral view; C, ventral view of ventral valves (Albrecht 1956).

1 V, ventral valve; 2 V, inner valve; 3 V, dorsal valve; a, b, c, basivalvular plates; piv, posterior intervalvula; aiv, anterior intervalvula; Spr, spermathecal aperture; Ap, apodeme.

Krauss's organ

In most genera of Pamphagidae, the second abdominal tergite bears at its lower anterior corner a specialised structure, Krauss's organ (Uvarov 1943). It is a more or less oval plate, clearly raised above the surface of the integument and surrounded by a distinct chitinous rim; above, it almost touches the tympanum, and on its lower posterior edge lies the second abdominal spiracle (fig. 19). The outer covering of the organ appears very rough and strongly sclerotised, but in live specimens it easily gives to pressure, returning to normal when pressure ceases. The surface of the plate is sometimes covered by tubercles, or ridges, or may be smooth. The internal structure is as follows (Shulov 1952 a, 1952 c). Under the outer cover there is a shallow cavity, somewhat sunk in the body wall. The cover itself has a thin cuticle and a layer of columnar hypodermal cells. Although the spiracle is embedded in the organ, it appears that its trachea has no communication with the cavity. In the muscles at the dorsal border of the organ there is a branch of a nerve, but no specialised sensory cells have been discovered. The muscles in the region of the organ are somewhat modified, apparently enabling the whole organ to be moved slightly in relation to the abdomen.

In the absence of a more detailed study, particularly of the innervation and of sensory elements, one can only guess at the possible function of this organ. It was previously thought to be stridulatory, but even the present incomplete knowledge of its structure makes this view doubtful—although Tinkham (1948) mentions that in *Haplotropis* a sound is produced by the organ. The behaviour of *Tmethis* hoppers and adults with the organ destroyed was normal in every respect. A suggestion has been made that the structure of the organ might make it responsive to air pressure, but neither normal, nor operated, insects responded in any way to a reduction in air pressure to about

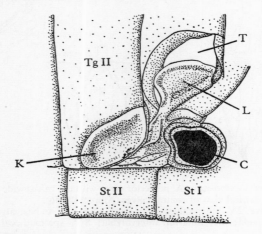

Fig. 19. *Tmethis*, Krauss's organ (Shulov 1952 *a*).
T, tympanum; L, tympanal lobe; Tg, tergite; St, sternite; C, coxa; K, Krauss's organ.

a quarter of the normal. Shulov's conclusion was that the organ merely serves as a cushion to protect the second abdominal spiracle from pressure by the hind leg during jumping, but it is strange that such an elaborate structure should have developed for this purpose. Its distribution in Pamphagidae is very general, except that the organ tends to disappear in wingless genera. On the other hand, it is present in some aberrant Romaleinae.

LEGS

The three pairs of legs have the same component parts, but present some differences in detail, particularly the third pair.

First (prothoracic) leg (fig. 20, A)

The basal segment is the small *coxa* which is attached to the membrane of the coxal cavity of the epipleuron; in this membrane another small sclerite, the *trochantin*, can be seen. The coxa is articulated with the short *trochanter*, which is joined firmly to the *femur*. The latter is long, rounded–triangular in section, with the lower surface flat or grooved; its lower edges may be somewhat serrate but there are never any spines. The femur is apically articulated with the tibia which is usually longer and more slender and is armed with a double series of immovable spines along its lower edges. Near the apex of the tibia there are two pairs of *spurs* which are similar to the spines but articulated and movable.

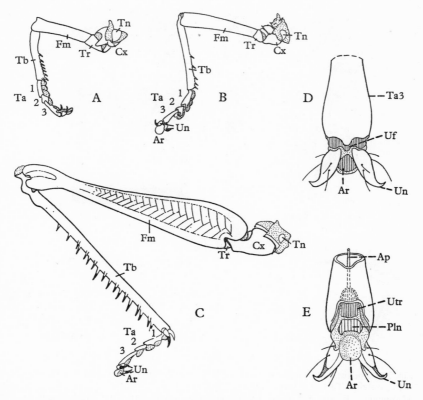

Fig. 20. *Nomadacris*, legs. A, prothoracic; B, mesothoracic; C, metathoracic (Albrecht 1956).
   Cx, coxa; Tn, trochantin; Tr, trochanter; Fm, femur; Tb, tibia; Ta, tarsus; Un, claw; Ar, arolium.
Dissosteira. D, distal end of tarsus, dorsal view; E, ditto, ventral view (Snodgrass 1929).
   Ta3, third article; Ap, apodeme; Uf, unguifer; Utr, unguitractor; Pln, planta; Un, claw; Ar, arolium.

Apically, the tibia is articulated with the *tarsus* (fig. 21) which consists of three well separated articles, the first and the last of them being usually longer than the middle. The first tarsal article is convex and well sclerotised above, but its lower surface bears three pairs of soft pads, which are called *pulvilli* (or euplantulae). The second article, which is the shortest, has only one pair of similar pulvilli. The third article is compressed laterally and has only one elongated and inflated pulvillus. The apex of the third article (fig. 20, D, E) projects dorsally and is excised ventrally where it is connected by two small sclerites (the *unguitractor plate* and *planta*) with the apical appendages—the *arolium* and a pair of *claws* (all these together are called by morphologists the *pretarsus*, but the term is illogical when applied to distal structures, and unnecessary). Detailed structure of the pulvillus and arolium of all legs is discussed below (p. 25).

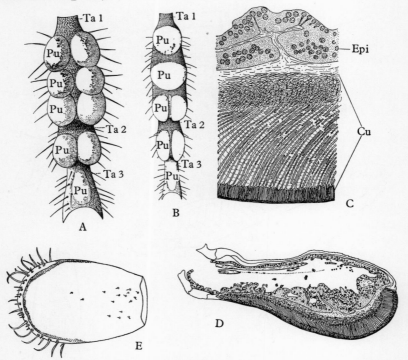

Fig. 21. *Dociostaurus*. A, prothoracic tarsus; B, mesothoracic tarsus (Jannone 1939*b*).
Pu, pulvilli; Ta 1, 2, 3, tarsal articles.
Melanoplus. E, arolium, ventral view; D, *ditto*, longitudinal section; C, integument of arolium (Slifer 1950*a*). Cu, cuticle; Epi, epidermis.

Second (mesothoracic) leg (fig. 20, B)

There is no substantial difference between this pair of legs and the first pair, except that the first two pulvilli of the first tarsal article are unpaired (fig. 21, B). The tibia in some Pamphagidae may be serrate along the upper edge, as a part of the stridulatory mechanism (p. 182).

Third (metathoracic) leg (fig. 20, C)

This leg differs considerably from the others, being transformed from an organ for walking to one for jumping. Its trochanter is still further reduced, the coxa is of a different shape, while the femur and tibia are very much enlarged. The femur is laterally compressed and its surfaces are divided by longitudinal ridges into well defined areas. Its externo-median area is somewhat convex and has a double row of elongated facets disposed in fishbone pattern; the furrows delimiting the facets correspond to ridges on the inside of the integument to which serial muscles are attached (p. 62); a similar pattern, though less distinct, can be seen on the interno-median area which may bear a longitudinal stridulatory ridge (p. 176). The lower surface is usually somewhat concave and the tibia fits into it when folded; on this surface a soft tubercle, Brunner's organ (p. 166), is found. The femur is narrowed towards the apex, which is enlarged to form a complex femoro-tibial joint, with strong lateral *genicular lobes* (Semichon 1924). The tibia is long, more or less rectangular in section, with a double row of strong spines along the posterior edges and two pairs of articulated preapical spurs. The tarsus is similar to that of other legs; the pulvilli of the first article are as in the second leg.

Pulvillus and arolium

These structures deserve separate discussion because of the peculiar specialisation of their integument and of its implications (Jannone 1939 *b;* Slifer 1950 *a*).

The *arolium* (fig. 21, C, D, E) is hollow, filled with blood and supplied with nerves and tracheae. The cuticle and hypoderm of its dorsal surface are normal, but the cuticle on the ventral surface is very thick and fibrous, the fibres being fine and dense near the surface where they form a very compact layer, covered by delicate epicuticle and a waxy deposit. The hypoderm of the ventral side is also modified, consisting of large cells, some of which might be secretory, but no ducts are present and their nature is doubtful. The fibrous structure of its ventral cuticle makes the arolium very pliable when it meets the substrate. The ventral surface bears a number of trichoid sensilla, probably tactile in function.

The *pulvillus* (or euplantula) has a structure similar to that of the arolium, though the special cuticular layer is thinner. It is also supplied with trichoid sensilla, as well as with others consisting of large sense cells and delicate tubules opening on the surface (Slifer, *t.c.*); these have not been studied in detail and it is not certain whether they are the same as described by Jannone (*t.c.*) as campaniform ones of a special type. Since these structures are in close contact with the substrate, their functions deserve careful study in relation to behaviour reactions.

The waxy surface layer of the pulvilli and arolia appears to prevent penetration of soluble dyes and of some insecticides (Mukerji & Chatterjee 1953), but the layer is easily abraded by contact with a rough substrate and the cuticle then becomes permeable.

The fact that the arolia are particularly large in species living on plants and very small in ground-living ones suggests that they play some part in climbing, which, however, requires detailed study.

Modifications of leg structure

As may be expected, the structure of the legs is subject to modifications related to special modes of life or activities—climbing, digging, swimming, sound production, etc., and such modifications will be discussed in the appropriate sections. Some variations in structure, however, are less obviously dependent on the environment or special activities.

The structure of the base of the hind femur presents two main types. In the most common one (fig. 22, L, O, S), the upper lobe of the notched base is large and overhangs the smaller lower lobe; in the other, the lower lobe is attenuated and the upper one reduced (fig. 22, Pc, Pp). The second type is characteristic of Pamphagidae and Pyrgomorphidae, while femora of intermediate type occur mainly in Romaleinae (fig. 22, R). Such variations must

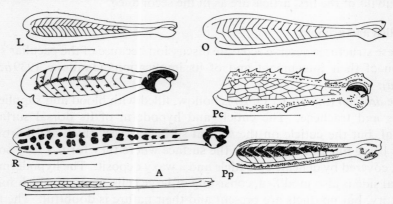

Fig. 22. Variations of metathoracic leg.
L, *Locusta*; O, *Oxya*; S, *Sphodromerus*; Pc, *Porthetis*; R, *Romalea*; Pp, *Poekilocerus*; A, *Acrida*. Line = 1 cm. (original by J. B. Mason).

affect the articulation mechanism and its functions, studies of which should include the coxa, trochanter (which is very much reduced in the second type) and relevant muscles.

A further feature of the femora of the second type is the distortion and partial obliteration of the fish-bone pattern, suggesting degradation of muscles; the fact that Pamphagidae are poor jumpers provides support for this suggestion.

TEGMINA AND WINGS

Morphologically speaking, both pairs of pterothoracic appendages are wings, but they differ considerably in their structure and in some of their functions. While the term wings, therefore, can be used to cover both pairs, it is confusing to use it when only the hindwings, or only the forewings (tegmina), are meant; the latter are sometimes called elytra, but this term properly applies to fully sclerotised structures found in beetles.

The *tegmen*, in its most common form, is approximately parallel-sided, with the apex rounded, but it varies from very narrow, with acute apex (e.g. *Acrida*, p. 415, fig. 241), to broad, leaf-like (*Systella*, p. 398, fig. 216). The length also varies greatly (p. 29).

The framework of a tegmen is formed by *veins*, which are hollow tubes with strongly sclerotised cuticle (fig. 23); their cavities being in communication with the general body cavity contain blood, and include branches of tracheae and of nerves arising from the mesothoracic ganglia (Zacwilichowski 1934; Fudalewicz-Niemczyk 1958; Afifi 1960). The membrane between the veins

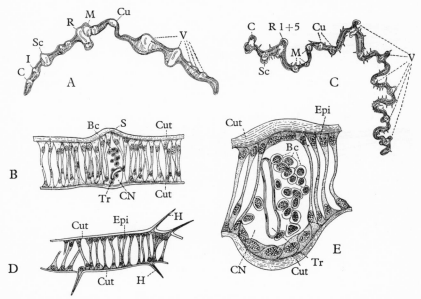

Fig. 23. *Dociostaurus*. A, B, sections of tegmen; C, D, E, ditto, of hindwing (Jannone 1939 b).
C, R, I, Sc, R, M, Cu, V, veins designated as in fig. 24; CN, cavity of a vein; Tr, trachea; Bc, blood cells; H, hair; Cut, cuticle; Epi, epidermal cell.

is formed by two thin cuticular layers, separated by a space in which blood can circulate; under the cuticle there are some hypodermal cells, more slender than in the veins where they are mostly bi-nucleate. The veins are provided with several kinds of sensilla, mainly trichoid and campaniform (p. 165), in which fine branches of nerves end.

The nomenclature of the main tegminal veins is important for taxonomy and has been subject to some controversy (Comstock & Needham 1899; Snodgrass 1929; Karandikar 1945; Smart 1953a, 1953b). Ragge (1955) reviewed it and provided a comparative table of previous systems; his system is adopted, with slight modification (fig. 24). Between the main veins and their branches there is a network of crossveins of variable regularity and density. Apart from differences in details of venation between taxonomic units, there is much variation due to the use of some veins and crossveins for stridulation and of the membranous areas between them as resonators (p. 176).

The *hindwing* has a larger area than tegmen and is approximately triangular in shape, with the outer margin more or less rounded. The venation (fig. 24) is homologous with that of the tegmen, but the posterior part is particularly large and clearly delimited from the anterior by the first anal vein which is therefore called the dividing vein; this posterior part is then called the *vannus*

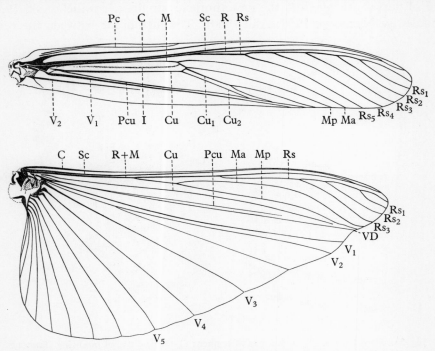

Fig. 24. *Locusta*, venation of tegmina and wings (original by V. M. Dirsh).
Pc, precosta; C, costa; Sc, subcosta; R, radius; Rs, radial sector; M, media; Ma, anterior media; Mp, posterior media; I, intercalate (false) vein; Cu, cubitus; Pcu, postcubitus; VD, dividing vein; V, vannal veins.

and the veins within it vannal veins (the first vannal corresponding to 2A, and so on, of other authors). The veins also include branches of tracheae and nerves and bear sensilla externally, while their lumens are in communication with the body cavity. The crossveins are usually less dense and finer than in the tegmen, and the membrane is also thinner, but otherwise similar in structure (fig. 23).

As can be seen from this brief description (for details see Jannone 1939 *b*), both tegmina and hindwings are not merely parchment-like appendages serving flight, but very complicated live organs, maintaining intimate connection with the rest of the body by nerves and tracheae, and by blood circulating through veins and between membranes, while also possessing their own sensory equipment. The physiology of the wings has been greatly and unduly neglected.

At rest, the tegmina and wings are folded against the body as shown in fig. 25. It appears that the base of the right tegmen usually overlaps the left, but this has not been investigated.

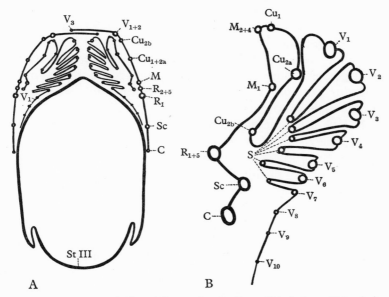

Fig. 25. *Dociostaurus*. A, folding of the tegmina; B, ditto, of hind wings. Veins designated as in Fig. 24, except that Cu_{2b} of hind wing corresponds to VD; S, secondary veins (Jannone 1939 *b*).

MEIOPTERISM

The normal, functional wings are subject to reduction from mere relative shortening to complete disappearance. This phenomenon has been broadly called brachypterism, and various terms have been proposed to designate the degree of reduction (Karny 1912; Puschnig 1914; Ramme 1951 *a*, p. 26), but La Greca (1954) proposed the all-embracing term meiopterism (reduction of flight organs), and the following categories can be distinguished:

Macropterism: normal, functional tegmina and hindwings, reaching at least to the end of the abdomen.
Brachypterism: tegmina shorter than the abdomen, but overlapping, or at least touching each other dorsally; hindwings as tegmina, or shorter, or absent.
Micropterism: tegmina lateral, not touching each other dorsally; hindwings absent.
Subapterism: tegmina minute, scale-like, without venation; hindwings absent.
Apterism: all wings absent.

There are no sharp dividing lines between these categories and further complications occur, for example when the tegmina are fully developed and only the hindwings are reduced (e.g. in the male of *Chorthippus parallelus*). The ultimate reduction to the apterous condition is also not always obvious;

thus the Pamphagid genera *Tropidauchen* and *Nocaracris* are usually regarded as apterous, but minute tegmina and vestiges of hindwings are revealed by careful examination (Mason 1959).

Sexual dimorphism in the degree of wing development is quite common. In macropterous species using the tegmina for stridulation (p. 176), the male tegmen is more highly specialised than the female one and, generally speaking, the degree of meiopterism in females is greater than in males of the same species. An extreme case is that of *Porthetis* and related Pamphagid genera (fig. 219, p. 400), males of which are fully winged while females are apterous. The cases of greater wing reduction in the male sex are, on the other hand, exceptional; for example, in an undescribed Australian genus related to *Macrotona* the male is normally brachypterous, while the female is macropterous (Dr K. H. L. Key, personal communication); and in a small desert grasshopper of Middle Asia, *Diexis chivensis*, the female has tegmina extending beyond the middle of the abdomen and short hindwings, while the male tegmina are very short and the hindwings hardly perceptible.

While the degree of meiopterism is usually characteristic of a species, in some cases there is considerable individual variation; for example, in some species of *Chrotogonus* (Pyrgomorphidae) both macropterous and brachypterous individuals occur, as well as transitional forms (Kevan 1959).

Wing reduction is correlated with substantial modifications in the morphology of the pronotum (p. 11), the pterothorax (p. 14) and the wing muscles (La Greca 1947; J. Thomas 1952, 1953, 1954*a*; Ewer 1954*d*, 1958; Atzinger 1957; Wiesend 1957). In the sexually dimorphic *Psophus*, both the direct and indirect wing muscles are very much reduced in the brachypterous female as compared with the macropterous male. In *Romalea*, the thoracic muscles which move only wings are strongly reduced, but those which also move legs are relatively robust (D. Wilson 1962). In the apterous female of *Lamarckiana* several important muscles are either absent, or represented by small strands, or are merely smaller than in the fully macropterous male (J. Thomas 1952). In the completely apterous *Lentula*, the indirect flight muscles and several of the dorso-ventral flight muscles are entirely absent, a condition not yet observed in any other acridoid (Ewer 1958). Many micropterous and apterous species lack the tympanum (p. 190).

A phenomenon of great interest is the occasional appearance of macropterous individuals in normally brachypterous species, for example, in the European *Chorthippus parallelus* and *Podisma pedestris* (J. Thomas 1953), North American *Dendrotettix quercus* (Rehn & Rehn 1938), African *Zonocerus elegans* (E. D. Burtt 1951*b*), Indian *Hieroglyphus nigrorepletus* (Uvarov 1922), Australian *Phaulacridium vittatum* (Key 1938), and so on. Such reversion is known to occur only in brachypterous species, not in micropterous ones. There has been much theorising on the causes of reversion, but reliable experimental evidence in support of the various hypotheses is lacking. A possible approach to the physiology of this phenomenon was suggested by Wiesend (1957), who pointed out that early instar hoppers have all muscles equally developed regardless of the eventual length of tegmina and wings, but in the later instars some factor inhibits muscle development in the individuals that eventually become brachypterous (see also J. Thomas 1953, 1954a; Atzinger 1957). Such an inhibiting factor may be hormonal (cf. Sellier 1955), but this awaits investigation. A change from the macropterous condition normal for a species to the brachypterous has been recorded only under exceptional experimental conditions. Thus, feeding on lucerne resulted in brachypterism in *Melanoplus sanguinipes* and in *Schistocerca* (p. 84).

It has been suggested in the past that the degree of wing development is connected with altitude (those living on high mountains tending to become brachypterous or apterous), or with dense vegetation which hinders movement, and so on. Such correlations will be discussed elsewhere in relation to ecology.

INTEGUMENT

In the past, the hard outer covering of insects has been regarded as exoskeleton (that is, an essentially supporting structure), but now it is regarded as 'one of the primary organ systems' (A. G. Richards 1951), serving a number of physiological functions. It covers not only the whole body and its appendages, but extends also to the walls of the tracheae (p. 124), foregut (p. 70) and hindgut (p. 73). General information on insect integument will be found in the book of A. G. Richards (*t.c.*) and in papers by Wigglesworth (1948, 1957); Beament (1961) and Ruddall (1963), but data on acridoids are far from adequate.

HISTOLOGY

The integument consists of several layers (fig. 26). The innermost is a very thin *basement membrane*, formed of delicate filaments embedded in amorphous substance; its general structure and properties are those of the connective tissue (Jannone 1939 *b*; Chauvin 1939 *b*, 1941 *b*; Slifer 1952; Baccetti 1956 *a*, 1956 *b*; Malek 1958 *b*).

The basement membrane lines very closely the inner surface of the *epidermis* (also called hypoderm), which consists of a single layer of essentially glandular cells, with various inclusions (e.g. pigment granules). These epidermal cells play an active part in many physiological processes, in addition to the production of the *cuticle*, which is a comprehensive name for the external non-cellular layers formed by solidified secretions of epidermal cells (Jensen & Weis-Fogh 1962; Andersen 1963). The most important substance is chitin (p. 91), but there are several of these layers, differing in their physical and chemical properties. The innermost layer, the *endocuticle*, is distinctly laminated and usually colourless; the laminae correspond to solidified layers deposited every 24 hours and reflect the growth of the cuticle (Neville 1963 *b*, 1963 *c*, 1963 *d*) see (p. 295). Above the endocuticle lies the *exocuticle* which is non-laminate and often hard and dark-coloured as a result of sclerotisation and tanning; the chemistry of these latter processes is still debatable (Malek 1957, 1958 *a*, 1961; Dennell 1958; Hackman 1959).

Above the exocuticle there is a thin coating of various non-chitinous materials, secreted by the epidermal cells and carried outwards along very fine *pore canals* traversing the deeper layers of the cuticle. This coating has been collectively called the *epicuticle*, but the latest suggestion (Lower 1959) is to restrict this term to the innermost proteinaceous layer (sometimes striated and impregnated with lipoid); it is overlaid by the *amphion*, consisting of secreted substances, which appear to vary according to the species. In

Schistocerca two layers of amphion were distinguished; the paraffin and the 'cement' layers (the latter being partly lipoid), permeated by wax (Malek, *t.c.*) with the melting point at 50–54° C (Pradhan & Bindra 1956). In *Melanoplus bivittatus*, there is an inner lipoprotein layer and an outer covering of wax, but no 'cement' layer (Chefurka & Pepper 1955*b*), though the latter statement was questioned by Malek (*t.c.*). The properties of the epicuticle and the amphion are of obvious importance for the permeability of the integument, which should affect water economy, humidity responses, action of contact poisons, and so on, and variation may be expected in relation to the ecology, but only the above two species have been studied in this respect.

There is a great diversity in the structure and properties of the integument of different body regions and parts. Thus, the intersegmental membranes of

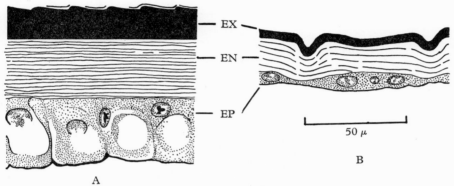

Fig. 26. *Schistocerca*, sections of cuticle. A, tergite; B, intersegmental membrane (Malek 1958*b*).
EX, exocuticle; EN, endocuticle; EP, epidermis.

the abdomen have very thin epidermal and cuticular layers (fig. 26, and p. 322), whereas these layers are extremely thick in, for example, the pronotum (fig. 29). Tegmina and wings are essentially integumental structures of a special kind (fig. 23).

Slifer (1951) has described in *Locusta* some areas of the integument with thin, poorly sclerotised cuticle, lacking cement layer and consisting almost entirely of exocuticle; cells under this cuticle are unusual, their cytoplasm having numerous processes. Such areas on the head are represented by a pair of *antennal crescents*, lying just above the antennal sclerite surrounding the membranous antennal base (antacorium). Areas of similar structure, called fenestrae by Slifer, are found dorsally on mesothorax, metathorax and the abdominal tergites I–VII, laterally; there is (in the female only) a pair on tergites II and III; ventrally, they are in the cervical membrane and on the mesosternum snf metasternum (fig. 27). Such specialised areas, hereafter called *Slifer's patches*, were found in 128 species studied, belonging to different families

3

and occurring in different habitats (Slifer 1953 *a*, 1953 *b*, 1954 *b*, 1957, 1958 *a*). The total size of the patches in a species in relation to its total surface was generally greater in females than in males and they were relatively larger in species of larger size and thicker integument; no relation was found between wing development and the size of the patches. It was thought that the specialised areas are particularly well developed in abundant and swarming species (*Locusta*, *Schistocerca*, *Nomadacris*), but a comparison between

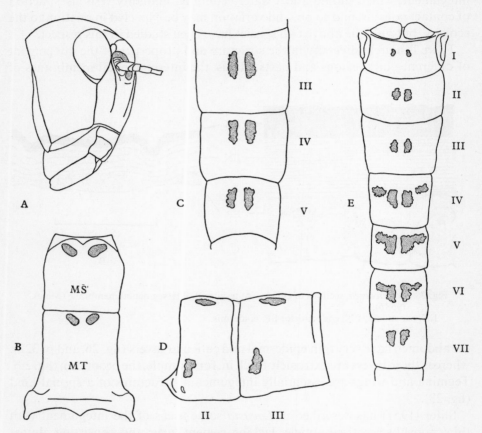

Fig. 27. *Locusta*, Slifer's patches of cuticle (stippled) (Slifer 1951).
A, male, head with the antennal crescent; B, female, mesothorax and metathorax; C, female tergites III, IV and V; D, female, sides of tergites II and III; E, male, tergites I to VII.

Dociostaurus maroccanus and non-swarming species of the genus did not support this (Slifer 1957). Slifer's original suggestion that these structures are connected with thermoreception has been disputed (p. 220) and their function remains obscure.

In adults, changes in the structure and properties of integument occur during development and growth (p. 295).

The importance of the cuticle as a protective covering is obvious, but no studies are available on, for example, its hardness in acridoids. Its permeability will be more conveniently discussed in connection with water relations (p. 225). Of great interest is the recent finding that the cuticle of hinge mechanisms of *Schistocerca* wings has special rubber-like elastic properties because it includes a peculiar protein, *resilin* (Weis-Fogh 1960; Bailey & Weis-Fogh 1960; Jensen & Weis-Fogh 1962; Neville 1963*b*; 1963*c*, Andersen 1963).

INTEGUMENTAL GLANDS

'All of the epidermal cells are glandular in that they participate in the production of the cuticle, but there are in addition certain larger cells which develop from epidermal cells and seem to be specialised for producing some special secretions' (A. G. Richards 1951). To this latter category belong the dermal moulting glands (p. 285), and the glandular hypodermal cells found on the dorsal side of the abdominal tergites of *Schistocerca paranensis* and *S. gregaria*, with fine canals carrying a secretion through the cuticle to its surface (Ogloblin 1947; Malek 1958*b*; Loher 1960, 1961). The secretion has a distinctive odour and is regarded as a hormone which plays a part in the inter-attraction of individuals, particularly prior to mating, and stimulates sexual maturation (p. 298). It has been suggested by Liebermann (1953) that a pair of integumental organs covered by hairs, found on the seventh abdominal sternite of *Trybliophorus modestus*, may be glandular and connected with mating.

Eversible thoracic glands

In adults of *Acrotylus* spp. and *Morphacris*, when captured, a whitish membranous trilobate vesicle is extruded behind the pronotum, between the bases of the elytra (fig. 28, D, E). This is a thoracic gland, which in the normal state is an integumental sac under the pronotum, with some of its hypodermal cells large and glandular (Jannone 1938*b*, 1939*a*). A similar structure in the non-everted state has been described by Vosseler (1902) in *Oedaleus* (fig. 28, A, B, C); according to Hollande (1926) it is eversible and is present in both hoppers and adults, as is the case in *Acrotylus*. The everted vesicle may burst under pressure of blood, which then flows out. Nikolskiĭ (1925) observed that when hoppers of *Locusta*, bred in cages, are taken in the hand there appears behind the pronotum a lobed sac which bursts at the apex and emits a jet of fluid to a distance of up to 60 cm. Hoppers of all instars are able to do this, but particularly those of the third and fourth, and seldom those of the fifth; Jannone (*tt.cc.*) failed to find this organ in the adult *Locusta*.

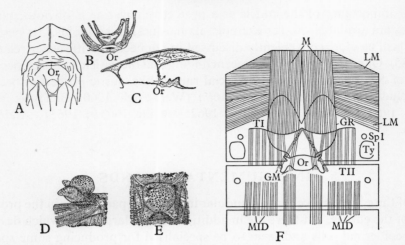

Fig. 28. Integumental glands. A, B, C, *Oedaleus*: A, view from above; B, gland isolated; C, longitudinal section (Vosseler 1902). D, E, *Acrotylus*: D, everted thoracic gland, side view; E, ditto, dorsal view (Jannone 1938). F, *Poekilocerus*, diagram of abdominal gland (Fishelson 1960).

M, LM, MID, muscles; GM, muscles of the gland; Or, orifice; GR, gland; TI, TII, abdominal tergites; Sp, spiracle; Ty, tympanum.

Abdominal repugnatorial glands

In several Pyrgomorphid genera (*Colemania*, *Atractomorpha*, *Pyrgomorpha*, *Phymateus*, *Zonocerus*, *Poekilocerus*) there is a large, bilobed sac-like gland (fig. 28, F), with the orifice in the membrane between the first and second abdominal tergites (Coleman 1911; Pavlowsky 1916; De Lotto 1950; Ewer 1957*c*; Fishelson 1960). Similar, but less developed, glands were noted by Pavlowsky in the membrane between the second and third tergite in *Phymateus*, which also has a glandular structure above the base of the hind leg. The secretion of the glands is a milky fluid, with alkaline reaction and pungent smell, and it may be ejected on strong excitation for a distance up to 30 cm. The opening of the gland is regulated by specialised alary muscles, but the ejection is probably due to an increase in haemocoelic pressure, which also causes jets of blood to be mixed with the secretion (Ewer *t.c.*). Not all Pyrgomorphidae possess such glands; they are absent in *Maura* and *Dictyophorus*, in which, however, expulsion of blood from other parts of the body occurs on excitation (Grassé 1937).

In *Physemophorus socotranus* the first tergite bears a hard cylindrical tubercle which projects between the suitable (and quite unusually) excised bases of the elytra, but its fine structure and function have not been studied.

SURFACE FEATURES OF CUTICLE

The surface of the integument on the exposed parts of the body is relatively seldom smooth and shiny, but the surface of the abdomen, covered by the wings while the insect is at rest, is usually smooth. Elsewhere, the integument is usually matt, owing to minute cuticular wrinkles, rugosities, tubercles and spinules. Some types of surface structure are connected with the ecology of the species, but detailed studies of cuticular sculpturing are lacking, although the finer structure of the surface may be of importance in relation to the wetting properties of the integument (Holdgate 1955).

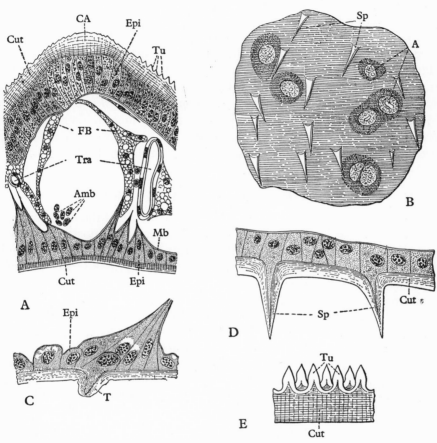

Fig. 29. *Dociostaurus*, cuticle. A, transverse section of pronotum; B, ventral face of the metazona of pronotum; C, D, sections of the same; E, greatly enlarged section of the dorsal cuticle of pronotum (Jannone 1939 *b*).

Cut, cuticle; CA, median carina; Epi, epidermis; Tu, tubercles (shown enlarged in E); FB, fat body; Tra, trachea; Amb, amoebocytes; Mb, basal membrane; Sp, spines; A, clear areas corresponding to tubercles (T); T, tubercle on the ventral face of metazone.

Various projections of the cuticle, in the shape of ridges, tubercles and spines, are common (fig. 29), but their fine structure has hardly been studied; some of them may be due merely to the superficial moulding of the cuticle surface, but others are more complicated and their structure involves one or more epidermal cells (Jannone 1939*b*). Particularly prominent are *spines*, which may be either rigid, such as those disposed in two series along the hind tibia, or set in membranous sockets (e.g. the movable apical tibial *spurs*). Spines may occur in somewhat unexpected places, for example on the underside of the pronotal integument (fig. 29, B) where their function is difficult to suggest.

Various sensilla, which are also essentially integumental structures, are dealt with elsewhere (p. 161).

Hairs are not a conspicuous general feature of Acridids, although in some of them they are well developed. Thus, the sternum of *Locusta* is covered with dense hairs which earned it the name of 'hairy-chested locust' in the Sudan. Dense hairs on some parts of the body are also characteristic of certain desert species, and paired patches of dense and long hairs have been described on the seventh sternite of *Trybliophorus modestus* by Liebermann (1953); similar groups of hairs can be seen on sternites in *Tropidopola* and *Oxya*. No information is available on the fine structure of hairs or their function, except the known, or presumed, hair sensilla (p. 161).

COLORATION AND PATTERN

Visible colours of insects are due either to the structure of the integument, or to the pigments in it. Structural colours of insects are mostly metallic or lustrous in appearance and these are very rare in Acridoidea; the few examples of such coloration are offered by *Leptacris*, a slender grasshopper of tropical grasslands, which has a silvery band along the lower edge of the head, pronotum and pleurae, and by the North American *Bootettix* which has silvery spots. The fine structure of the silvery parts has not been studied, but this appearance is probably due to the scattering of light by very thin lamellae (as in the butterfly *Argynnis*; Fox & Vevers 1960).

White colours are also probably structural. Newly moulted hoppers and adults are whitish, until pigments are formed. All the thinner parts of the integument, for example intersegmental membranes, remain colourless or whitish. Pure white features of pattern are sometimes associated with particularly thickened cuticle. For example, the pronotal carinae are frequently white, or light, in colour; their whiteness is probably due to the scattered reflexion of light either by the numerous colourless lamellae or by solid colourless material in thick layers of the cuticle (Fox & Vevers 1960; A. G. Richards 1951). Some data on the histological location of pigments in pattern morphs (p. 39) of *Chortoicetes terminifera* were given by Byrne (1962).

More usual are the colours due to pigments present in the integument. The chemical nature of pigments is reviewed below (p. 42), while here the visible coloration and its pattern are discussed only as a morphological problem. Ecological aspects of coloration will be dealt with in the second volume.

The range of colours in acridoids as a whole is less extensive than, for example, in butterflies or beetles, and as a group they appear rather uniformly coloured in shades of brown (from pale-straw to black), grey and green; such bright colours as red, blue or yellow appear normally on hind wings and often on hind legs, but seldom on other parts.

Completely uniform coloration, however, is not a general rule, and disruptive patterns, composed either of different colours or of contrasting shades of the same colour, are common. While the earlier authors have been content with describing colour patterns in a purely subjective way, more detailed studies on the different types of variation—genetic, environmental, developmental—have demanded an objective approach. Vorontsovskiĭ (1928) in his study of parallel colour variation in forty-eight species of grasshoppers established thirty-two categories of pattern and called them varieties, with suggestive Latin names. Thus, uniformly green specimens were called var. *viridis*; green with purple elytra, var. *porphyroptera*; green on the sides but brown above, var. *hyalolateralis* or var. *prasinolateralis*; and so on. Rubtzov (1935a) adopted the same principle, but distinguished only six, more clearly defined, categories amongst twenty-six closely allied Siberian species. Ramme's (1951b) eleven pattern categories, diagrammatically illustrated in colour for twenty-one European species, were denoted not by names, but by one-letter symbols. Key (1954), in studying pattern variation in *Chortoicetes* and *Austroicetes*, established twelve 'forms' (called 'pattern morphs' by White & Key 1957) defined by morphological distribution of colours and denoted by standardised Latin names (fig. 30).

A different method of recording complex combinations of colour and pattern was proposed by E. J. Clark (1943). The description of each colour form is by a formula, composed of symbols which denote both the general and the detailed distribution of colours. Clark's notation system, as simplified by O. W. Richards & Waloff (1954), is given below, with some modifications.

The insect to be described is regarded as being in the resting position, with tegmina and wings closed.

Colours. Colour symbols are italic initial letters of the corresponding Latin adjectives: white, *a*; brown, *b*; yellow, *f*; grey, *g*; black, *n*; purple or pink, *p*; straw, *s*; green, *v*.

Markings. Coarse spotting or banding, m (not in italics); fine spotting, p; colour of spots may be indicated as above (e.g. *n*p; *b*m).

Total coloration, T. The dorsal and lateral surfaces are recorded separately in that order, so that an entirely green insect is T*vv*, and one grey dorsally and green laterally is T*gv*; one with the reverse distribution of colours is T*vg*.

Tegmen, E. The tegmina in the resting position are divided into three longitudinal zones, each recorded separately, the dorsal zone first (e.g. E*vbb*). Pale stripes, often present at the outer edge of the dorsal zone and just above the lower edge of the tegmen, are denoted as sp and ls, respectively. A spot often present in the distal third of tegmen is st (stigma).

Abdomen, A. Hidden in the resting adult; if its description is needed, the usual pattern features are the dorsal stripe, fm, which may be flanked by lateral lines, ll, and the sides of the abdomen, l.

Hind femur, F. The colour of the dorsal, outer and lower surfaces is recorded separately, in that order.

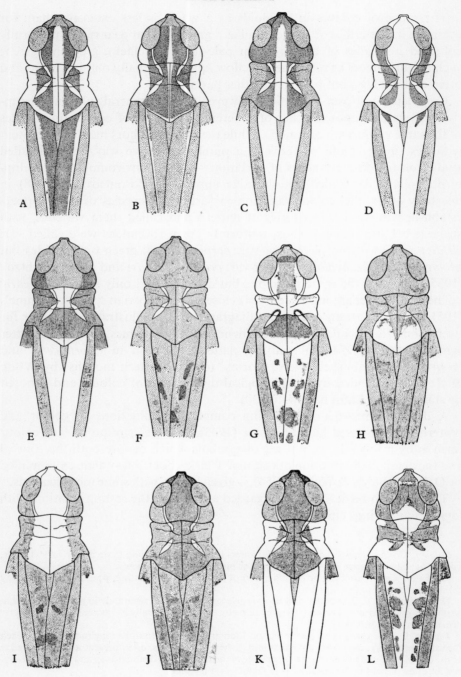

Fig. 30. *Chortoicetes terminifera*, pattern morphs. A, *trilineata*; B, *lineosa*; C, *albomedia*; D, *nigrovirgata*; E, *fusco-collaris*; F, *rubiginosa*; G, *transmaculata*; H, *sagittata*; I, *acruciata*; J, *nigrosuperficies*; K, *posteroalba*; L, *leopardina* (Key 1954).

Hind tibia, Tib. Colour recorded in the usual way; when particoloured, fractions may be used (e.g. Tib 1/3*s* 2/3 *r*). Tibial spines, if of a distinct colour, are denoted as Ts.

Head, C. The medio-dorsal stripe is denoted by fm; it may include a median line, m. A post-ocular stripe is fpd. The vertex, V, may need separate notation.

Pronotum, P. There is a dorsal stripe, fd, and the median carina, cm. A pale-coloured line, often coinciding with the lateral carina, is cl. The dorsal stripe may be bordered by a darker band externally, fdl, or internally, fdi. Often there is an oblique mark on the pronotal lateral lobe, zl.

Here are examples of applying this notation to two varieties of *Chorthippus parallelus*:

T*vv*; E*vvb* (or *vvv*) st*n*; F*vv*; Cfpd*g*; Pcl*s* fdi*n* (entirely green; tegmen green except the lowest zone which may be brown with a black stigma; femur green dorsally and laterally; head with a grey postocular stripe; pronotum with a straw-coloured median stripe, flanked internally by black).

T*vb*; E*vvv*; F*bb*; Cfp*dn*; All*n* (green dorsally and brown laterally; tegmen entirely green; femur dorsally and laterally brown; head with black postocular stripe; abdomen with black lateral lines).

Clark's notation system has been so far tested only on a few British grass-hoppers and may need modification for more general use, but its principle appears logical. Moreover, as Richards & Waloff (1954) recognised after extensive tests, it allows a shorthand recording of copious data (e.g. when studying a population) for later analysis.

A much more precise method of recording colours and patterns has been developed for an objective investigation of colour variation in hoppers of *Schistocerca* by Stower (1959), depending on the instar and the environmental and inherited factors. The essential components of total coloration are the ground colour and the dark pattern. The ground colour in these hoppers varies from green to red and is rarely the same over the whole body; it has therefore to be considered separately for a number of body regions of which the following were selected: frons, postocular patch, pronotum, hind femur, abdominal tergites. The colour of each region was determined exactly by comparison with plates in *The Munsell Book of Color* (1929-42), which makes it possible to record by special symbols the *hue* (e.g. red, yellow, green), the *value* (luminance) and the *chroma* (intensity, or degree of saturation of a hue). The symbols are read off the Munsell plates and the data, being numerical, are convenient for segregation into classes; three such classes, each characterised by respective ranges of hue, value and chroma, were defined.

The pattern of *Schistocerca* hoppers is formed by black or brown markings, the extent of which varies widely on different regions of the body; for practical purposes it was estimated by Stower over the main regions and the mean dark pattern index was calculated; on the basis of the index, classes were established. Thus, an objective numerical representation of both colour and pattern was obtained, permitting statistical analysis of the variation in different populations and in relation to the various factors. Stower's method is very laborious, but this disadvantage may diminish if the number of body regions to be studied is reduced as a result of detailed investigation of particular material. It should be particularly valuable as a tool for precise research, for example in studies of the variation of single chromatic characters.

The coloration of the wings presents somewhat different problems from that of the rest of body. Thus, the tegmen coloration has to be resolved in that of the membrane and the veins. A morphological approach to the pattern of acridoid tegmina was made by Lemche (1935), who suggested that the dark transverse bands (e.g. in *Schistocerca*) are based on forks of the main veins. The membrane of the hindwings is usually colourless, but in some species it is bright blue, yellow or red; brown or black pigment may be suffused throughout the wing, but more frequently forms a curved band across the wing or an apical spot. The deposition of pigments in both wings is, presumably, correlated with the haemolymph circulation (p. 106).

While much of the colour and pattern may be stable and inherited (Byrne 1962), this is not always the case. It will be seen later that striking changes normally occur in an individual in the course of its hopper development (p. 283), and of the ageing and maturation of the adult (p. 297), as well as under the influence of density (p. 336) and the external conditions (p. 44, 52). This underlines the view that the integument, even of adult acridoids, is not a mere outer covering, but a living system.

PIGMENTS

There has been in the past a tendency to regard pigments merely as chemical substances in the integument concerned mainly with the external appearance of an insect. More recent work has shown that this is only a subsidiary, and often incidental, function of pigments, most of which play a part in various metabolic processes, and attention is now turned to their biochemistry and their physiological role. Such studies of very complex and imperfectly known organic substances naturally require highly specialised knowledge and 'attempts made by entomologists at identifying pigments by a few simple reactions, followed by giving them long but meaningless names, should be discouraged as they are likely to introduce more confusion than clarity' (Uvarov 1948; A. G. Richards 1951). General treatment of insect pigments will be found in the following publications: Timon-David 1947; Wigglesworth 1949; Baraud 1955; Cromartie 1959; Fox & Vevers 1960; Gilmour 1961; R. H. Thomson 1960. A comprehensive review of pigments involved in the coloration of locusts was given by Goodwin (1952*a*). Since, as will be seen, the same substance (or a slight modification of it) may produce more than one visible colour, while similar colours may be due to chemically different pigments, it is more correct to group pigments according to their chemical nature.

Melanins

In spite of their name, pigments of this group are not always black and may be brown, reddish, or yellowish. In fact, it is far from clear which of the black, brown and grey components of coloration common in acridoids are due to melanins and which to ommochromes (p. 44).

Melanins are considered to be derived from the amino-acid tyrosine, found in haemolymph which is oxidised with the aid of the copper-containing enzyme phenolase (tyrosinase) and then polymerised, the resulting products being insoluble in most solvents; this latter fact is largely responsible for their exact chemical nature still being insufficiently known (Gilmour 1961).

Reliable records of melanin in adults of acridoids are few. Chauvin (1941b) found melanin in adult *Schistocerca* only in pericardial cells and salivary glands, not in the integument. However, according to Goodwin (1952a), some vestiges of melanin are present in the blackish tegminal spots, mandibles, leg joints and spines of *Schistocerca* and *Locusta* adults. Many other adult acridoids possess large areas of integument with deep black coloration, but it is not known whether this is due to melanin.

On the other hand, the black areas of the integument of gregarious hoppers of *Locusta* and *Schistocerca* are definitely due to melanin deposited in the cuticle; cuticular exuviae shed in moulting show the black pattern of the previous instar. Melanisation of the new cuticle has, therefore, to occur repeatedly after each moult. It has been thought that melanisation of cuticle is closely associated with its hardening (sclerotisation) but recent views are that two different chemical processes are involved (Goodwin 1952a; Malek 1957, 1961; Jones & Sinclair 1958; Gilmour 1961; Karlson & Schloss-berger-Recke 1962). In fact, the cuticle of the solitarious and the albino hoppers (p. 46) from both of which melanin is absent, is just as hard as that of the normal gregarious ones. The absence of melanin from the cuticle of solitarious locust hoppers and its presence in gregarious appears to be broadly connected with different levels of metabolism and activity in the two phases. These effects however are not direct, but associated with the differences between phases in their hormonal balance which influence melanin meta-bolism.

The sources and the metabolism of the substances involved in melanin production are little known; it was often suggested that its source is the amino-acid tyrosine, but direct proofs are lacking (see review by Fuzeau-Braesch 1960). The enzyme phenolase (tyrosinase) is present already in the egg of *Melanoplus* (Bodine & Boell 1935) and Bodine & Fitzgerald (1948a) studied changes in the copper content of developing eggs, this element entering the composition of phenolase. Melanin formation in the *Locusta* embryo is subject to hormonal control (Jones 1956a), while there are indications that carotene and vitamins such as ascorbic acid and inositol are needed in the diet of *Schistocerca* and *Locusta* for the development of normal melanin patterns in hoppers (Dadd 1960a, 1961a, 1963).

There are empirical indications that some stage in the formation, or deposi-tion, of melanin is affected by external factors. Thus, gregarious hoppers of

Schistocerca reared at 24°C develop an unusually deep and extensive black pattern, at 33°C the pattern is reduced, and at 44°C it is almost absent (Husain & Ahmad 1936*b*); a similar effect of high temperatures was noted in the field (Stower 1959). While great reduction of black areas at high temperatures can be reasonably ascribed to deficiency of melanin, the general darkening at low temperatures may also be due to excess production of dark insectorubin (see below). Another set of experiments indicated that solitarious hoppers of *Schistocerca* reared in an atmosphere with an excess of carbon dioxide developed the black pattern of the gregarious phase (Husain & Mathur 1936); this result is difficult to interpret, if melanisation involves oxidation.

Ommochromes

As already mentioned, some blackish, brown, red and yellow pigments produce coloration similar to that due to melanins, but they are chemically different from them.

Chauvin (1941*b*) extracted from the integument of *Schistocerca* a wine-red pigment which became orange when oxidised; he called it *acridioxanthin* and believed it to be anthocyanin derived from food, but this view is no longer accepted. Becker (1942) extracted substances of this type from eyes of various insects (not including acridoids) and named them ommochromes. Goodwin 1950*b*, 1952*a*; Goodwin & Srisukh 1950) obtained redox pigments from *Schistocerca* and *Locusta*, found them similar to Chauvin's acridioxanthin and Becker's ommochromes, and proposed to call them *insectorubins*. The name ommochromes has been adopted for a group of pigments supposed to be derived from the amino-acid tryptophan and characterised by being soluble in cold dilute alkalis, formic acid and mineral acids and by showing reversible redox changes, that is, being brown, orange or yellow when oxidised and red when reduced. They are found not only in insects, and in insects not only in their eyes (Butenandt, Biekert & Linzen 1958; Linzen 1959; Fox & Vevers 1960; Gilmour 1961). Since the group is still inadequately known the name insectorubin may be retained for the locust pigments of the ommochrome group.

Insectorubin is synthetised in the locust egg and its amount continues to increase through the hopper life (fig. 31) but its concentration drops after the final moult. Unlike melanin, it is found not diffused in the cuticle, but in the hypodermal cells in the form of granular inclusions (Nickerson 1956; Bellamy 1958). A significant feature of its distribution is concentration of such granules under the melanised spots of the cuticle, suggesting some connection between insectorubin and melanin (p. 45).

Although present in gregarious hoppers of both *Locusta* and *Schistocerca* insectorubin contributes little to their coloration, but the pink colour of the gregarious *Schistocerca* fledglings is due to its reduced form. Chauvin (1941*b*) suggested that it is eliminated in excreta on sexual maturation, but this is not the case, and it is still present in the mature adult, but masked by yellow carotenoid (p. 47), especially in the males, while the brownish colour of mature females is due to insectorubin combined with protein (Goodwin 1952 a).

Ommochromes in grasshoppers have been studied only by Okay (1948, 1954) who concluded that brown components of integumental colour in *Acrida* and *Calliptamus* are due to insectorubin. In *Acrida*, reared at low temperature (21°C), some reddish-violet colour appearing especially on the underside of the body is due to ommochrome, which is present as brown granules of protein-bound pigment in hypodermal cells, and to reddish, or violet, reduced free pigment penetrating into the endocuticle.

Insectorubin production in locusts is affected by temperature in a way similar to melanin, since it is almost completely inhibited at 38–40°C, but at

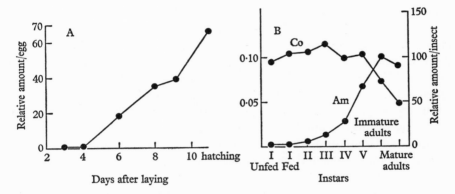

Fig. 31. Changes in the insectorubin content in *Locusta* and *Schistocerca* during life. A, eggs; B, hoppers and adults (after Goodwin 1950 b). Co, concentration; Am, relative amount.

28°C its amount is three times that of the normal; the size of insectorubin granules at high temperature is definitely reduced (Bellamy 1958). It is possible, therefore, that visible changes in the general darkness of the integument correlated with temperature are not solely due to variation in the melanin deposition, but also to the rate of insectorubin production. Since insectorubin is mainly contained in the hypoderm and melanin in the cuticle, the exuviae shed at moults can provide information on the relative parts played by the two pigments in the general coloration.

A possible metabolic connection between insectorubin and melanin has been suggested by Goodwin (1950 b) and by Dadd (1961 c), but this could not be the case if it is true that the first originates from tryptophane and the second from tyrosine (Fuzeau-Braesch 1960). Dadd (t.c.) found also that the absence of carotene from the diet of *Schistocerca* suppressed the pink coloration of immature adults which is due to insectorubin.

It is of particular interest that in the green solitarious hoppers of *Schistocerca* some red-brown pigment is found only in the eyes (Goodwin 1950*b*; Linzen 1959), where it is presumably responsible for the dark stripes (p. 198) which are almost invisible in the gregarious hoppers because the interspaces between stripes are equally dark, possibly as a result of excessive insectorubin; gregarious hoppers reared at 40°C have striped eyes, presumably because the insectorubin production is inhibited by high temperature. However, the chemical constitution of the reddish-brown pigment of locust eyes, regarded by Goodwin as insectorubin, has been questioned by Gilmour (1961). Linzen (personal communication) found xanthommatin in *Schistocerca* eyes.

Hereditary melanism and albinism

While general darkening of the integument in cool and humid conditions is due to the increased production of both melanin and insectorubin (p. 44), it is not known whether such environmentally induced change is transmitted to the next generation. On the other hand, a definite case of melanic mutation was recorded by Volkonsky (1938*a*) in *Schistocerca*. By rearing hoppers at 18–19°C, very dark coloration was obtained. Amongst the next generation, reared at 25°C and exposed to sunlight, 24 hoppers out of the total 1500 were almost entirely black, the few light parts being whitish, without any brown or yellow; no hoppers were intermediate between the melanic and the normal ones. The resulting adults were almost entirely black, with brownish-black tegmina. In immature adults, pink insectorubin coloration was visible only on the intersegmental membranes of the abdomen; when mature, they remained brownish-black, with some yellow carotenoid showing only on a part of the pronotum, on the tegminal veins, abdomen and hind tibiae. These melanic forms bred true for a number of generations, but proved to be recessive in crosses with the normal type. When kept in isolation, melanic hoppers still remained almost black, but any light parts were green; in adults there appeared light stripes on the pronotum, and the tibiae of all legs were bluish or greenish. Thus, their insectorubin, carotenoid and bilin metabolism was affected by density in a way similar to that in the normal strain. Unfortunately, it is not known whether the overall darkening was due to excessive melanin in the cuticle, or also to excessive insectorubin in the epidermis; this could have been established by examining the exuviae. It is of interest to add that no such extreme melanic coloration is known amongst the numerous American species of the genus *Schistocerca* except *S. melanocera* from the Galapagos Islands.

Occasional albino individuals have been recorded in *Locustana* (Faure 1932), *Schistocerca* (Hunter-Jones 1957) and *Melanoplus sanguinipes* (Putnam 1958). They appeared as a few mutants in normal cage cultures and were normal in every respect except colour and bred true, but the albinism proved to be recessive in crosses with the normal individuals. The *Schistocerca* albinos have the background colour creamy-white (instead of yellow due to β-carotene) and no black melanic pattern, although a faint shadow-pattern, probably due to a small amount of insectorubin (some 15% of the normal; Bellamy 1958) is visible. Young crowded adults develop pink coloration due to reduced insectorubin and become yellow on maturation; their morphometrics and the respiratory metabolism are as in the normal gregarious *Schistocerca*, which suggests that the dark pigmentation is a less reliable criterion of the gregarious phase than has been assumed in the past (Pener 1963). When reared in isolation hoppers are green without any dark pattern. Thus, the melanin production in albinos appears to be suppressed and that of insectorubin greatly reduced, while β-carotene and the bile pigment contributing to the green colour are normal.

An albino strain in permanent culture at the Anti-Locust Research Centre proved to be of value in histochemical studies on melanisation of cuticle (Malek 1957; Karlson & Schlossberger-Recke 1962).

Carotenoids

Carotenoid pigments of animals were formerly called *lipochromes*, because they are frequently found dissolved in fat. It is now established that insects and other animals are unable to synthetise carotenoids and that they are always derived from plant food (Goodwin 1952a; Fox & Vevers 1960; Gilmour 1961). Chemically, they are hydrocarbons of complicated chain structure, soluble in fat and organic solvents; oxidation transforms them into *xanthophylls* and they can also combine with proteins forming *chromoproteins*. In their various combinations they are responsible for a surprisingly wide range of colours in acridoids (e.g. yellow, orange, red, blue and green).

Carotenoids have been best, though still insufficiently, studied in locusts. In *Schistocerca* a mixture of carotenes and xanthophylls was reported by Lederer & Volkonsky (Lederer 1935), and Chauvin (1941b) reported carotenoids in the same species. Since then, these pigments have been specially investigated, on the initiative of the Anti-Locust Research Centre, in *Schistocerca* and *Locusta* in the University of Liverpool (Goodwin 1949, 1950a, 1951, 1952a, 1952b; Goodwin & Srisukh 1949; Dadd 1961c, 1963).

The two main pigments of this group in locusts are *β-carotene* and *astaxanthin*, the latter being an oxidised carotenoid, widely distributed in Crustacea and insects. Their distribution in locusts is not the same, since β-carotene is found in the integument, wings, eyes, haemolymph, fat and eggs, whereas astaxanthin does not occur in the haemolymph.

Quantitative changes in the carotenoid content of locusts during the life-cycle are as follows. Newly laid locust eggs contain only β-carotene and its quantity does not change much during the first half of the incubation period, but towards the end of the period it begins to fall, while astaxanthin appears and its amount increases (fig. 32). After hatching, the amount of both pigments slowly increases at about the same rate, but a striking change is seen in adults, in which the astaxanthin content falls while that of β-carotene increases in relation to sexual maturation, especially in the female (fig. 32 and table 4).

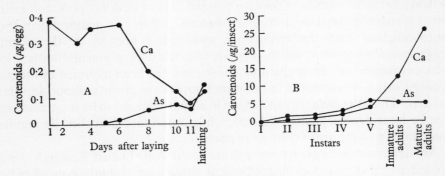

Fig. 32. Changes in carotenoid contents of *Locusta* during life. A, eggs; B, hoppers and adults (Goodwin 1949).
Ca, carotene; As, astaxanthin.

The reciprocal relation of β-carotene and astaxanthin in the developing egg suggests that the latter is formed by oxidation of the former, but the amount of astaxanthin produced is less than that of the β-carotene that disappears. Thus, the metabolism of these substances in the egg is still not clear (Goodwin 1949). As regards changes during sexual maturation, the great increase of β-carotene

Table 4. *Mean carotenoid content of locusts in μg per insect*
(*Goodwin* 1949)

In each case the upper figure is for β-carotene, the lower for astaxanthin

	Hopper instars					Male		Female	
	I	II	III	IV	V	Immature	Mature	Immature	Mature
LOCUSTA									
gregarious	0·13	0·38	0·4	2·1	3·0	8·4	15·4	10·7	35·8
	0·21	0·97	1·4	1·8	5·5	3·5	3·4	3·0	5·4
solitarious	—	—	—	—	—	11·4	19·1	11·4	12·5
	0·22	—	—	2·9	5·0	5·8	7·1	5·8	12·6
SCHISTOCERCA									
gregarious	0·026	0·63	1·7	1·7	8·7	22·9	44·0	13·6	55·8
	0·13	0·72	1·6	4·1	7·6	12·5	3·5	8·3	16·5
solitarious	—	—	—	5·5	26·4	25·3	47·5	25·3	47·5
	0·39	—	—	5·6	17·7	10·1	16·2	10·1	16·2

in maturing adults cannot be accounted for by slight reduction in astaxanthin and it must be obtained from food.

As regards coloration, β-carotene is responsible for the yellow background colour of gregarious *Schistocerca* hoppers and for the yellow colour of mature gregarious males of both *Locusta* and *Schistocerca*, but this is due not to an increase in the total pigment content, but to the diffusion of

48

β-carotene into, or close to, the cuticle. Mature females of *Schistocerca* and *Locusta* are less yellow; they appear mostly brown, owing to the presence of hypodermal insectorubin (p. 44). Gregarious *Locusta* hoppers which have no yellow component in their coloration have no β-carotene in the integument; their orange-coloured areas are due either to the tanned cuticular protein or to diffuse and weak melanisation.

The green coloration of solitarious hoppers of *Schistocerca* is not connected with any difference from the gregarious hoppers as regards the carotenoid content, which is approximately the same, but is due to a mixture of yellow carotenoids with a blue bilin pigment (p. 50).

Temperature, which is so important in the production of melanin and insectorubin, has no effect on the carotenoid metabolism of locusts (Goodwin 1951). The carotene content of food is, of course, of importance; when reared on a diet without carotene, *Schistocerca* hoppers and mature adults failed to become yellow (Chauvin 1939 a; Dadd 1960 a, 1961 c, 1963) and their blood was blue, not the normal yellow.

The physiological role of carotenoids is not sufficiently known, but their connection with testes, ovaries and eggs in locusts suggest their importance for reproduction. In *Melanoplus bivittatus* carotenoids were found particularly concentrated in the gonads (Grayson & Tauber 1943). A direct indication that either the metabolism of yellow carotenoids or its translocation to the cuticle of maturing adult *Schistocerca* is under the hormonal control of the corpora allata has been obtained by Loher (1960, 1961; see p. 298).

The presence of β-carotene and astaxanthin in locust eyes suggests their possible role as visual pigments, particularly because β-carotene is regarded as a precursor of vitamin A which is of importance in the vision of other animals (Goodwin 1952; Dadd 1961 a). However, no work on the histochemistry of locust eyes has ever been attempted, although the need for it is obvious.

A somewhat special case is the bright coloration of the hindwings which is particularly common in the otherwise very sombrely coloured Oedipodinae. Lederer (1938) found that the intense red colour of the hindwings of *Oedipoda germanica* was a mixture of β-carotene and a xanthophyll. Okay (1945) considered that the bright rose wings of *O. miniata* contain a chromoprotein and a bilin pigment, but later (1947, 1949) he established the presence only of a free carotenoid soluble in water and of a red chromoprotein identical with astaxanthin but not of bilin. The same substances were found by Okay in the wings of *Acrotylus insubricus* and *Calliptamus* sp. and by Goodwin & Srisukh (1949) in wings of *Nomadacris*.

The blue wings of *Oedipoda caerulescens* and *O. schochi*, according to Okay, contain the same astaxanthin (which can be blue) but no yellow carotenoid. The yellow wings of *O. aurea* contain a similar carotenoid, and some other yellow water-soluble pigment. Occasional blue individuals of *Locusta* owe their abnormal colour also to astaxanthin (Goodwin 1949).

Astaxanthin in Crustacea is known to produce many different external colours and it is not surprising that the same happens in grasshoppers. Moreover, its colour is easily changed by even weak chemicals and temperature, which should account for the variability of wing colour observed in many Oedipodinae.

Bile pigments

Green coloration, common in acridoids, has been in the past attributed to the chlorophyll of food plants. However, this colour develops also in insects fed on plants without chlorophyll (Chauvin 1939 *a*) and it is due not to a single green substance, but to a mixture of yellow chromoproteins with blue pigments of the *bilin* group, which are common in the bile of vertebrates. Such a mixture was called *insectoverdin* (Junge 1941) but the name is only one of convenience.

Solitarious hoppers of *Schistocerca* and *Locusta* usually have almost uniformly green integument and green haemolymph, but this similarity of the colour is not due to the same composition. The blue component is in both cases *mesobiliverdin*, but the yellow of the haemolymph is due only to β-carotene, whereas in the integument free astaxanthin is also present in *Schistocerca*, though not in *Locusta* (Goodwin & Srisukh 1951 *a*; Goodwin 1952). Mesobiliverdin is absent from the gregarious hoppers, which have yellow haemolymph and yellow ground colour of the integument, but it appears in such hoppers, replacing the yellow, if they are reared on carotene-free diet (Dadd 1961 *c*).

Okay (1953) found blue pigment in the peripheral fat body of green *Locusta* and *Schistocerca* hoppers and suggested that it might be synthetised there. The pericardial cells of green *Locusta* hoppers were found by him to contain a blue pigment the quantity of which increases with their age, but which is gradually replaced by reddish-brown pigment; in immature adults there may still be some blue pigment, but it disappears in mature adults of both sexes. This led him to suggest a transformation of the blue bilin pigment into the reddish-brown insectorubin in the pericardial cells, but this has not been investigated.

Stower (1959) pointed out that the green post-ocular patch in solitarious *Schistocerca* hoppers has a higher blue component than other green parts, and suggested that this region of the head may be 'the site of intensive production of the blue component of insectoverdin'; in gregarious hoppers this patch is coloured reddish, possibly by insectorubin; however, the nature of this blue pigment is not known and it may be carotenoid.

Pterins

These pigments, related chemically to uric acid and guanine, may be white, yellow, or red; they are often fluorescent in ultra-violet light. They are widely distributed in insects (Ziegler-Günder 1956), but data on their occurrence in acridoids are very scanty.

A yellow fluorescent pigment, soluble in water, reported in the eyes of *Schistocerca* (Busnel & Drilhon 1942) and *Locusta*, was identified as *xanthopterin* (Goodwin & Srisukh 1951 *b*). De Lerma (1950 *a*) found *isoxanthopterin* in the haemolymph of *Paracinema tricolor*, and Busnel & Drilhon (1942) discovered small quantities of it in the integument of *Schistocerca*. More frequently pterins have been reported from the eggs of *Locusta* (De Lerma 1951 *a*, 1952; Goodwin & Srisukh 1951 *a*), *Schistocerca* (Goodwin & Srisukh 1951 *b*) and *Melanoplus differentialis* (Bodine & Fitzgerald 1948 *b*; Burgess 1949).

The metabolic role of pterins in acridoids has not been studied, but they appear to have some connection with the next group, the flavins.

Flavins

Although flavins do not contribute to the external coloration of insects, they should be discussed here because they often accompany pterins, to which

Table 5. *Riboflavin content (in μg per gram of fresh weight)*
of Schistocerca (*Busnel & Chauvin* 1942)

Egg in the ovary	25·1
Egg 11 days old	30·5
Young hopper	10·0
Hopper 3rd instar	14·5
Mature gregarious male	17·0
,, ,, female	18·1
Malpighian tubes of young hopper	700·2
,, ,, ,, adult male	1045·6
,, ,, ,, old adult male	2150·3

they are also related chemically, differing mainly in the addition to their structural formula of a benzene ring.

Riboflavin is a yellow water-soluble substance found in the eggs of *Locusta* and *Schistocerca* (Busnel & Chauvin 1942; Busnel & Drilhon 1942; De Lerma 1952), and of *Melanoplus* (Bodine & Fitzgerald 1947 *a*, 1947 *b*, 1948 *b*; Burgess 1949), and more abundantly in the Malpighian tubes (Busnel & Drilhon *t.c.*). The quantitative distribution of riboflavin in the different stages of *Schistocerca* is shown in table 5; its high concentration in the Malpighian tubes is noteworthy (p. 121).

An important point is that the quantity of riboflavin increases during incubation, but later it may be reduced since no free riboflavin is found in hatchlings of *Melanoplus*. On the other hand, other fluorescent substances, resembling pterins, appear later. This suggests a possibility of riboflavin being used for the formation of pterins (Bodine & Fitzgerald, *tt.cc.*; Burgess *t.c.*).

Special interest is attached to riboflavin because it is considered, from the metabolic point of view, to be vitamin B_2. The vitamin properties of apparently

51

the same substance from *Melanoplus* eggs have been demonstrated by its action on blood cell production in mice (Burgess, Clarke & Rolfe 1956; Burgess & Rolfe 1959).

The function of riboflavin in the Malpighian tubes is obscure; it may be merely accumulated and stored there (Busnel & Drilhon 1942).

HOMOCHROMY

The general resemblance of the coloration of grasshoppers to the prevailing colour of the environment is well known (Chopard 1938) and will be more appropriately discussed later as an ecological problem. Here we are concerned with the phenomena in their integument to which such resemblance may be due.

Table 6. *Results of experiments of rearing locusts on a coloured background (Faure* 1932)

		Number of hoppers in each category of resemblance to background			
	Number	None	Slight	Fair	Good
Locustana					
White	27	1	3	12	11
Black	19	1	2	—	16
Urania blue	3	—	—	2	1
Mouse grey	9	—	2	1	6
Aniline yellow	10	—	2	3	5
Brown	10	—	—	1	9
Totals and % in brackets	78	3(3·8)	9(11·4)	19(24)	48(60·8)
Locusta					
White	20	—	2	9	9
Black	15	1	1	2	11
Grey	7	—	—	1	6
Aniline yellow	5	—	—	1	4
Brown	3	—	—	—	3
Totals and % in brackets	50	1(2)	3(6)	13(26)	33(66)

Experimental work by Faure (1932) in rearing solitarious hoppers of *Locustana* and *Locusta* in painted boxes provided evidence that general coloration of hoppers and of the resulting adults comes to resemble the background.

The results (table 6) show that 84·8% of *Locustana* and 92% of *Locusta* hoppers assumed fair or good resemblance to the background, even when that colour was quite unusual in their normal environment (e.g. white or yellow). Thus, in the case of *Locusta*, adults almost white (with pink flush) and blue were produced. Results with pink and green background were negative but hoppers transferred to non-green background tended, at least, to lose green colour. In somewhat similar experiments with *Locusta*, but with the estimation of the wave-length values of the colours used, Hertz &

Imms (1937) generally confirmed the effects of the background colour, although no complete adjustment was observed, except in the case of the black background. Their important new result was that changes of colour were considerably influenced by the difference between the intensity of the incident light and of that reflected from the background. On a black background, nearly all locusts become black in bright daylight with frequent sunshine, but the results were less definite in poor daylight or in the light transmitted through the yellow or violet screen; hoppers on a black background

Table 7. *Colour changes of* Acrida *hoppers on coloured background* (*Ergene* 1952*a*)

Original hopper colour	Background colour	Number of hoppers	
		Total	Finally coloured as background
Yellow	Green	41	36
Green	Green	14	13
Green	Yellow	22	19
Yellow	Yellow	9	8
Green	Orange	13	11
Yellow	Orange	6	6
Green	Red	43	39
Yellow	Red	13	10
Green	Violet	20	16
Yellow	Violet	8	6
Green	White	16	9
Yellow	White	8	8
Green	Black	10	6
Yellow	Black	8	6
Green	Light-blue	13	0
Yellow	Light-blue	8	0
Green	Dark-blue	26	0
Yellow	Dark-blue	10	0

kept in darkness developed only light-grey colour. Wilde & Staal (1955) reported similar results with *Locusta*.

Striking results of chromatic adaptation were obtained by Ergene (1952*a*) in her experiments with hoppers of *Acrida* which normally are either green or straw-yellow (table 7).

Coloured photographs in Ergene's paper show an amazing range of colours of the resulting hoppers, including some never found in nature. This range, however, does not appear to exceed that due to variations in the colour of insectorubin, which is, presumably, responsible, although no histochemical studies were made.

Ergene's results with a green background diverged from those of Faure (1932) and Hertz & Imms (1937) who failed to obtain homochromy of hoppers on it and maintained that green pigmentation develops only if hoppers are fed on fresh grass and kept in very humid air. The over-riding importance of fresh food for achieving green colour in *Acrida* was particularly stressed by Okay (1953); later (1956) he suggested that high humidity (not below 71%)

and a certain temperature (between 21 and 44 °C, with 33°C as the optimum) are required in addition to green food. Jovančič (1953, 1960) also found that a temperature about 30°C and humidity not below 40% were essential for obtaining green coloration in *Acrida*, *Oedaleus decorus* and *Pezotettix giornae* (the addition of the last species is odd, since no green form of it is known). Okay's general conclusion was that green coloration is definitely not produced by a green background. However, Ergene (1950, 1954 b, 1955) provided evidence that the colour of hoppers and adults of *Acrida* changed from straw-yellow to green and vice versa in response to the background colour and regardless of whether the food was green or not, provided the insects were kept in light, with occasional sunshine. Yellow insects kept in light on a yellow or white background failed to become green, although fed on fresh grass at 22–28°C and 70–80% relative humidity. A condition necessary for adaptation to take place, stressed by Ergene, was the length of exposure; some hoppers changed their colour within a few days, but the majority only after some fifteen days (fig. 33); in Okay's experiments the length of exposure was not specified.

Ergene (1954 c) has also shown that the haemolymph of *Acrida* hoppers changed its colour according to that of the background before a moult, but the colour of the integument changed only after a moult. Similar results were reported for *Oedaleus decorus* (Ergene 1955a).

Such flatly contradictory conclusions of two recent investigators are difficult to reconcile, but the weight of evidence is not in favour of Okay's uncompromising statements. Jovančič (1960) quite rightly stressed that the problem is a physiological one; it can hardly be resolved by further insufficiently controlled experiments and only a thorough study of all environmental conditions affecting the production of the blue bilin component of green coloration and its translocation to the integument can help to elucidate it.

Another special case of homochromy is the black coloration of grass-hoppers on burnt ground. This phenomenon has particularly attracted the attention of field naturalists in tropical Africa, where vast tracts of grassland are subject to grass fires during the dry season (Poulton 1926; Burr 1927–30), and it also occurs in *Chorthippus brunneus* on burnt heathland in Britain (Burton 1960). Poulton suggested that such homochromy is due to an ability of some species to change their colour to black within a few days and direct experimental evidence of this was obtained by E. D. Burtt (1951 a) by putting *Phorenula werneriana* in gauze-covered cages placed on burnt ground and exposing them to strong sunlight; control cages were kept in shade. A change from the usual greyish colour to coal-black occurred in the majority of those on burnt ground, in some cases after only two days. The change occurred not only in recently emerged adults, but also in those some five months old. Similar results were obtained with *Tylotropidius speciosus* which changed from light-brown to black in seven days. Ergene (1953b, 1954a) repeated Burtt's experiments with *Oedipoda* and *Acrida* and also obtained complete

54

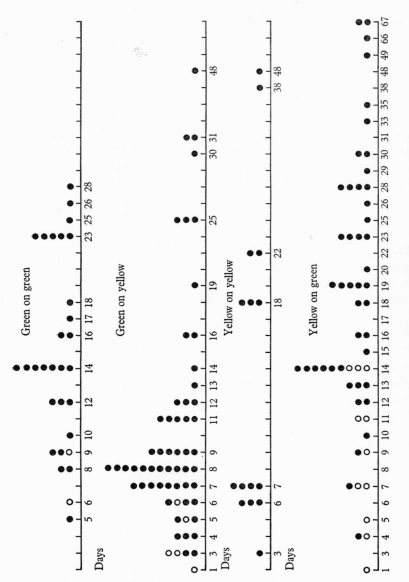

Fig. 33. Colour changes of green and yellow *Acrida* hoppers on the different backgrounds. Each circle represents a hopper; black circle, colour changed to correspond with the background; empty circle, no change (after Ergene 1950, modified).

blackening of integument within seven to thirty days. She also insisted on the importance of strong sunlight for the change, and attempted to investigate whether the stimulus to change was a visual one. Individuals with eyes covered by black lacquer acquired black coloration as usual; when one tegmen was lacquered, it did not become black but the other did. This suggests that the stimulus is received by the integument, not through the eye; this conclusion was reached also with regard to the adaptation to a green background (Ergene 1953 b).

There is no information as to what pigment is involved in such intense overall blackening. As we have seen, general darkening occurs as a result of melanin and insectorubin over-production at low temperatures, but strong sunshine should result in high body temperature of the insect (p. 211), which inhibits the production of both melanin and insectorubin (pp. 44, 46). The biochemistry and the histology of this process are quite obscure, but it should be possible to arrange carefully controlled investigations.

DIURNAL COLOUR CHANGES

Rapid changes of colour due to contraction and expansion of special chromatophore cells are known in many animals, but not in insects. The only known case of a similar nature is the diurnal change of the integumental colour in *Kosciusciola tristis*, an apterous Australian alpine grasshopper (Key & Day 1954 a, 1954 b). The male of this species has a general greenish-blue coloration in day time and almost black at night; similar but less striking changes occur in the female. Observations in nature and laboratory experiments have shown that light intensity, background colour (white or black), relative humidity and degree of crowding have no effect and the only factor influencing colour change was the temperature, the pale colour being obtained above 25° C and the dark under 15° C. By comparing the colour of the insect with a chart of graded colours, a quantitative assessment of the changes was made and the diurnal variation is shown in fig. 34.

Histological studies of the different colour forms revealed that the change in the visible coloration is due to the different distribution of two kinds of pigment granules in the epidermal cells (fig. 35). In the light-blue form, a dense layer of fine pale-blue granules occupies the upper portion of each cell, while the lower is filled with larger brown granules; in the dark form, the latter move to the top and the former to the bottom; in the intermediate colour forms, transitional distribution of the two types of granules is seen. The pigments involved have not been studied.

Similar, but less striking, changes were observed in another species of the same genus, and it is probable that other alpine grasshoppers (*Podisma*, *Conophyma*, *Kingdonella*, etc.) which are often olive-green in colour exhibit the same phenomenon. It need not be restricted to alpine grasshoppers either, since in at least one common Australian lowland species, *Oedaleus australis*, general darkening, particularly of the face, was observed after a two-and-a-half hours' exposure to 4°C (Key & Day 1954*a*).

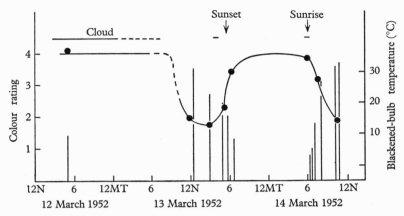

Fig. 34. Diurnal changes in the dark coloration of *Kosciusciola tristis* in relation to the temperature (Key & Day 1954*a*). Black circles, colour rating; vertical lines, temperatures.

Another, and possibly more important, case of pigment movements is that observed in the compound eyes of *Chorthippus* sp. by Stefanovska (1890). In individuals kept for several hours in darkness, brown pigment granules, with distinct contours, are concentrated near the bases of the crystalline cones,

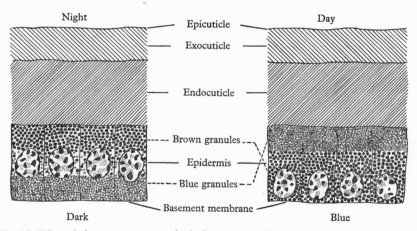

Fig. 35. Diurnal pigment movements in the integument of *Kosciusciola tristis* (Key & Day 1954*b*).

but after one hour's exposure to sunlight, the granules lose their clear outlines and become dispersed so that the whole retinula appears more uniformly pigmented; moreover, some of the brown granules are changed into red droplets. These observations were not very exact and more than one kind

57

of pigment may have been involved, but pigment movement in relation to illumination is well known in other nocturnal insects, and many acridoids have night-flying habits. Stefanovska's observations on this point have been overlooked, or ignored, by subsequent authors, and the subject needs a re-examination. Rao (1960) recorded changes in the pattern of *Schistocerca* eyes, where the usual dark stripes (p. 198) became well defined only in the locusts kept in sunlight, while in those kept in shade the eyes remained uniformly coloured; this suggests movement of dark insectorubin in the inter-stripes, although it might also have been due to suppression of this pigment by high temperature (p. 46).

HORMONAL CONTROL OF COLORATION

Weed Pfeiffer (1945*a*) obtained evidence that the implantation of extra corpora allata induced haemolymph of *Melanoplus* to become green, and P. Joly (1952) achieved the same results, as well as a change of the integumental colour to green, by implanting corpora allata of various grasshoppers into hoppers of *Acrida*. This hormonal effect on green coloration, as well as the role of hormones in other colour changes in locust phases, is discussed in more detail elsewhere (p. 376).

MUSCULAR SYSTEM

The muscular system is conventionally divided into the *somatic* (or skeletal) muscles, stretched between sclerotised segments and appendages of the body and regulating their movements, and the *visceral* muscles which serve the internal organs, although some of them also originate on body walls. Only the somatic muscles are discussed; the visceral ones are mentioned in descriptions of the respective organs.

Muscles consist of transversely striated contractile fibres, *myofibrils* (or sarcostyles), bundles of which are enveloped in cellular membrane, *sarcolemma,* which has essentially the character of connective tissue (Baccetti 1956*a*). Muscle bundles are supplied with oxygen by abundant fine tracheae and tracheoles (Bennett 1953; Tiegs 1955; Hoyle 1957). They are also provided with motor nerves which enter them and terminate in branched *end-plates* (p. 65). Very detailed descriptions of the histology of the different types of *Locusta* muscles are given by Vogell, Bishai *et al.* (1959).

Each muscle has its point of *origin*, usually on a relatively stationary part of the integument (or of the endoskeleton) and, at its other end, a point of *insertion* (or attachment) on the part to be moved when the muscle contracts. The connection between the myofibrils and the basement membrane of the integument is a direct one, there being no tendon-like structure (Buchthal & Weis-Fogh 1956). The places of origin of the main muscles are usually very conspicuous on the inside of the integument as heavily sclerotised edges of sclerites or ridges which often appear as furrows on the outside, for example on the pronotum and sternum (p. 12, 16).

Muscles are given names, indicating either their function, inferred from their position (abductors, levators, depressors etc.), or the position itself (tergal, tergo-pleural, pleuro-alar etc.). It is also customary to designate muscles by consecutive numbers, first introduced by Snodgrass (1929, 1935*a*) for *Dissosteira*; when extra muscles were found in other species, they were given letters in addition to the Snodgrass numbers, but some authors (Misra, Jannone) adopted number systems of their own, thus creating confusion. In the following brief description, the numbers of Albrecht (1953*a*, 1956) who followed the Snodgrass system are given in brackets.

Nearly 300 different skeletal muscles have been described in acridoids; practically all of them are paired, and many are branched, or consist of several discreet bundles. This makes the muscular system so complicated that its detailed description would be disproportionately long. Therefore its treatment here will be restricted to a somewhat simplified description of the muscles on which depend movements of the main parts of the body and its appendages. Students concerned with the detailed anatomy of the muscular system should refer to general descriptive papers by Berlese (1909, *Anacridium*), Snodgrass (1928–37, *Dissosteira*), Maki (1938, *Locusta*), Jannone (1939*b*, *Dociostaurus*), Misra (1946, 1947, 1950, *Schistocerca*), Albrecht (1953, *Locusta*; 1956, *Nomadacris*), Luh Chin-Jen & Yu Pei-Yu (1957, *Locusta*), Ewer (1953–8, *Acanthacris, Locusta, Zonocerus, Phymateus, Lentula*, etc.) and Alicata (1962*a*, 1962*b*, *Eyprepocnemis*), as well as to others referred to below and dealing with parts of the muscular system.

MUSCLES OF HEAD

The *antenna* as a whole can be moved upwards by two levator muscles (fig. 6, C) and downwards by two depressors, and its flagellum (which has no

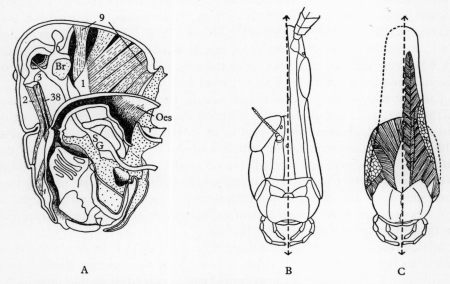

A   B   C

Fig. 36. A, *Nomadacris*, longitudinal section of head (Albrecht 1956).
   9, adductor of mandible; 2, 3, retractors of labrum; 38, retractor of mouth angle; Br, brain; Oes, oesophagus; SG, suboesophageal ganglion.
B, frontal view of the head of *Acrida* compared with the more normal type of head. C ditto, muscles (Strenger 1942).

muscles in it) is moved outwards by an abductor and inwards by an adductor. It is noteworthy that the adductors can only bring the two antennae almost parallel to each other, but cannot cause them to cross. The *mandibles* (fig. 36, A) are worked by powerful adductors (9) consisting of numerous large bundles, and small abductors. Figure 36, C shows the arrangement of adductors in the elongate head of *Acrida* (Strenger 1942). The *maxilla* has a rather large number of muscles, particularly those connected with movements of the palps which, in contrast to the antennae, have muscles inside each segment except the apical, and are therefore very flexible; the same applies to the *labium* and its palps. Within the head are also found some of the muscles of the anterior sections of the alimentary tract (hypopharynx, pharynx and foregut).

Two pairs of muscles (fig. 9, C—muscles 52, 53), originating on the ridges of the pronotum and a pair arising on the first phragma (49) move the head in the vertical plane; a pair originating on the prosternum (55) pulls the lower part of the head backwards; and a pair arising on the episternum (57) moves the head sideways. Contractions of all these muscles regulate head movements directly, but, in addition, there are eight pairs of muscles, originating on cervical sclerites, which affect head movements indirectly, by pulling on the neck membrane. The head can thus be moved in all directions in relation to the body, but only to a limited extent. Muscles of the neck of *Melanoplus* were described by L. M. Henry (1958).

MUSCLES MOVING THE PROTHORAX

A pair of muscles (fig. 9, C, 58), each divided into three bundles arising on internal pronotal ridges and attached to the membrane between the prothorax and mesothorax, serves to move the former in relation to the latter; this movement is also achieved by an intersegmental pair and by three pairs of ventral longitudinal muscles.

MUSCLES OF LEGS

The muscular system regulating the movements of the first leg is very complicated (fig. 9, D), there being six pairs of muscles (63–9) moving the coxa, and three pairs (71) attached to the trochanter, which together provide a range of movement in all directions. They originate on the various ridges and similar structures on the inside of the prothoracic integument. The femoral movements are governed by one strong pair originating on the trochanter. The tibia has three pairs of muscles; two originate in the femur, and one in the tibia itself, the latter possibly representing a scolopazium (p. 167). The tarsus has two pairs of muscles originating in the tibia and femur and inserted at the base of the first tarsal segment; they move the whole tarsus, its segments having no intrinsic muscles, but being able to bend on each other, presumably because of the action of the muscles of the claws originating in the femur and tibia, the apodemes of which traverse the tarsus.

A feature of the musculature of the base of the second pair of legs is that the total number of muscles is greater than in the first pair; some of the extra muscles, while originating at the leg base, are attached to parts of the meso-thorax taking part in the movement of the tegmina. The other muscles are the same.

The basal musculature of the third pair of legs (fig. 37, A) is as in the second, but some of the femoral and the tibial muscles, although the same in number as in other legs, are very much enlarged in connection with jumping. The origin of many of the coxal muscles is on the rims of the sternal segments, and the shape of these segments (p. 16) accordingly reflects the mode of movement peculiar to the species. Some of these muscles are also concerned in movement of the wings.

The most conspicuous muscle of the jumping leg is the levator (or extensor) of the tibia, which lies within the large inflated femur, occupying its greater part (fig. 37, B, 135). It consists of a double series of groups of short muscle fibres; each group, or *muscle unit*, is enveloped in tracheolated membrane, separating it from other units; the units originate on the interior wall of the femur, between the 'fishbone' ridges (p. 25) of its external surface. Each

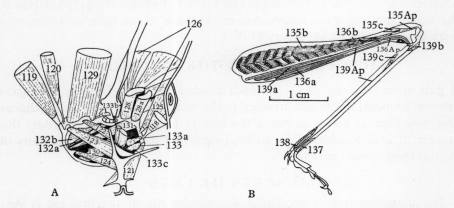

Fig. 37. *Nomadacris*, muscles of hind leg. A, muscles moving coxa and trochanter; B, muscles of femur, tibia and tarsus (Albrecht 1946).

unit is supplied with a nerve, terminating in an end-plate (p. 66) and with tracheae (Hoyle 1955 *a*, 1957).

MUSCLES OF WINGS

Apart from general anatomical works, wing musculature is specially discussed in papers by Tiegs (1955, *Chortoicetes*), La Greca (1949, *Anacridium*), Thomas (1952, 1954 *a*, *Lamarckiana*; 1953, *Omocestus*, *Podisma*, *Chorthippus*; 1954*b*, *Locusta*), Ewer (1953–8), Atzinger (1957), Wiesend (1957), J. I. Campbell (1961, *Locusta*), D. Wilson (1962, *Melanoplus*, *Romalea*), and D. Wilson & Weis-Fogh (1962, *Schistocerca*).

The wing muscles, which are all found within the mesothorax and metathorax, are referred to two functional groups: *indirect wing muscles*, inserted on sclerotised structures of the pterothorax near the wing bases and mainly concerned in up and down movements of the wings by altering the curvature of the tergum; and *direct wing muscles* which are inserted on the wing bases and immediately govern other wing movements.

The most conspicuous of indirect wing muscles (fig. 38, B) are the longitudinal dorsal muscles (81 and 112) and tergo-sternal muscles (83, 84 and 113).
In addition there are in adult *Schistocerca* (Misra 1950) and *Anacridium*
(La Greca 1949) tergo-pleural and oblique dorsal muscles, which also occur
in hoppers of *Locusta* (Thomas 1954*b*) and *Acanthacris* (Ewer 1954*a*) but
disappear in adults (p. 282).

The direct wing muscles (fig. 38, A) in the mesothorax are: a pair of flexors
(85) closing the tegmina; two pairs of rotators (97, 98), giving the tegmen an
inward rotation at the end of the down stroke; and a pair of depressor ex-
tensors (99) opening the tegmina. In the metathorax, a similar group of
muscles serves movements of wings.

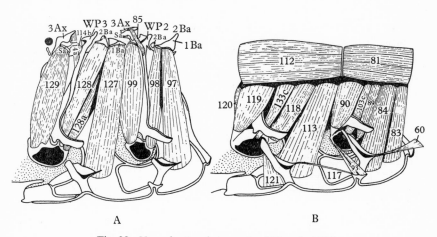

Fig. 38. *Nomadacris*, wing muscles (Albrecht 1946).

D. Wilson (1962) has shown that some thoracic muscles can be used in
moving wings for flight and for stridulation, as well as moving legs, particularly
for climbing.

Reductions of musculature in brachypterous and apterous species are
discussed on p. 30.

ABDOMINAL MUSCLES

The muscles of abdominal segments III to VII are almost the same. The
main muscles of the typical third segment (fig. 39) are five flat bundles of
dorsal muscles (167, 168) and a paradorsal muscle (169); they originate on a
preceding tergite and are inserted on the anterior edge of the following one,
thus enabling telescopic movements of the tergites; a similar effect on the
sternites is achieved by ventral muscles (172, 173). Dorso-ventral dilation of
the abdomen is produced by the external lateral muscles (177) attached to the
apodemes of the sternites (p. 17), while the internal lateral muscles (175, 176)

produce the opposite effect; these movements are of importance in respiration.

Modifications in segment I are due to the presence of an intersegmental pair of muscles, connecting the abdomen and mesosternum, and of special muscles of the tympanum (p. 188).

The musculature of segment VIII in the male is as in the preceding ones, but in the female this segment and the following ones contain special powerful muscles of the ovipositor. In the male, special muscles of parts of the phallic complex are found in the IXth and the following segments. In both sexes, the posterior segments also have muscles connected with the rectum, anus and cerci (in addition to general works, see Guarino 1935, *Anacridium*; Ford 1923, *Melanoplus*; Pichler 1952, *Calliptamus*).

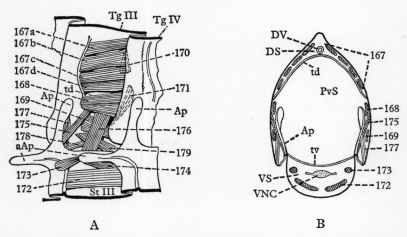

A   B

Fig. 39. *Dissosteira*, abdominal muscles. A, side view; B, cross-section (Snodgrass 1935)
DS, dorsal sinus; PvS, perivisceral sinus; VS, ventral sinus; td, dorsal transversal muscle; tv, ventral transversal muscle; DV, dorsal blood vessel; VNC, ventral nerve cord; Tg, tergite; St, sternite; Ap, apodeme.

More specialised muscles of the abdomen are those regulating movements of the tympanal organ (Pichler 1953), spiracles (Hoyle 1959), Krauss's organ (p. 21) and eversible glands (p. 35).

One might expect considerable variations in the musculature of different species, but a comparison between *Locusta, Dissosteira, Dociostaurus, Schistocerca* and *Nomadacris* (Albrecht 1956) revealed only relatively minor differences (see Ewer 1953–8, for variation in various species).

Of special interest are differences in musculature connected with meiopterism (p. 30). Equally, if not more, interesting would be a detailed comparative study of the musculature of species with strongly different habits, such as the ground-dwellers and the climbers on shrubs, trees and grass-stems; they are noticeably different in parts of the exoskeleton, for example the sternum from which muscles of the legs originate, but the muscles themselves have not been studied.

A special point is the existence in hoppers of certain wing muscles, which disappear in adults (p. 282).

MUSCLE FUNCTION

A muscle contracts in response to electrical impulses transmitted to it from a ganglion along the motor nerves (p. 155). The innervation of the muscular system is even more complex than the system itself, since every muscle receives more than one axon; an anatomical description of it cannot be offered here, but some general notes are given elsewhere (p. 154).

The electrical nature of both the nervous and the muscular activity makes possible studies of neuro-muscular mechanisms by precise experimental methods. Such studies, however, are still in their early stages and they have been concentrated almost entirely on muscles of the jumping leg and wings. Either the whole decapitated live insect or a part of it is kept in physiological saline solution (since legs and wings receive their nerves from thoracic ganglia, removal of the brain does not affect their activity; see Bethe 1897), with the nerve leading to an exposed muscle, and electrical stimulation is applied either to the nerve or to the muscle (externally or internally). The effects are recorded mechanically by a connection with a kymograph needle, or electrically as changes in the electric *action potential* in the muscle in relation to its *resting potential*, which is the difference in the electric charge between its outer surface and the inside, due to difference in the ionic concentration of the body fluid and muscle cell contents.

Only a brief account of the results of neuro-muscular studies can be given here; details of the technique, findings and current theories (often controversial) will be found in, for example, the following papers: Voskresenskaya (1947, 1950, 1959); Hoyle (1953, 1955b, 1957, 1958); Castillo, Hoyle & Machne (1953); Ewer & Ripley (1953); Ripley & Ewer (1953); Hagiwara & Watanabe (1953); Buchthal & Weis-Fogh (1956); Weis-Fogh (1956a); Buchthal, Weis-Fogh & Rosenfalk (1957); Hamori (1961); D. Wilson (1962, 1964); D. Wilson Weis-Fogh (1962); Neville & Weis-Fogh (1963); Neville (1963a).

Each muscle unit (e.g. one of the many bundles of the tibial extensor of the jumping leg) receives one to three, but commonly two, nerve fibres (Hoyle 1957). A double fibre consists of a *fast* axon (transmitting impulses) resulting in vigorous contractions of the muscle (e.g. jumps), and of a *slow* axon which induces slow movements (e.g. walking). The two axons enter the muscle unit together and their branches reach every fibre of it, terminating in *end-plates* (fig. 40).

If the fast axon impulses causing a strong contraction, or *twitch*, are rapidly repeated, individual contractions fuse into a prolonged strong contraction called *tetanus*. Repeated impulses of the slow axon appear to induce a steady contracted state or *tonus*, which is responsible for some prolonged postures.

The effects of impulses on muscles are subject to temperature. Thus, the electrical activity of a jumping muscle increases sharply when the temperature of the saline bath in which it is immersed is raised (Castillo, Hoyle & Machne 1953; fig. 41). The contraction of a locust wing muscle is nearly tripled when the temperature rises from 11° to 35°C (Weis-Fogh 1956d). Boistel (1960) suggested that the greater excitability of the jumping muscle of the hind leg of *Locusta* at higher temperature may be due to a rise in the respiratory rate causing a higher concentration of CO_2 in the tracheal air.

Another aspect of the neuro-muscular mechanism which may be of importance in behaviour is the effect of the ionic concentration of the blood (p. 110), which affects the resting potential of a muscle and its responses to

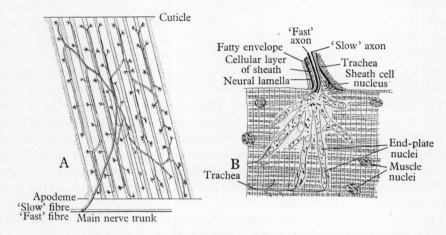

Fig. 40. Diagram of a nerve ending in a muscle. A, the axons and end-plates; B, end-plate enlarged (after Hoyle 1957).

electric impulses. It has been suggested (Hoyle 1953) that an increase of potassium concentration in the blood reduces the resting potential of a locust muscle and the magnitude of its responses. If so, food with a high potassium content, as in many plants, might depress activity, but this has not been proved, possibly because of efficient elimination of potassium by the organism (p. 110; Chapman 1958). Moreover, the presence of other ions (barium, strontium, calcium and sodium) has modifying effects on the resting potential (Werman, MacCann & Grundfest 1961; Wood 1963).

Since electro-physiological studies of muscular activity are still in their early stages and are restricted to experiments on single muscles, it is premature to expect them to supply an explanation of the mechanisms involved in movements of the whole insect. Hoyle (1957) described an arrangement which may make it possible to apply electro-physiological technique to behaviour studies. An insect is provided with small electrodes, implanted through the cuticle into a muscle and attached to fine insulated copper wires, which allow the insect to move about, while muscle impulses are transmitted through them to an electro-encephalograph; thus the electrical activity in the muscles and behaviour can be observed simultaneously, but no data are available on any studies carried out with this technique.

Locust flight muscles do not entirely depend for their rhythmic action on active contraction under nervous control. Their sarcolemma includes elastic elements which contribute to the rhythmic movements of wings by passive contraction after stretching. In addition, the integument of the pterothorax, and the cuticle generally contains a rubber-like component, which makes a contribution to rhythmic deformations of the thorax during flight

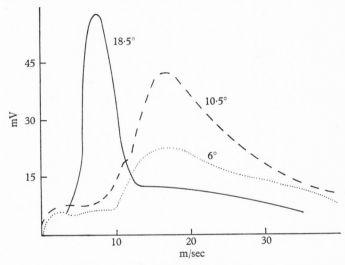

Fig. 41. Electrical activity of a jumping muscle of the hind leg in relation to the temperature (after Castillo, Hoyle & Machne 1953).

(Buchthal, Weis-Fogh & Rosenfalk 1957; Weis-Fogh 1959, 1960; Bailey & Weis-Fogh 1960; Jensen & Weis-Fogh 1962). The mechanics of flight will be discussed in the second volume of this work.

BIOCHEMISTRY OF MUSCLE

The activity of muscles ultimately depends on transformation of chemical energy into electric, a process very little known even in vertebrates. Studies of chemical processes connected with muscular contraction in acridoids are fairly numerous, but still fragmentary.

It is generally assumed that the sequence of chemical events in an active muscle comprises the breaking up of glycogen and the combination of some of the products with phosphate compounds, a process in which special enzymes take part, the final product being lactic acid; the whole process is regarded as reversible, leading during rest to re-synthesis of glycogen as the main energy source for muscular action. However, recent work (Weis-Fogh 1952) suggested that, at least in *Schistocerca*, the main fuel for flight is fat not glycogen, but there is also evidence to show that not all muscles depend on the same reserve substances (Bishai & Zebe 1959). Some indications as to the nature of substances used in muscular activity can be obtained by studies of the respiratory quotients of muscles (Krogh & Weis-Fogh 1951; D. Gilmour 1941; Kubišta 1956, 1958, 1959; Kubišta & Bartoš 1960). A comparative study of several muscles of *Locusta* has shown considerable differences in their metabolism, particularly in glycolysis and phosphorylisation, and in the enzymes involved (Vogell, Bishai *et al*. 1959). Further data on muscular chemistry will befound in papers by Gilmour & Calaby (1952, 1953*a*, 1953*b*); Gilmour (1953, 1961); Zebe (1958); Zebe & McShan (1957); Humphrey & Siggins (1949); Bellamy (1958); K. Rees (1954); Perez-Gonzales & Edwards (1954); Kermak & Stein (1959); Bücher & Klingenberg (1958); Kerly & Leaback (1957); Sacktor (1961) and Wood (1963).

The metabolism of fat as a source of muscular energy has received little attention, possibly because the mobilisation of fat for flight may occur elsewhere than in the muscles (Weis-Fogh *t.c.*), although in flight muscles of *Schistocerca* active lipase was found (George, Vallyathan & Scaria 1958).

The actual contractile properties of muscles are believed to depend on actomysin (a complex protein) in the myofibriles. Actomysin extracted from the jumping leg of *Locusta* was of extremely high viscosity, compared with that from wing muscle; this need not mean a difference in their contractile properties (Gilmour & Calaby 1953*a*, 1953*b*).

Most biochemical studies have been carried out on extracts from muscles or isolated muscles and the properties of live muscles may be more complicated.

CONNECTIVE TISSUE

Most of the internal organs are enclosed in loose membranous connective tissue. This generally consists of branched filaments with the chemical properties of a protein related to collagen found in the skin, tendons and bones of vertebrates. Between filaments there is an amorphous or finely laminated substance, with properties of a neutral polysaccharide, possibly secreted by special cells; various other cells, including haemocytes, may be adhering to, or mixed with, the tissue. Tissues of this type, with variations, are found in the basement membrane of the integument (p. 32), muscular (p. 59) and neural (p. 154) sheaths, membranes round the fat body (p. 96), the alimentary canal, and so on. Their main function is, probably, to provide support for the organs concerned. Detailed histological and histochemical data will be found in papers by Riedel (1941, 1946, *Romalea* and *Brachystola*); Baccetti (1955 *a*, 1955 *b*, 1956 *a*, 1956 *b*, 1957 *Anacridium*, 1961 *a*, 1961 *b*, *Aiolopus*); Ashurst (1959); Ashurst & Chapman (1961, *Schistocerca*) and E. G. Gray (1959, *Locusta*).

ALIMENTARY SYSTEM

ANATOMY AND HISTOLOGY

In most acridoids the head is orthognathous and the opening of the mouth is ventral, but in those with elongated head and strongly oblique face (p. 4) this opening is directed almost backwards.

The first section of the alimentary canal (fig. 42) is the *preoral* or *buccal cavity*, the anterior wall of which is formed by the inner surfaces of the clypeus and labrum bearing sensory hairs and pits; this surface is sometimes called the epipharynx (fig. 43, B). The upper wall of the cavity is largely formed by the *hypopharynx* (tongue) (fig. 43, A) which is somewhat sclerotised and densely covered with hair sensilla (Jannone 1939*b*, *Dociostaurus*; Karandikar 1939, Misra 1946, *Schistocerca*).

On the lower surface of the hypopharynx, near its tip, one can see the opening of the salivary cup, into which open two salivary ducts leading from the paired *salivary glands* (fig. 43, C). The glands are grape-like clusters (acini) of small globules, each consisting of several cells. The cells are of two kinds: in some the secretion (presumed to be serous) is scattered in the cytoplasm in fine granules; in others there is a glistening drop of mucous secretion. Between the glandular cells there are scattered small cells containing black pigment (melanin according to Chauvin 1941*b*).

Into the preoral cavity opens a short anterior portion of the *foregut*, the *pharynx*, which has thin walls sheathed in a layer of circular muscles; its inner surface has irregular longitudinal ridges, some of them bearing hair sensilla. The pharynx widens behind and passes into the curved *oesophagus*, which in its turn widens into the large *crop*, and the latter narrows into the *gizzard* (proventriculus). There are no definite external limits between oesophagus, crop and gizzard, but internally they differ in the arrangement of surface folds and the sclerotised armature. In the oesophagus, the folds are longitudinal and less sclerotised than in the crop, where they are obliquely transverse, while the gizzard has again longitudinal, well sclerotised, folds. The armature of the folds consists of sclerotised spines of different sizes, arranged in certain patterns (fig. 44). The patterns appear to be characteristic of taxonomic groups (Bordas 1898; Bryantseva 1951, 1953; L. H. Williams 1954), and the type of armature may also be related to the mechanical properties of the usual food.

The gizzard is gradually narrowed posteriorly and at the hind end its inner surface bears a ring of six V-shaped sclerotised and pigmented elevations which together form the *cardiac valve* (sphincter), separating the gizzard from the

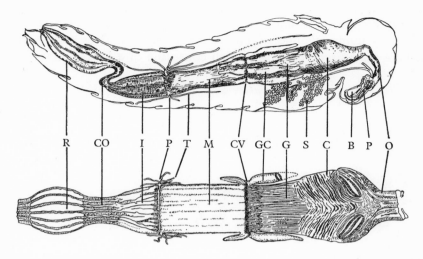

Fig. 42. *Locusta*, alimentary system, side view and dorsal view (after Liu & Leo 1955). B, buccal cavity; P, pharynx; O, oesophagus; C, crop; S, salivary glands; G, gizzard; GC, gastric caeca; CV, cardiac valve; M, midgut; T, Malpighian tubes; P, pyloric valve; I, ileum; CO, colon; R, rectum.

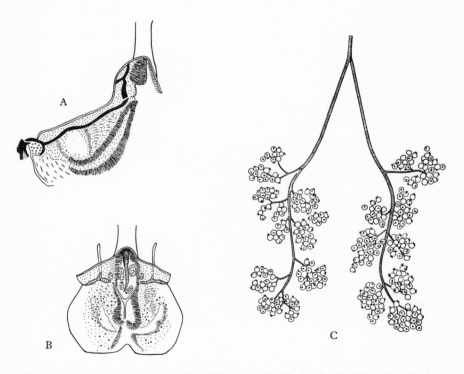

Fig. 43. *Locusta*. A, hypopharynx; B, epipharynx; C, salivary glands (Albrecht 1953 a).

71

midgut (ventriculus, stomach). The midgut is cylindrical and has transparent membranous walls; its inner surface is not cuticular, smooth, and it is surrounded by numerous fine strands of longitudinal muscles. At its anterior end there arise six *gastric caeca*, each consisting of a longer anterior and a

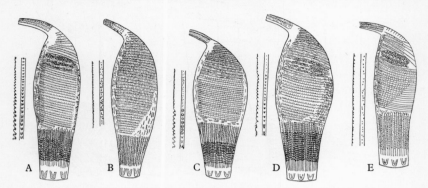

Fig. 44. Variations in the armature of the gizzard wall (after Bryantseva 1951).
A, *Asiotmethis* (Pamphagidae); B, *Pyrgomorpha* (Pyrgomorphidae); C, *Calliptamus* (Calliptaminae); D, *Sphingonotus* (Oedipodinae); E, *Chorthippus* (Gomphocerinae).

shorter posterior lobe. The latter is sometimes reduced to a very small tubercle (*Rhadinotatum*, Hodge 1940) or even absent (fig. 45). The epithelium of the midgut and the caeca consists of elongated columnar secretory cells, with a fine brush border (Nenyukov & Parfent'ev 1929; Woodruff 1933; Pilat 1935 a; Newell & Baxter 1936; Hodge 1936, 1939; Beams & Anderson

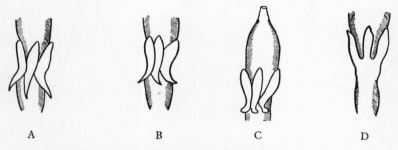

Fig. 45. Gastric caeca. A, *Oedipoda*; B, *Psophus*; C, *Chorthippus*;
D, *Euthystira* (T. Kaufman 1959).

1957; Hafez & Ibrahim 1959; Baccetti 1961 c). According to Khan (1961), the brush border develops in newly-emerged adult *Locusta* as soon as the secretory cells produce the digestive enzyme, which is within twenty-four hours.

The midgut is separated from the hindgut by the *pyloric valve* (sphincter), which appears externally as a simple constriction of the gut, marked also by the attachment of the Malpighian tubes (p. 118). The *hindgut* (or intestine) is divided into the ileum, the colon and the rectum; its inner walls are cuticular as are those of the foregut. The *ileum* (large intestine) is a short straight tube, tapering posteriorly; its inner walls have six slightly pigmented folds (the fine structure of the walls has been described by Baccetti 1960). The six folds are better defined in the narrower *colon* (small intestine), which tends to be S-shaped dorso-ventrally but is straight in the Pyrgomorphidae and Pamphagidae (Bordas 1898). The main portion of the *rectum*, also called the *rectal sac*, is wider than the colon and can be recognised externally by six bands of strong longitudinal muscles; its inner wall has six long, flat *rectal pads* (papillae), lying opposite the intervals between the external muscular bands. The pads are covered with thick cuticle, under which lies epithelium which includes cells with a striated border, as in the midgut; this is followed by well-developed connective tissue which is well supplied with tracheae, each ending with a nucleated tracheal cell giving off numerous tracheoles (Marshall 1945; Palm 1949*b*; Day 1949; Baccetti 1956*b*, 1962; Phillips 1964).

A structure common to the midgut and the hindgut is the *peritrophic membrane*. This is a very thin lining of the whole of these two sections of the alimentary canal and also of the *gastric caeca* (Beretta 1935, 1937; Khan 1961). The membrane is cuticular (A. W. A. Brown 1937*c*) and the electron microscope has revealed its structure as a fibrillar network (Mercer & Day 1952).

The above is a considerably simplified description of the alimentary tract, based mainly on that of *Locusta* (Nenyukov & Parfent'ev 1929; Hodge 1939; Albrecht 1953; Liu & Leo 1955). Some variations of the structures are known in other acridoids, particularly in relation to the general shape of the body. Thus, in strongly elongated species the alimentary canal is correspondingly long and the colon straight (*Rhadinotatum*, Hodge 1940; *Leptysma*, *Opshomala*, Hodge 1943; *Acrida*, Hafez & Ibrahim 1959). As mentioned above, the armature of the gizzard and the shape of the caeca and the colon are variable, and it is possible that more extensive studies would reveal substantial divergencies from the generalised picture, correlated either with the taxonomy or with feeding habits. The number of species studied in this respect is still very small (in addition to the above references, see Dufour 1841, *Oedipoda*; Visart 1894, *Anacridium, Oedipoda*, etc.; Cuenot 1895, *Acrida*, etc.; Bordas 1898, *Schistocerca, Poekilocerus, Pamphagus, Calliptamus*, etc.; Hodge 1936, 1937, *Melanoplus*; Jannone 1939*b*, *Dociostaurus*; Albrecht 1956, *Nomadacris*; Judd 1948, several species, foregut only; Ibrahim 1963, *Chrotogonus*; Baccetti 1961*c*, *Aidopus*).

DIGESTION

The digestion is one of the least studied aspects of acridoid physiology, in spite of its obvious importance in relation to feeding habits, effects of food on growth and reproduction, and insecticide action.

The mechanism of food ingestion, or feeding, will be more appropriately dealt with as an aspect of behaviour and here only the fate of the food during its passage through the alimentary canal is discussed.

The fate of food in the alimentary canal was investigated in *Schistocerca* and *Locusta* hoppers by Goodhue (1958, 1962, 1963) by feeding them on grass or bran impregnated with a radio-opaque substance and following the passage of a meal by X-ray photography. The food, cut into small particles by the mandibles, passes through the oesophagus into the foregut and enters the anterior part of the midgut and the posterior lobes of the gastric caeca. In the gizzard it becomes less radio-opaque, indicating a dilution by the digestive fluids produced partly by the salivary glands and partly by the secretion from the gastric caeca (Schlottke 1937). The secretory function of the latter appears to be restricted to their anterior lobes, which become enlarged but remain free of food, while the posterior ones are filled with food and some absorption of it occurs in them. Thus, the foregut is partly involved in the digestion of food, while its other function may be to crush food particles by the armature of its cuticle (p. 70); however, the mechanical effect cannot be great since the fragments remain recognisable as to the species of plants (Chapman 1957).

The main processes of digestion and absorption of food substances occur in the midgut and the caeca. The secretion of the digestive enzymes by the midgut epithelium is, according to Woodruff (1933) and Khan (1961), of the merocrine type (that is, the secretory cells do not break down in the process) although Hodge (1936, 1937) believed that the secretion may be either merocrine or holocrine. The food mass in the midgut becomes enveloped in the peritrophic membrane, which is, however, permeable to digestive enzymes and to products of digestion (Waterhouse & Day *in* Roeder 1953). The membrane persists through the hindgut and envelops the excreta pellets (A. W. A. Brown 1937a, 1937c); it is continually renewed by delamination from the gut epithelium.

Food in the posterior end of the midgut is isolated from the rectum by the pyloric valve and the bend of the colon; this bend straightens out when the abdomen elongates for passing a faecal pellet. Goodhue (1962) suggested that the function of the bend is to break the peritrophic membrane enveloping the whole food bolus into fragments covering the faecal pellets.

According to Baccetti (1960), a function of the ileum is the absorption of fluid from the faeces.

During its passage through the rectum, the volume of food decreases; possibly because of further absorption of water and inorganic ions (Shaw & Stobbart 1963; Phillips 1964) from it in the rectal pads (Baccetti 1962).

Rate of digestion

The rate of digestion of food is relatively high. In *Locusta* hoppers, fed on plants sprayed with colouring substances, coloured excreta appeared after about one hour at a temperature of 32°C (Nenyukov & Parfent'ev 1929). Voskresenskaya (1936), feeding the same insects after a long period of starvation and dissecting them at intervals, found that in ten minutes after feeding the whole foregut was filled and some food reached the midgut; after one hour the whole canal was filled; after two hours the foregut became clear, but the whole canal was not cleared until after about six hours (fig. 46, A).

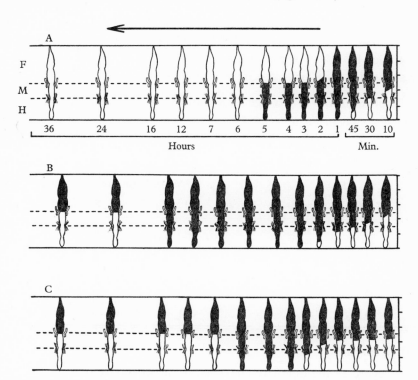

Fig. 46. Passage of food through the alimentary canal of *Locusta* hoppers (after Voskresenskaya 1936). A, normal food; B, food with Paris Green; C, food with sodium
arsenite.
F, foregut; M, midgut; H, hindgut.

Chauvin (1946) observed, by X-ray method, that in *Schistocerca* fed on crushed lettuce with barium the food passage took about four hours. Monchadskiĭ & Skoblo (*in* Predtechenskiĭ 1935), however, found that the rate of passage of food in *Schistocerca* hoppers depends on the introduction of new food; while normally the food passes through the canal in one-and-a-half hours on the average, its passage is greatly slowed down in starving individuals and some food remains in the midgut and hindgut after three to four days of starvation. This would suggest physiological regulation of the rate of digestion, but the delay may be merely due to the absence of pressure from the newly in-gested food. Goodhue (1962) provided information on the rate of food passage through the different regions of the alimentary canal, which shows that food with a higher water content passed more quickly than dry food (table 8).

The rate of passage of food is also affected by stomach insecticides (fig. 46, B, C). This should be of toxicological importance, since the slow passage of poisoned food lengthens the time available for the poison to be absorbed. In the case of sodium arsenite up to 35% of the dose ingested by *Locusta* was found outside the alimentary tract after thirty-six hours, and with Paris Green 44% of the dose had been absorbed after twenty-four hours (Voskresenskaya 1936). The effects of poisons on the cells of the midgut epithelium of *Locusta* were studied by Pilat (1935). Nervous control of food movement in the fore-gut was studied by Clarke & Grenville (1960)

Table 8. *Rates of passage* (*in minutes since the ingestion when the leading edge of the meal reaches each area*) *of different foods through the alimentary canal of* Schistocerca *hoppers* (*Goodhue* 1962)

G, grass; M, moist bran; D, dry bran

Instar	Food		Foregut	Midgut, segments					Hindgut segments			
	Kind	% water		1	2	3	4	5	6	7	8	9
III	G	80				10	20			30		
IV	G	80			10		20			30		
V	G	80			10		20		30			
III	M	35		10		20	30			40		
IV	M	35		10		20	30		40			
V	M	35		10		20	30			40		
III	D	10		10	20	30	40	50	60			
IV	D	10		10	20	30	40	50	60			
V	D	10		10	20	30	40	50		60		

Digestive enzymes

With regard to the digestive enzymes, some information exists for *Locusta* (Nenyukov & Parfent'ev 1929; Day 1949; Powning, Day & Irzykiewicz 1951; Robinson, Smith & Williams 1953; Robinson 1956; Khan 1961, 1962, 1963 *a*, 1963 *b*, 1963 *c*, 1964), *Schistocerca americana* (Swingle 1931), *S. gregaria* (Chauvin 1941 *b*; Drilhon & Busnel 1945 *a*, 1945 *b*; Robinson, Smith & Williams 1953; Kikal & Smith 1959; D. W. Payne 1961), *Calliptamus* (Tareeva & Nenyukov 1931) and *Stenobothrus* (Schlottke 1937). These data are summarised in table 9 which shows, as might be expected, a predominance of carbohy-drases over the enzymes taking part in the digestion of fats and proteins. Some of the recorded enzymes, such as β-glucuronidase and arylsulphatase, may be not from the locust secretions but of microbiological origin, since there is a rich bacterial flora in the gut.

Schlottke (1937) determined the concentration of each enzyme in different parts of the alimentary canal of *Stenobothrus* at different intervals after feeding. Reng (1961) attempted quantitative estimations of the activity of four main

Table 9. *Digestive enzymes in* Locusta *(L),* Schistocerca americana *(Sa),* S. gregaria *(Sg),* Calliptamus *(C), and* Stenobothrus *(St).*

Enzymes	Salivary glands					Foregut					Caeca					Midgut					Hindgut					Malpighian tubes				
	L	Sa	Sg	C	St	L	Sa	Sg	C	St	L	Sa	Sg	C	St	L	Sa	Sg	C	St	L	Sa	Sg	C	St	L	Sa	Sg	C	St
Carbohydrases																														
Amylase	+			+		+	+	+	+	+		+	+	+	+	+	+	+	+	+	+	+	+	+	+				−	−
Maltase	+	+	−	+		+	+	+	−	−	+					+	+	+	+	+	+	+	−	+	−				−	
Sucrase (invertase)	+	+				+			−	+				−	+	+				−	+	+							−	
Cellulase	+								−																					
Lichenase																														
Trulinase	−		+					−								+		+											−	
Dextrinase							+	+																						
β-glucuronidase																					+									
Glucosidase																+														
Esterases																														
Lipase	+			+	+	+			−	+	+				+	+	−		+	+	+	+		+	+	−			−	
Phosphatase	−					+	+							−		+	+		+		+	+		+				+		
Arylsulphatase																+			+	+	+	+		+						
Proteinase	−	−				+	+		+	+	+			−	+	+	+		+	+	+	+		+	+				+	+
Peptidase	+			−		+	+		+	+	+				+	+	+		+	+	+			+					+	+

enzymes, by the methods used in vertebrate enzymology, in two acridoids and obtained very similar figures (table 10).

Table 10. *Enzyme activity in two species*

	Amylase	Lichenase	Proteinase	Esterase
Stenobothrus sp.	0·0026	1·18	0·35	0·2
Locusta	0·003	2·2	0·34	1·3

Reng's data were based on the contents of the whole alimentary tract, and it can be seen from table 9 that the various enzymes are not distributed throughout the tract. In fact, D. W. Payne (1961) found that in *Schistocerca* the foregut possessed greater carbohydrase activity than other gut regions, indicating that digestion occurs mainly in the foregut, while carbohydrase and reducing sugar concentrations were extremely low in the hindgut, suggesting their absorption by the midgut.

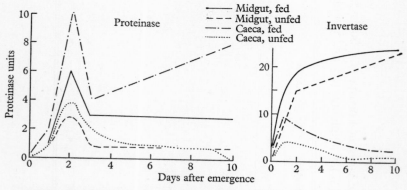

Fig. 47. Changes with the age in the rates of secretion of digestive enzymes in the alimentary tract of adult *Locusta* (after Khan 1963 c).

Khan (*tt.cc.*) has shown further, that in the newly-emerged *Locusta* adult there is abundant proteinase in the lumen of the gut, but the tissues of the midgut and of the caeca show only negligible activity of invertase and proteinase. These enzymes are synthetised in the tissues within two days and their concentration increases, and then fluctuates, provided the insects are fed. Starvation depresses the production of the enzymes, but feeding after starvation stimulates the secretion of invertase in the midgut earlier than in the caeca, whereas the secretion of proteinase is stimulated first in the caeca (fig. 47). In hoppers provided with food, the midgut and caeca tissues have maximal invertase in the middle of the instar, but it becomes very low before the next moult.

Since enzyme action is affected by the changes in the acidity and alkalinity of the digestive fluid, considerable attention has been paid to the hydrogen-ion (pH) concentration in the alimentary canal; the available data have been reviewed by Uvarov (1948), Grayson (1951) and Srivastava & Srivastava (1956), while D. W. Payne (1961) studied the pH in detail in *Schistocerca*. The figures for a wide range of species from America, Europe and India do

Table 11. *Hydrogen-ion concentration in the alimentary canal*

	Foregut	Midgut	Hindgut	Reference
Melanoplus differentialis	5·0–5·9	5·6–7·2	5·9–7·4	Grayson 1951
Schistocerca americana	5·2–6·0	5·9–7·5	6·5–7·5	,, ,,
Chortophaga viridifasciata	5·7–6·1	6·1–7·5	6·1–7·4	,, ,,
Acrida exaltata	6·0–6·4	6·6	6·2	Srivastava & Srivastava 1956
Chrotogonus sp.	6·2–6·4	6·2	6·2–6·3	,,
Hieroglyphus nigrorepletus	6·0–6·4	6·6–6·8	6·0–6·2	,,
Schistocerca gregaria	5·4	6·2–7·1	7·0	D. W. Payne 1961

not suggest any substantial differences that might be ascribed to the species, or to the food. In table 11 a few examples of the original determinations in some Indian species (Srivastava, *t.c.*) and in *Schistocerca gregaria* (D. W. Payne, *t.c.*) are given. It will be seen that the pH of the tract increases in alkalinity along its length. Skrjabina (1936), however, recorded changes in

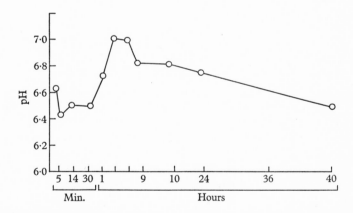

Fig. 48. Changes in pH of the midgut during the passage of food (after Skrjabina 1936).

pH of the gut contents of *Locusta* and *Calliptamus* during the food passage and suggested that the acidity in the midgut increases as soon as acid food reaches it but that later the alkalinity increases, probably owing to the secretion of digestive fluid (fig. 48). Points of this kind may be of importance in relation to the effects of stomach insecticides, the solubility of which would depend on the reaction in the gut.

UTILISATION OF FOOD

The coefficient (percentage) of food utilisation is obtained by dividing dry weight of food consumed, less dry weight of excreta, by dry weight of food consumed and multiplying by 100.

In P. M. Davey's (1954) experiments, *Schistocerca* hoppers fed on grass utilised 78·2% of food in the first instar, 51·5 in the second, 45 in the third, 34 in the fourth and 35 in the fifth. Dadd (1960 *e*) found the coefficient of grass utilisation by fifth instar *Schistocerca* to be 28–43% and by *Locusta* 28–53%. Adult *Schistocerca* utilised 32·6–33·4% of endive leaves (Chauvin 1946); males of that species utilised 23–53% of dry grass (Norris 1961). Adult males of *Dociostaurus brevicollis*, according to Nagy (1952), utilised 44–66% of food consumed during twenty-four hours (table 12); in females there was great variation, from 28 to 62%, possibly in relation to the state of ovarian development, an aspect not yet studied in detail. Males of 11 species of European

Table 12. *Utilisation of food consumed by adult males of* Dociostaurus brevicollis *in 24 hours. Weight in mg.* (*Nagy* 1956)

| | Food Plant | | | |
	Cynodon	Festuca	Polygonum	Mean
Green food consumed	45·3	48·1–60·2	35·7–54·0	48·7
Dry „ „	20·1	29·5–33·5	15·2–22·5	24·2
Dry excreta	7·1	10·2–12·8	7·6–7·8	9·1
Dry food utilised	13·0	19·3–20·7	7·6–14·7	14·7
Percentage utilised	64·82	61·83–66·35	43·91–65·6	60·48
Number of individuals	6	12	12	30

grasshoppers utilised 45–60% of the daily food and females 64–83% (T. Kaufmann 1959). Misra (1962) provided data on utilisation of different grasses by *Camnula pellucida*.

Nagy's work, suggesting that the coefficient of utilisation depends on the food plant, was supported by the detailed findings of D. S. Smith (1959) who reared *Melanoplus sanguinipes* on wheat, oats and *Agropyrum*. A particularly interesting result of his work was that the coefficient of utilisation of the different foods varied according to the age of hoppers (fig. 49). During the first five days, utilisation of all three foods was highest, with *Agropyrum* leading, but it fell progressively to the end of the hopper period, when *Agropyrum* took the last place. The general falling off with age, also found by P. M. Davey (*t.c.*) in *Schistocerca* and Misra (*t.c.*) in Camnula, suggests that younger hoppers utilise food for energy rather than growth. This suggestion is supported by the data on the *efficiency of food conversion*, calculated as the gain in dry weight, divided by dry weight of the food utilised and multiplied by 100 (fig. 49).

As regards the food substances utilised, A. W. A. Brown (1937*b*) fed *Melanoplus bivittatus* (late instar hoppers and adults) on finely chopped lettuce with the addition of determined quantities of various carbohydrates and estimated the percentage of the latter in the excreta. Monosaccharides (glucose, galactose, xylose) were utilised completely, while polysaccharides (inulin, dextrin, pectin, glycogen) passed through the gut almost without any being absorbed (but see p. 86); starch grains were not utilised at all. Proteins, however, were entirely absent from the excreta, suggesting that they formed the main nutritive substance absorbed. On the other hand, D. S. Smith (1958),

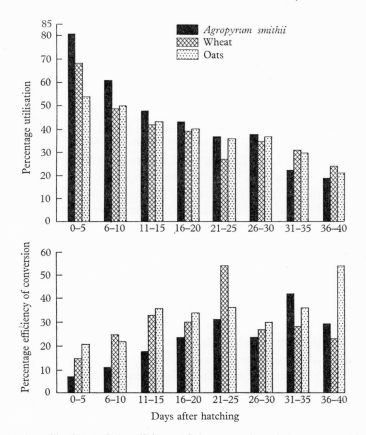

Fig. 49. The utilisation and the efficiency of the conversion of three types of food by hoppers of *Melanoplus sanguinipes* in relation to their age (after D. S. Smith 1959).

who investigated the consumption, utilisation and conversion of nitrogen by *Melanoplus sanguinipes*, found that 35·8–42·2 % of the nitrogen consumed was utilised and 16·1–22·8 % converted to tissue nitrogen; there was no relation to the nitrogen content of the food, but the latter had an effect on hopper development (p. 83).

Chauvin (1941 b) pointed out that in *Schistocerca* the rate of absorption of different substances changed with the development of the insect; hoppers and sexually mature adults utilised more sugars, while maturing adults used proteins at a higher rate.

EFFECTS OF FOOD ON DEVELOPMENT

Rearing of *Locusta m. migratoria* on a wide range of plants led Kozhanchikov (1950) to suggest the following grouping of food-plants according to their effects on the development of this species:

(1) Plants on which the complete life-cycle can be accomplished—Gramineae and Cyperaceae.
(2) Plants on which hopper development is completed, although with considerable or high mortality, but adults do not mature sexually—Compositae, Cruciferae, some Gramineae (e.g. *Avena*), Plantaginaceae, Leguminosae and Urticaceae.
(3) Plants on which hoppers can reach the last instar, but hopper mortality is considerable at the final moult, or immediately after—Rosaceae, Saxifragaceae, Caryophyllaceae.
(4) Plants on which only early instars survive—Typhaceae, Ranunculaceae.
(5) Plants eaten only by first instar hoppers, which fail to moult—Labiatae, Onagraceae, Chenopodiaceae, Liliaceae, Geraniaceae, Ericaceae, Betulaceae.
(6) Plants not eaten by first instar hoppers, even when starved—Primulaceae, Polygonaceae, Convolvulaceae, Rubiaceae, Ulmaceae, Caprifoliaceae, Salicaceae.

As shown in table 13, the kind of food affects both the rate of development and the growth of hoppers. The shortest hopper period was for hoppers reared on *Phragmites*, which also reached the heaviest weight at the Vth instar and their mortality was the lowest; those fed on *Plantago* took twice as long to develop to the Vth instar, in which they had one-third of the normal weight, and there was heavy mortality. Similar data are available for *Locusta m. manilensis* in China (Chin, Quo & Cheng 1957). An additional point of importance is that the effects of the same plant may depend on its stage of development; for example, *Phragmites* proved to be a better food in spring than the same plant in summer.

Experimental work with *Melanoplus differentialis* (Hodge 1933) and *M. sanguinipes* (Pfadt 1949; Smith, Handford & Chefurka 1952; Barnes 1955) has also shown a definite correlation between food, length of hopper period and mortality; in the case of members of this genus, the best food plants were not Gramineae, but members of other families. Of interest was the fact that a mixed diet of several plants resulted in faster development, greater weight of resulting adults and lower mortality, than did a diet of any single plant.

These data appear to indicate that the nutritional value of a given plant is not the same for different species or even different instars, although it has been suggested that the basic food requirements of all phytophagous insects are similar and that they can develop on any green food, provided they eat enough of it (Fraenkel 1959). According to that view, the amount eaten depends on the attractiveness and the palatability, or otherwise, of the plant to the insect rather than on its nutritional value. Thus, hoppers of *Melanoplus sanguinipes* reared on oats had slow development, high mortality and produced adults of low weight, although the efficiency of conversion of oats to body tissue (p. 81) was just as high as for wheat which was in all respects a more satisfactory food. The conclusion was that both foods were equally nutritious, but oats were eaten less (D. S. Smith 1959).

Some food plants have special effects on development. Hoppers of *Melanoplus sanguinipes* reared on lucerne (alfalfa) produced small adults with abnormally short tegmina (Brett 1947; fig. 50). Very high mortality and extended hopper period in the same species and *M. differentialis* fed on lucerne

Table 13. *Effects of food plants on the length of the hopper period, mean weight in mg at end of Vth instar and mortality of* Locusta *hoppers (after Kozhanchikov 1950)*

Plants	Mean length in days	Mean weight at end of Vth instar	Mortality percentage by instars					
			I	II	III	IV	V	Total
GRAMINEAE								
Phragmites communis, spring	24·0	1508	0	10	10	2	2	24
Phragmites communis, summer	27·0	1382	16	10	16	2	15	59
Calamagrostis epigeios	29·4	1054	8	23	0	7	7	45
Dactylis glomerata	30·3	1309	22	15	12	17	2	68
Agropyrum repens	27·3	1272	9	6	7	5	10	37
Poa pratensis	26·0	1160	25	10	10	5	5	55
CYPERACEAE								
Carex sp.	26·3		33	11	15	4	2	65
COMPOSITAE								
Taraxacum officinale	31·0		3	47	3	13	14	80
Sonchus oleraceus	26·6	1311	14	14	3	3	17	51
Artemisia vulgaris	38·0		83	12	0	0	0	95
CRUCIFERAE								
Raphanus raphanistrum	35·0	803	50	12	13	0	0	75
URTICACEAE								
Urtica urens	36·0	675	68	10	0	5	10	93
LEGUMINOSAE								
Trifolium pratense	36·0	825	90	0	0	0	5	95
PLANTAGINACEAE								
Plantago major	45·6	500	44	6	6	12	4	72
ROSACEAE								
Ribes rubrum	66·0	250?	92	0	0	0	8	100
Potentilla anserina	—		57	15	18	10	0	100
CARYOPHYLLACEAE								
Stellaria media	—		28	45	12	5	10	100
RANUNCULACEAE								
Ranunculus acer	—		90	10	—	—	—	100
TYPHACEAE								
Typha latifolia	—		95	5	—	—	—	100
ERICACEAE								
Vaccinium myrtillus	—		100	—	—	—	—	100

were recorded also by Barnes (1955, 1963) and Pfadt (1949). The latter author noted also that the effects of lucerne are particularly serious for the first instar hoppers, while it appeared to be a suitable food for older hoppers (initially given other plants). *Schistocerca* hoppers fed on lucerne (Telenga 1930) took thirty-seven days to develop, as against twenty-eight to thirty on other plants; some of them developed in twenty-nine days passing through only four instars, instead of the normal five. The resulting adults were abnormally small, with the tegmina not reaching the end of the abdomen, but they matured, copulated and one female laid eggs. Therefore, feeding on lucerne caused lengthening of the normal hopper period in some individuals, while in others the development was accelerated by elimination of an instar. Some *Schistocerca* hoppers fed on cabbage also passed through four instars and produced brachypterous adults (Mukerji & Batra 1938). As can be seen in table 13, feeding *Locusta* on another leguminous plant, *Trifolium*, also resulted in high mortality, long hopper period and very small adults; in this case, and in the observations

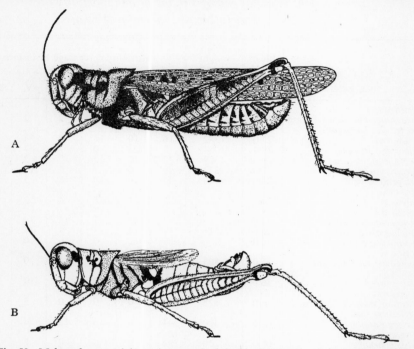

Fig. 50. *Melanoplus sanguinipes*. A, normal adult; B, adult bred on lucerne (Brett 1947).

on *Melanoplus sanguinipes* recorded above, no reference to the number of instars was made.

The unfavourable effects of oats on *Melanoplus sanguinipes* were accompanied by a high percentage of individuals having an extra instar (D. S. Smith 1959), an effect opposite to that caused by lucerne. Since the instar number is under hormonal control (p. 289) relations between the nutritional value of food and the course and rate of development may be less simple than has been assumed in some experimental studies.

NUTRITIONAL REQUIREMENTS

The above data on the very dissimilar effects of different food plants on survival and development indicate a need for fundamental investigations on the substances in food that are essential for the completion of the normal life-cycle. An approach to the problem can only be made through the use of artificial diets of precisely known composition. The need for evolving a completely sufficient artificial diet has been long felt by laboratory workers on locusts since, while it was possible to control all the major physical environmental factors (temperature, humidity, light), natural food (grass or any other plant) appeared to be subject to variation in quality, depending on the source, stage of growth, season and so on, and this sometimes tended to confuse experimental results. It was with a view to investigating the possibility of developing a standard artificial diet for locusts that Dadd (1960–63) carried out a series of studies on their nutritional requirements. A fully satisfactory

Table 14. *Basic synthetic diet for locust hoppers (Dadd* 1960 *a)*

Cholesterol	50 mg
Linoleic acid (B.D.H. technical grade)	0·2 ml
Casein, fat and vitamin free (B.D.H.)	6·0 g
Bacteriological peptone (B.D.H.)	2·0 g
Egg albumen powder (B.D.H.)	2·0 g
Salt mixture (Glaxo DL.6)	1·5 g
Cellulose powder (Light and Co.)	15·0 g
Carbohydrate (dextrin)	10·0 g
Ascorbic acid	100 mg
Vitamins in 10 ml of 20% ethanol:	
Thiamine	25 μg/g diet
Riboflavin	25 μg/g diet
Nicotinic acid	100 μg/g diet
Pyridoxine	25 μg/g diet
Folic acid	25 μg/g diet
Inositol	250 μg/g diet
Pantothenic acid	50 μg/g diet
p-Aminobenzoic acid	25 μg/g diet
Choline chloride	1250 μg/g diet
Biotin	1 μg/g diet

artificial diet was not achieved, but valuable information was obtained by rearing locust hoppers on a basic diet, which could be varied by addition, subtraction, or the quantitative modification of ingredients; its composition is given in table 14.

Full results of these investigations cannot be discussed here, but the main conclusions are as follows.

Both *Locusta* and *Schistocerca* hoppers grew satisfactorily on a diet containing a mixture of such proteins as casein, albumen and peptone; *Schistocerca* hoppers grew also on casein alone, but those of *Locusta* did not. There was also a difference between the species when proteins were replaced by a mixture of amino-acids, on which *Schistocerca* developed but *Locusta* failed to survive. It was of great interest that chlorophyll (a chromo-protein) which is so common in the normal food of locusts proved to be unnecessary.

The quantity of available nitrogen appears to be of importance, since in experiments of D. S. Smith & Northcott (1951), in which hoppers of *Melanoplus sanguinipes* were reared on wheat grown in solutions with different nitrogen content, the latter appeared to have a direct nutritional effect (table 15).

Dadd (*t.c.*) found that requirements in *fatty acids* were satisfied by linoleic and linolenic acids and cholesterol. Tocopherol was not required, and carotene had no effect on growth of *Locusta* and *Schistocerca*, but was essential for pigmentation of *Schistocerca* (p. 48).

Carbohydrates were found essential and without them both locust species failed to complete development. Growth occurred with 13% glucose or sucrose in the diet, but was satisfactory only with 26%; with 39% complete development was obtained, but the rate of growth was slower. Requirements for carbohydrates appeared to increase with the hopper instars. Amongst other carbohydrates tested, pentoses, sorbose and galactose were not utilised, but all hexoses, oligosaccharides, dextrines and starches were. A high amount

Table 15. *Effects of nitrogen content of wheat on length of hopper period and mortality of* Melanoplus sanguinipes (*D. S. Smith & Northcott* 1951)

Nitrogen percentage		Hopper period days	Mortality percentage
In solution	In wheat		
High	6·16	49	52
Low	4·29	61	70
Zero	3·33	—	100

of indigestible cellulose was found to be important, since without it the growth was less satisfactory than on grass, even though diets without cellulose had much higher coefficients of utilisation.

Requirements for *salts* appeared to be not very great. Both species grew well with only four salts, at the minimum rate of 1–2% of the diet, and tolerated up to 10%.

Amongst *vitamins*, it was found that ascorbic acid, thiamin, riboflavin, nicotinic acid, pyridoxine, folic acid, calcium pantothenate or choline were essential for growth of hoppers to the adult. Inositol and biotin were also of importance; omission of inositol, apart from retarding growth, resulted in a reduction of melanin (p. 43) and of cuticular carotenoids. The need for ascorbic acid is of interest because other insects are able to synthesise it, but locusts apparently cannot do so, although it was found in the cytoplasm of nerve cells of *Schistocerca* (Moussa & Banhawy 1960). In Dadd's experiments, no hoppers of *Schistocerca* reached the adult stage without ascorbic acid in the food; *Locusta* did better, but the few adults obtained were small and not viable. For both species 1·4 mg of ascorbic acid per gram of diet appeared to be optimal for growth. Indications were obtained that ascorbic acid plays some part in processes occurring during moulting and that it may be of importance in the sclerotisation and melanisation of the cuticle.

Dadd's synthetic diets proved to be inadequate for the practical purpose of continuous breeding of locusts in the laboratory though Cavanagh (1963) found that *Schistocerca* hoppers and adults developed on it as rapidly as on grass, but adults laid fewer eggs, unless given daily a small quantity of fresh grass. An artificial diet of less rigid composition developed by Howden & Hunter-Jones (1958) consisted of bran, two parts; dried whole milk, two; grassmeal, two; dried brewer's yeast, one (all by volume). On this diet, hoppers of *Schistocerca* developed normally, but mortality was high and adults failed to mature. However, when a very small quantity of chopped fresh grass was added, *Schistocerca* developed, matured and reproduced normally, but *Locusta* developed slowly, and mortality was high, possibly because its normal food is grass (p. 82) for which it has a much higher requirement than *Schistocerca*. This artificial diet is now regularly used for standard cultures of *Schistocerca* in the Anti-Locust Research Centre and some other laboratories. Grass-hoppers in the Belleville Laboratory, Canada, are reared on a similar diet, consisting of 75 g alfalfa meal (Cerogras), 25 g powdered dry milk, 5 g dried brewer's yeast, 0·5 g sodium chloride; lettuce leaves or wheat blades may be added, but are not necessary (R. W. Smith 1952). *Melanoplus* spp. in Montana were reared from egg to adult by Kreasky (1962) on the following diet (amounts in brackets in grams): casein (5·0), l-cystine (0·1), glycine (0·15), sucrose (8·0), corn oil (1·0), cholesterol (0·3), Wesson's salts (0·7), choline chloride (0·1), powdered cellulose (4·0), brewer's yeast (1·5), ascorbic acid (0·5), agar (4·0). This diet, however, enabled the hoppers to reach the adult stage only if water extract of 12–24 g of dried lettuce was added to it. The chemical nature of this indispensable 'lettuce factor' has not been discovered, except that it was not a nucleic acid derivative, but some organic substance, extremely resistant to heating, acids and weak alkalis. One can only comment that, since culti-vated lettuce is not a normal food of the grasshoppers, this substance must be present in some other plants. The need for adding a small quantity of grass to the locust diet also suggests that there is some special growth factor in grass, possibly the same as in lettuce.

It is to be noted that the scanty available information on the essential food substances refers only to their effects on hopper growth, while the effects on the maturation of adults and their fecundity have, so far, been studied only as far as the species of food plants are concerned. Data on this subject (p. 380) suggest the need for investigating the nutritional basis of adult development and reproductive physiology.

STARVATION

The effects of starvation are not easy to study by themselves, as they are complicated by loss of water, particularly at lower humidities (p. 228).

Data on the length of survival of starving hoppers and adults of *Schisto-cerca* are presented in table 16.

Table 16. *Length of life, in days, of starving* Schistocerca

| R.H. percentage | Hopper instars | | | | | Adult | Reference |
	I	II	III	IV	V		
0	—	4·4	4·1	—	1·0	2·0	Bodenheimer *et al.* 1929
20	—	1·0	2·7	—	1·8	3·0	,, ,, ,,
40	—	3·0	5·3	—	1·5	3·0	,, ,, ,,
60	—	3·4	5·5	—	3·0	4·8	,, ,, ,,
80	—	1·5	6·1	—	2·5	3·0	,, ,, ,,
100	—	3·5	4·7	—	3·0	5·8	,, ,, ,,
Not known	2	5	5	10	15	—	Telenga 1930

In Mikhelson's (1922) experiments the mortality of starved gregarious hoppers of *Locusta m. migratoria* occurred in the Ist instar in four to six days, in the IInd to IVth in six, in the Vth in nine, and in adults in 10·5 days. His results and those of Telenga indicate that the survival time increases with the

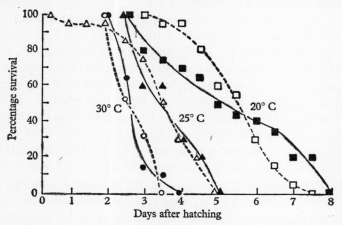

Fig. 51. Survival times of unfed hatchlings of *Melanoplus sanguinipes* (broken line) and *Camnula pellucida* (solid line) in relation to the temperature (after D. S. Smith 1960 *b*).

instar, while Bodenheimer's figures are too irregular to be taken at their face value. The maximum figures of twelve to fourteen days were obtained by F. B. Isely (1938) for adults of *Melanoplus ponderosus*; most of the other species tested by him died within a week.

As might be expected, the survival time of unfed hatchlings decreases with a rise in temperature (fig. 51).

Blackith & Howden (1961) studied the food reserves of hatchling locusts which may enable them to survive starvation. The fat content of the hatchlings of *Locusta* proved to be subject to great individual variation, from zero to 14·14%, but individuals which were almost without any fat on eclosion survived as well as those with high fat content, although fat was undoubtedly depleted during starvation (table 17).

Table 17. *Percentage of fat to dry weight in starving locust hatchlings* (*Blackith & Howden* 1961)

Species	Phase	Original	At death
Locusta	solitarious	7·5	2·8
	gregarious	10·7	2·2
Schistocerca	solitarious	5·3	2·4
	gregarious	9·3	4·9
Nomadacris	gregarious	13·0	2·8

These authors suggested that the main source of energy used during starvation was attributable to substances other than fats. No glycogen, which appears to be important in older insects (see below), was discovered in hatchlings. Amongst sugars, trehalose was partly exhausted by starvation, but glucose was not affected, while most of the amino-acids were exhausted. The amount and the percentage content of chitin actually increased

The metabolism of starving hoppers of the later instars appears to be substantially different from that of hatchlings, if one can compare the three locust species with *Chortophaga* studied by Ludwig (1950 *a*). His data on the losses of different substances during complete starvation (table 18) indicate that most of the weight loss was due to water, glycogen was nearly exhausted and fat and glucose much reduced, while nitrogen was, apparently, not used at all (Ludwig 1950 *b*); however, the figures for it were calculated ones, and the basis of the calculations has been questioned by Tassoni (1957).

Table 18. *Changes in weight and composition of starved* Chortophaga *hoppers* (*Ludwig* 1950 *a*)

	Original		Final		Loss	
	Weight mg	Percentage	Weight mg	Percentage	Weight mg	Percentage
Whole insect	138·1	—	82·0	—	56·1	40·6
Water	100·58	72·83	59·66	72·75	40·92	40·6
Fat	5·58	4·04	1·75	2·13	3·83	68·6
Glycogen	2·36	1·71	0·07	0·08	2·29	97·0
Faeces	—	—	—	—	6·53	—
Nitrogen	3·89	2·82	3·98	4·85	—	—

CHEMICAL COMPOSITION

Most of the available information on the chemical substances in the acridoid body and on their metabolism is included in the chapters dealing with the various systems or processes: integument (p. 32), alimentary (p. 70), excretory (p. 118), secretory (p. 156), respiratory (p. 124), and nervous systems (p. 151), fat body (p. 96), eggs (p. 249), water relations (p. 225), and so on.

There remains, however, a certain amount of analytical data on the gross composition of some species, summarised below, merely for reference purposes. Great caution is needed in using such data, since the treatment of insects before analysis and methods of the analysis and of presenting the results have varied widely. Also, exact indications of the age, state of maturity, etc., of the insects used are nearly always lacking, while in many cases whole insects (including the contents of the alimentary canal) were analysed.

TOTAL ANALYSES

There are only very few and incomplete total chemical analyses of whole insects and the data are presented in Table 19.

Table 19. *Total analyses of acridoids*

(D, dry weight; W, wet weight)

Species	Material	Percentage of	Crude protein	Fats	Carbo-hydrates	Ash	Reference
Melanoplus sp.	Adults	D	75·28	7·21		5·61	McHargue 1917
Oxya sp.	Adults	D	74·713	5·735	4·033	6·526	Ichikawa 1936
„ „	Adults	D	67·44– 68·13	4·42– 4·61		3·67– 3·88	Korigawa 1934
Nomadacris septemfasciata	Hopper Ist instar	W	15·3	2·7	7·2	1·0	Rosedale 1945
Nomadacris septemfasciata	Hopper VIth instar	W	18·6	2·4	6·8	0·8	Rosedale 1945
Nomadacris septemfasciata	Adults	W	20·8	3·9	7·5	1·7	Rosedale 1945
Schistocerca gregaria	Adults	D	61·75	16·95			Das 1945
Schistocerca paranensis	Adults	D	51·08	18·4	16·066	4·234	Basso Stajano & Escalante Rossi 1947
Sphenarium	Adults	D	50·62			18·92	Massieu, Cravioto *et al.* 1959

PROTEINS

Quantitative differences in the crude protein content between the few species analysed (table 19) are not necessarily specific and may depend on the growth stage. As regards the qualitative characteristics, McHargue (1917) recorded the following percentages of the different nitrogen-containing groups in the protein of *Melanoplus* sp.: 9·14 ammonia, 3·42 melanin, 14·98 arginine, 5·62 histidine, 0·23 cysteine, 8·0 lysine, 52·87 amino-nitrogen (in filtrate from bases), 4·32 non-amino nitrogen (in filtrate from bases). In *Oxya* sp., the nitrogen was distributed as follows: water soluble nitrogen 46·80, albumin 8·16, globulin 7·41, prolamine 7·87, gluteline 21·96, insoluble nitrogen 11·00 per cent of the total (Korigawa 1934). In *Sphenarium* ten amino-acids were recorded (Massieu, Cravioto *et al.* 1959). Ichikawa (1937) provided data on the relative percentages of nitrogenous compounds in the two sexes of *Oxya* (table 20); bearing in mind possible variation due to age, etc., there did not seem to be much sexual difference.

Table 20. *Percentages of nitrogenous compounds in the two sexes of* Oxya *sp.* (*Ichikawa* 1937)

	Male	Female
Water soluble	36·49	35·00
Albumin	6·68	10·22
Globulin	8·51	7·10
Prolamine	1·51	1·84
Gluteline	21·84	21·81
Chitin	25·00	24·03

The mean nitrogen content of *Locusta* undergoes some changes during the adult life (Cheu 1952) but they are not very serious (see table 26, p. 98). Changes due to starvation were investigated by Ludwig (p. 89) and by Tassoni (1957); the latter author insisted that the usual method of calculating protein content from the total nitrogen produces figures which are too high and that protein and non-protein nitrogens should be determined separately.

The possible importance of blood proteins for evaluating taxonomic relationships was suggested by the preliminary investigations of Stephen (1961).

CHITIN

This most important constituent of the cuticle is a very stable polysaccharide, chemically related to cellulose (Gilmour 1961), and associated with protein; a tentative scheme of its synthesis from glucose was offered by Candy & Kilby (1962). In most studies on chitin, protein is removed during purification of chitin by weak alkali (usually KOH or NaOH), so that the available quantitative data do not necessarily apply to the substance as found in the intact integument (A. G. Richards 1951).

A few quantitative determinations of chitin in locusts are given in table 21.

The figures for adult *Schistocerca* show that the percentage chitin content increases during adult life. In fact, the actual increase is even greater, because the total weight of an adult locust also increases (p. 300). A two-day-old male contained only 0·0377 g of chitin, but one two months old had 0·1197, an almost three-fold increase.

Table 21. *Chitin content of three locust species*

	Locusta Percentage of dry weight (Rothman 1929)	*Schistocerca* Percentage of fresh weight (Millot & Fontaine 1938)	*Nomadacris* Percentage of fresh weight (Rosedale 1945)
Hopper instar I	4·72	—	7·2*
,, ,, II	6·53	—	—
,, ,, III	7·31	2	—
,, ,, IV	6·93	1·7	—
,, ,, V	9·22	2·2	—
,, ,, VI	—	—	6·8*
Adult, age unknown	10·20	—	7·5*
,, fledgling	—	1·3	—
,, 2 days old	—	2·2	—
,, 4 ,, ,,	—	2·5	—
,, 7 ,, ,,	—	3·2	—
,, 3 weeks old	—	3·7	—
,, 2 months old	—	4	—

*These figures appear too high, probably because chitin was estimated in insects from which fat was extracted.

It was suggested by Blackith & Howden (1961) that the production of chitin is a continuous process. A newly laid egg of *Schistocerca* has practically no chitin, but one ready to hatch contains some 12% of dry weight of chitin; most of it is lost with shedding the provisional cuticle at hatching (p. 270). Increase in the chitin content of hoppers, even starving ones, is very rapid and substantial (table 22).

Table 22. *Percentage content of chitin to dry weight in starving locust hoppers* (*Blackith & Howden* 1961)

Species and phase	Newly hatched	Four days old
Locusta, solitarious	5·74	10·14
,, gregarious	4·89	10·42
Schistocerca, solitarious	5·17	9·18
,, gregarious	5·03	7·78
Nomadacris, gregarious	5·01	9·34

Some additional data on chitin content have been given for *Oxya*, in which it was 3·67–3·71% of dry weight (Korigawa 1934) and for a number of European grasshoppers in which it varied from 0·63 to 2·42% of fresh weight (Hochrainer 1942). The latter series suggests somewhat higher chitin content in species from drier habitats, and comparative determinations in species with different ecology would be of interest, provided care is taken to compare insects of similar physiological age.

OTHER CARBOHYDRATES

The most prominent carbohydrate is chitin, the distribution and properties of which are reviewed above, while sugars in blood are mentioned on p. 112, and glycogen is discussed in relation to muscular activity (p. 68). Other data are too fragmentary to be of value.

Data on carbon alone, which is, of course, found not only in carbohydrates, obtained by Kunasheva (1932) for seven European species (table 23), suggest that males usually contain more carbon than females, and hoppers less than adults.

Table 23. *Percentage carbon content (Kunasheva* 1932)

Species, sex and instar	Live weight	Dry weight
Chorthippus parallelus ♂	14·72	47·67
„ „ ♀	13·88	48·27
„ „ I instar	12·38	41·90
„ „ II „	13·13	46·30
„ „ III „	13·46	46·17
„ „ IV „	13·23	42·51
„ *albomarginatus* ♂	14·94	48·10
„ „ ♀	15·61	48·00
„ „ II instar	13·70	44·80
„ „ III „	12·77	46·52
„ „ IV „	13·07	47·22
„ *montanus* ♂	14·09	34·70
„ „ ♀	16·22	37·54
Calliptamus italicus ♂	15·40	42·53
„ „ ♀	16·02	43·86
Bryodema tuberculata ♂	15·67	43·02
„ „ ♀	15·97	50·69
Dociostaurus brevicollis ♂	15·00	39·41
„ „ ♀	15·45	42·23
Mecostethus grossus ♂	14·69	45·54
„ „ ♀	16·92	45·66

FATS see pp. 96, 249, 267.

INORGANIC CONSTITUENTS

A summary of available data on the inorganic constituents of acridoids is presented in table 24, which should be regarded with the usual reservations (p. 90).

The predominance of phosphorus, which stands out clearly, is due to the importance of this element for most tissues, but particularly the nervous system, and for protein (Tassoni 1957) and fat metabolism. The role of sodium and potassium in blood plasma is discussed on p. 110. Calcium and silicon are also present in considerable quantities, possibly mainly in the cuticle and other supporting tissues. In *Schistocerca gregaria* the silicon content in the immature (red) was higher than in the mature (yellow) adults, but this may be because whole insects were analysed and the immature ones

Table 24. Inorganic chemical constituents of bodies

(A, ash; D, dry weight; W, wet weight; +, present)

Species	Material	Percentage of	Si	Cu	Fe	Mn	Na	K	Ca	Mg	Ti	Ni	P	S	Se	Reference
Schistocerca gregaria	Dry, large scale	A	11·9	0·13	2·06	0·16	6·2	18·2	6·2	4·9	0·16	0·009	32·4	2·56		E. B. Uvarov 1931
" "	Red adults, dry	A	14·7	0·26	1·73	?										" "
" "	Yellow adults, dry	A	6·27	0·29	1·27	?										" "
" "	Adults dry, eviscerated	A	15·2	0·17	4·57	?										" "
" "	Adult males boiled in salt water, dry	D	0·3696	+	0·357	0·0013	+	+		+	+		0·562	0·323		Lapp & Rohmer 1937
" "	Adult females, do.	D	0·1736	+	0·267	0·0014	+	+		+	+		0·441	0·316	+	" "
" *paranensis*	Immature adults, dry	D						0·98	0·35	0·37			1·41			Brodskis 1944
" "	Adults, air dried	D			0·21			0·84	0·59	0·16			1·20			Das 1945
" "	Eggs	D			0·16			0·40	0·03	0·32			0·21			Schröder 1909
" "	Hoppers	D	1·40		0·12			0·80	0·02				1·40			" "
" "	Adults	D						0·76	0·01				0·70			Collens 1915
" "	Adults	W						0·94					1·44	?		F. Giral 1954
Acanthacris ruficornis	Adults, dry	A	6·33	0·43	1·92					+						E. B. Uvarov 1931
Melanoplus sp.	Residue of liquid pressed out of adults	A	12·1				5·08	7·42	13·26	8·51			50·71	1·05		Packard *in* U.S. Ent. Commission 1878
" *bivittatus*	Adults, dry	D	0·600		1·07	0·008	0·335	1·202	0·360	0·394			1·190	0·380		McHargue 1917
" "	Adults, fresh	W		0·216												Melvin 1931
" "	Adults, dry	D		0·693												Moxon 1939
" sp.	Adults fresh	W												0·03	4·66	J., F. & M. Giral 1943, 1946
Locusta m. migratoria, solitarious	Adult males	W				0·0021										Vinogradov & Neustrueva 1930
Locusta m. migratoria, solitarious	Adult females	W				0·0014										Vinogradov & Neustrueva 1930
Oxya sp.	Adult males	A	8·638		1·593	0·255	17·102	21·776	1·053	5·437			40·095	0·671		Ichikawa 1937
" "	Adult females	A	9·611		0·687	0·306	20·208	19·230	0·735	3·852			46·263	0·272		
Tropidacris dux	Adults	D						1·16					1·63			Collens 1915
Taeniopoda auricornis	Adult males	W												0·1		F. Giral 1941, 1954; J., F. & M. Giral 1944
" "	Adult females	W			0·003									0·04		
Sphenarium "	Adults	D							0·27				0·79			Massieu, Cravioto *et al.* 1959; F. Giral 1946

may have had more silicon in the grass in the alimentary canal, although the eviscerated specimens also had a very high silicon content. A relatively high copper content was found in *Acanthacris* and *Melanoplus femur-rubrum*; in the latter case, copper was more abundant in cast skins than in the insects themselves (Melvin 1931). Sulphur is an important constituent of proteins and fats (p. 101).

The only element on which more extensive studies were made is manganese (Vinogradov & Neustrueva 1930). In thirteen species the Mn content varied between 0·0011 and 0·0031% of live weight. It was found to be higher in hoppers than adults of *Chorthippus albomarginatus*, and in adult males than females of *Locusta* and *Pararcyptera*.

A special case is that of selenium which was found in *Melanoplus bivittatus* feeding on plants with high selenium content (Moxon 1939), but it appears that the whole insects were analysed and the selenium might have been in the food in the alimentary canal. Records of lithium, barium and strontium (Lapp & Rohmer 1937) were obtained from locusts (*Schistocerca*) boiled in salt water, bought in a Moroccan market.

The data on the inorganic constituents might be more suggestive if separate parts of the body, or particular tissues, were analysed, rather than whole insects often even including food in the alimentary canal.

FAT BODY AND FAT METABOLISM

STRUCTURE OF FAT BODY

The fat body is a discrete organ, enclosed in a connective tissue membrane which also divides it into many lobes (Baccetti 1955 b). It extends throughout the abdominal and thoracic cavities, where it closely adheres to various internal organs (particularly air-sacs) and it can be divided into a main central part, a peripheral sheet under the dorsal integument and a series of pads underneath the ventral nervous system (Buys 1924, *Melanoplus*; Coupland 1957, *Schistocerca*). The colour of the main fat body is various shades of yellow, but the peripheral sheet is whitish in the gregarious hoppers of *Schistocerca* and *Locusta* and blue in the solitarious (Okay 1953).

The cells of the fat body are large with chromatic nuclei, the vacuoles containing fat and granular inclusions (Pospelov 1926a, 1926b; Coupland, *t.c.*). Included amongst the fat cells are large oenocytes (p. 103), which are particularly numerous near its periphery. The whole of the fat body tissue is penetrated by a dense network of fine branched tracheoles.

The body is discernible already in Ist instar hoppers as a single or double white layer of cells, with small fat droplets in cytoplasm, which increase in size in the later instars. In *Locusta* adults striking changes are observed in the fat cells, particularly on sexual maturation, when cell membranes become difficult to discern, fat globules increase in size and granular inclusions become more numerous; the whole fat body increases in size so that it causes the air-sacs to be compressed (Pospelov *t.c.*). This maximum development of fat body occurs before the first oviposition, while the largest eggs are still not quite mature (stage III, see p. 304). It is followed by a rapid reduction, and only a few shreds of fat body remain when eggs are fully formed (Phipps 1950). The fat body of a newly emerged adult *Melanoplus* female is also quite small, but already after the first day it becomes enlarged and the maximum development is reached in about sixteen to twenty-three days, after which a reduction occurs (Weed Pfeiffer 1945 b).

FAT CONTENT

The fat body is certainly the main depository of fat, although a certain proportion of fat is found elsewhere; thus, in adult *Schistocerca* the average total lipid content (which is mainly in the fat body) was estimated as 9·6% of fresh weight, while the legs contained 0·4% and wings 0·3% (Weis-Fogh 1952).

The available data on the fat content of hoppers of several locust species are summarised in table 25, which illustrates phase differences (p. 351), but there is no information on the changes in fat content from instar to instar, or within an instar.

Changes in fat content of *Locusta* during adult life are illustrated by table 26 which shows that in both sexes a rapid increase occurs during the first two weeks, at the end of which it reaches some 30% of dry weight in the gregarious phase and 15–20% in the solitarious. In the female sharp reduction occurs just before the first eggs are laid; this reduction, therefore, is not due to the elimination of fat with eggs as might be thought, but to the reduced feeding at this period (Cheu 1952). That the fat is being utilised for movement is suggested by the more substantial drop in fat content in gregarious locusts than in solitarious. At the time of the first oviposition, a gregarious female has some 165 mg of fat, and some 46 mg of it are removed with the egg-pod. During subsequent life and repeated ovipositions, the fat content must be

Table 25. *Fat content (per cent of wet weight) of locust hoppers*

Species	Phase	Hatchling	Vth instar	Reference
Locusta	solitarious	7·5		Blackith & Howden 1961
,,	gregarious	10·7		,, ,, ,,
,,	solitarious		11·02	Matthée 1945
,,	gregarious		14·02	,, ,,
,,	solitarious		12·53	Vuillaume 1955
,,	gregarious		17·57	,, ,,
Locustana	solitarious		12·79	Matthée 1945
,,	gregarious		14·63	,, ,,
Schistocerca	solitarious	5·3		Blackith & Howden 1961
,,	gregarious	9·3		,, ,, ,,
Nomadacris	gregarious	13·0		,, ,, ,,

repeatedly renewed, as it appears to be almost stationary, and a five-week-old female, after laying four to five times, has a fat content not lower than it had just before laying the first pod. Towards the end of life, however, the lost fat is no longer replaced and the content declines. In males it also falls with age. Osman & Schmidt (1961) also gave some data on fat content in adult *Locusta*.

A similar picture is presented by *Melanoplus*, according to Weed Pfeiffer (1945b), who also estimated the changes in fat content in tissues other than eggs. As a newly laid egg of this species contains approximately 0·352 mg of fat and since on average 100 eggs are laid at one time, some 35·2 mg of fat in a female ready to lay should be in eggs, leaving an average of 80·4 mg in the fat body and other tissues. Thus, nearly one-third of the total amount of fat is likely to be lost after one oviposition, but the fact that it remains almost constant (fig. 52) suggests a continued rebuilding of fat from food. Moreover, females with the ovaries removed maintained their fat content at about the normal level, but it suffered depletion in later life.

Table 26. *Fat and protein content at various stages of development of adult* Locusta *(Cheu 1952)*

Phase and sex	Age	Fat		Protein			Dry body weight mg per locust
		Percentage to dry weight	mg per locust	Percentage to dry weight	Percentage to fat-free dry weight	mg per locust	
Gregarious ♀	1 day	13·9 ± 1·7	40 ± 7	55·0	62·0	169 ± 16	284
	1 week	25·1 ± 3·7	152 ± 27	45·4	59·9	237 ± 39	523
	2 weeks	30·1 ± 5·4	317 ± 56	40·3	61·4	414 ± 35	1,052
	Before 1st laying	15·5 ± 1·5	165 ± 27	56·2	66·5	607 ± 62	1,063
	After 1st laying	14·9 ± 2·0	119 ± 26	56·5	66·7	462 ± 57	798
	5 weeks	17·8 ± 9·5	143 ± 87	—	—	—	802
	7 weeks	12·1 ± 4·9	93 ± 48	—	—	—	771
	After 6th laying	8·5 ± 1·9	68 ± 13	60·5	66·3	484 ± 57	802
	At time of death	7·2 ± 1·7	42 ± 13	—	—	—	—
Solitarious ♀	1 day	5·3 ± 0·3	18 ± 2	57·4	62·5	197 ± 38	346
	1 week	13·5 ± 2·4	99 ± 34	52·9	61·3	376 ± 42	710
	Before 1st laying	15·0 ± 6·8	178 ± 99	55·0	65·3	667 ± 96	1,212
	After 1st laying	14·4 ± 8·0	136 ± 95	54·6	64·4	528 ± 128	968
	After 6th laying	10·8 ± 5·4	103 ± 52	58·1	65·3	552 ± 68	956
Gregarious ♂	1 day	11·8 ± 0·2	28 ± 4	—	—	—	233
	1 week	22·9 ± 4·8	90 ± 27	—	—	—	392
	2 weeks	29·9 ± 5·6	169 ± 66	—	—	—	565
	5 weeks	23·3 ± 12·2	123 ± 87	—	—	—	526
	7 weeks	21·6 ± 6·5	110 ± 49	—	—	—	508
	At time of death	5·4 ± 2·0	20 ± 9	—	—	—	—
Solitarious ♂	1 day	7·3 ± 0·8	15 ± 3	—	—	—	202
	1 week	10·9 ± 2·1	38 ± 9	—	—	—	353
	2 weeks	19·4 ± 2·2	96 ± 15	—	—	—	493
	5 weeks	23·4 ± 12·2	117 ± 77	—	—	—	500
	7 weeks	10·6 ± 4·7	44 ± 15	—	—	—	—

In the case of males, the importance of food in building up fat was shown in experiments with *Schistocerca* fed during the last hopper instar and the first two weeks of adult life on partly dried grass (with 33% of water, as compared with 80% in fresh grass); the adults at the end of two weeks had 130–281 mg fat as against 298–477 mg in the controls fed on fresh grass (G. G. Cavanagh, unpublished).

As regards the utilisation of fat, it has been shown by Weis-Fogh (1952) that the main source of energy for flight in *Schistocerca* is the reserve fat,

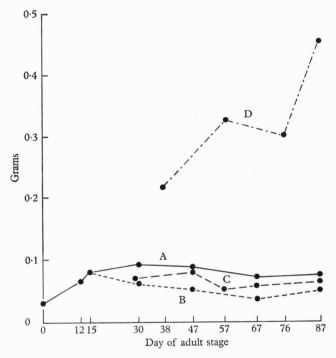

Fig. 52. Fat content of adult female of *Melanoplus differentialis* in relation to age (Weed Pfeiffer 1945 b).
A, normal female; B, ditto, fat other than in eggs; C, castrated female; D, female with corpora allata removed.

which is expended. Locusts flying in a wind-tunnel for five hours used, on average, 60 mg of fat per individual out of the total 175 mg. In *Locusta*, also, fat is used for flight (Zebe 1960).

Field data on gregarious *Schistocerca* in migrating swarms (fig. 53) show that the total fat content of fledgling males rose from 10–15 mg per locust to 30–40 mg (3–4% of fresh weight) in the second week. In other observations, the mean fat content of males rose in the first four weeks to 150 mg per locust and in swarms five to six weeks old and still immature reached 140 mg (8% of fresh weight); even much higher figures, up to 200 mg per male and over 300 mg per female, were obtained from swarms moving slowly and feeding on lush vegetation (Z. Waloff, 1961). This confirms that the fat expended in movement and in egg-laying is continually rebuilt, allowing continued migration and the maturation of further eggs. In laboratory-bred *Schistocerca* a much higher fat content was recorded than in the field, 600 mg per male being reached in four weeks and up to 900 mg in six weeks (G. G. Cavanagh,

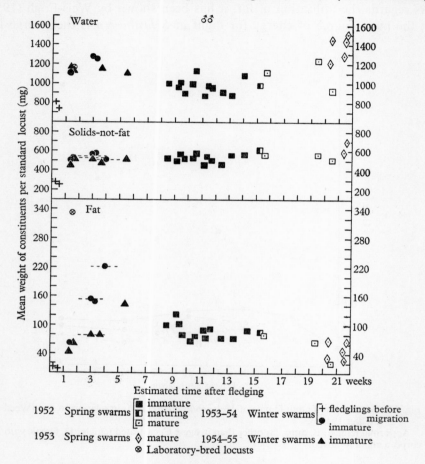

Fig. 53. *Schistocerca*, gross composition of males in migrating swarms
(Z. Waloff, original).

unpublished). This must be due to a lower level of activity and abundant regular feeding.

All these data indicate that fat reserves are used not only for the formation of egg-yolk, but perhaps more as a source of energy; also, that fat in yolk is not necessarily obtained at the expense of the fat body, but possibly metabolised from food and transported in the blood.

In view of the great variation of total fat content even in one individual during its life, casual quantitative estimates available for a few species present little value, since in most cases there is no indication of the sex, age, physiological condition, etc., of the specimens analysed, while the methods of extraction and evaluation are also not always comparable. It would not be safe, therefore, to draw any conclusions from such data and merely a list of references is given below:

Schistocerca gregaria: Dubois 1893 (eggs); Timon-David 1930; Lapp & Rohmer 1937; Brodskis & Rungs 1944 (eggs, immature and mature adults of both sexes); Gueutal 1941 (eggs, hoppers, adults); G. Albrecht 1961 (immature adults).

Schistocerca paranensis: Trevithick & Lewis 1939; Basso Stajano & Escalante Rossi 1947; F. Giral 1954.

Nomadacris septemfasciata: Rosedale 1945 (hoppers, adults).

Locusta migratoria: Matthée 1945 (hoppers of two phases).

Locustana pardalina: Matthée 1945 (hoppers of two phases).

Anacridium aegyptium: Timon-David 1930; Marcuzzi 1960.

Dociostaurus maroccanus: Timon-David 1930.

Oxya japonica: Tsujimoto 1929.

Pezotettix giornae and *Acrida bicolor:* Marcuzzi 1960.

Taeniopoda and *Melanoplus:* F. Giral 1941, 1946, 1954; J., F. & M. Giral 1943, 1944, 1946.

Papers containing information on fat and its metabolism in eggs only are referred to on pp. 249, 266.

PROPERTIES OF FATS

Some characteristics of fats of the different species are listed in Table 27.

Table 27. *Properties of fats*

Species	Percentage wet weight	Iodine index	Saponification index	Reference
Dociostaurus maroccanus	3·3	109·9	181·0	Timon-David 1930
Anacridium aegyptium	2·57	97·6	198·9	,, ,, ,,
Schistocerca gregaria ♂		106·68	224·0	Lapp & Rohmer 1937
,, ,, ♀		92·71	224·0	,, ,, ,,
,, *paranensis*		65·2	194·5	Trevithick & Lewis 1939
Oxya japonica	3·00	122·6	171·5	Tsujimoto 1929
Taeniopoda auricornis ♂	2·52	111·5	196·5	F. Giral 1941
,, ,, ♀	2·76	101·3	185·0	,, ,,
Melanoplus sp.		75·3	216·3	J., F. & M. Giral 1943
Nomadacris septemfasciata Vth instar hoppers		140	136	Rosedale 1945

As regards the chemical components of fat, that of *Melanoplus* sp. contained some neutral fat, but mainly free fatty acids, including stearic (9·1%), palmitic (6·7%), arachidic (2·1%) and several unsaturated acids (82·1%). In *Taeniopoda auricornis* sexual difference in the composition of fat was found: female fat contained 35% unsaturated acids, 6·5% oleic and 58·5% linoleic acid, while that of males consisted of 15·5% saturated, 24% oleic and 60·5% linoleic acid; the sulphur content was 0·247% in females and 0·096% in males

(J. Giral, F. Giral & M. L. Giral 1943, 1944, 1946). The lipids of adult *Locusta* consist mainly of triglycerides, particularly the palmitic and oleic acids; phospholipoids form 10–15% of the total fat (Osman & Schmidt 1961). In *Schistocerca* adults, only palmitic and stearinic acids were found in the saturated fraction (Gerd 1961; G. Albrecht 1961). All such data have only a limited value, as substantial changes in the composition of fat must be expected in relation to age and physiological state of the insects.

FUNCTIONS OF FAT BODY

Studies on the metabolic activities of the fat body of *Schistocerca* are all very recent and still in progress; a general review of the problem was recently published by Kilby (1963). The results are incomplete and some of them contradictory, but they already serve to show that this organ is not merely a store of reserve materials (fats, proteins and carbohydrates), but also an important organ of intermediate metabolism. It has been suggested that the fat body may play a part similar to that of the vertebrate liver in transaminating amino-acids, thus making them available for metabolism of other tissues, and in the conversion of carbohydrates and proteins into fat.

More specifically there is evidence that the fat body of *Schistocerca* is able to convert acetate, glucose and amino-acids into fat (Clements 1959; A. Tietz 1961). The synthesis of trehalose from glucose in the fat body of the same species was established by Candy & Kilby (1961), and the part played by it in some transamination reactions described by Kilby & Neville (1957). Oxidation of fatty acids was investigated by Meyer, Preiss & Bauer (1960).

Of some interest is the presence in the fat body of acridoids of glycogen which in other insects provides energy for flight. Its presence was suspected by Pospelov (1926a) in the granular inclusions of fat body cells in *Locusta*; Coupland (1957) found a large amount of glycogen in the cells of hoppers, but less in adults of *Schistocerca*; Trivelloni (1960) recorded it in *Schistocerca paranensis*; Clements (1959) regarded glycogen in *Schistocerca* as a minor product of fat body synthesis. According to Weis-Fogh (1952) the total glycogen content of adult *Schistocerca* ranged from 16 to 33 mg per individual; this amount could provide energy for only one to two hours of flight, and the main source of energy for flight must be fat.

Following is a list of enzymes involved in metabolic activities within the fat body: dehydrogenases (isocitric, malic, glutamic, glycerophosphate, succinic, lactic, hydroxybutyric, etc.); oxidases (cytochrome, succinic and amino-acid); arginase; aconitase; fumarase; trehalase; lipase; phosphatases (Bellamy 1958; Bücher & Klingenberg 1958; Candy & Kilby 1961; Clements 1959; Coupland 1957; George & Eupen 1959a, 1959b; George & Heydekar 1961; George, Vallyathan & Scaria 1958; Hearfield & Kilby 1958; Howden & Kilby 1956; Hess, Scarpelli & Pearse 1958; Kilby & Neville 1957; Zebe &

McShan 1957; Zebe 1960, 1962; Meyer, Preiss & Bauer 1960; A. Tietz 1961).

It has been suggested, with regard to other insects, that enzyme activity in the fat body might be due to the presence of symbiotic micro-organisms, but none were found in the fat body of *Schistocerca* (Coupland 1957).

HORMONAL CONTROL OF FAT METABOLISM

While in normal adult females the initial rapid increase of fat content ceases after about two weeks and thereafter the content becomes almost stationary, a strikingly different picture was presented by females of *Melanoplus* from which corpora allata were removed during the first four days after emergence (Weed Pfeiffer 1945 b). In such females, the fat content continued to increase at the initial rate for as long as eighty-seven days and rose to some 40–50 % of the dry weight, as compared with the average 11·6 % in the normal females of the same age (fig. 52); at the same time the amount of water was reduced below the normal. The hypertrophy of the fat body in the operated females was clearly shown. This suggests that a hormone secreted by the corpora allata prevents storage of fat, and the changes in the rate of fat increase in normal females can be linked up with secretory activity of the corpora allata. Mendes (1948) has shown that the corpora allata in *Melanoplus* are inactive at the beginning of the adult stage, and this leads to the accumulation of stored fat; later on, however, their secretory activity increases markedly, resulting in an inhibition of fat storage on the one hand, and the beginning of yolk formation in oocytes on the other. Removal of the corpora allata has the opposite effect, favouring the storage of fat and impeding yolk formation. These conclusions have also been confirmed for *Locusta* (L. Joly 1955, 1960), but only as regards the ovarian development.

The suspension of sexual maturation in many insects is known to be accompanied by accumulation of fat reserves (Lees 1955), but Weed Pfeiffer's findings concerning the connection between corpora allata activity, fat storage and yolk deposition suggest valuable lines of research. Comparative investigations of fat content in normal and diapausing adults of the same species should produce interesting results.

OENOCYTES

Oenocytes are large cells (fig. 54) with large nuclei and chromatic inclusions, found in different parts of the body close to the hypoderm, but particularly grouped near the abdominal spiracles and tracheae, on the under surface of the ventral septum, and on the periphery of the fat body; they are also found free in the body cavity (Chauvin 1938, 1941 b; Coupland 1957; Duarte

1939). Their appearance is subject to cyclical changes connected with the moulting process (table 28 and fig. 54).

In oenocytes of *Schistocerca*, glycogen, proteins, ribonucleic acid and granular pigment inclusions were found (Chauvin *tt.cc.*; Coupland *t.c.*).

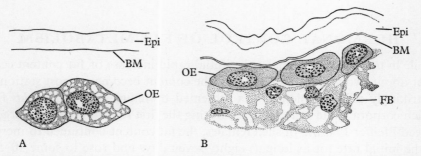

A   B

Fig. 54. Oenocytes of *Locusta* hoppers. A, three days after a moult; B, five days after a moult (Duarte 1939).
Epi, hypoderm; BM, basal membrane; OE, oenocyte; FB, fat body.

Table 28. *Changes in oenocytes, cuticle and hypoderm in*
IIIrd instar Locusta hoppers (Duarte 1939)

Time after moult	Hypoderm and cuticle	Oenocytes
30 hours	Homogeneous	Homogeneous
3 days	Cell division	Increase in size and maximum vacuolisation
4 days 20 hours	Digestion of old cuticle and formation of new; moulting glands appear	Decline of vacuolisation
5 days 10 hours	Maximum activity of moulting glands	Homogeneous

The functions of oenocytes in insects generally are very insufficiently known (A. G. Richards 1951). They have been supposed to play some part in the intermediate metabolism (Kessel 1960), and their accumulation near spiracles suggests some connection with respiration. Although their secretory activity has some relation to the moulting cycle, their presence in adults certainly suggests some other functions.

CIRCULATORY SYSTEM

STRUCTURE

The circulatory system is not a closed one, and consists of a pulsating organ, corresponding to the heart, but there are no blood vessels and the blood circulates through body cavities, reaching the exterior of the various organs (fig. 55).

The body cavity is divided by two longitudinal *diaphragms* into three communicating *sinuses* (fig. 39 B): dorsal (pericardial), large central (perivisceral)

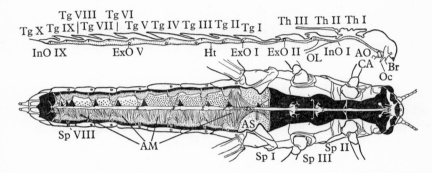

Fig. 55. *Schistocerca shoshone*, circulatory system. Top: longitudinal section of dorsal blood vessel; bottom: general view (after Nutting 1951).

AM, alary muscles; AO, aorta; AS, air-sac; Br, brain; CA, corpora allata; ExO, excurrent ostia; Ht, heart; InO, incurrent ostia; Oc, occipital ganglion; OL, ovariole ligament; Sp, spiracle; Tg, tergites; Th, thoracic segments. Heavy black dots, pericardial cells.

and ventral (perineural). The dorsal diaphragm extends from the first to the ninth abdominal segments and consists of membranous connective tissue, intertwined with paired alary muscles. There are ten pairs of alary muscles in many species, eleven in *Taeniopoda* (Nutting 1951), eight in *Dissosteira* (Snodgrass 1935), *Locusta* (Albrecht 1953 *a*) and *Dociostaurus* (Jannone 1939 *b*), and seven in *Nomadacris* (Albrecht 1956) and *Locusta m. manilensis* (Liu, Lee & Leo 1960); more extensive studies are needed. The ventral diaphragm is mainly membranous, but includes some muscle strands and nerves (A. G. Richards 1963).

The *dorsal blood vessel*, or *heart*, is a long straight tube lying in the pericardial sinus and extending from the head to the tenth abdominal segment. Its part lying within the head and thorax is called the *aorta* and its anterior end, expanded into a funnel and attached to the hypoderm of the frons just below the median ocellus, is open below (*Locusta*, Pavlova 1895). Nutting

105

(*t.c.*) and Jannone (*t.c.*) described the aorta ending just behind the brain but this was not confirmed by Albrecht (1953 *a*). The aorta forms expansions (diverticula) in the mesothorax, metathorax and first abdominal tergite.

The dorsal vessel proper forms dilations (heart chambers or *ampullae*) in each segment of the abdomen from the second to the eighth, then tapers and ends blindly in the tenth. Each ampulla has a pair of dorso-lateral openings, the incurrent *ostia*, with valve-like flaps; according to Nutting (*t.c.*) there are twelve pairs of such ostia in all species studied by him, but not all are shown in his diagram (fig. 55). Kowalevsky (1894*a*, 1894*b*) recorded in *Locusta* and *Calliptamus* five pairs of slit-like ventro-lateral openings which he regarded as also possibly incurrent; this view was accepted by Wigglesworth (1953), but Nutting believed them to be excurrent and considered seven pairs as typical for acridoids.

The blood vessel is in close relation to the two dorsal tracheal trunks (p. 126) and is innervated by a pair of lateral nerves. It was claimed by Kowalevsky (*t.c.*) that Malpighian tubes in *Locusta* penetrate the walls of the heart, but Jannone (*t.c.*) did not find this to be the case in *Dociostaurus*.

CIRCULATION

While it is possible that respiratory movements of the body walls (p. 128) affect blood pressure and thus influence circulation, the latter is caused essentially by the rhythmic contractions of the blood vessel. These contractions begin usually at the posterior end of the vessel and a peristaltic wave moves forward; a reversal, however, also occurs. This causes blood from the perivisceral cavity to be drawn into the heart through the incurrent ostia, impelled forward and discharged through the anterior opening of the aorta into the general body cavity. During the contracting phase of heart beat, some blood is expelled from the heart through the excurrent ostia. The ventral diaphragm of *Melanoplus* pulsates at the rate of 30/min (A. G. Richards 1963), but the effects of this on circulation are not known. The circulation of blood through the body cavity remains unstudied.

The only accessory pulsating organs definitely known in acridoids are a pair of *antennal ampullae*, which lie below the bases of the antennae; their position is marked externally by small oval swellings of the integument just below the edge of the antennal sockets. Each ampulla emits a vessel into the antenna and has special muscles (fig. 56). The fine structure of the ampullae has been described by Pavlova (1895) in *Locusta* and other species, but they have been overlooked by most later authors.

Circulation in grasshopper wings was observed more than 200 years ago (H. Baker, *The Microscope Made Easy*), but received no further attention, except in a short paper by Guignon (1936), according to whom blood circulates in *Psophus* hoppers along the wing veins, as well as between the wing membranes, whereas in adults it is confined to the former. However, the fact that pigments can spread throughout the adult wing (p. 299) and the presence of haemocytes between its membranes (Jannone 1939*b*) contradict the latter

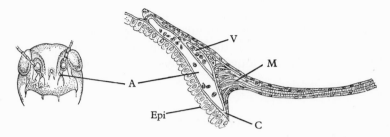

Fig. 56. *Locusta*, antennal ampulla; frontal view of head and a section of an ampulla (after Pavlova 1895).
A, ampulla; C, cuticle; Epi, hypoderm; M, muscle; V, valve.

suggestion. Clare (1953) studied circulation in the wings by direct observation of live insects under the microscope. According to him, the haemolymph flows from the thoracic haemocoele along the costal, subcostal and radial veins, as well as the medial and cubital; towards the apex, the flow divides

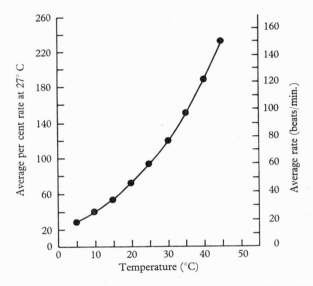

Fig. 57. *Melanoplus*, rates of heart beat at different temperatures (Jahn & Koel 1948).

along the branches of the veins, then returns towards the base along the post-cubital and vannal veins and enters a pulsatile chamber at the base of the tegmen. The flow in the hindwings is similar. Some variation in the pattern of circulation was mentioned, but was not described in detail.

The *rate of heart-beat*, as shown by electro-cardiograms (Jahn & Koel 1948), varied in *Melanoplus* from twenty beats per minute at 5°C to 150 at 45°C; near the zero, the rate was ten per minute (fig. 57). Studies on the effects of chemicals on circulation, which may be important in relation to insecticide action, are almost non-existent. Nicotine and atropine caused a depression of circulation, while acetylcholine stimulated the heart (H. L. Hamilton 1939). In carbon dioxide and monoxide the heart pulsations continued for six hours, and in pure hydrogen for as long as five days (Walling 1906).

HAEMOLYMPH

The fluid freely circulating in the body cavities of insects is the haemolymph, often called blood, although the mode of its circulation and its properties and functions differ from those in higher animals. It consists of a liquid component (*plasma*), and free cellular elements (*haemocytes*).

The volume of haemolymph per insect is not easy to determine, and the only reliable data exist for *Schistocerca* (R. M. Lee 1961), in which the volume was determined not by itself, but in relation to the unit of body weight, in millilitres per gram. As shown in fig. 58, the volume rises during the latter half of each hopper instar, attains its highest level just before a moult, and falls sharply some twenty-four hours after a moult. Variations in the volume are not entirely due, as might be thought, to the intake or the loss of water, but also to the changes in the distribution of water between the haemolymph and body tissues (fig. 59). Breakdown of tissues before a moult releases water into the haemolymph; after a moult, the dry weight of the insect falls, owing to the loss of old cuticle, and the percentage of total water rises in proportion, but the ratio of haemolymph volume to the unit weight decreases, suggesting the utilisation of water from the haemolymph for the growth of new tissue. In an adult locust, the dry weight increases owing to the growth (p. 300) at the expense of the haemolymph volume per unit weight so that the absolute haemolymph volume does not alter with age, but its percentage falls.

Changes in the haemolymph volume probably affect the *pressure of blood*, which, however, can be also greatly affected by the compression of the body in respiration (p. 128), moulting (p. 284) and oviposition (p. 324).

The *reaction of haemolymph* in a number of North American species was found to be mostly weakly acid, the mean pH values being 6·3–6·9 (Bodine 1925 b; Boche & Buck 1942; Hastings & Pepper 1943); in six Indian species it was 6·4–6·6 (Srivastava & Srivastava 1956), but Russian authors obtained indications of alkaline reaction, the values being 7·1–7·3 in *Calliptamus*, 7·29 in *Locusta* and 7·39 in *Dociostaurus* (Tareeva & Nenyukov 1931; Skrjabina 1936). However, in all cases considerable variation was found between species (from 6·0 to 7·6) and between individuals of the same species; any constancy of reaction in metabolically very active blood can scarcely be expected.

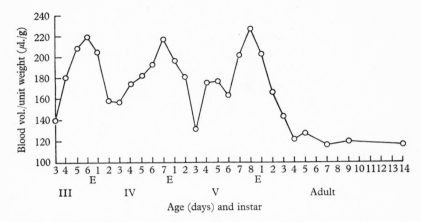

Fig. 58. *Schistocerca*, variation of haemolymph volume during the life-cycle (after R. M. Lee 1961). E, moult.

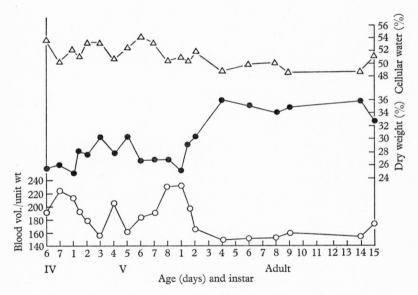

Fig. 59. *Schistocerca*, variation of haemolymph volume, cellular water and dry weight during the life-cycle (after R. M. Lee 1961).

The *buffering capacity* of blood (ability to resist changes in reaction on the addition of either an acid or a base) was very weak in the few species studied (Hastings & Pepper 1943); this may be of importance in relation to the action of insecticides with pronounced acid or basic properties.

109

The more common *inorganic constituents* of haemolymph (Phillips 1964; Shaw & Stobbart 1963) are sodium and potassium. Quantitative determinations of calcium and magnesium are available for one species only (table 29); other elements may be present in small quantities, for example copper was reported in blood of *Melanoplus* and *Dissosteria* (Muttkowski 1921). Phillips (*t.c.*) found a high chloride content in *Schistocerca* haemolymph.

It has been suggested (Hoyle 1954, 1956) that a rise in potassium concentration in *Locusta* hoppers fed on grass was due to the fact that grass is rich in potassium and much of it may pass into the blood; an increase in potassium concentration in haemolymph after feeding (fig. 60) was suggested as a reason for reduced muscular activity (p. 66) and thus may have an effect on behaviour (Ellis & Hoyle 1954). Chapman (1958) carried out systematic estimations of potassium in the haemolymph of *Nomadacris* also feeding on grasses and found that the potassium concentration rose from the mean value of 15 m equiv./l.

Table 29. *Some inorganic constituents of haemolymph*

(Data in m equiv. per litre; those marked with an asterisk are recalculated from the original ones in mg per cent.)

	Na	K	Ca	Mg	Reference
Stenobothrus stigmaticus	61	62			Boné 1945
Romalea microptera	64	18			Tobias 1948
Locusta, hopper, fed	72–130	15–43			Hoyle 1954
„ „ starved	83–140	9–25			„ „
„ adult, fed	64–154	12–29			„ „
„ „ starved	73–156	7–16			„ „
Locusta, adult	74–102	15–33			Ramsay 1953
Schistocerca, adult, starved	108	11			Phillips 1964
Chortophaga viridifasciata	62*	3·4*	3*	12·8*	Barsa 1954

in the morning to about twenty during the heat of the day, and fell again in the evening (fig. 61). The increase in the concentration was not connected with feeding, since the concentration was falling in the afternoon when the main meal was taken. Cage experiments indicated that the quantity of grass eaten at a meal contained about 0·82 mg potassium per locust, which was approximately ten times the total quantity in the haemolymph; a marked increase in concentration would therefore be expected, if potassium were absorbed, but this was not observed. On the other hand, locusts in cages exposed to high temperature showed an increase in potassium value, though less marked than in the field, while there was a slight decrease if they were provided with abundant water. These data, although admittedly not very exact, suggested that there is efficient elimination of potassium taken with food and that the potassium concentration in the haemolymph is affected by variations in the total blood volume, while the quantity of potassium remains the same. The sodium concentration in these experiments did not show diurnal variations.

The information on haemolymph *proteins* is fragmentary. The plasma of

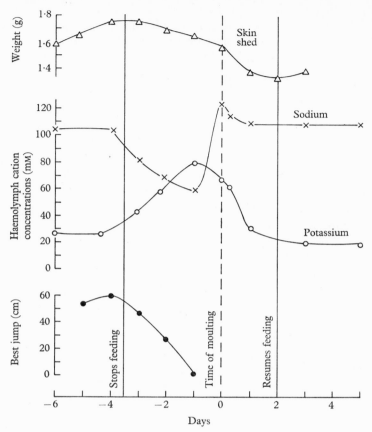

Fig. 60. *Locusta*, changes in the potassium and sodium concentration in the haemolymph of hoppers in relation to feeding and moulting (after Hoyle 1956).

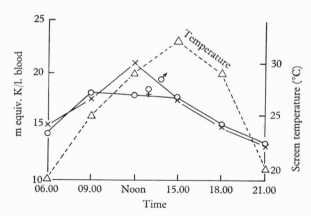

Fig. 61. *Nomadacris* adults, diurnal changes in the potassium concentration in the haemolymph (after Chapman 1958).

III

adult *Schistocerca* contained about 770 mg protein per 100 ml (Bowen & Kilby 1953). Numerous amino-acids were found in blood of *Locusta* hoppers, as follows: alanine, arginine, aspartic acid, glutamic acid, glycine, histidine, isoleucine, leucine, lysine, phenylalanine, proline, threonine, tyrosine, valine; their total amount was 549·8 mg/100 cc (Duchateau & Florkin 1958; Duchateau, Florkin & Sarlet 1952). In the blood of adult *Schistocerca* females most of these acids were also found, with the addition of glutamine, methionine, tryptophane and serine, the serine and glycine being at higher concentrations than others, but a high degree of quantitative variation in these and other amino-acids was observed (Treherne 1959; Howden & Kilby 1960, 1961; Blackith & Howden 1961; Benassi, Colombo & Allegri 1961). In *Anacridium* blood, a small quantity of tryptophan was found, in addition to the same amino-acids (Benassi, Colombo & Peretti 1959). Some preliminary data on the electrophoresic properties of blood proteins were given by Stephen (1961). The

Table 30. *The mean uric acid content (mg per cent)*
of the haemolymph of Vth instar locust hoppers
(*Matthée* 1945)

	Min.	Max.	Mean
Locusta migratoria			
solitarious	20·74	22·92	21·22
gregarious	12·59	15·78	14·36
Locustana paradalina			
solitarious	18·64	21·82	20·31
gregarious	11·36	15·45	13·78

protein concentration in the haemolymph and its changes during the sexual maturation of *Schistocerca* have been investigated by L. Hill (1962 *d*).

The uric acid in blood of Vth instar *Schistocerca* hoppers varied from 26·6 to 31·0 mg/ml. In *Locusta* and *Locustana* there is consistent difference in the uric acid content between hoppers of the two phases (table 30).

The *blood sugar* content of five grasshoppers was found to range from 30 to 49·4 mg/100 cc (Blumenthal 1927). In the haemolymph of female hoppers of *Schistocerca* the glucose content varied from zero at the beginning to 150 mg/100 g towards the end of the Vth instar. Glucose from food is absorbed from the alimentary canal into the haemolymph and is then rapidly converted into trehalose by the action of the enzyme trehalase (Howden 1957; Howden & Kilby 1960, 1961; Treherne 1958 *a*, 1958 *b*). The concentration of this, and of other reducing substances, undergoes striking changes within the same instar (fig. 62). The trehalose content of adult *Schistocerca* falls sharply after one hour of flying, which suggests that it may be a source of energy (Howden & Kilby 1960); it is not clear to what extent this replaces, or supplements, the energy known to be obtained from fat (p. 99).

Amongst other carbohydrates the presence of a substance showing reactions similar to glycogen was indicated, but it did not appear to be true glycogen (Howden & Kilby 1961).

Some other, entirely fragmentary, data on the biochemistry of the haemolymph can be found in the literature, but the information summarised above demonstrates a great variability in the composition of haemolymph, connected with growth (even within a hopper instar), feeding, activity and external conditions. Such quantitative determinations as are made without exact indication as to the sex, age, physiological state and environmental conditions have little value and may be only misleading.

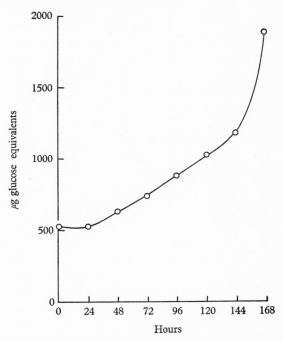

Fig. 62. *Schistocerca*, changes in the concentration of reducing substances in the haemolymph during the life of Vth instar female hoppers (after Howden & Kilby 1960).

The physical properties of haemolymph are insufficiently investigated. *Specific density* determinations (table 31) show little difference between species, and no difference between sexes was found.

The *osmotic pressure*, depending on the concentration of soluble substances in the blood, is known for a few species only, in which its value varied from 10·6 to 12·5 atmospheres (Rouschal 1940; Barsa 1954), but Mazek-Fialla (1941) recorded variations from 4·1 to 11·3 atmospheres in field specimens, depending on the weather, the lowest values obtaining in cool, damp conditions.

The *colour* of blood, usually yellowish or green, depends on soluble pigments, which are reviewed elsewhere (pp. 50, 51). It differs between the phases of locusts

8

(p. 50) and, in *Schistocerca*, also in relation to ovarial development (L. Hill 1962, 1963).

Precipitin tests of the blood plasma, intended to suggest the relationship between taxonomic groups, are in their infancy and the only conclusion arrived at was a confirmation of an obvious view that Acridoidea are more closely related to Gryllodea than to Mantodea (Leone 1947; Pauly 1955).

Table 31. *Specific density of haemolymph, in g/ml*

Species	Ist instar	Vth instar	Adult	Reference
Melanoplus sanguinipes			1·0257–1·0264	House & Stephens 1958
,, *bivittatus*			1·0262–1·0281	,, ,, ,,
Schistocerca		1·0377		Howden & Kilby 1960
,,	1·0220		1·0285–1·0298	Blackith & Howden 1961
Nomadacris			1·0352	,, ,, ,,
Locusta	1·0257		1·0314	,, ,, ,,
Chorthippus parallelus			1·0293–1·0306	,, ,, ,,

HAEMOCYTES

The cellular elements of blood, or haemocytes, are mostly found adhering to the surfaces of different organs bathed by blood and they tend to assume many different shapes. They are also found, though in smaller quantities, circulating

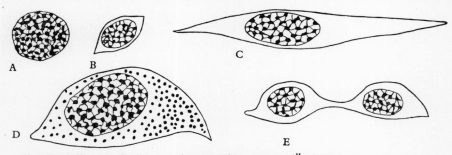

Fig. 63. *Calliptamus barbarus*, main types of haemocytes (Ögel 1955).
A, mother cell; B, proleucocyte; C, phagocyte; D, granular leucocyte; E, phagocyte dividing.

freely in the blood and here also they vary in shape, size and properties. Several attempts at the classification of haemocytes have been made (C. B. Mathur & Soni 1937, *Schistocerca*; Lepésme 1938, *Schistocerca, Locusta*, etc.; Millara 1947, *Acrida, Schistocerca, Anacridium*; Ögel 1955, 22 Turkish species; Taddei 1949, *Anacridium*; Crouzel 1960, *Schistocerca paranensis*).

The following four main types (fig. 63) have been distinguished by Ögel:

Mother cell (macronucleocyte of Lepésme; proleucocyte of Millara): round, with large nucleus, surrounded with cytoplasm, which is reduced, vacuolated and may disappear. Mother cells divide and give rise to the next type.
Proleucocyte (young leucocyte of Millara): small, spindle-shaped, with cytoplasm not vacuolated. These grow to become either of the next two types.

Phagocyte (micronucleocyte of Lepésme): large, spindle-shaped, with abundant, sometimes vacuolated, cytoplasm. According to Ögel, division occurs in phagocytes.
Granular leucocyte: as phagocyte, but cytoplasm with granular inclusions.

It is reasonable to assume that these types are really stages in the development of cells, and intermediate types certainly occur, as well as degenerating cells.

All haemocytes, except granular leucocytes, are phagocytic, particularly mother cells. Phagocytes circulating in the blood are only a portion of their total number, the majority forming dense aggregations along the upper surface of the dorsal diaphragm, close to the excurrent ostia (Kowalevsky 1892, 1894 b; Cuénot 1895; Nutting 1951).

A special category (or stage ?) of 'hyaline haemocytes', discernible only with a phase contrast microscope and characterised by instability, was stated to play an important part in the *coagulation of blood plasma*. These cells, when in contact with a solid surface (glass plate), tend to shrink and burst, discharging their contents, and initiate the clotting of the plasma. Patterns of coagulation in different insect groups are not the same, but they are uniform in all the species examined (Gregoire 1955, 1957, 1959, *Schistocerca, Locusta, Calliptamus*, etc.; Gregoire & Jolivet 1957, *Nomadacris, Cyrtacanthacris*, etc.; Hinton 1954).

In addition to haemocytes, some fat globules, particles of tissue, etc., are also found in the blood.

Haemocyte counts

All authors found enormous variations in the number of haemocytes per unit volume of blood (Tauber & Yeager 1935; Tareeva & Nenyukov 1931; C. B. Mathur & Soni 1937; Webley 1951; Ögel 1955; see table 32 and fig. 64).

Table 32. *Haemocyte counts/cu mm of blood (Ögel 1955)*

	Last instar hoppers		Adults	
	Mean	Range	Mean	Range
Acrida anatolica	15709	4500–36000	10969	3000–23000
Calliptamus barbarus	13330	4000–22000	7825	2250–18000
Oedaleus decorus	14559	5500–28000	9231	4000–27000
Oedipoda miniata	19464	4750–36000	8725	3000–18000
Pyrgodera armata	9250	8000–12500	17875	4650–37000

These variations depend on many factors, such as moulting, injury and so on, but particularly on the total blood volume (Webley 1951), and the counts may reflect variation not in the number of cells, but in the total haemolymph volume (p. 108).

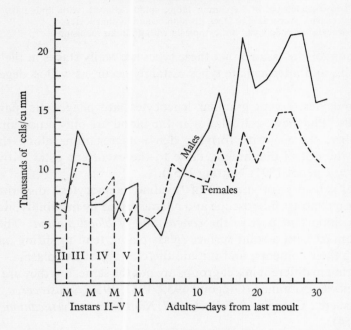

Fig. 64. *Locusta*, variation of haemocyte counts during the life-cycle
(Webley 1951). M, moult.

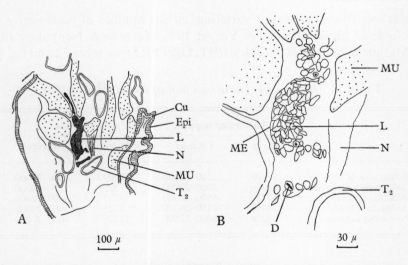

Fig. 65. *Locusta*. A, section through the base of coxa of IInd instar hopper; B, ditto,
enlarged (after Ögel 1959).
Cu, cuticle; Epi, hypoderm; L, leucopoeitic tissue; N, nerve; ME, connective tissue
membrane; MU, muscle; T_2, trachea.

Origin of haemocytes

The production of haemocytes has been sometimes regarded as a function of a layer of cells (fig. 67) adhering to the pericardial membrane (Cuénot 1895; Kowalevsky 1894a, 1894b), but it is now known that these cells are phagocytes and not the source of haemocytes. Centres of production of the latter were found in the thorax of *Locusta* embryos, while in hoppers they are represented by special (leucopoeitic) tissue found in each coxa near a tracheole (fig. 65). In this tissue various types of haemocytes were found, including mother cells, giving rise to other types. This tissue increases in size at each moult which may account for rises in haemocyte counts observed during moults, but it disappears in the adult (Ögel 1959). Crouzel (1960) suggested that haemocytes may be produced in the optic lobe of the brain.

FUNCTIONS OF HAEMOLYMPH

The principal functions of the haemolymph are the intermediate metabolism and transport of chemical substances between different organs; the maintenance of pressure inside the body; localised changes in the pressure, for example during moulting, respiratory movements and oviposition; storage of water; and phagocytosis by haemocytes. In addition to dissolved and suspended substances, insect haemolymph also carries oxygen and carbon dioxide, but no quantitative data exist for acridoids. Kreps & Chenykaeva (1942) claimed to have found in *Locusta* and *Anacridium* a substance inhibiting the hydration of CO_2, but this was disproved by Levenbook & Clark (1950).

EFFECTS OF INSECTICIDES

Very little work has been done on this important subject. Tareeva & Nenyukov (1931) observed disintegration of haemocytes in *Calliptamus* under the influence of sodium arsenate, and Pilat (1935b) confirmed this in *Locusta*. The latter author, however, also suggested that, simultaneously with disintegration, there is an energetic formation of new haemocytes, considered by him as a regenerative process.

The effects of insecticides may be increased by the use of substances with strong acid or basic properties, owing to the poor buffering capacity (p. 109) of the haemolymph (Hastings & Pepper 1943). The need for further work is obvious.

EXCRETORY SYSTEM

MALPIGHIAN TUBES

The main excretory organs are the numerous long, thin Malpighian tubes, joined basally to the posterior end of the mid-gut and blind apically. In *Melanoplus* they are 192–312 in number; about half of them are directed forwards, the others backwards and they are gathered in twelve groups. Each group (fig. 66) at its base arises from an ampulla which in its turn opens into one of the twelve longitudinal folds (excretory furrows) of the mid-gut (Stuart 1935 *a*). According to Kowalevsky (1894 *a*) in *Locusta* and to Chauvin (1941 *b*) in *Schistocerca*, the tubes penetrate the heart, but Jannone (1939 *b*) did not find this in *Dociostaurus*.

The number of tubes and their grouping vary in different species as will be seen from table 33.

Table 33. *Numbers of Malpighian tubes*

	Number	Groups	Reference
PAMPHAGIDAE			
Asiotmethis muricatus	150–200	10	Faussek 1887
Pamphagus elephas	60–80		Bordas 1898
PYRGOMORPHIDAE			
Poekilocerus	100–120		,, ,,
ROMALEINAE			
Romalea microptera	500		Riedel 1941
Brachystola magna	600		,, ,,
CANTANTOPINAE			
Melanoplus sanguinipes	150	10	U.S. Ent. Com. 1877
Melanoplus differentialis	192–312	12	Stuart 1935 *a*
Leptysma marginicollis	72–80	6	Hodge 1943
Opshomala vitreipennis	72–75	6	,, ,,
CYRTACANTHACRIDINAE			
Schistocerca gregaria	220–294	12	Savage 1956
OEDIPODINAE			
Locusta m. migratorioides	300	12	Albrecht 1953 *a*
Dissosteira carolina	70	6	H. M. Tietz 1923
Psophus stridulus	70–80		Bordas 1898
Oedipoda caerulescens	80–100		,, ,,
Mecostethus grossus	50–60		,, ,,
ACRIDINAE			
Acrida pellucida	165–175	12	Hafez & Ibrahim 1960
TRUXALINAE			
Truxalis nasuta	40–50		Bordas 1898
Stenobothrus lineatus	30–40		,, ,,
Dociostaurus maroccanus	120–130	12	Jannone 1939 *b*

The number of tubes does not appear to be of taxonomic significance, but the very high number in the two Romaleinae may be a subfamily character. It is not clear whether the relatively high number in the five injurious species

(*Locusta, Dociostaurus, Schistocerca* and *Melanoplus*) is of significance, and an examination of related species would be of interest. The number of tube groups appears to be related to the total number of the tubes.

Each Malpighian tube is intertwined with a double band of striated muscle (Palm 1946) and with a trachea. In *Schistocerca* each tube consists of a short distal segment, which is colourless, and a long proximal segment which is opaque-yellowish and frequently contains crystals (Savage 1956). The wall of a tube consists of a single layer of relatively large epidermal cells, covered

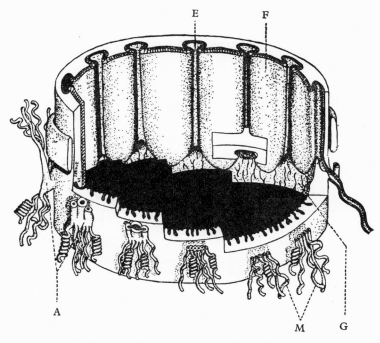

Fig. 66. *Melanoplus*, diagram of the junction of Malpighian tubes with the mid-gut (Stuart 1935 *a*).
   A, ampulla; G, gastric mucosa; M, Malpighian tubes; F, intestinal fold; E, excretory furrow.

externally by thin basement membrane; the internal border of the cells is provided with numerous protoplasmic processes forming a brush (Beams, Tahmisian & Devine 1955; Mazzi & Baccetti 1957). Amongst the ordinary epidermal cells, which are often pigmented, there are found special cells, secreting a mucous polysaccharide substance (Martoja 1959, 1961). The muscle bands are responsible for peristaltic contractions of the tubes, which are not under the control of the central nervous system, since they are not affected by nerve-paralysing substances and since even pieces of the tubes exhibit such movements (Palm 1946). Hormonal control of peristalsis was suggested by the fact that extracts of brain and corpora cardiaca stimulate it (Koller 1955; M. L. Cameron 1953).

EXCRETION

Some data on the quantitative relation between food consumed and the undigested residue excreted have been given when discussing the utilisation of food (p. 80).

The *faecal pellets* are generally oblong, spindle-shaped, and enveloped in thin wrinkled peritrophic membrane (A. W. A. Brown 1937*a*), but their shape is variable even in the same species depending on the food (Gangwere 1962). Their size is roughly proportional to the level of food consumption. In adult *Schistocerca* males three to eight days old the average weight of a pellet was 4·8 mg; during the fourth week it was 3·1 mg and declined to 1·9 mg during the fifth week (Norris 1961) and the total amount per male varied approximately parallel to the amount consumed (fig. 205).

Table 34. *Weight and water content of the faeces produced,*
per individual, by isolated males and groups of Schistocerca (*Norris* 1961)

	Isolated			Grouped		
	Faeces, mg		Percentage water	Faeces, mg		Percentage water
Time of day	Wet	Dry		Wet	Dry	
10–10.45 a.m. (before feeding)	25	22	12	25	24	4
11–12 a.m. (after feeding)	200	76	62	640	154	76
12–1 p.m.	558	208	63	1042	246	76
1–2 p.m.	450	184	59	728	216	70
2–3 p.m.	298	188	37	222	100	55
Total	1531	678	56	2657	740	72

The water content of the faeces may be of importance in relation to the possible regulation of the total water in the body Norris (1961) observed that the pellets of *Schistocerca* adults were both very few and very dry in the morning, when only dry grass of the previous day remained in the cage, but the excretion increased rapidly soon after feeding on fresh grass and the pellets became very wet (table 34). The effects of the quality of food on the water content of faeces were observed also by Miss Z. Waloff (personal communication) in *Schistocerca* swarms in Somalia, where the fresh pellets were dry during the hot dry season, but became full of moisture with the onset of rains and the appearance of lush vegetation.

The difference in the amount of faeces and their water content between the isolated and the grouped males (table 34) indicated a higher level of excretion by crowded males, which merely reflected their greater feeding activity, but also indicated that the grouped males absorbed a smaller percentage of water from the same food as the isolated ones.

The *chemical constituents of faeces* of *Melanoplus* included mainly uric acid, but also urea and the amino-acids arginine and phyllobombicin (A. W. A. Brown 1937*a*). In the excreta of *Locusta* and *Schistocerca* adults, uric and allantoic acid were recorded (Razet 1961). Chauvin's (1941*b*) analyses have shown that the quantitative composition of excreta varies between different stages of *Schistocerca*, those of a hopper and the sexually mature adult being rather similar, while an immature adult excretes relatively more urea, uric acid and sugars (table 35).

Table 35. *Composition of the excreta of* Schistocerca *fed on lettuce (in mg per gram of dry excreta) (Chauvin* 1941 *b*)

	Hoppers		Adults	
	IVth instar	Vth instar	Immature	Mature
Total nitrogen	1·61	1·36	1·855	1·575
Soluble nitrogen	0·56	1·05	1·61	0·78
Ammonia	0·2048	0·2652	0·72	0·4692
Urea	—	—	0·50337	—
Uric acid	1·008	1·092	2·35	1·176
Cholesterol	—	0·0026	0·0015	0·008
Sugars	—	1·49	2·75	0·93

The available information on the mineral composition of urine inside the Malpighian tubes is limited to its sodium and potassium content in *Locusta*. The potassium content of the urine was found to be some six times that of the haemolymph, providing evidence of active secretion of potassium into the tube; the sodium content, on the other hand, was a little lower than in the haemolymph (Ramsay 1953).

Studies on the excretion of vital dyes by the Malpighian tubes of *Chorthippus brunneus* (Palm 1952) showed that colloidal dyes (e.g. trypan blue) are not excreted, while neutral red is. Lison (1937, 1938) has shown that, in the same species, certain acid dyes are deposited in the cytoplasm of the Malpighian tubes in the form of granules.

The presence of glycogen, insectorubin and some vitamins in the tissues of the Malpighian tubes suggests that their function is not restricted to excretion. *Schistocerca* is said to be one of the insects very rich in riboflavin (vitamin B_2), which is concentrated in the Malpighian tubes (table 5, p. 51). Other fluorescent substances found there are lumiflavin, lumichrome and pterin (Busnel & Chauvin 1942; Busnel & Drilhon 1942; Drilhon & Busnel 1945*a*; De Lerma 1949). The presence of the enzyme phosphatase has already been mentioned (p. 77, table 9).

The role of the secretory mucous cells (see above) is not known but it is hardly likely to be directly concerned in excretion.

TISSUES AND CELLS WITH POSSIBLE EXCRETORY FUNCTIONS

In the pericardial sinus several different kinds of cells and loose tissues can be found, but views on their nature and even nomenclature are somewhat confused. The name *pericardial cells* (or nephrocytes) is usually applied to loose strands and groups of cells suspended in the sinus (fig. 67); they are variable in size, frequently contain two nuclei, vacuoles, crystals and pigment granules (for histological details see Palm 1952; Kessel 1961). Similar cells are also found attached to strands of connective tissue on the dorsal surface of the alary muscles of the heart (Nutting 1951).

Closely adhering to the dorsal pericardial membrane there are three to six layers of flattened cells, closely packed to form *phagocytic tissue* which some authors have regarded merely as an accumulation of haemocytes (Kowalevsky

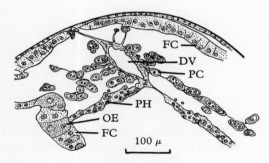

Fig. 67. *Chorthippus brunneus*, cross-section of the pericardial cavity (after Palm 1952). DV, dorsal vessel; FC, fat cells; OE, oenocytes; PC, pericardial cells; PH, phagocytes.

1892, 1894*a*, 1894*b*; Chauvin, 1941*b*; Palm *t.c.*), while others have apparently failed to distinguish these cells from the pericardial (Cuénot 1895).

Cells with phagocytic properties also occur in many other parts of the body, for example round salivary glands and at the bases of all legs (Bruntz 1909); the last-named situation (not described in detail) suggests a possibility that these may be the cells regarded as leucopoeitic by Ögel (1959; p. 117).

Since the nature, origin and possible interrelations of such cells and tissues are not clear, it is not surprising that views on their functions differ widely. They were considered by some authors as phagocytes, similar to or even identical with haemocytes, while others regarded them as organs of storage excretion and called them nephrocytes. Hollande (1922) described them as playing a part in transforming colloidal substances into simpler crystalloid ones, which are then rejected into the blood and excreted by the Malpighian tubes. Palm (*t.c.*) has carried out extensive investigations on the storage and excretion of vital dyes by various insects, including grasshoppers, but refrained from formulating any general conclusions. Snodgrass (1935*a*) has summed the situation up by a broad statement that 'the pericardial cells and presumably also the similar cells in other parts of the body play an important part in the physiology of the insect'. A similar view was expressed by Kessel (1961). One reason for this unsatisfactory state of affairs is the tendency of most investigators to form conclusions of wide general value, rather than to study each type of cell and tissue in one insect in relation to its physiological state, growth, activities and so on.

It should be noted, finally, that excretion probably occurs, not only through specialised tissues and organs, since, for example, pigments in the integument are largely final products of metabolism and their deposition may be regarded as storage excretion; the whole integument cast off at moulting contains substances in the same category.

RESPIRATORY SYSTEM

STRUCTURE

The respiratory system consists of segmentally placed paired spiracles, branched tracheae, and air-sacs (Vinal 1919, *Dissosteira*; du Buisson 1924, *Chorthippus*; Albrecht 1953 *a*, *Locusta*; Albrecht 1956, *Nomadacris*; Jannone 1939 *b*, *Dociostaurus*; P. L. Miller 1960, *Schistocerca*).

The *spiracles* are the outer openings of the respiratory system through which the air enters and leaves it. Their total number is ten pairs, two on the thorax, and the rest on the first eight segments of the abdomen (figs. 68 and 71).

The first (mesothoracic) spiracle (fig. 69, A, B, C) lies in the membrane between the prothorax and the mesothorax and is normally concealed under the edge of the pronotum. It is larger than the others, and has a two-lipped valve for closure, the posterior lip being a soft flap which fits into a groove of the hard anterior lip and is moved by a pair of muscles. On the inside, this spiracle gives rise to two tracheae and some authors (e.g. Amoroso 1936) regard it as two fused spiracles. The second (metathoracic) spiracle (fig. 69, D, E, F) lies between the mesothorax and metathorax and has two hard lips, both with muscles (Hoyle 1959).

The first of the eight abdominal spiracles lies in the first tergite, close to the anterior edge of the tympanal organ; the rest are situated in the antero-lateral corners of the abdominal tergites. Each of them (fig. 69, G, H) is a simple oval slit leading to a wider cavity, the atrium, opening into a trachea; their closing mechanism consists of two sclerotised lips, the posterior one being immobile and the anterior (manubrium) provided with a muscle. The last (tenth, or eighth abdominal) spiracle is somewhat larger than the others.

A. G. Hamilton (1937) has supplied measurements of the outer spiracular openings in adults of *Locusta* and *Schistocerca*; the figures obviously indicate the maximum values which may be reduced even to zero by the action of the closing apparatus and they serve only as an indication of the size of solid particles (i.e. insecticidal dusts) able to enter the tracheae.

The *tracheae* are elastic tubes of varying diameter, profusely branched to supply air to all internal organs. They develop as invaginations of the integument and their walls, therefore, include the same elements in the reverse order (fig. 70). The inner layer (intima) is cuticular and is thickened at intervals to form spiral, or ring-like, threads (taenidia) which serve to keep the tracheae open; then follows an epithelial layer, which is covered by a thin membrane of connective tissue (A. G. Richards & Korda 1950; Souza Santos *et al.* 1954).

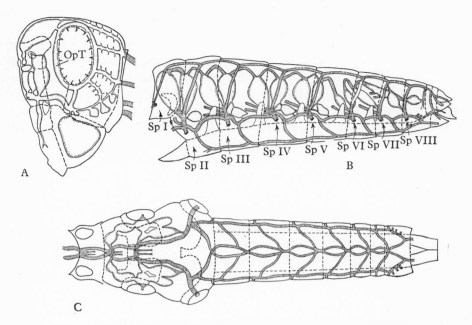

Fig. 68. *Nomadacris*, respiratory system. A, head; B, lateral view; C, ventral view (dorsal view, see fig. 71, N). OpT, ophthalmic trachea (Albrecht 1956).

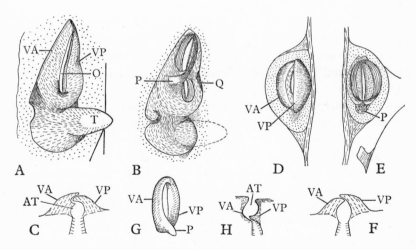

Fig. 69. *Schistocerca*, spiracles. A, mesothoracic, external view; B, ditto, internal view; C, ditto, section; D, metathoracic, internal view; E, ditto, external view; F, ditto, section; G, abdominal, internal view; H, ditto, section (after Karandikar 1939).

VA, anterior valve; VP, posterior valve; O, orifice; Q, muscle attachment; T, P, processes; AT, atrium.

The *tracheal system* is very complicated (figs. 68, 71) and only its main features are outlined below.

In the head there are two main trunks, arising from the mesothoracic spiracle. One is the upper cephalic trachea which divides into a network of thin-walled tracheae, converging to an ophthalmic trachea round the compound eye. Deeper in the head lies the median cephalic trachea which is divided into two branches, one supplying the air-sac lying above the brain; the other branch supplies mainly the foregut. The lower portion of the head is served by two branches of the cephalo-thoracic trachea which receives air through both of the thoracic and the first abdominal spiracles; it supplies air also to a pair of large mandibular air-sacs.

The thoracic system is represented by the tracheae arising from the first pair of abdominal spiracles; each of them is divided into three branches, supplying the dorsal longitudinal muscles and the very large paired thoracic air-sacs; some branches supply air to the wing muscles and to the wing veins. The legs receive air directly from the first and second thoracic spiracles. On the ventral side of the thorax runs a pair of cephalo-thoracic tracheae, which are linked by transverse trunks and supply the thoracic ganglion and the head.

The abdominal tracheal system comprises a pair of lateral spiracular tracheae connected with the spiracles; a pair of dorsal trunks connected in each segment by transverse tracheae with the spiracular tracheae, but not with each other; a pair of ventral tracheae connected with each other and with the spiracular tracheae and supplying mainly the nerve cord; and two pairs of alimentary tracheae, supplying the gut.

The finer branches of all tracheae, or *tracheoles*, differ from the tracheae mainly in the thinner walls and smaller diameter, for example in *Melanoplus* down to 0·3 microns (A. G. Richards & Korda 1950). The finest terminal tracheoles examined by electron microscope are said to enter muscle cells (Bennett 1953).

Air-sacs are merely expanded sections of the tracheae and they differ from the latter only in thinner walls and less developed, but still present, taenidia. Apart from those in the head and thorax mentioned above, there is a segmented system of paired air-sacs in the abdomen embedded in fat body; their number and grouping differ specifically (fig. 71). Thus, in *Locusta* and *Dissosteira* each of the abdominal spiracles three to six supplies one sac, while in *Nomadacris*, *Schistocerca* (Albrecht 1956) and *Acrida* (Hafez & Ibrahim 1960) each of these sacs is a double one. In *Chorthippus* (du Buysson 1924) and *Dociostaurus* (Jannone 1939 *b*) the first three and the last three pairs of sacs converge in the middle to form six-lobed groups. In *Nomadacris* there are also additional air-sacs supplying the reproductive organs and the ventral side of the gut; these are not found in *Locusta*. These findings suggest possible differences between Oedipodinae (*Locusta* and *Dissosteira*), Acridinae (*Acrida*), Cyrtacanthacridinae (*Schistocerca*, *Nomadacris*) and Gomphocerinae (*Chorthippus*,

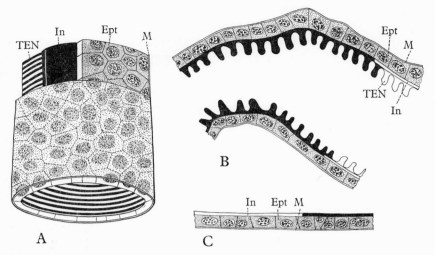

Fig. 70. *Dociostaurus*, trachea. A, diagram, partly in section; B, longitudinal section of a trachea; C, section of a wall of air-sac (Jannone 1939 b).
In, intima; TEN, taenidia; Ept, epithelium; M, connective tissue membrane.

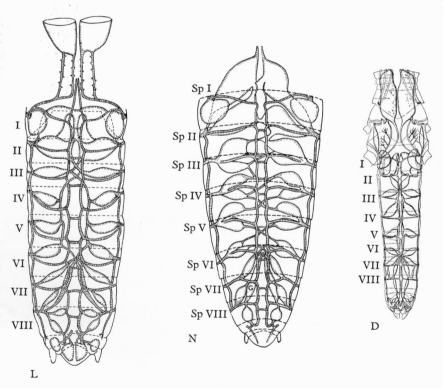

Fig. 71. Air-sac patterns of *Locusta* (L), *Nomadacris* (N), and *Dociostaurus* (D) (Albrecht 1953 a, 1956; Jannone 1939 b).

Dociostaurus), but more representatives of each group should be examined to confirm this. It would be of value to study the air-sacs, and the tracheal system generally, in all groups of Acrididae. Of particular interest would be such studies on non-flying species, since air-sacs may play an important part in ventilation during flight.

Apart from the larger air-sacs, many of the finer branches of tracheae have small sac-like expansions, especially amongst the muscles and close to other organs.

MECHANISM OF VENTILATION

Since air must enter and leave the body by the spiracles, a great deal of attention has been paid to establishing which of the spiracles serve for inspiration and which for expiration (M. O. Lee 1925; du Buisson 1925; McArthur 1929; McGovran 1931; Fraenkel 1932*a*, 1932*c*; A. G. Hamilton 1937; McCutcheon 1940; Watts 1952; Miller 1960). The general view now is that at rest the first four pairs of spiracles normally serve for inspiration and the last six for expiration. However, in *Schistocerca* the tenth pair was claimed to be inspiratory at rest, and expiratory during flight (A. G. Hamilton, *t.c.*), but P. L. Miller (1960) found that it opens only towards the end of expiration and may also be open during inspiration.

The *circulation* of air through the body is achieved by four types of ventilation movements (du Buisson 1925; Fraenkel 1932*c*; Weis-Fogh 1956*e*; P. L. Miller 1960), as follows:

(1) Active compression and expansion of the abdomen in the vertical direction, due to the action of lateral muscles causing sliding movements of the tergal parts of segments over the ventral.
(2) Longitudinal telescoping movements of abdominal segments.
(3) Protraction and retraction of the head.
(4) Protraction and retraction of the prothorax.

In addition Misra (1947) suggested the possibility of vertical expansion of the thoracic air-sacs by two pairs of special small muscles.

Observations on the *rate of ventilation* movements are few and apply only to the vertical abdominal movements. In a resting adult *Schistocerca* it was twenty per minute according to Fraenkel (1932*a*), and forty according to Chauvin (1941*b*), who determined the rate for the Vth instar hopper as sixty and for the flying adult as sixty to seventy. The rate is greatly affected by the temperature, as illustrated by table 36.

Table 36. *Effects of temperature on the number of abdominal ventilatory movements per minute in a female of* Melanoplus femur-rubrum *(after Lee, M. O.* 1925)

°C	0	9·5	11·0	15·0	16·6	19·5	22·0	24·0	25·5	26·6
Rate	0	5·8	7·5	9·7	11·0	15·0	18·1	20·8	26·0	26·6

Crozier & Stier (1925) suggested that in *M. femur-rubrum* the regular rhythmic movements do not occur below 14–16·5°C, while at temperatures above 40°C they become abnormally high. In *Calliptamus* (Kozhantschikov 1934), the rate at 40°C was forty per minute; at 45°C it rose to 100 and at 55° to 160; this suggests a disturbance effect. All such figures should be used with great caution, since they refer to one type only of ventilation movements, and because of the great individual variability even under uniform conditions (Herber & Slifer 1928). Mean values, often based on a few records obtained from insects kept under abnormal conditions of restraint, can only be misleading.

A *normal cycle* of respiratory movements in resting insects, proposed by McCutcheon (1940), confirmed by Watts (1959) and generally accepted, is

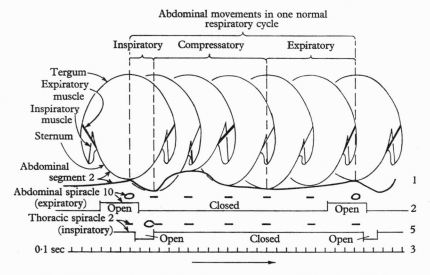

Fig. 72. Scheme of a cycle of respiratory movements (McCutcheon 1940).

based on simultaneous recording of the vertical movements of the abdominal walls, the opening and closing of spiracles and the intra-tracheal air pressure (fig. 72). Inspiration occurs through the anterior spiracles when the abdomen expands and the intra-tracheal pressure drops to zero, the posterior spiracles being closed. This is followed by the compressatory phase, during which the anterior spiracles close, the abdomen contracts, the posterior spiracles remain closed and the air pressure in the tracheae rises. Further contraction of the abdomen causes expiration through the posterior spiracles which then open, while the anterior ones remain closed, and the intra-tracheal pressure drops sharply. This normal cycle may be replaced by the, so-called, *dyspnoeic cycle*, during which all spiracles close at the beginning of the abdominal contraction and the intra-tracheal pressure rises rapidly, then all spiracles open, but the anterior ones do so first and most of the air is expired through them. In this scheme still only one type of ventilation movement is taken into account.

The cycle is modified during flight. During the first seconds of flight, the vertical abdominal contractions cease entirely, but are subsequently resumed with increased frequency and amplitude and the other three types of ventilation movements do not appear (Miller 1960); this appears to correspond to the dyspnoeic type. At the same time, the volume of the thorax during flight is subject to changes due to wing movements and the ventilatory rate is affected by this more than by abdominal movements (Weis-Fogh 1956 e). This additional ventilation during flight serves mainly the flight muscles, while the vertical abdominal movements ventilate mainly the central nervous system, the two mechanisms being largely independent (Miller t.c.).

The *function of the air-sacs* is a major problem, but it is most inadequately studied. The most complete hypothesis is that by McCutcheon (1940), according to which the air-sacs permit the building up of sufficient pressure to supply the air to the smaller tracheae. The main air-sacs fill with air during inspiration and the pressure inside them rises because of the lesser diameter and more resistant walls of the tracheae connecting them; thus the air pressure in the lesser tracheae should be greater than at the spiracles. During the normal respiratory cycle in resting *Schistocerca obscura* the intra-tracheal pressure fluctuated between 0·6 and 1·0 mm of mercury; during the dyspnoeic cycle, occurring at high activity, it was in the range 7–10 mm of mercury (Watts 1952); according to Wigglesworth (1953), such pressure changes amounting only to less than one per cent cannot be of material importance in air circulation, which he considers as being due to diffusion; according to his view, the main function of air-sacs is to increase the volume of the air within the body. It has been suggested in the past that air-sacs increase the buoyancy of flying insects, the air within them, heated by muscular action, being lighter than the outer air, but this idea found no confirmation. The mechanical functions of air-sacs will be discussed in relation to moulting (p. 284) and egg-laying (p. 324).

It is clear that knowledge of the mechanism of respiration is still inadequate and the respective quantitative data are particularly questionable, because most of them are based on observations with insects kept under abnormal conditions of restraint and excitation.

REGULATION OF RESPIRATION

The regulation of respiration through the opening and closing of spiracles and through ventilation movements depends partly on spontaneous rhythmic impulses from the central nervous system and partly on such impulses induced by chemical action of tracheal air on ganglia (Fraenkel 1932a, 1932b, 1932c, 1932d; Miller 1960). The existence of over-riding direct nervous control is suggested by the abnormal high frequency of movements caused by handling. As can be seen from the diagram (fig. 73), a stimulus applied to the central nervous system may be directly transmitted to the metathoracic and the abdominal ganglia inducing rhythmic movements of the IIIrd, IVth and abdominal spiracles and of the ventilatory muscles. On the other hand, cephalic and thoracic ganglia are receptive to carbon dioxide concentration in the

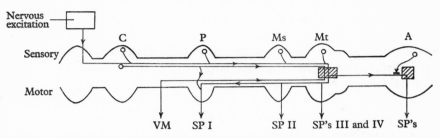

Fig. 73. Diagram of the nervous control of respiration (after P. L. Miller 1960). C, cephalic; P, prothoracic; Ms, mesothoracic; Mt, metathoracic; A, abdominal ganglia; VM, neck and prothorax ventilation; Sp, spiracles.

tracheal air and respond by modifying the rhythm. Abdominal ganglia do not modify ventilation unless connected with the thoracic ganglia. In addition, there is an effect of carbon dioxide concentration on the muscles regulating the closing mechanism of the second spiracle; this is particularly effective when the haemolymph has a high potassium concentration which causes the contraction of the muscle (Hoyle 1960, 1961). An excess of CO_2 may cause a reversal in the direction of tracheal ventilation (McGovran 1932); Hoyle (1960) found that CO_2 reduces the response of the muscle to electric stimulation. Changes in the composition of tracheal air due, for example, to movement, are illustrated in table 37.

Table 37. *Mean percentage composition of tracheal air in hind leg of grasshopper* (*Krogh* 1913)

	CO_2	O_2	N_2
Grasshopper inactive	1·9	15·7	82·4
„ after being chased	4·2	5·4	90·4

RESPIRATORY METABOLISM

Quantitative data on the volume of air used in the ventilation of the tracheal system are fragmentary. In resting *Schistocerca*, 7·3–20·5 cu. mm of air is transported in a second and it was calculated that a complete renewal of air should require from fifty seconds to thirty minutes (Fraenkel 1932 *d*); in the same locust during flight, ventilation of the thorax alone amounted to 350 litres of air per μg body weight in an hour (Weis-Fogh 1956 *e*). In *Chortophaga*, the air is passed at the rate of 0·222 cc per gram body weight in a minute at 28°C, and 0·107 cc at 23°C (McGovran 1931).

More detailed quantitative information exists on the rates of *oxygen consumption* and *carbon dioxide production*. The essential general point is that, as can be expected, there are great changes in the intensity of respiratory metabolism during growth of the insect, as well as variations caused by external conditions.

A much discussed general question is whether the respiratory rate is correlated with the weight or the surface area of an insect. Bodine (1921) and Butler & Innes (1936) considered that respiratory rate reflects increase in the surface area better than increase in the weight, but Gardiner (1958) found direct correlation with weight, while A. G. Hamilton (1958) concluded that weight and CO_2 output in adults are not correlated, much variation being due to physiological processes of maturation. In *Locusta* hoppers a high degree of correlation between weight and oxygen consumption is found in early instars, but not in the older ones (K. U. Clarke 1957a). As regards the surface area, its estimation is very laborious and most authors who have studied its relation to respiratory rate have not attempted to carry it out with the necessary accuracy. Indeed, the argument appears somewhat academic, particularly because of the short-term variations in the respiratory rate in the same individual, due to a number of internal and external factors (as shown below).

Early data by Bodenheimer and Reich (Bodenheimer *et al.* 1929) indicated that in hoppers of *Schistocerca* the amount of oxygen consumed per unit body weight decreased in successive instars. More exact determinations by Clarke (*t.c.*) made on individual *Locusta* hoppers have shown that increases in weight and in oxygen consumption per animal were practically parallel in the early instars, but in the later ones the consumption changed much more than the weight (fig. 74, A); it will be seen that the relations between weight and oxygen consumption in the adult are different from those in hoppers.

The rate of adult metabolism and striking changes in it are shown in fig. 74, B (A. G. Hamilton 1958, 1959, 1961, 1964), based on CO_2 production during the adult life of the male *Schistocerca*. The initial drop in weight and in CO_2 output on the first day after adult emergence is attributed to exhaustion during the final moult and to lack of feeding. When feeding starts on the second day, there is a sharp increase in weight, due to the building up of tissues, and the CO_2 output increases also but at a much greater rate. The increase in weight continues until about the fifteenth day (Norris 1954), but the CO_2 output falls after only five days; this indicates not a decrease in the intensity of metabolism, but a change in its chemistry, a greater production of CO_2 suggesting an accelerated formation of fat. When fat reserves have been built up, the CO_2 output gradually falls and in later life, its curve runs parallel to that of weight in the male. No such data are available for the female, where further changes in weight (p. 300) and fat content (p. 97) occur in connection with egg production. Apart from the changes in the rate of CO_2 output during the development of an adult, the mode of its discharge also changes, contrary to the earlier assumption that it is a smoothly continuous process. A. G. Hamilton (1961), using the Infra Red CO_2 Analyser, has obtained the records shown in fig. 75. A male of *Schistocerca* three hours after emergence discharges CO_2 in bursts at the rate of twenty-five to thirty per hour; these bursts are the result of closing the spiracles and stopping ventilation movements for about one-and-a-half minutes; at the end of this period, the movements start again and the spiracles open and close at the rate of one opening per second; this continues for fifteen to thirty seconds. In an adult one day old, the bursts of CO_2 are reduced in amplitude and this coincides with the drop in CO_2 produc-

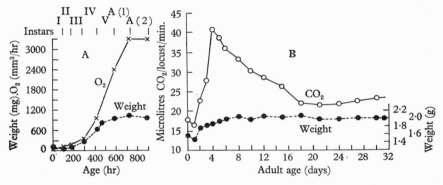

Fig. 74. A, *Locusta*, rates of oxygen consumption in relation to weight, during the life-cycle (K. U. Clarke 1957a). B, *Schistocerca*, rates of carbon dioxide production in relation to weight, during the adult life (A. G. Hamilton 1958).

tion as a result of exhaustion after the moult. In later life, the CO_2 discharge gradually increases, and becomes continuous, occasional bursts occurring only as a result of movement. Corresponding records for *Nomadacris* revealed an important difference; in that species there is a delay in sexual maturation (p. 309) and a steady discharge of CO_2 is achieved only after ninety days, when adults also reach their maximum weight and sexual maturity. Thus, this method makes it possible to detect a period of suspended adult maturation. An important source of variation in the respiratory rate is activity; in two groups of *Romalea* (one more active in the forenoon and another in the afternoon), the oxygen consumption exhibited striking parallel changes (fig. 76). Even more striking are the effects of such strong activity as flying (Krogh & Weis-Fogh 1951). In adult *Schistocerca* at rest, the oxygen consumption averaged 0·63 1/kg/hr, but in flight it rose to 10–30 1/kg/hr; calculated for an average male locust, the consumption was 18 cu. mm per minute at rest and 300–900 cu. mm in flight, thus increasing fifteen to fifty times. After flight, the consumption fell again, but not to the resting level, so that an 'oxygen debt'

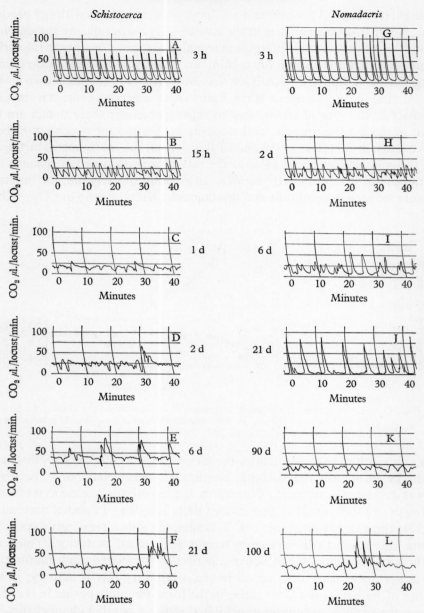

Fig. 75. Changes in the rhythm of carbon dioxide production during adult life of *Schistocerca* and *Nomadacris* females (after A. G. Hamilton 1961). See text.

obtained, and this was not abolished until after one to two hours at rest (fig. 77). The respiratory quotient value in resting locusts averages 0·82, but in flight it fell to 0·75 indicating utilisation of fat for energy (Weis-Fogh 1952; also p. 99).

134

Effects of temperature on the respiratory rate (fig. 78) are probably directly attributable to activity. A depression of the rate in grasshoppers whose compound eyes were blackened (Bodine 1922) was probably also indirect, through reduced activity.

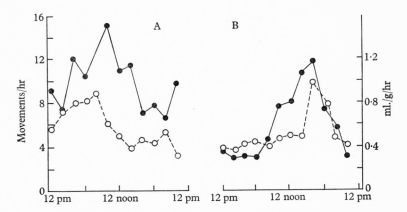

Fig. 76. *Romalea*, daily-rhythms of locomotor activity (solid line) and of oxygen consumption (dotted line) in two groups of individuals, one (A) active before midday, the other (B) in the afternoon (after Fingerman, Jago & Lower 1958).

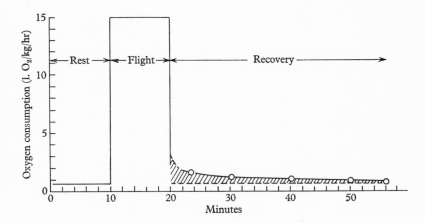

Fig. 77. *Schistocerca*, effects of flight on oxygen consumption (Krogh & Weis-Fogh 1951).

Numerous attempts to express the relation between temperature and respiratory rate by some mathematical formula have been made; all such formulae 'have some descriptive value but none of them is of sufficiently general application to be regarded as embodying any rational principle' (Wigglesworth 1953).

The nutritional state of an individual has a profound influence on its respiration rate. The oxygen consumption of a *Locusta* hopper begins to fall some

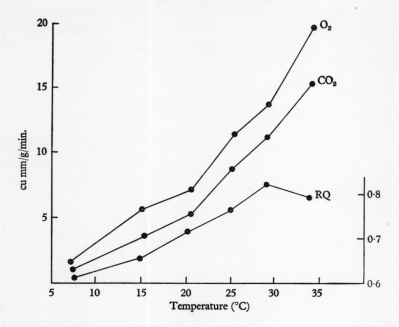

Fig. 78. *Chortophaga viridifasciata* hoppers. Rates of oxygen consumption, carbon dioxide production and the respiratory quotient, in relation to the temperature (after Kleinman 1934).

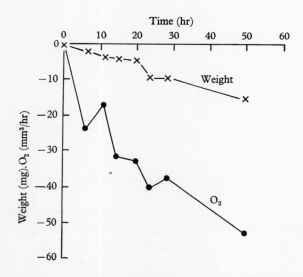

Fig. 79. *Locusta*. Decrease in the weight and in the oxygen consumption of a starving hopper (K. U. Clarke 1957a).

136

one-and-a-half hours after it has stopped feeding, and after some five hours it drops considerably (fig. 79); in a hopper starved for fifty hours and then fed, the consumption still continued to fall for four hours, but showed a great and sudden increase five-and-a-half hours after the commencement of the meal (K. U. Clarke 1957a).

Not enough is known about the specific differences in respiratory rate, though hoppers of *Melanoplus femur-rubrum* of about the same weight as those of *Dichromorpha viridis* have a higher CO_2 output (Bodine 1921), which may merely reflect their greater activity. The differences in the respiratory rate of gregarious and solitarious locusts may also be due to their different activity levels (p. 336).

It is clear that the physiology of respiration in acridoids is far from being well studied. Many earlier data need verification, since most of the authors did not pay sufficient attention to such aspects as age, physiological state, activity and previous history of the experimental insects, and this makes generalisations premature.

DIFFUSION OF GASES THROUGH INTEGUMENT

Several authors have suggested a possibility of an additional respiration by diffusion, particularly of carbon dioxide, through the integument, but this problem awaits more thorough investigations (Krogh 1913; M. O. Lee 1925; Gilmour 1941; A. G. Hamilton 1959).

REPRODUCTIVE SYSTEM

MALE

The internal reproductive organs of the male (fig. 80) comprise the paired testes and seminal ducts opening into the ejaculatory duct, which receives also numerous accessory glands and terminates in the phallic complex.

The *testes* are paired, but so closely adpressed as to appear as a single body enveloped by yellowish connective tissue, lying above the alimentary canal and under the dorsal diaphragm. Each testis consists of a large number of slender tubular follicles, bound together by connective tissue; the follicles are attached to the long paired *seminal ducts* (vasa deferentia) which run backwards to join the *ejaculatory duct*. Laird (1943) studied the gross structure of the testes in about a hundred species and distinguished three main types (fig. 81).

The simplest type is the *pinnate* (inappropriately called 'radiating' by Laird), in which follicles, usually very numerous, join the seminal duct along the whole length of the testis. This type was found in the families Pyrgomorphidae, Pamphagidae and Ommexechidae, as well as in Romaleinae and some genera of Catantopinae. In the other extreme type, the *fountain*, less numerous follicles enter the seminal duct near its blind end, in a cluster; this type is found in Oedipodinae, Acridinae and Gomphocerinae, as well as in some Catantopinae. The difference between the two types is not sharp, and a third type, the *intermediate*, had to be recognised; in this, the follicles enter the seminal duct, as in the pinnate type, but only along about one-half of the testis length; this type is common in Catantopinae and found also in some Romaleinae. The study of post-embryonic development of the testis has shown that in all cases the testes in hoppers are of the pinnate type, and either remain so in the adult, or become of the intermediate or the fountain type; this suggests less specialisation in Pyrgomorphidae and Pamphagidae in comparison with subfamilies of Acrididae. More extensive studies are required to evaluate the taxonomic importance of the testis morphology, including the number of follicles, on which the scanty data available refer to *Locusta* (300–400, Albrecht 1953 *a*), *Romalea* (up to 320, Laird, *t.c.*), *Acrida* (34, Hafez & Ibrahim 1960) and several Oedipodinae (18–36, Nolte 1939). Laird pointed out the variability of testis structure even within a single species: for example, in *Schistocerca americana* all three types were found. Aberrant types of testis should be expected; thus, in *Opshomala* and *Leptysma* (Catantopinae) the two testes are not fused but lie one behind the other, apparently as an adjustment to the strongly compressed and elongated bodies of these insects (Hodge 1943).

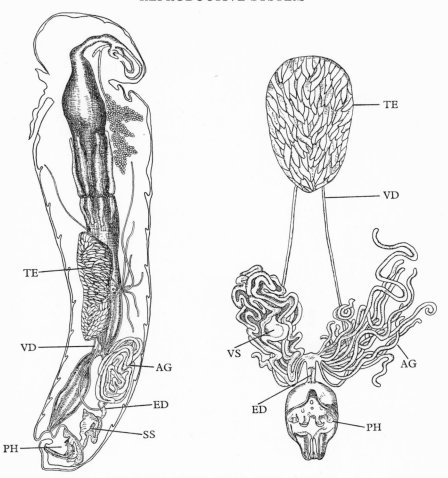

Fig. 80. *Locusta.* Male reproductive organs (after Liu & Leo 1959).
TE, testis; VD, seminal duct (vas deferens); ED, ejaculatory duct; SS, ejaculatory sac; VS, seminal vesicle; PH, phallic complex; AG, accessory glands.

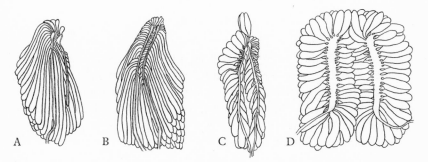

Fig. 81. Types of the testis. A, fountain, *Xanthippus corallipes*; B, intermediate, *Melanoplus mancus*; C, pinnate, *Sphenarium mexicanum*; D, pinnate, *Romalea microptera* (after Laird 1943).

The *ejaculatory duct* is sac-like and its wall in its upper part consists of an outermost layer of fat tissue, a poorly developed muscular layer, a layer of cells resembling connective tissue, a basement membrane, a layer of hypodermal cells and a cuticular lining; in the lower part, there is no muscular sheet (Gregory 1961).

Into the ejaculatory duct open, in addition to the seminal ducts, long tubular *accessory glands*. In *Locusta* eighteen tubes on each side were recorded by

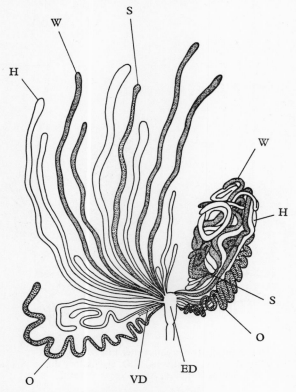

Fig. 82. *Locusta*, male accessory glands (Gregory 1961).
S, seminal vesicle; W, white glands; H, hyaline glands; O, opalescent gland; VD, vas deferens; ED, ejaculatory duct.

S. A. Ivanova (1926) and fifteen by Albrecht (1953 a), but Mika (1959) found sixteen tubes and Gregory (1965 a) who described them in detail confirmed this number. In other species the tubes of each side number fourteen in *Dociostaurus* (Jannone 1939 b), *Anacridium* (Ito 1924; Fedorov 1927), and *Chortophaga* (M. A. Payne 1933) and nine to twelve in *Pamphagus, Tmethis, Oedipoda, Oedaleus, Chorthippus* and *Acrida* (Fenard 1896); Hodge (1943) found only two glands in *Opshomala* and *Leptysma*, but this needs confirmation.

On the basis of their appearance and the contents, four types of tubular accessory glands can be distinguished in *Locusta* (fig. 82). There are four *white glands*, filled with milky-white secretion; ten *hyaline* glands, of varying length, with completely colourless content; one *opalescent* gland, the contents of which are opalescent and with minute granules; and one *seminal vesicle*, which is also tubular, but very much coiled, the whole coil being enclosed in a thin yellowish connective tissue membrane, thus presenting the appearance of an oval body; the lumen of the vesicle in a mature male is filled with seminal fluid and spermatozoa. The distal part of each accessory gland is thin-walled and filled with fluid which is, presumably, secreted in this part (for histological details, see Gregory, *t.c.*).

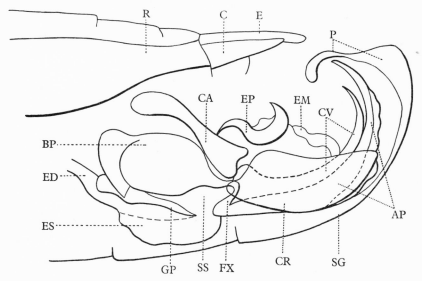

Fig. 83. *Locusta*, diagram of the phallic complex (original by V. M. Dirsh).
R, rectum; C, cercus; E, epiproct; ED, ejaculatory duct; ES, ejaculatory sac; SS, spermatophore sac; GP, gonopore; BP, basal valve of penis; FX, flexure of penis; AP, apical lobes of penis; CA, apodeme of cingulum; CR, ramus of cingulum; CV, valve of cingulum; EP, epiphallus; EM, ectophallic membrane; P, pallium.

The secretions of the accessory glands are insufficiently known; they include proteins, lipoids and mucous substances; their pH varies between 6·3 and 6·7. The secretions serve to form different parts of the spermatophore (p. 316).

The *phallic complex* comprises a number of membranous and sclerotised structures (Chopard 1920) and their nomenclature has become greatly confused; the latest terminology is that by Dirsh (1956*a*) in whose work earlier synonyms can also be found; Eades (1961) introduced further changes which are, however, debatable. The whole phallic complex is an oval sclerotised body which can be easily extracted from the end of the abdomen. Internally (fig. 83), it begins with an enlargement of the ejaculatory duct called the *ejaculatory sac*;

its cavity is connected by a narrower *gonopore* with the *spermatophore sac*. The *penis* (aedeagus) consists of wide *basal valves*, lying above the spermatophore sac and connected by the *flexure* with the long, curved *apical lobes*, which are normally concealed under the membranous *pallium*, but are extruded during copulation. Above the basal valves lies the *cingulum*, a

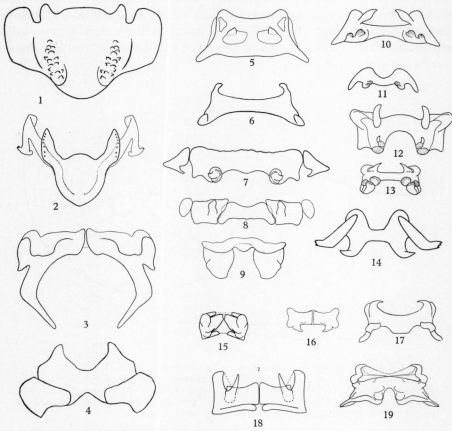

Fig. 84. Epiphalli (original by V. M. Dirsh).
   1, *Pamphagus elephas* (shield-like); 2, *Charilaus carinatus* (ditto); 3, *Acrophymus cuspidatus* (divided); 4, *Tropidacris latreillei*; 5, *Calliptamus italicus* (plate-like); 6, *Mecostibus mopanei*; 7, *Lathicerus cimex*; 8, *Graea horrida*; 9, *Anacridium aegyptium*; 10, *Acrida turrita* (bridge-shaped); 11, *Machacridia conspersa*; 12, *Dociostaurus maroccanus*; 13, *Ochrilidia gracilis*; 14, *Taphronota calliparea* (bridge-shaped, with dorso-lateral appendages); 15, *Notopleura saharae*; 16, *Oxya hyla* (divided); 17, *Catantops melanostictus*; 18, *Sudanacris pallida* (divided); 19, *Cataloipus oberthüri*.

strongly sclerotised structure consisting of a pair of *apodemes*, a pair of wide *rami*, and the long, curved *valves of the cingulum* adjoining the apical lobes of the penis. The cingulum is derived from the *ectophallic membrane*, on which also lies the *epiphallus*, a strongly sclerotised and somewhat complicated structure.

The above diagrammatic description is based essentially on *Locusta*, but there is great variation in the general structure of the phallic complex and its parts which makes it of outstanding value for taxonomy. Attempts to use some of the features of the phallic complex for taxonomic purposes at the species level have been made in the past (e.g. Znoiko 1928, *Omocestus*; Hubbell 1932, some *Melanoplus*; Jannone 1937, *Calliptamus*) and Roberts (1941) produced a general study of the complex on which he based a classification of subfamilies. A comprehensive treatment of the phallic complex in the whole of the Acridoidea by Dirsh (1956*a*, 1961) has thrown a new light on the higher classification within the group, and he erected several new families and subfamilies on the basis of phallic characters. Particularly good taxonomic characters are provided by the epiphallus (fig. 84), which may be shield-like (Pamphagidae), bridge-shaped (Acrididae and Lentulidae), bridge-shaped with dorso-lateral

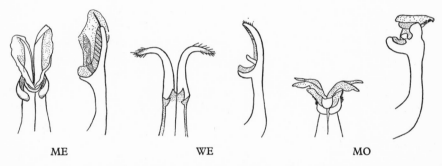

ME   WE   MO

Fig. 85. Apical valves of penis in three species of *Anacridium*, dorsal and side views (Dirsh & Uvarov 1953).
ME, *A. melanorhodon*; WE, *A. wernerellum*; MO, *A. moestum*.

appendages (Pyrgomorphidae), plate-like (Calliptaminae), divided (Euryphyminae), and so on. The value of the epiphallus is considerable also in specific classification, if care is taken (as in all taxonomic work) to bear in mind possible individual variation. The apical valves of the penis are also of value (fig. 85), particularly in classifying species, with the same proviso. Both these characters can be studied in relaxed dry material and they should be included amongst the essential characters in all new descriptions of species and genera. An example of such study is a work by Barnum (1959*a*) in which the phallic complexes of 123 North American species (mostly of Oedipodinae) are described. Lal & Parshad (1961) described phallic complexes in twenty-three Indian species.

The functions of parts of the male phallic complex are imperfectly understood, the only description being that by Boldyrev (1929) for *Locusta*. During copulation, the whole phallus is filled with blood. In addition to the blood pressure, the penis, epiphallus and other sclerotised parts are subject to the action of special visceral muscles, which govern the actual copulation and the transmission of sperm from male to female; these processes are described elsewhere (p. 314).

FEMALE

The female reproductive system (fig. 86) consists of paired ovaries, each with an accessory gland and an oviduct, and of vagina and spermatheca.

The *ovaries* are paired, but enclosed together in a connective tissue membrane and may therefore be mistaken for a single organ (e.g. Ogloblin 1950, *Schistocerca paranensis*). In fully mature females, the ovaries occupy the greater part of the abdomen, lying above the alimentary canal. Each ovary is composed of a number of *ovarioles* (egg-tubes), attached by their bases to the oviduct, while their apices converge to the middle line of the body and are produced into thin terminal filaments, which fuse to form a single ligament extending into the mesothorax and attached there to the aorta.

Each ovariole widens basally but is joined to the oviduct by a narrow pedicel; it contains a series of eggs, the more mature ones being nearest its opening into the oviduct. Considerable changes in the size of ovarioles and of the whole ovaries occur during the maturation of the eggs (p. 304).

There are wide specific differences in the number of ovarioles, which has been studied by Rubtzov (1934), Voy (1949), N. Waloff (1954, many species from different regions), Phipps (1959, 1962, many species from East and West Africa) and Robertson & Chapman (1962, forty species from Tanganyika), Bryantseva (1958, U.S.S.R.), Kaufmann (1959, Germany). The lowest number ever recorded is four (two in each ovary) in *Aeropedellus clavatus* and in *Stenobothrus lineatus* (in which, however, the most frequent number is eight); the highest is 393 (201 + 192) in *Phymateus* sp. The last figure indicates an asymmetry in the ovariole number in the two ovaries, which is not uncommon (Phipps, *t.c.*; Roonwal 1947c).

There is some correlation of the ovariole number with taxonomy. Thus, the commonest number in Gomphocerinae is about ten; in Pyrgomorphidae it is from twenty-seven to forty-three, except in the group Phymatei in which it varies from 69 to 393; in Cyrtacanthacridinae it is usually high, for example 150 to 169 in *Anacridium*, 199 in *Cyrtacanthacris*, 179 in *Nomadacris*, 85 to 145 in *Schistocerca*. There are some striking differences also within a genus; for example 152 in *Heteracris coerulescens* and sixty-seven in *H. pulchripes* (Phipps 1959). Further notable correlation is with the length of the female; thus the long-bodied *Acrida* has more than twice the number of ovarioles common in its group. N. Waloff calculated the number of ovarioles per 1 mm length of female and found this index to be taxonomically suggestive, the Gomphocerinae having the lowest index (0·43) and Catantopinae the highest (0·83); Phipps found a similar correlation, but it was not always significant.

There is an indication of a geographical (possibly climatic) factor affecting the ovariole number: the temperate species of the same taxonomic groups tend to have a smaller ovariole number than the tropical ones. Rubtzov (1934) suggested that the ovariole number in a single species is also subject to

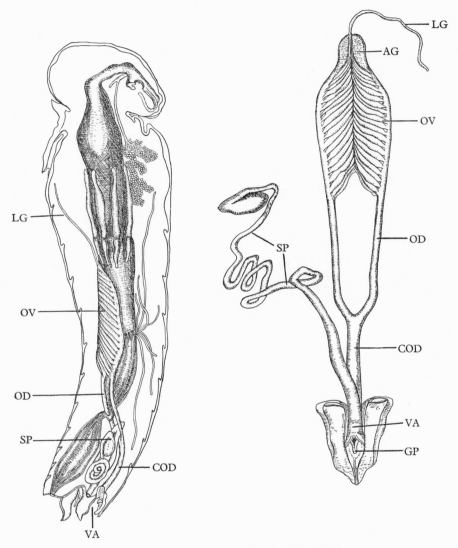

Fig. 86. *Locusta*, female reproductive organs (after Liu & Leo 1959).
LG, ligament; AG, accessory gland; OV, ovary; OD, oviduct; COD, common oviduct; SP, spermatheca; VA, vagina; GP, gonopore.

geographical variation and Phipps (1962) found that the same species in East Africa usually had more ovarioles than in West Africa.

A further quantitative feature of ovaries is the number of egg rudiments (oöcytes) per ovariole, which also varies by species, but is usually low, rarely exceeding twenty-five, though in *Acrotylus insubricus* up to sixty-eight oöcytes were found (N. Waloff 1954). There does not appear to be any correlation between the ovariole and the oöcyte numbers.

Most of the above data are based on dissections limited in the number, the area, or the period of sampling. Better information on variation in ovariole numbers exists with regard to some locust species where it is one of the phase phenomena, connected with parental density (p. 353). Roonwal (1947 *c*) suggested that variation in ovariole number in adult *Schistocerca* may be due to reduction of the number found in a hopper because of a competition between ovarioles for space and nutrition, while Richards & Waloff (1954) thought that some variation may be due to the weather of the season. The

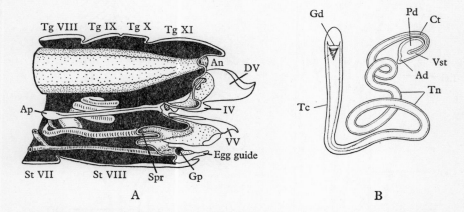

A   B

Fig. 87. *Locusta*, female. A, diagrammatic sagittal section of end of abdomen (after Albrecht 1953 *a*). B, spermatheca (Gregory 1965 *a*).

Ap, apodeme of ovipositor; An, anus; Tg, tergites; St, sternites; DV, dorsal ovipositor valve; IV, inner valve; VV, ventral valve; GP, gonopore; Spr, aperture of spermatheca; Gd, base of spermathecal duct; Tc, thick tube; Tn, thin tube; Ct, constricted tube; Vst, vestibule; Ad, apical diverticulum; Pd, preapical diverticulum.

problem will be further discussed in relation to fecundity (p. 327) and to phase variation (p. 353).

The paired *accessory* glands are blind anterior prolongations of the oviducts, usually long and curved, but short and straight in Pamphagidae (Bryant-seva 1955); their size varies with degree of maturation and their epithelium is glandular (Baccetti 1961*d* calls them pseudo-colleterial, since the true colleterial glands in other Orthoptera open into the vagina; no such glands are present in acridoids). Their secretion is supposed to produce the covering of the egg-pods; it is proteinaceous but its nature is insufficiently known.

The two oviducts converge behind to the *vagina*, a short and broad tube, ending behind with the *gonopore*, the opening of the genital chamber between the ovipositor valves. Just anteriorly of the gonopore, the vagina receives the long coiled *spermathecal duct* ending in a small oval vesicle, the *spermatheca* (or *receptaculum seminis*). The general structure of the spermatheca in a large number of species was studied by Fenard (1896), Slifer (1939, 1940, 1940*a*, 1940*b*, 1943), Voy (1949) and Dirsh (1957*a*), while Katiyar (1956*a*) and Gregory (1965*a*) described in detail the structure and histology of the spermatheca of *Locusta* (fig. 87, B). The spermathecal duct can be divided into three regions: nearest to its base is the *thick tube*, which is the widest and has thick cuticular lining; it runs straight for some distance, then bends at a right angle; the next region is the *thin tube*, which forms several coils and passes into the *constricted tube* curving round the *preapical diverticulum* and leading into the latter through a *vestibule*. The preapical diverticulum is oval in shape and en-

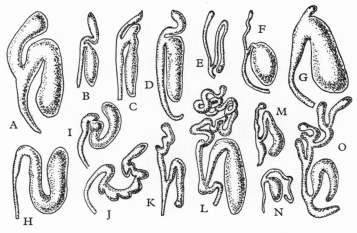

Fig. 88. Variations in the apical portion of the spermatheca (Uvarov 1948, after Slifer). A, *Acrida*; B, *Gomphocerus sibiricus*; C, *Aulocara elliotti*; D, *Chorthippus*; E, *Orphulella concinnula*; F, *Stauroderus scalaris*; G, *Arphia xanthoptera*; H, *Ocneridia* sp.; I, *Tmethis cisti*; J, *Poekilocerus vittatus*; K, *Hieroglyphus annulicornis*; L, *Anacridium aegyptium*; M, *Melanoplus femur-rubrum*; N, *Paraidemona mimica*; O, *Teratodes monticollis*.

closed in a fatty connective tissue. The apical diverticulum in *Locusta* is a small tubercle, but in other species it may be elongated. In fact, the distal part of the spermathecal duct is subject to considerable variation (fig. 88), being coiled, bifurcate, branched, or expanded into a vesicle. These variations are characteristic for some taxonomic groups. Thus, the spermatheca of Pamphagidae has a single apical diverticulum (fig. 88, H, I), although the same type occurs in other families; Acrididae, as a family, are characterised by a spermatheca with two apical diverticula (e.g. fig. 88, E), but again, this type is not exclusive to members of this family. Spermathecal differences are observed between species of the same genus (*Melanoplus*, Slifer 1940*b*), but a considerable variation within a species is also known (Slifer 1940*c*), so that Barnum (1959) considered it valueless as a specific character. On the whole, the structure of the spermatheca may be regarded as a subsidiary taxonomic character of the higher categories, but it should be used with caution (Dirsh 1957). The histology of the spermatheca and the details of its connection with the vagina have been described by both Voy and Slifer (*tt.cc.*).

The anterior end of the vagina in members of the subfamilies Catantopinae, Calliptaminae, Cyrtacanthacridinae, Ommexechinae and Egnatiinae has a pair of large plaited pockets (Vardé 1929, 1934; Slifer & King 1936; Slifer

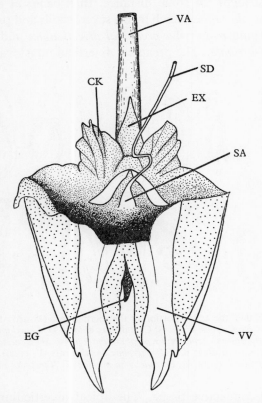

Fig. 89. *Nomadacris*, internal view of the female genital chamber (Albrecht 1956).
VA, vagina; SD, spermathecal duct; EX, median extension of the chamber; SA, spermathecal aperture; EG, egg-guide; VV, ventral ovipositor valve; CK, Comstock-Kellog gland.

1940*b*) called *Comstock-Kellog glands*, which are eversible and have glandular epithelium (fig. 89). These glands were observed in the everted state before copulation and possibly play some part in the attraction of the male by the female (Hubbell & Cantrall 1938, *Appalachia*; Laub-Drost 1959, *Schistocerca*, *Anacridium*, *Nomadacris*, *Acanthacris*, *Ornithacris*, *Tylotropidius*; Thomas 1965.

On the inner ovipositor valves there is an opening leading to a short invagination which has been regarded as a rudimentary accessory gland (Nel 1929; Agarwala 1952–54), but this is doubtful.

Table 38. *Recorded cases of gynandromorphism*

Species	Male characters	Female characters	Reference
Melanoplus sanguinipes	Dorsal half and ventral left half of body; left legs; external genitalia except ventral right side.	Ventral right side of abdomen; lower right ovipositor valve.	Severin 1943
Melanoplus sp.	Left half of external genitalia.	Whole body; right half of ovipositor subgenital plate; right cercus.	Severin 1955
Melanoplus adelogyrus	Whole body, and right half of genitalia.	Left lower ovipositor valve; distorted upper valve.	Hubbell 1932
Podisma pedestris	Whole body and left half of genitalia.	Right half of genitalia.	Baccetti 1954
Parapodisma sapporensis (hopper)	External genitalia; testis with sperm.	Ovarian tissue attached to testis; egg rudiments.	Natori 1931
Schistocerca paranensis	Whole body except left half of genitalia.	Left half of ovipositor.	Morales Agacino 1957
Schistocerca gregaria	Genitalia of right side; accessory glands; seminal vesicle.	Genitalia of left side; deformed ovary with ovarioles.	Dirsh 1957b
Anacridium melanorhodon	Dorsal parts of body including genitalia; testes; accessory glands; phallic complex (partly distorted).	Genitalia of ventral part, spermatheca.	Potter, 1940
Pardalophora phoenicoptera	Whole body, except ventral right side; phallic complex.	Ventral right ovipositor valve.	Friauf 1947
Sphingonotus caerulans	Whole body and genitalia, except rudiments of ovipositor.	Rudiments of lower ovipositor valves.	Dirsh 1957b
Trimerotropis citrina × *T. maritima*	Whole left side, including genitalia.	Genitalia, ovary and oviduct of right side.	Carothers 1939
Camnula pellucida	Whole body, epiproct, epiphallus, both cerci; paraproct and subgenital plate of left side.	Paraproct, subgenital plate and ovipositor of right side.	Friauf 1947
Locusta migratoria	External genitalia, left side.	External genitalia, right side.	Verdier 1960 (unpublished)
,,	External genitalia, testis (showing spermatogenesis) and seminal duct on the right side.	External genitalia and ovary (with oocytes) on the left side.	P. Joly 1960
Chorthippus parallelus	External genitalia (imperfect); testis.	Abbreviated tegmina; reduced stridulatory pegs; shape of the foveolae of vertex.	Karaman 1959

149

GYNANDROMORPHS

Several described cases of individuals with mixed male and female characters are recorded in table 38. Two additional schistocerca gynandromorphs have been described in great detail by Pener (1964). One had a normal phallic complex, another a deformed one; the testes were absent in both; both had a normal, or almost normal ovary on one side and a reduced one on the other. Both exhibited male behaviour which disappeared after some time. There were no attempts to dig for egg-laying, although eggs reached full size (p. 304) and the ovipositor valves were present on one side.

In most cases, there was a bilateral division of male and female external characters, but in some it was dorso-ventral. In a few cases the internal reproductive organs were also involved; in others they have not been examined, or were unaffected.

NERVOUS SYSTEM

The nervous system is usually divided into the central, peripheral and visceral (or sympathetic) systems, although the division is one of convenience rather than basic. The following brief description, as far as the anatomy is concerned, is based mainly on that of the nervous system of *Nomadacris* (Albrecht 1956) and *Locusta* (Albrecht 1953 *a*; Afify 1959, 1960; Clarke & Langley 1963 *b*) and *Schistocerca* (Delphin 1963 *a*); a detailed general description is available also for *Dociostaurus* (Jannone 1939 *b*), apart from papers on parts of the nervous system by different authors quoted below.

CENTRAL NERVOUS SYSTEM

This includes the brain (sometimes called the supraoesophageal ganglion), the suboesophageal ganglion and the ventral nerve chain with its segmentary ganglia.

The brain (fig. 90) is a conspicuous white body lying in the anterior part of the head and largely covered by muscles and air-sacs. It consists of three paired lobes. The first pair is the *protocerebrum*; from it arise anteriorly a pair of ocellar stalks innervating the lateral ocelli, and a similar stalk leading to the median ocellus, as well as a pair of large *optic lobes,* providing the nerves of the compound eyes. Internally, the two protocerebral lobes and their median connection (*pars intercerebralis*) have an extremely complicated system of ganglion cells and nerve fibres, the more conspicuous features being the *central body* and a pair of *mushroom bodies* (corpora pedunculata), which are important centres of synaptic nervous coordination. According to Huber (1955), the mushroom bodies in *Gomphocerippus* are of importance in the integration of sound perception and stridulation.

The second part of the brain is the *deutocerebrum*, a pair of round lobes, each of them giving rise to an antennary nerve. Some difference between sexes in the nerve cells of the lobes was recorded in *Locusta* (Afifi 1959).

The posterior part of the brain is the *tritocerebrum*, consisting of two conical lobes, from which arise nerves of parts of the head, including the labrum, as well as those forming post-oesophageal commissures connecting the tritocerebral lobes with the frontal ganglion, which itself is connected with the brain by the recurrent nerve (p. 154); there are two such commissures in *Locusta* and only one in *Dociostaurus* (Jannone 1939*b*) and *Nomadacris* (Albrecht 1956).

Detailed histological studies of the brain and of the nervous pathways within it will be found in papers by Viallanes (1887), Hanström (1940),

151

Tortajada (1960), Jawlowski (1954), Satija (1957, 1958), Afifi (1960), Clarke & Langley (1963 c); the last five concern *Locusta*.

Large circumoesophageal commissures connect the tritocerebrum with the *suboesophageal ganglion* which lies below the oesophagus and emits several pairs of nerves to the mandibular muscles, hypopharynx, maxillae, labium, salivary ducts and neck membranes (Schmitt 1959; histology, Kessel 1961).

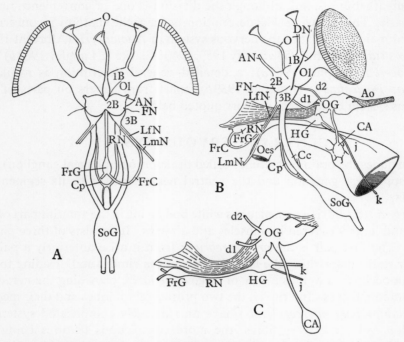

Fig. 90. *Nomadacris*, brain and associated ganglia, nerves and endocrine organs. A, anterior view; B, lateral view; C, endocrine organs and their connections (Albrecht 1956).

1 B, protocerebrum; 2B, deutocerebrum; 3B, tritocerebrum; O, ocellus; Ol, optical lobe; DN, dorso-tegumentary nerve; AN, antennal nerve; FN, frontal nerve; OG, corpus cardiacum (oesophageal ganglion); d1, d2, nerves connecting corpus cardiacum with the brain; Ao, aorta; HG, hypocerebral ganglion; RN, recurrent nerve; FrG, frontal ganglion; LfN, labro-frontal nerve; LmN, labral nerve; FrC, frontal connective; Oes, oesophagus; Cp, post-oesophageal commissure; Cc, circumoesophageal commissure; SoG, suboesophageal ganglion; CA, corpus allatum; j, k, oesophageal nerves.

The tritocerebrum and its commissures are also connected with the corpora cardiaca (p. 157) and the corpora allata (p. 158).

The *ventral nerve chain* lies on the floor of the body cavity and is formed by a series of paired ganglia in the thorax and abdomen which are connected by a pair of nerve trunks and a thin median sympathetic nerve (p. 154). The three pairs of thoracic ganglia give off nerves to the legs of the respective segments and those in the meso- and metathorax also to the wings; the meta-thoracic pair sends nerves also to the first three abdominal segments and is, therefore, regarded as a result of fusion of a thoracic and three abdominal pairs (Schmitt 1959; Delphin 1963 a). Accordingly, the positions of the abdominal ganglia do not correspond to the segmentation (fig. 91). The last abdominal pair, lying in the VIIIth segment, is large and regarded as a result of fusion of three pairs, since it supplies nerves to the rest of the abdomen. This

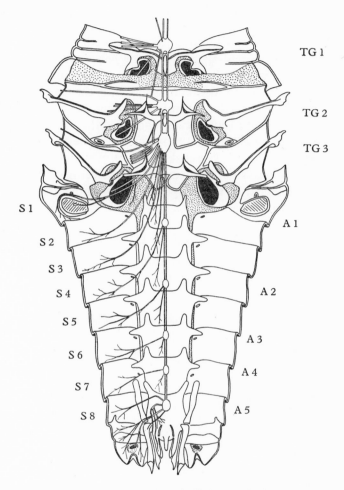

Fig. 91. *Nomadacris* female, ventral nerve chain (Albrecht 1956).
TG 1–TG 3, thoracic ganglia; A 1–A 5, abdominal ganglia; S 1–S 8, abdominal sternites.

ganglion includes some large cells, giant fibres from which extend through the abdominal nerve chain to the metathoracic ganglion (P. M. Cook 1951); on the other hand, it has been suggested that some giant fibres arise from cells in the brain (Satija 1957, 1958) and transmit stimuli from the eyes and the aerodynamic organ on the head (p. 162).

153

The finer structure of the abdominal ganglia in *Locusta* has been described by Tsvileneva (1953).

VISCERAL NERVOUS SYSTEM

The visceral (sympathetic, stomatogastric or stomodaeal) nervous system is closely connected with the central system (Clarue & Langley 1963*b*, 1963*c*, 1963*d*; Delphin 1963*a*, 1963*b*; Melis 1961). It consists (fig. 90) of the *frontal ganglion*, connected by two frontal connectives with the tritocerebrum, the *recurrent nerve* and two *oesophageal ganglia* (*corpora cardiaca*); the latter have a mainly secretory function and will be considered later (p. 157), together with the corpora allata which are also connected with the oesophageal ganglia. The slender *median nerve* of the ventral nerve chain also belongs to the visceral system and it sends off four nerves regulating the opening and closing of spiracles and respiratory abdominal movements, as well as wing movements (T. S. Ivanova 1952, 1956; Voskresenskaya 1950, 1959); this suggests that the division of the nervous system into central and visceral systems is becoming outdated. Moreover, most of the ganglia are now known to have also some secretory functions (p. 157).

PERIPHERAL NERVOUS SYSTEM

This comprises the numerous ramifications of nervous trunks, formed of fibres (axons) which arise either from the nerve cells in ganglia, or from the

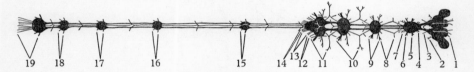

Fig. 92. *Psophus*, diagram to indicate which of the ganglia send out nerves to the different body regions (after Huber *in* Jacobs 1953).

1, lateral ocellus; 2, antenna; 3, labrum; 4, mandible; 5, maxilla; 6, labium; 7, anterior neck muscles; 8, other neck muscles; 9, prothorax; 10, mesothorax; 11, metathorax; 12, first abdominal segment; 13, second ditto; 14, third ditto; 15–18, fourth to seventh ditto; 19, eighth and the following segments.

various sensory cells. A nervous trunk usually contains a bundle of fibres covered by a sheath (*neurilemma*) which has a cellular layer and a laminated outer membrane; this sheath also envelops the ganglia and is said to be identical with the connective tissue membrane covering other organs (Baccetti 1955*a*, 1956; Ashurst 1959; Ashurst & Chapman 1961).

The whole system of repeatedly branched nerves is exceedingly complicated and it would not be possible to provide here an adequate general description of it, even if one existed; apart from the works already quoted, descriptions of the innervation of the regions and parts of the body will be found in the papers by La Greca (1949, pterothorax, *Anacridium*), Ewer (1953, 1954*a*, 1954*c*, 1957*a*, thorax, *Acanthacris*), T. S. Ivanova (1952, 1956, *Locusta*), Schmitt (1955, abdomen; 1959, neck and thorax, *Dissosteira*; 1962, review), J. I. Campbell (1961, mesothorax, *Locusta*), Alicata (1962*b*, thorax, *Eyprepocnemis*), Guthrie (1964, flight apparatus, *sonistocerca*); references to the innervation of various organs and parts of the body are made where necessary and fig. 92 illustrates diagrammatically the nerves arising from different ganglia.

FUNCTIONS OF THE NERVOUS SYSTEM

The axons arising from ganglia are the motor nerves, transmitting impulses to organs and parts of the body, while those arising from the sensory cells carry signals to ganglia. The transmutation of a sensory signal into a motor impulse occurs in ganglia, where the terminal fibril of the two kinds of axons are interlocked, forming a synapse; a synapse may not be direct, but through special association neurones (Melis 1961). The connection between the motor nerves and muscles is discussed on p. 65.

Both the motor impulses and the sensory signals are electrical in nature and are conducted along the nerves as waves of electric potential. This provides a basis for studies of the function of sense organs and of locomotory activity by recording changes in the electric potential of a nerve in relation to the stimuli experimentally applied to definite sense organs or to the nerves leading from them. A great deal of useful information has already been obtained by electrophysiological methods, but it has to be borne in mind that an electric response to a stimulus does not necessarily mean that a particular sense organ is designed to receive only this particular stimulus. In fact, some sense organs have proved to be electrically responsive to a variety of stimuli, including some certainly never met with by an insect. Another application of the electrophysiological technique is electrical stimulation of definite parts of the brain and of other ganglia in order to find out on which particular centres certain types of muscular activity depend; this method is supplementary to operations involving the removal of the ganglia, or their parts. References to the results obtained in studies of this kind will be made in the chapters on sense organs, muscles, and behaviour.

Since nerves are in contact with the haemolymph, the composition of the latter has an effect on nerve conductivity. The concentration of potassium in blood of other animals was found to affect unfavourably the transmission of electrical excitation through nerves, though *Locusta* tolerates high potassium concentrations (p. 110), apparently because the connective tissue sheath covering its nerves is less permeable to the potassium ions than that of other animals (Hoyle 1953, 1954); Ashurst (1959) and Treherne (1961) did not support this view.

Many cells of the brain and ganglia are secretory and the material is transmitted along the connecting nerves (p. 157).

NEUROSECRETORY AND ENDOCRINE ORGANS AND CELLS

Until relatively recently, the organs of internal secretion of insects have been regarded as a separate endocrine system; but it is now recognised that such organs, with primarily endocrine functions, are closely connected with the nervous system, while many of the nerve ganglia include secretory cells, and both are the sources of hormones stimulating and regulating a variety of physiological and developmental processes (Scharrer & Scharrer 1963). Investigations of neurosecretory organs and cells in acridoids are now in such active progress that the following brief review is certain to be out of date before it is published. It is restricted to the structural aspect of the organs, while such information as exists with regard to the effects of the secretions on the physiology and development will be found in the appropriate chapters.

The main endocrine organs are concentrated in a retro-cerebral complex in the head (P. Joly 1939; Cazal 1948; Cazal & Guerrier 1946), illustrated diagrammatically in fig. 93.

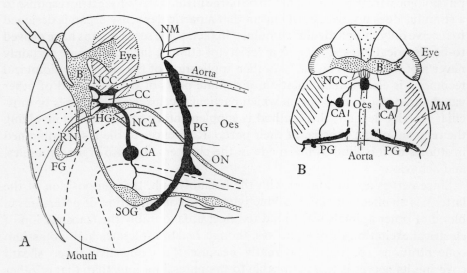

Fig. 93. *Locusta*, diagram of the neuro-endocrine system in the head. A, lateral view; B, dorsal view (Staal 1961).

B, brain; NM, neck membrane; NCC, nerve of the corpus cardiacum; CC, corpus cardiacum; CA, corpus allatum; HG, hypocerebral ganglion; NCA, nerve of the corpus allatum; RN, recurrent nerve; FG, frontal ganglion; PG, prothoracic gland; Oes, oesophagus; ON, external oesophageal nerve; MM, mandibular muscles.

NEUROSECRETORY CELLS OF THE
BRAIN AND GANGLIA

In the intercerebral part of the protocerebrum of *Schistocerca* there are two closely apposed groups of numerous small cells, covered by a layer of vacuolated cells. Secretory inclusions in the cells vary cyclically in their amount and the secretion, which is thought to be not a hormone but a carrier protein, is passed along a connecting nerve to the corpora cardiaca (Highnam 1961) and has a stimulating effect on their activity and ovarian development (p. 311).

Neurosecretory cells of several distinct types have been found also in all the ganglia of the ventral nerve cord of adult female *Schistocerca*, but not in the frontal, hypocerebral or ingluvial ganglia (F. Delphin 1963*a*, 1963*b*; Panov 1962). The cells are broadly similar to the kinds reported in other insects, are arranged in a pattern which is more or less characteristic of each ganglion, and appear to undergo changes correlated with sexual maturation. The histological appearance of the cells of both sides of a given ganglion is always the same in a given insect, suggesting that they operate in phase with each other. The secretory material is discharged backwards and forwards along the ventral nerve cords. No definite secretory pathways can be found in the ventral ganglia.

CORPORA CARDIACA

These have also been termed corpora para-cardiaca, corpora pharyngea, pharyngeal bodies, and the oesophageal ganglia. They are elongated paired

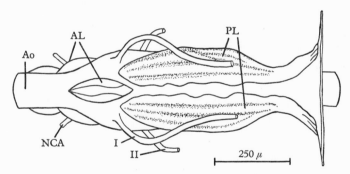

Fig. 94. *Schistocerca*, corpora cardiaca (after Highnam 1961). Ao, aorta; AL, anterior lobe; PL, posterior lobe; NCA, nerve of the corpus allatum; I and II, nerves of the corpus cardiacum.

bodies (fig. 94) lying behind the brain, with which they are connected by a nerve, and they are closely adherent to the aorta (*Locusta*, Pavlova 1895, Albrecht 1953 *a*,Özbaş1957*a*,1957*b*; *Nomadacris*,Albrecht 1956; *Schistocerca*, Highnam 1961, Delphin 1963*a*; *Chorthippus*, Hanström 1940). Their relative size and shape vary in the few species that have been studied (fig. 95). They consist of a pair of anterior lobes which project into the aorta, and a pair of folded posterior lobes which are largely secretory (De Lerma 1937; Cazal & Guerrier 1946; Cazal 1948; Nayar 1954; Özbaş 1957 a; Sugiyama 1958). Their secretion is related to moulting (p. 290), the maturation of ovaries (p. 311), pigmentation (p. 377) and the peristaltic movement of the Malpighian tubes and the hindgut (M. L. Cameron 1953; Koller 1955).

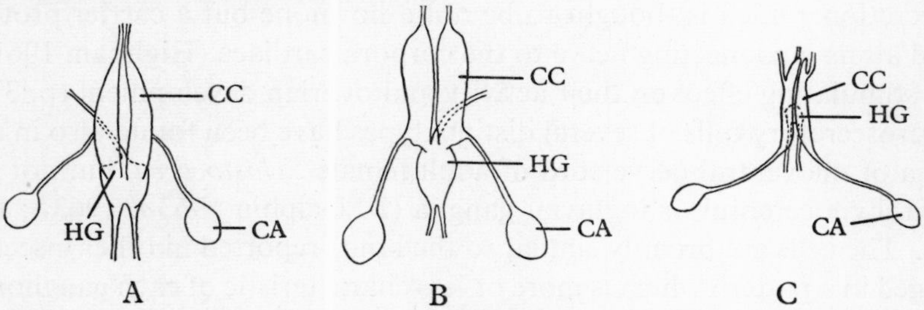

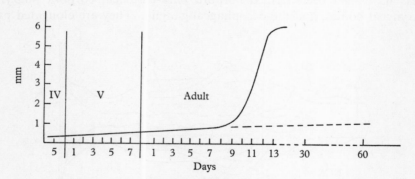

Fig. 95. Variation in the endocrine glands (Özbaş 1957a).
A, *Locusta*; B, *Acrida bicolor*; C, *Glyphotmethis escherichi*. Lettering as in fig. 93.

CORPORA ALLATA

A thin nerve arising from each corpus cardiacum leads to a corpus allatum, a conspicuous oval white body, lying close to the oesophagus on either side. It is connected by a nerve also with the suboesophageal ganglion (in the case of

Fig. 96. The growth of the corpus allatum in late hopper and the adult
(after L. Joly 1960).

Glyphotmethis the connections are different, see fig. 95) and it emits several thin nerves (L. Joly 1960; see also references under corpora cardiaca). The histology of the corpora allata was described by Mendes (1948), De Lerma (1937, 1950 b) and in more detail by Özbaş (1957 b). Their secretory cells are of two kinds, normal and giant ones.

The size of a corpus allatum increases in both sexes throughout the hopper life (table 39) and the increase continues in the adult of *Locusta* (fig. 96),

Chorthippus brunneus and *Omocestus viridulus*, particularly in the females (Palm 1949a).

Active secretion in hoppers occurs in cycles, each commencing two to three days after a moult, the secretion being released into the blood before the next moult. There are indications that secretory activity partly depends on the nervous connection with the corpora cardiaca and the brain, and that more than one hormone may be produced (Staal 1961).

Physiological effects of the corpora allata secretion have been demonstrated, or suggested, with regard to moulting (p. 289), growth (p. 290), pigmentation (p. 376), fat metabolism (p. 103), sexual maturation (p. 311) and phase polymorphism (p. 375).

Table 39. *Growth changes in the mean size (in microns) of corpora allata (Özbaş 1957a)*

	Locusta		Acrida	
Instar	Male	Female	Male	Female
Third	110 × 80	120 × 85	90 × 67	93 × 71
Fourth	150 × 107	180 × 155	100 × 80	170 × 85
Fifth	204 × 130	247 × 160	148 × 93	170 × 118
Adult	250 × 160	305 × 224	194 × 140	232 × 162

PROTHORACIC GLAND

This organ is also sometimes called the ventral cephalic, or ventral, gland, but in acridoids it is actually found in the occipital part of the head, close to the neck membrane, and the name occipital gland would be more appropriate. The other names have been used because of the supposed functional homology with the similar glands in other insects where their position is different. However, the accepted term is the prothoracic gland.

It is a thin vertical sheet of cells (fig. 93) extending from the posterior part of the occiput, where its strands penetrate between the mandibular muscles, down each side of the oesophagus towards the tentorium and ending in a long filament (Strich 1955; Strich-Halbwachs 1958, 1959; Staal 1961). Its size varies considerably between species and it is particularly visible in hoppers, increasing in size from instar to instar. It was supposed to disappear soon after the final moult (Pflugfelder 1947, 1958; P. Joly 1958; Cazal 1948; Strich-Halbwachs, *t.c.*), but this view was mainly based on observations on crowded *Locusta*, whereas in isolated individuals of that species and of *Schistocerca* it persists throughout the adult life (Carlisle & Ellis 1959); it also persists in adults of several grasshopper species, but may disappear if they are reared crowded (D. Carlisle, personal communication).

The histological picture of the gland varies in cycles related to moults, cell limits becoming ill-defined and the cytoplasm granular during a moult; then the cytoplasm becomes more homogeneous and all nuclei are enlarged and charged with chromatin (Strich 1955). Secretory activity of the gland falls rapidly after the final moult, particularly in crowded locusts.

The physiological role of the gland is not clear, except that it has a definite effect on moulting (p. 289); it was claimed also to affect ovarian development and hardening of the integument after moulting (Strich-Halbwachs 1959), but this remains unconfirmed (D. Carlisle, personal communication). Its persistence in adults implies that it continues to play some part after the final moult.

OTHER ORGANS OF INTERNAL SECRETION

Suggestions regarding possible endocrine activities of the fat body cells, the oenocytes and the corpora lutea of the ovarioles (Iwanoff & Mestscherskaya 1935) were based on insufficient evidence, but removal of ovaries has an apparent effect on neuro-secretion (p. 313). However, systematic investigations of neurosecretion in acridoids are only beginning and new sources of hormones may be discovered. Cases of interaction between different neuro-endocrine organs have been recorded and this makes experimental studies of the effects of their secretions particularly difficult. Such studies have been based on observing the effects of surgical elimination, or implantation, of certain organs, but their possible interaction, as well as the resulting balance of the various secretions, introduce serious complications.

CHEMICAL NATURE OF HORMONES

Only indirect indications were obtained by Nickerson (1956) that some of the hormones affecting phase changes in the coloration of *Schistocerca* may be related to steroids, and Carlisle & Ellis (1963) suggested that the active ingredient of the moulting hormone (p. 289) secreted by the prothoracic gland may be related to cholesterol. Otherwise, there is no information on the chemistry of hormones in acridoids. Stamm (1959) claimed that the two kinds of ecdysone, isolated in crystallised form from adults of *Dociostaurus*, had the same chromatographic and other properties as those from the lepidopterous pupae, for which an empirical formula $C_{18}H_{30}O_4$ has been suggested (C. M. Williams 1958).

SENSE ORGANS

In spite of the paramount importance of sensory perception for behaviour and ecology, the present knowledge of sense organs is very meagre. Even purely descriptive data on their morphology, particularly the fine structure, are fragmentary, while their function until recently has been largely inferred from their structure, or from behaviour responses. The introduction of the electron microscope makes it possible now to investigate the finest structures (Slifer 1961), and electrophysiological methods provide information on the stimuli received by sense receptors and their transmission to the nervous system, but investigations with these new techniques are still very scarce. An excellent review in which acridoids figure prominently has been provided by Dethier (1963). Thomas (1965) provided a detailed study of abdominal sensilla of *Schistocerca* female.

In the following pages, sense organs are grouped according to their known, or suspected, function, but their classification is one of convenience and not rigid.

The organs of vision are treated in a separate chapter (p. 196), and so are the auditory organs, discussed in relation to the sound-producing mechanisms (p. 176).

MECHANORECEPTORS

The organs for the perception of mechanical stimuli of various kinds are partly the external integumental sensilla and partly the so-called scoloparia which are internal.

Trichoid sensillum

Hairs and bristles occur on most parts of the integument and are often grouped into organs with special sensory functions.

The fine structure of most of the hairs is not known, and some of them (perhaps the majority) may have no nerve cells, nor any connection with the nervous system. Here we are concerned only with such hairs as are known to have a nervous component.

A trichoid sensillum is a long hair or bristle with its base level with the surface of the integument and inserted in a socket (fig. 97, D, E, F); its cuticular walls are thick, the central lumen, which is not open at the tip, contains nerve fibres leading to the sensory cells in the hypoderm which are connected by a nerve with the central nervous system (Slifer 1954a, 1961; Riegert 1960). These sensilla are not permeable to water-soluble dyes and are therefore unlikely to respond to chemical stimuli, but they respond to touch and to air movements.

11

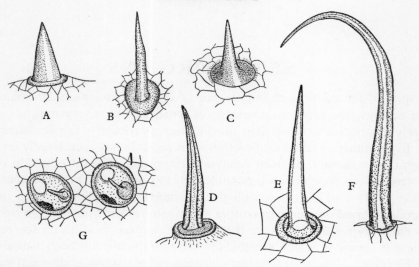

Fig. 97. *Melanoplus bivittatus*, main types of sensilla. A, B, C, basiconic; D, E, F, trichoid; G, coeloconic (after Riegert 1960).

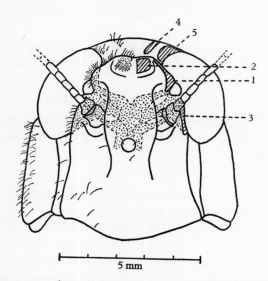

Fig. 98. *Schistocerca*, aerodynamic organ. 1–5, areas bearing trichoid sensilla (after Weis-Fogh 1956c).

Aerodynamic organ

Five groups of trichoid sensilla are found on the head (fig. 98) where they form an aerodynamic organ (Boyd & Ewer 1949; Weis-Fogh 1956c), innervated by the dorsal tegumentary nerve. If a jet of air is blown on the hairs, they bend slightly and vibrate and the insect responds by forward movement, walking if a hopper, or flying if an adult. Electrophysiological investigation has shown that a movement of the hair tip by only 0·25 μ was sufficient to cause electric discharges in the nerve, but only if the hair was bent backwards or to the side. This enables a locust to orientate into the wind which is essential for taking off from the ground; if the hairs are covered the reaction is lost. The hairs also act as air-speed indicators (Haskell 1959*b*, 1960).

Other wind-sensitive hairs are found on the thorax and the abdomen, but they respond to rather fast air flow and are non-directional (Haskell 1960).

There are also numerous trichoid sensilla on the tegmina and wings, particularly along the main veins (Zacwilichowski 1934; fig. 100); their detailed structure and function have not been studied, but air-flow over the wings of a locust elicits a flight response (Weis-Fogh 1956*c*), which may be due to the trichoid sensilla.

Cercal sensilla

Wind-sensitive hairs have been found also on the cerci; those in *Schistocerca* responded to an air-flow of only 4 cm per second (Haskell 1960); a puff of

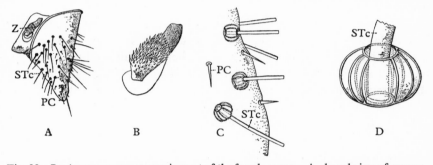

Fig. 99. *Dociostaurus*, sensory equipment of the female cercus. A, dorsal view of cercus; B, basal appendix of the cercus (brustia); C, tactile sensilla of two types; D, base of a specialised sensillum (Jannone 1939*b*).
STc, specialised tactile sensillum; PC, trichoid sensillum; Z, brustia.

air directed at the cercus produced an electrical response in the abdominal nerve chain of *Locusta* (P. M. Cook 1951), and a jumping reaction in *Disso-steira* (Hoyle 1958). Responses from cercal hairs to sound were regarded as evidence of their acoustic function, but it is more probable that they respond to air vibration (Pumphrey 1940).

The cercal sensillum of *Chorthippus* (Sihler 1924), *Schistocerca* (Thomas (1965) and of *Dociostaurus* (Jannone 1939*b*) is a long hair arising from the bottom of a globular cup with a complicated structure (fig. 99); this suggests an articulation mechanism which may play a part in registering movements of the air, either by air-flow or by pressure.

Neck organs

The first cervical sclerite of *Dociostaurus* (Jannone 1939*b*), *Schistocerca*, *Locusta* and other species (Goodman 1959; Haskell 1959*a*, 1960; L. M. Henry

1958) bears a cervical hair plate (fig. 8), with numerous trichoid sensilla of several kinds, innervated by a branch of the second pair of nerves from the first thoracic ganglion. These sensilla register movements of the head, particularly its rotation; they are of importance in maintaining the horizontal position in flight, and also possibly in scanning movements while on the ground, since they are present in both adults (including wingless species) and in hoppers.

The anterior edge of the pronotum also bears tactile hairs and their function may also be connected with movements of the head relative to the thorax. It would be of interest to study both the cervical plates and the pronotal hairs in the climbing species, where they might act as gravity recorders.

Prosternal process

In a large number of groups (Cyrtacanthacridinae, most Catantopinae, Pamphagidae, etc.) important taxonomic characters are the presence and the shape of the prosternal process (p. 13). Its finer structure has been described only for *Schistocerca* (Chauvin 1939*b*; Rowell 1961), in which it is a hollow cylinder, thickened and rounded apically, with thick cuticle and pigmented hypoderm. It is abundantly supplied with flat air-sacs and bears 100–140 hair sensilla, which are up to 0·8 mm long, conical, with round bases inserted in a sclerotised cup of hour-glass shape; there are also a few much shorter setae. The sensilla are innervated by branches of the second nerve of the prothoracic ganglion, which also supplies branches to the similar hair sensilla on the coxa and femur of the first leg. The prosternal process in *Schistocerca* is absent in the first instar and develops gradually. The function of this organ is certainly tactile. A drastic treatment, such as its removal or cauterisation, produced no effect on behaviour, but if the hairs were covered by paraffin, movements of the first legs were disturbed to the extent of both being raised vertically. Direct electrical recordings from the nerves involved have shown responses to the bending of the sensilla, by either pressure or puffs of air; similar responses were obtained from the hair sensilla on the sternum and coxa (Rowell *t.c.*). It has been pointed out (Uvarov 1948) that the prosternal process is particularly well developed and presents great variation of structure in species with climbing habits, and its ability to control movements, particularly of the front legs, which are of dominant importance in climbing (La Greca 1948), tends to support this idea. *Schistocerca* is only an occasional climber and it would be more promising to study this organ in such species as *Tropidopola* or *Nomadacris* which normally sit on grass stems.

Other trichoid sensilla are distributed widely over the body, particularly in the situations where they are likely to be of value as *tactile receptors*. On the antennae they are more numerous on the scape and the pedicel than on the flagellum; they are also conspicuous near the tips of palps and maxillae and on the coxae, pulvilli and arolia of the tarsi (Jannone 1939*b* Röhler 1906; Slifer 1950*a*; Riegert 1960).

Stridulatory pegs

As described elsewhere (p. 178), femoral stridulatory pegs of Gomphocerinae are modified trichoid sensilla and, apart from their mechanical part in sound production, they probably serve to record and control rhythmic stridulatory movements of the hind femora, but no studies of these points have been made. The long bristles on the stridulatory ridge of Truxalinae (p. 179) which have no articulated pegs may have the same function, but even their fine structure has not been studied.

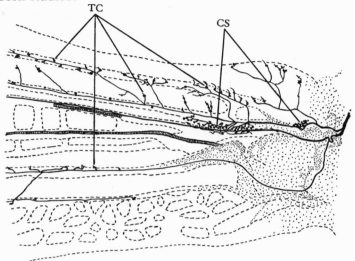

Fig. 100. *Chorthippus*, underside of tegmen, showing groups of trichoid (TC) and campaniform (CS) sensilla (after Zacwilichowski 1934).

Campaniform sensillum

This has been called also the cupola, bell, umbrella and plate sensillum, olfactory pore and Hicks's organ, although some of these names may apply either to variations of the same type, or even to different types. It consists (fig. 104, D) of a deeply sunk chamber, the orifice of which is covered by a cuticular cap, which may be either flush with the surface of the integument, or sunk in it; a large basal sensory cell sends a neuron to the inner, open end of the cap. Campaniform sensilla appear to be very widely distributed; thus, McIndoo (1920) recorded 'olfactory pores' from nearly all body parts, but he may have included under this name also some coeloconic sensilla. Jannone (1939b) has found 'Hicks' organs's on the maxillae, trochanter, femur and tarsus of *Dociostaurus*; on the antennae they occur in this species (fig. 102) and in *Schistocerca* (Aziz 1958) only round the distal end of the pedicel; Sihler (1924) recorded them from the cercus of *Chorthippus* and Thomas (1965) from the ovipositor of *Schistocerca*. Of particular interest is the occurrence of campaniform sensilla on the tegmina and wings. In *Chorthippus* there are two groups of them on the underside of the tegmen at the base of the subcostal vein (fig. 100), and there is one group in a similar position on the hind wings. The campaniform sensillum is regarded as a mechano-receptor, sensitive to strains in the exoskeleton and is considered of possible importance in the maintenance of balance in flight (Pringle 1957) or in the regulation of wing beat (D. M. Wilson 1961). McIndoo's (*t.c.*) contention that it has an olfactory function can no longer be supported. Grant (1949) suggested, on purely structural grounds, that sensilla of this type might be suitable for receiving infra-red radiation, thus being thermoreceptors.

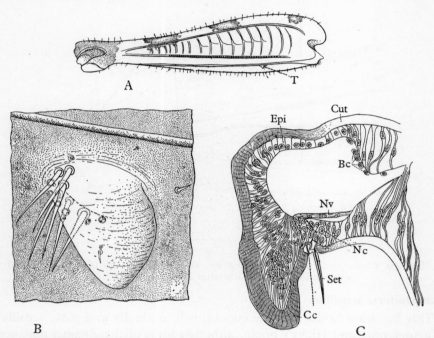

Fig. 101. *Dociostaurus*, Brunner's organ. A, inner face of the hind femur; B, Brunner's organ; C, ditto, section (Jannone 1939*b*).

T, Brunner's organ; Cut, cuticle; Epi, hypoderm; Bc, amoebocytes; Nv, nerve; NC, nerve cells; Set, trichoid sensillum; Cc, campaniform sensillum.

Brunner's organ

In acridoids, with few exceptions, there is on the lower ridge of the inner face of the hind femur (fig. 101) a small tubercle called Brunner's organ (Slifer & Uvarov 1938; Jannone 1939*b*, 1950). In live insects the tubercle is soft and pliable, resembling a fluid-filled blister. In sections, the tubercle is covered by a thin cuticle and its interior is filled with a cuticular deposit from the underlying hypodermal cells. Near the base of the tubercle there are several large curved trichoid sensilla, and a group of campaniform sensilla, innervated by neurones from a branch of a femoral nerve; in *Stenobothrus lineatus* there are no campaniform sensilla in the first instar hopper (Roscow 1961). Brunner's organ is found in representatives of all acridoid families and there is little variation in its size and outward appearance in different genera, except that the sensory bristles may be either shorter, or longer, than the tubercle. No clear relation has been found between the habits of species (ground-living, climbing, etc.) and the degree of development of the organ (Slifer & Uvarov, *t.c.*; Rehn 1952).

The function of the organ is almost certainly tactile, but the mechanism of its action is uncertain. Its position is such that when the tibia is adpressed to the femur (as it normally is at rest) the tubercle is flattened; this naturally led to a suggestion that it must be of importance in the jumping reflex. However, the excision, or cauterisation, of the tubercle does not eliminate jumping; on the other hand, a pressure on the integument in the immediate vicinity of the tubercle provokes a jumping reflex. The latter observation suggested to P. Joly (1951) that the sensitivity to pressure is not restricted to Brunner's organ, but obtains also in the surrounding integument. Another suggestion, based on the fact that the tubercle is depressed by the tibia when at rest, is that its role may be to maintain the resting position, although grasshoppers with the tubercles removed still rested with tibiae firmly adpressed to femora. Roscow (1961) suggested that the organ may be of particular use to hoppers, while in adults the close contact between femur and tibia becomes a matter of acquired habit. There is need for detailed electrophysiological investigation, bearing in mind that there are at least two kinds of sensilla involved. Previous experiments have been based on treating the whole organ, but the bristles and the campaniform sensilla may play different roles. It might be suggested, further, since the tubercle appears to be partly filled with blood, that its depression may affect blood pressure in the femur, causing a stress in the cuticle round the campaniform sensilla or affecting scolopophores (p. 170).

It should be added that a jumping reflex exists in tettigoniids, gryllids and proscopiids (Rehn, *t.c.*), which have no trace of Brunner's organ. Nevertheless, there is no reason to dismiss this somewhat complicated organ as a 'simple morphological differentiation of integument' (P. Joly, *t.c.*).

Scoloparia

These organs are also often called *chordotonal*, because the general structure of some of them suggests that they may be sound receptors. There are, however, variations in their structure, while their function, apart from a special case of the tympanal organ (p. 188), is still a matter of conjecture. Therefore, the term scolopophorous organ, or scoloparium (Snodgrass 1935 b), based on structure, is preferable.

The essential feature of a scoloparium is a bundle of simple sensilla (scolopophores), usually stretched between two points on the body wall. A scolopophore usually consists of a distal cap cell attached to the cuticle, an enveloping cell and a sensory cell connected basally with a nerve and extended apically, ending in a peg-like *scolops* (or *scolopale*, plural *scolopalia*).

Antennal scolopophores are found in the basal segments (scape and pedicel) of the antennae. They were described in *Gomphocerus* (Eggers 1928), *Schisto-cerca* (Debauche 1938), *Dociostaurus* (Jannone 1939 b) and *Melanoplus* (McFarlane 1953). There has been some confusion as to the number of discrete groups of antennal scoloparia to which the name *Johnston's organ* has been somewhat loosely applied and it appears best not to use this term in relation to acridoids, the more so because there is a vast difference in the structure (and probably function) between their relatively simple antennal

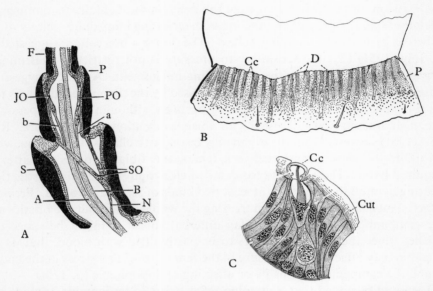

Fig. 102. Antennal scolopophores. A, *Melanoplus sanguinipes*, section of antennal base (after McFarlane 1953); B, *Dociostaurus*, apex of antennal pedicel and the base of the next segment; C, section of pedicel with a campaniform sensillum (Jannone 1939 b).
F, first segment of flagellum; P, pedicel; S, scape; JO, pedicellar scolopophore ('Johnston's organ'); PO, another pedicellar scolopophore; SO, scapal scolopophores; A, B, a, b, nerves of pedicellar scolopophores; N, nerve of scapal scolopophores; Cc, campaniform sensilla; D, depressions on the pedicel corresponding to points of attachment of scoloparia; Cut, cuticle.

scoloparia and the complicated original Johnston's organ of mosquitoes and other Diptera in which it has an auditory function.

There are two large scoloparia in the scape (fig. 102, A), basally attached a little above its base; they diverge and are apically inserted at the base of the pedicel, near the insertion of the pedicel muscles (fig. 6, C). In the pedicel, there are two organs. One of them (to which alone the term Johnston's organ might apply according to Debauche 1938) consists of twelve to fourteen scoloparia arising from the antennal nerve and apically attached round the periphery of the pedicel to the membrane between it and the first flagellar segment; the points of attachment are visible externally as small depressions (fig. 102, B).

The second pedicellar organ is a single scoloparium, separately innervated and terminating also in the membrane between pedicel and flagellum.

Finally, there is a small organ, consisting of a single scolopale, in the distal part of the apical segment of the antenna (Slifer 1936; McFarlane 1953).

It will be noted that the scoloparia of the antennal base are all restricted to the scape and the pedicel which are the only segments provided with muscles controlling movements of the flagellum. Electrophysiological studies on *Locusta* have shown that the antennal nerve by which scoloparia are in-

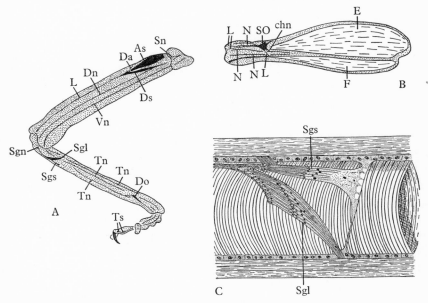

Fig. 103. Leg scolopophores. A, *Melanoplus sanguinipes*, anterior leg; B, ditto, hind femur (after McFarlane 1953); C, *Oedipoda caerulescens*, diagrammatic longitudinal section of middle tibia (after Friedrich 1929).

As, femoral aggregated scoloparium; Sn, its nerve; Ds, dispersed scoloparium; Da, its attachment; Dn, dorsal femoral nerve; Vn, ventral femoral nerve; Sgn, subgenual nerve; Sgl, subgenual scoloparium; Sgs, distal subgenual scoloparium; Tn, tibial nerve; Do, distal tibial scoloparium; Ts, tarsal scoloparia; L, ligament; SO, femoral scoloparium; N,chn, nerves; E, extensor muscle; F, flexor muscle.

nervated responds to the bending of the flagellum in relation to the pedicel. The scoloparia, therefore, are considered to be tension receptors stimulated by the stretching of the intersegmental membrane. The bending of the flagellum may be caused also by air currents and by movements of the insect, when a similar response is suggested (Uchiyama & Katsuki 1956). In this connection, it may be significant that the antennae during flight are kept in a very rigid state at an angle to the body and may serve to record changes in the direction of air currents. The possible function of the scoloparium in the terminal antennal segment is obscure, but it would be of interest to investigate the behaviour of that segment during flight and the effects of its amputation.

Leg scolopophores. Scolopophores in the femur, tibia and tarsus of the first leg have been described by several authors (Friedrich 1929; Debaisieux 1938; Slifer 1935; McFarlane 1953) (fig. 103).

In the first femur (fig. 103, A) there is a large scoloparium, consisting of 240 scolopalia aggregated in a cylindrical body lying dorsally near the base of the femur; it is innervated by a branch of the femoral nerve and a ligament arising from it extends to the membrane between femur and tibia. Below it lies a smaller dispersed scoloparium, innervated by another branch of the femoral nerve (Hubbard 1959). In the tibia, there are two *subgenual organs*, a larger near the base at the central side of the tibia, and a smaller one close to it; there is also a small distal organ near the apex of the tibia. Finally, there are two small scoloparia in the apical segment of the tarsus. The arrangement in the second tibia (fig. 103, C) and in the tibia and tarsus of the third is the same, but in the third (jumping) femur there is only one large scoloparium, near the apex (fig. 103, B).

Other scoloparia are widespread and Slifer (1936) who carried out a general survey of scoloparia in *Melanoplus* listed seventy-six pairs of them. In addition to those described above, scoloparia of varying sizes were found in the maxillary and labial palps, paraglossae, head, thorax, abdomen and wing base.

The functions of scoloparia have not been studied directly, but, as already suggested, the antennal scoloparia appear to be suited for the reception of mechanical pressure and air-movement. It is also very probable that the leg scoloparia serve to record stresses connected with posturing and movement, while there is also some evidence that the subgenual organs may be concerned with recording vibrations of the substrate (Autrum & Schneider 1948). Debaisieux (1938) stressed the fact that leg scoloparia lie in blood sinuses, so that the subgenual organ may almost prevent circulation; therefore they may be affected by changes in blood pressure caused, for example, by respiratory movements.

Muscle receptors

Slifer & Finlayson (1956) have briefly reported the presence in the dorsal longitudinal muscles of *Locusta* and *Romalea* of sensory neurones, connected by a slender fibre to the muscle, and have suggested that these organs may record the stretching of abdominal muscles (e.g. during oviposition; see also Thomas 1965) their possible role in regulating respiratory movements of the abdomen needs investigation.

A stretch receptor and a scoloparium were briefly described in the thorax of *Schistocerca* by Gettrup (1962). The former is found on a strand of the connective tissue between the pleuron and the mesophragma and its destruction causes the wing-stroke frequency of a flying locust to drop (see also Pabst & Schwartzkopff (1962).

CHEMORECEPTORS

The two main types of sensillum, known, or reasonably assumed, to be connected with the chemical sense (odour and taste), are the basiconic which looks like an acute peg arising from the level of the integument (fig. 104, A, B) and the coeloconic, also peg-like but lying within a cavity of the integument (figs. 97, G, 104, C). Slifer (1954*a*, 1955) distinguished three different types of the basiconic sensilla, but later (Slifer, Prestage & Beams 1957, 1959; Slifer 1961) admitted only two types, differing substantially in their internal structure and properties. Riegert (1960) recognised three types with different basal articulation (fig. 97, A, B, C), but here Slifer's views will be adhered to.

Long, thick-walled basiconic sensillum (fig. 104, A). This has thick cuticular walls, and its lumen, which contains a branched nerve bathed in fluid, is open at the tip, so that the nerve is in contact with the air. Sensilla of this type are found on all parts of the body, including all segments of the antennae, which makes an experimental proof of their function very difficult.

Short, thin-walled basiconic sensillum (fig. 104, B). This has very thin cuticle and its surface is impermeable to water and dyes, but it has a permeable spot near the base.

The coeloconic sensillum (fig. 104, C) is similar to the basiconic, but its peg is very short and placed at the bottom of a pit which Hauser (1880) has erroneously shown as covered by a membrane. The peg is permeable at the tip, but since it does not project outside the cavity which is filled by air, it was thought that this type cannot possibly act as a chemoreceptor. However, when air was displaced by a mild detergent, the tip of the peg proved to be permeable to a water-soluble dye (Slifer 1955). Apart from a few occurring on other parts of the body, including ovipositor (Thomas 1965), coeloconic sensilla are essentially restricted to the antenna and, moreover, to its distal segments (table 40).

Thus, the distal segments of the antenna bear two kinds of permeable sensilla, the short basiconic and the coeloconic, and it was significant that in Slifer's (1955) experiments, normal *Melanoplus* adults were able to detect water vapour and the odours of certain foods (dandelion leaves, wheat bran) from a distance at least as great as 40 cm; but adults with the antennae amputated, although still able to find dandelion leaves, were completely insensitive to water vapour (table 41) and wheat bran.

In experiments with *Schistocerca* hoppers, Aziz (1958) found that antennaless hoppers were less able to discriminate between high and low air humidities in a chamber where two humidities were offered; his figures, however, are not very convincing. Ibrahim (1959) found that the amputation of nine apical antennal segments of *Aiolopus thalassinus* and *Sphingonotus carinatus* made the insects non-responsive to air humidity. In Riegert's (1960) experiments the removal of eight apical segments eliminated humidity responses of *Melanoplus*

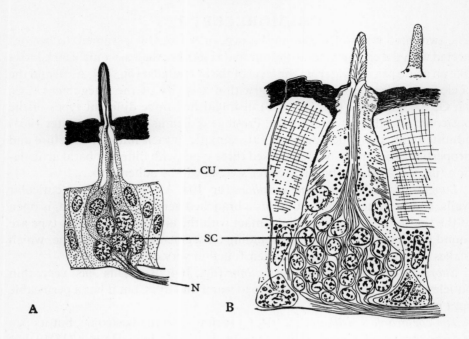

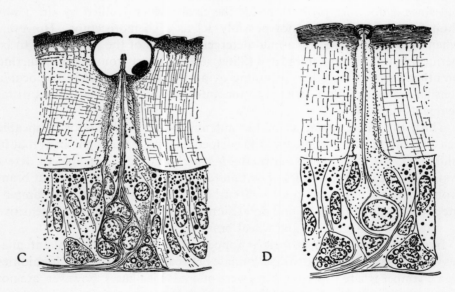

Fig. 104. *Melanoplus*, types of sensilla. A, long thin-walled basiconic; B, thick-walled
basiconic; C, coeloconic; D, campaniform (after Slifer, Prestage & Beams 1959).
CU cuticle; SC, sensory cells; N, nerve.

Table 40. *Distribution of the main types of sensilla on the antennal segments*

T = trichoid; Bl = basiconic long; Bs = basiconic short; Co = coeloconic; Ca = campaniform

Segments	Schistocerca gregaria IV hopper (Aziz 1958)					Melanoplus bivittatus adult ♀ (Riegert 1960)		Dociostaurus maroccanus adult ♀ (Jannone 1939c)		Acrida bicolor adult ♀ (Röhler 1906)		
	T	Bl	Bs	Co	Ca	Bl+Bs	Co	Co	Ca	T	Bl+Bs	Co
1 (Scape)	32	4	0	0	0	0	0	0	0	3–6	0–30	0
2 (pedicel)	16	6	0	0	22	0	0	0	35	4	0–6	0
3	0	13	0	0	0	0	0	0	0	21–28	20–24	0–19
4	0	13	0	0	0	0	2	4	0	3–4	14–16	0–4
5	0	10	0	0	0	0	3	4	0	3	16–27	0
6	0	13	0	0	0	0	0	6	0	0–1	11–12	0
7	0	10	0	0	0	0	3	0	0	0–2	17–29	0–8
8	0	15	0	2	0	3	0	7	0	0–1	15–38	0–9
9	0	14	4	2	0	11	8	14	0	0	30–132	11–87
10	0	17	5	19	0	24	4	8	0	0	26–229	37–117
11	0	21	7	1	0	44	12	26	0	0	136–213	90–159
12	0	27	16	20	0	71	11	21	0	0	205–241	102–148
13	0	30	19	7	0	62	26	25	0	0	105–183	77–161
14	0	31	31	36	0	74	29	53	0	0	117–123	40–87
15	0	33	25	26	0	87	35	34	0	0	47–79	27–57
16	0	28	25	38	0	91	29	53	0	0	47–50	25–82
17	0	26	29	36	0	85	42	31	0	0	43–49	
18	0	27	28	64	0	96	37	55	0			
19	0	22	27	38	0	80	37	29	0			
20	0	17	17	38	0	80	36	29	0			
21	0	10	14	28	0	76	40	32	0			
22	0	19	9	23	0	58	23	26	0			
23	0	36	16	38	0	32	23	33	0			
24	0					46	14	13	0			
25	0						21					
26	0											

bivittatus. On the whole, it is possible to suggest that the antenna as a whole (and particularly its distal half) may be the seat of hygroreceptors, but there is no definite evidence whether the coeloconic or the short, thin-walled basiconic, or the hair sensilla, or all of them, are concerned; since they occur on the antennal segments together, it will be difficult to obtain separate experimental evidence of their respective functions by the amputation method and the only hope is for electric recording from a single sensillum, if such were possible.

Table 40 provides some information on the variation in the sensory antennal equipment between species, sexes and instars.

Table 41. *Number of times water was found within one hour by* Melanoplus *deprived of food and water for* 24 *hours. In each experiment* 10 *normal and* 10 *antenna-less grasshoppers were used (Slifer* 1955)

Experiment No.	Sex	Normal	Antenna-less
1	♀	20	2
2	♀	17	0
3	♀	8	2
4	♀	20	5
5	♀	16	3
6	♂	23	3
7	♂	6	0
8	♂	15	5
9	♂	22	2
10	♂	8	2
	Total visits	155	24

As regards species, the highly specialised ensiform antenna of *Acrida* is remarkable for the very high number of both basiconic and coeloconic sensilla, as compared with other species possessing simple filiform antennae. It is also of interest that in *Acrida* the number of sensilla on the antennal surface facing downwards and outwards is twice that on the inward surface (Röhler 1906).

There is also a very marked sexual difference in *Acrida* in which Röhler recorded total of 1692–2046 basiconic and 2030–2190 coeloconic sensilla per antenna in males, and 920–1410 basiconic and 1217–1292 coeloconic sensilla in females; since the female antenna has a larger surface, the density of sensilla in the male is also distinctly greater than in the female. No such striking sexual difference was found by Riegert (1960) in *Melanoplus bivittatus*, which has simple antennae.

A gradual increase in the number of sensilla in hopper instars would be expected as a result of the increase in the number of segments (p. 276). In *Melanoplus bivittatus*, the number of the basiconic sensilla rose from 207 per antenna in the first instar to 725 in the fifth, and of the coeloconic from 115 to 455 (Riegert, *t.c.*).

Tarsal sensilla, apparently of coeloconic (or possibly campaniform) type, have been reported by Slifer (1950 a) on the tarsal pulvilli of *Melanoplus differentialis*, where they appear appropriately placed for chemical perception but neither their structure nor function has been studied. The possibility of some chemoreceptors occurring on legs, however, has found support in Slifer's (1954 d, 1956) experiments, in which *Romalea* responded to strong smelling substances (oils of camphor, eucalyptus, bergamot, thyme, etc.) kept at a few millimetres from a leg, by slowly lifting the leg. The response was strongest with the legs intact; and there was some indication that amputation of the tarsus lowered the sensitivity, although some sensitivity remained even if the whole leg, except the basal half of the femur, was amputated.

SENSILLA OF UNKNOWN FUNCTION

Jannone (1939 b) described the disposition in *Dociostaurus* of several groups of special sensilla inside the preoral cavity, particularly on the epipharyngeal surfaces of the labrum and clypeus, which he called *placoid* sensilla but for which he provided no detailed description; their position suggests that they may be gustatory. The same author recorded a row of minute 'placoid' sensilla near the tip of the penis valves, and some undefined 'circular' sensilla on the epiphallic membrane.

On the internal surface of a small basal apodeme of the lower ovipositor valves of *Dociostaurus* Jannone observed a characteristic group of about forty sensory spinules, with long canals arising from their bases. Agarwala (1952) also noted them in *Locusta* and Thomas (1965) in *Schistocerca*, but neither author provided any structural details; their position suggests that these sensilla may be connected with the perception of soil condition during oviposition.

There is, obviously, a great variety of sensilla and sense organs and even their structure is very inadequately known. Slifer (1961) stressed the need for electron microscope studies and one can only support her statement that 'as knowledge of the structural details of insect sense organs increases, it should be possible to plan in a more rational manner experiments intended to discover their function'.

SOUND PRODUCTION AND HEARING

Aristotle may have been the first naturalist to mention stridulation of grass-hoppers. More recent studies of their sound-producing mechanisms are numerous, but they deal mainly with European and North American species, which offer only a limited range of such mechanisms, while their surprisingly great variety in the families occurring outside these two continents remains largely unstudied. A comprehensive review of all mechanisms would be out of place here, and only the main types will be surveyed (for fuller, but still incomplete data see Kevan 1955; Jacobs 1953; Faber 1929, 1932, 1936, 1953; review and bibliography by Frings & Frings 1958, 1960; Busnel 1963).

The best studied mechanisms result in the type of sound called stridulation, but there are other sounds produced by some grasshoppers which are certainly not stridulatory, although often called so.

STRIDULATORY MECHANISMS

A stridulatory mechanism consists of two component parts; a *file* consisting of a series of tubercles, or articulated pegs, on one part of the anatomy and a *scraper*, which is a hard ridge on another part, friction between the two resulting in vibration of the integument. These pairs of components are found on different parts of the legs, tegmina and abdomen which are subject to friction produced by their relative movements.

The femoro-tegminal mechanism (fig. 105), which is the most specialised and best studied, is often regarded as typical of Acridoidea, although in fact it is restricted to three subfamilies (Gomphocerinae, Truxalinae and Eremogryllinae). The file is a raised ridge on the inner surface of the hind femur bearing a series of articulated *stridulatory pegs*; the scraper is a vein of the tegmen raised into a sharp edge. The up-and-down movement of the femur held close to the body causes the pegs to strike against the scraper vein and results in vibration of the tegmen. The resultant sound is often amplified by tympanate areas of the tegmen, that is, expanded areas between some veins which may be thickened (as in fig. 106). When the tegmina are closed in a stridulating grasshopper, the space between the opposing tegmina forms a resonating chamber (Faber 1932). In some species, the median area of the hindwing, which forms the outermost portion of a folded wing, is also expanded and, possibly, increases the resonating power of the chamber. This latter specialisation is not confined to any taxonomic group and is found, for example, amongst the species of the genus *Stenobothrus* only in *S. eurasius* and allied species, in the N. American *Orphulella*, S. American *Clinocephalus* and *Dichromorpha*, and so on.

The file varies considerably in its length relative to the femur, extending over almost two-thirds of the latter in some genera (*Stenobothrus, Chorthippus, Mesopsis*), half of it in others (*Mermiria, Dociostaurus*), and sometimes even

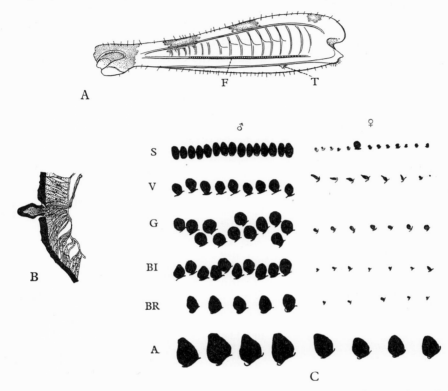

Fig. 105. Femoro-tegminal stridulatory mechanism. A, *Dociostaurus*, inner surface of hind femur; B, ditto, a stridulatory peg (Jannone 1939 *b*); C, arrangement of stridulatory pegs in several grasshopper species (Jacobs 1953).

F, stridulatory file; T, Brunner's organ; S, *Stenobothrus lineatus*; V, *Omocestus ventralis*; G, *Gomphocerus sibiricus*; BI, *Chorthippus biguttulus*; BR, *Chorthippus brunneus*; A, *Arcyptera fusca*.

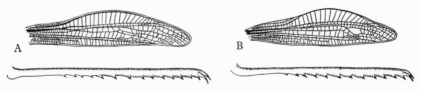

Fig. 106. Tibio-tegminal stridulatory mechanism of A, *Brachycrotaphus tryxalicera*; B, *B. sjöstedti* (Uvarov 1932).

less (*Orphulella*). The size, number and density of pegs also vary according to genera and species (fig. 105, C; table 42); such differences sometimes provide excellent specific characters, for example between three closely allied species of *Chorthippus* (Perdeck 1958). Individual variation in the number of pegs may be considerable, and although their number in females is nearly the same as in males of the same species, their density is always much less in females which are larger. The density, however, varies also within the file, the pegs being usually more closely placed in the basal part than in the distal. Only scanty data are available on possible geographical variation; the numbers of pegs in *Stauroderus scalaris* and *Chorthippus apricarius* from Kazakhstan (Marikovskiĭ 1955) proved to be within the range for the German representatives of these

Table 42. *Numbers of stridulatory pegs in some European grasshoppers (from Jacobs 1953)*

(F = length of femur in mm;   R = length of stridulatory file in mm;
N = total number of pegs; D = number of pegs per mm, or mean density)

Species and sex	F	R	N	D
Chrysochraon dispar ♂	10·2–12·2	3·4– 5·3	87–128	24·9
„ „ ♀	14·5–15·6	5·2– 6·5	94–132	18·9
Stenobothrus lineatus ♂	9·9–11·9	4·3– 7·3	302–453	58·7
„ ♀	12·5–15·3	7·3– 8·9	328–397	43·7
„ *stigmaticus* ♂	7·4– 9·0	2·3– 3·2	87–118	35·8
„ „ ♀	8·7–10·9	2·7– 3·9	84–108	28·5
„ *nigromaculatus* ♂	9·1–11·0	4·0– 5·4	146–185	33·9
„ „ ♀	12·3–14·3	6·0– 6·7	137–163	24·7
Omocestus viridulus ♂	9·5–10·9	3·6– 4·9	108–138	29·2
„ „ ♀	12·4–13·7	4·8– 6·4	93–132	21·2
„ *ventralis* ♂	8·2– 9·6	3·3– 4·1	98–127	31·7
„ „ ♀	10·9–12·9	4·1– 5·4	96–120	24·0
Chorthippus vagans ♂	8·3–10·8	3·4– 4·1	120–173	39·0
„ „ ♀	10·7–12·4	4·5– 5·2	126–155	28·3
„ *biguttulus* ♂	8·0– 9·3	2·7– 3·9	81–122	30·3
„ „ ♀	9·7–11·9	3·2– 4·5	79–115	24·3
„ *brunneus* ♂	8·6–10·8	2·1– 3·4	49– 86	21·7
„ „ ♀	11·4–13·4	3·2– 4·2	42– 58	15·1
„ *mollis* ♂	7·5– 9·2	2·9– 3·7	104–131	35·2
„ „ ♀	9·5–11·8	3·4– 4·7	85–116	28·1
Gomphocerus sibiricus ♂	10·5–11·5	4·9– 6·2	134–188	29·7
„ „ ♀	10·7–12·8	5·1– 6·3	124–180	25·1
Gomphocerippus rufus ♂	8·9–10·4	3·2– 4·7	144–236	50·1
„ „ ♀	11·5–12·9	4·2– 5·2	134–194	35·2
Arcyptera fusca ♂	15·3–16·8	6·2– 8·2	87–115	12·9
„ „ ♀	18·0–21·0	7·7–10·2	89–109	10·8
Pararcyptera microptera ♂	12·4–13·8	3·2– 3·4	50– 56	16·1
„ „ ♀	15·6–16·9	3·6– 4·5	52– 59	13·6

species (Jacobs 1953; Faber 1953), but British specimens of *Stenobothrus lineatus* were found to differ from the continental ones in having much higher density of pegs, although their numbers did not differ significantly; moreover, French females had better developed pegs, while in the British females the pegs were hair-like (Roscow 1961, 1963).

The finer structure of the pegs is insufficiently studied. Old descriptions (Landois 1867; Graber 1871; Petrunkewitch & Guaita 1901) made it clear that a peg is inserted into the ridge with a ring-like articulation and is presumably somewhat movable. Illustrations by these early authors show also some fibres at the bases of pegs, which look like either nerves or muscles and Jannone (1939*b*) gave a clear figure of a peg of *Dociostaurus*, showing that it has nerve cells and a nerve (fig. 105, B). Pegs, therefore, are not mere projections of integument but specialised trichoid sensilla (p. 161). This is supported by their development from hairs in hoppers, though in females some hairs fail to transform into pegs even in the adult (Jacobs 1953). Roscow (1963) observed that in the male of *Stenobothrus lineatus* there is a sudden increase in the size of pegs at the last moult (p. 296; fig. 175).

The femoral file in Truxalinae consists of a series of rigid tubercles which strike the tegminal scraper during stridulation. Each tubercle bears, on its lower surface, a long and stiff bristle which is articulated and is, presumably, a modified hair sensillum (fig. 243); this arrangement is sufficiently different from that in Gomphocerinae to be regarded as a subfamily character (p. 417). In either case, however, it may be suggested that the articulated peg, or bristle, is deflected on impact with the scraper and a stimulus is transmitted by its nerves to the central nervous system; this may well play a part in controlling the rhythm of stridulatory leg movements.

The scraper is normally the radial vein (R) of the tegmen, which is perceptibly compressed and is raised into an acute edge, but there are exceptions. Thus, in *Syrbula*, both the cubitus and the radius, and in *Peruvia* only the cubitus are raised.

The femoro-tegminal mechanism is found in all members of Gomphocerinae, providing the best character by which members of this subfamily can be distinguished from those of Acridinae, which otherwise very closely resemble them. The same mechanism occurs elsewhere only in Eremogryllinae, a small subfamily of desert grasshoppers; its modification in Truxalinae is described above. A very exceptional case is offered by two closely allied South American species of Catantopinae, *Atrachelacris unicolor* and *Leiotettix viridis*, in which the males have definite stridulatory pegs, which are, however, very irregularly spaced and do not form a series; the scraper veins of the tegmina are the costal, but they are very weakly raised. Other species of these and related genera have no traces of pegs, or of any other stridulatory mechanisms, and it can only be suggested that this is a case of rudimentary convergent development.

The *tibio-tegminal mechanisms* are less uniform than the femoro-tegminal. One type is found in the subfamily Hemiacridinae, members of which are characterised by having a series of regular, parallel, thickened transverse veinlets between the radius and the media (radial area) of the tegmina (p. 407; fig. 231); these veinlets are, presumably, rubbed by either the inner spines or the spurs of the hind tibia which have striations and sharp edges, but direct observations on the action are lacking.

A modification of this type is found in the Oedipodine genera *Heteropternis* of tropical Africa and Asia, and the Australian *Chortoicetes*, in both of which the medial area of the tegmen is filled with dense, thick oblique veinlets which are probably rubbed by the tibial spurs; the intercalate vein is also serrate.

Another type consists of highly modified, expanded and ridged inner spines of the hind tibia (fig. 106), rubbing against the usual scraper vein of the tegmen (p. 179). It is remarkable that this type occurs in several genera of African and Asian savannas in addition to the usual femoro-tegminal mechanism, stridulatory pegs being also very well developed in these genera which thus possess two kinds of file and one type of scraper; they also have well developed tympanate areas of the tegmina.

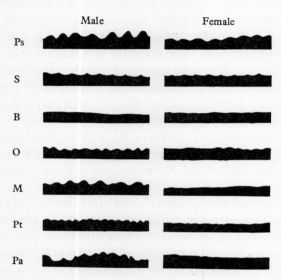

Fig. 107. Tegmino-femoral stridulatory mechanism. Profiles of the intercalate vein forming the file (Jacobs 1953).

Ps, *Psophus stridulus*; S, *Sphingonotus caerulans*; B, *Bryodema tuberculata*; O, *Oedipoda caerulescens*; M, *Mecostethus grossus*; Pt, *Paracinema tricolor*; Pa, *Parapleurus alliaceus*.

Still another type is found in the subfamily Porthetinae of Pamphagidae, for which it is characteristic. It consists of a close series of strongly-raised oblique veinlets in the costal area of the tegmen (p. 398; fig. 219); the counterpart is presented by modified hind tibial spurs (E. D. Burtt 1946).

A primitive type of tibio-tegminal stridulation is found in *Nomadacris* (Golding 1934; Laub-Drost 1960), in which the male during copulation holds the almost folded hind legs vertically and strikes the tegmina with the spines (or possibly spurs) of the tibiae; there are no obvious morphological specialisations on either part of the mechanism, but a distinct sound is produced.

Another common mechanism is the *tegmino-femoral*. In it, the friction is (as in the femoro-tegminal type) between the hind femur and the tegmen, but their roles are interchanged; the femur has a simple acute scraper ridge which rubs against a specialised intercalate vein bearing a series of non-articulate knobs, or tubercles (fig. 107). This file is formed not by a regular vein, but by an intercalate one in the medial area, which is normally absent in species with a femoro-tegminal mechanism. The serration of the file varies considerably, and sometimes it occurs also on portions of other closely adjoining veins. This mechanism is typical of the Oedipodinae, and is the only character separating them from Acridinae; the serration of the file in some Oedipodinae is very weak and there are transitional genera between the two groups; it is, however, still a convenient dividing feature. The tegmina in grasshoppers with this mechanism normally have no tympanate areas; on the other hand, in a number

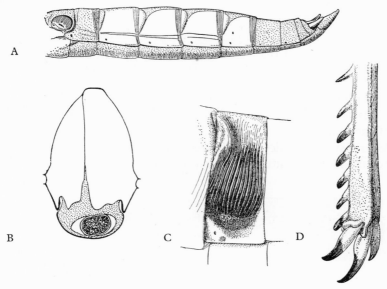

Fig. 108. A, *Phonogaster cariniventris*, abdomen with longitudinal ridges; B, its transverse section showing large air-sacs. C and D, *Charora pentagrammica*, abdominal tergite with ridges and hind tibia with modified spines (Henry 1942).

of genera there is an additional specialisation of the hindwings for producing flight noises (p. 183).

An extremely aberrant *femoro-abdominal* mechanism was found in an acridine, *Phonogaster cariniventris* (fig. 108, A, B), in which the hind femur has a long series of stridulatory pegs and the sides of abdominal tergites IV–V each bear a pair of sharp longitudinal ridges; these ridges are not covered by the very narrow tegmina and presumably serve as scrapers instead of the tegminal veins. In addition, the abdomen has thin integument through which very large air-sacs are visible; this arrangement, presumably, serves to increase the resonance (Henry 1942).

A somewhat similar *tibio-abdominal* mechanism is characteristic of the Egnatiinae, which have a number of oblique ridges on the sides of the abdomen and specialised spurs of the hind tibia (fig. 108, C, D).

A *tibio-alar mechanism* occurs in the group Batrachotetrigini of the family Pamphagidae, in which the hindwings have modified venation, with thick sinuate veins and tympanate areas; the middle tibia has a dentate upper edge and the sound is produced by its friction against the rapidly vibrating, slightly opened, wings (fig. 109; Pantel 1886; Uvarov 1943).

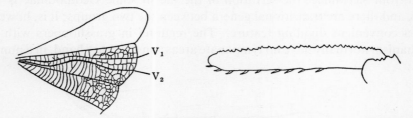

Fig. 109. Tibio-alar stridulatory mechanism of *Prionotropis flexuosa*; wing with specialised veins and tympanate areas and serrated middle tibia (Uvarov 1943).

A very peculiar *tegmino-alar mechanism* is characteristic of the predominantly tropical American subfamily Romaleinae (fig. 110). The first vannal area of the hindwing is narrow and its membrane is convex, with a series of parallel transverse veinlets which are serrate; when the wing is closed, this convex tube-like structure lies at the dorsal edge of the wing, and comes into

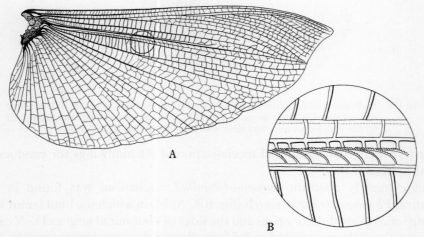

Fig. 110. Tegmino-alar stridulatory mechanism of *Colpolopha obsoleta*. A, wing; B, enlarged stridulatory veinlets (original by V. M. Dirsh).

contact with the strongly raised scraper veins on the underside of the tegmen (Dirsh 1961); rapid vibration of the closed wings results in stridulation.

A similar type of sound production in *Schistocerca, Anacridium, Locusta, Nomadacris*, etc., was found by Laub-Drost in 1953 (Faber 1953, p. 45, footnote; Faber 1957; Laub-Drost 1959, 1960) and studied by Loher (1959) in

Schistocerca. The sound is produced when the tegmina and wings are closed; a rapid (hardly visible) vibration in a horizontal direction causes friction of the overlapping bases of the tegmina, producing a stridulatory sound; the sound is produced also by the wings when both tegmina are removed (Laub-Drost, *t.c.*). The principle is the same as in Tettigoniidae and Gryllidae, but without morphological specialisation. It is possible that this type will be found more widespread if specially looked for. The sound is modified when the tegmina are slightly raised. In *Sphingonotus savignyi*, a very loud sound is produced by the resting male, with tegmina somewhat raised and both tegmina and wings vibrating rapidly (personal observations); this species has also a well developed tegmino-femoral mechanism, and is able to produce a crepitation sound in flight as well, thus possessing three different methods of sound production.

OTHER SOUND-PRODUCING MECHANISMS

All the above mechanisms are classified as stridulatory, and they result in rhythmic sounds with high frequency. Other mechanisms producing more or less occasional sounds also exist and they have also often been called stridulatory, but it is reasonable to restrict the term to those based on friction.

A fairly common method is *wing crepitation*. It occurs in species with unusually wide hindwings, with thickened main veins as well as regular crossveins (fig. 111). In flight, a rattling noise is produced (as by a fan), by the partial folding and rapid expansion of the wing. It has been suggested that the noise is due to the wings beating either against the hind legs or against the tegmina (Pierce 1948), but both views have been already disproved by amputating tegmina (Karny 1908) and hind legs (Stäger 1930); neither operation affected the noise, but crushing the thick veins of the wings suppressed the sound (Isely 1936). This type of mechanism is regularly found in some Oedipodinae (*Bryodema, Psophus, Circotettix, Dissosteria, Helioscirtus*, etc.), but also occurs in a number of entirely unrelated genera of other groups (European *Stauroderus scalaris*, African *Panzia*, Australian *Froggattia*). This type is merely an extreme specialisation for sound production, since some noise is always produced in flight even by species without any modification of wings, e.g. during the mating flight of male *Locusta* (Descamps 1961). Such *flight noise*, possibly produced by all flying species, has been studied only in *Schistocerca*, flying swarms of which, consisting of millions of individuals, can be heard at some distance. Recordings of swarm flight noise indicated that its average sound level was 61–56 decibels above the human threshold at several metres from the microphone. When a locust is not in full flight, its hind legs hang down and a different *wing-beat* noise is produced, probably by impact of wings on legs; its average level was 67·2 decibels above the human threshold at 10 cm from the insect (Haskell 1957*a*).

Another mechanism, of somewhat sporadic occurrence, is the *mandibular*.

The American *Oedaleonotus* and *Dissosteiar carolina*, Indian *Mesambria*, European *Calliptamus* and *Locusta*, as well as *Schistocerca*, *Nomadacris*, *Tylotropidius* and others, have been observed to produce clicking noises with their mandibles (Lutz 1924; Varley 1939; Henry 1942; Faber 1949; Loher 1959; Laub-Drost 1959; Alexander 1960); this was also observed in hoppers.

Some Oedipodinae produce sounds by *drumming* the posterior tarsi, abdomen, or partly opened tegmina against the ground (Faber 1936, 1953), but no morphological specialisations are involved.

A method of sound production entirely different from all described above is *hissing* which accompanies the emission of frothing liquid through some

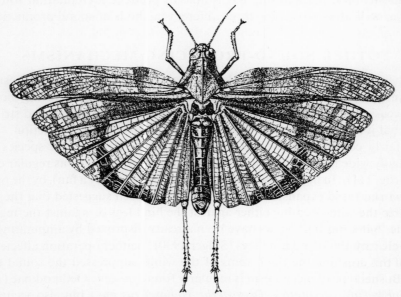

Fig. 111. *Bryodema tuberculata*, male wings, specialised for crepitation
(Faber 1936). × 1·5.

spiracles by hoppers and adults of *Taeniopoda* and *Romalea* (Duncan 1924; Rehn & Grant 1961).

The above is only a brief review of the main sound-producing mechanisms. Their diversity suggests that sound production and perception must play an important part in the life of our insects and this will be discussed in the second volume. An important general point is that most of these mechanisms are based on rhythmic or other movements originally unconnected with sound production, since they occur also in species which do not produce any sounds, as well as in hoppers (Smit & Reyneke 1940; Weih 1951). In fact, although it is generally believed that stridulation is a typical general attribute of grasshopper behaviour, this is far from being so. This belief is merely a result of the concentration of studies on grasshoppers of the temperate regions where such accomplished songsters as Gomphocerinae and Oedipodinae constitute the bulk of the fauna. Actually, the majority of the acridoid world fauna is formed by Catantopinae, Pyrgomorphidae and Acridinae, which have no sound-producing mechanisms, or only poorly defined ones, some of which have been mentioned above. It is worthy of notice that an expansion of the medial area of the hindwing, forming a tympanate area, occurs not infrequently in some Acridinae in which no specialised sound-producing organs are known, for example in *Acrida, Amphicremna, Eutryxalis* and others; *Acrida*, however, makes a distinct flight noise.

It must be stressed that insects without obvious morphological modifications are not necessarily 'dumb'. The tegmino-alar stridulation, for example, of *Schistocerca* (p. 182), is produced without any special mechanism and is not easily observed or heard, and it is possible that detailed studies of behaviour in other supposedly dumb species will lead to discoveries of some, at present unsuspected, means of production of sounds, including those at ultra-sonic frequencies, not audible to man (p. 190). Special attention should be paid to various rhythmic movements during courting and mating, when sound production serves as a means of expression and communication, as will be discussed in the second volume.

PROPERTIES AND STUDY OF SOUNDS

Early workers on this subject attempted to describe grasshopper 'songs' as heard by the human ear, either by phonetic transcription or by musical symbols, but little real progress was possible until the conceptions and the electronic technique of acoustics were applied to their study. Detailed treatment of this approach will be found in the recent books by Haskell (1961) and R. G. Busnell (1963); (see also Evans 1952; Pimonov 1955; Broughton 1955; Pasquinelly 1955; Pasquinelly & Busnel 1955; Loher & Broughton 1955; Loher 1957) and only a brief review is presented below.

A sound is a result of the vibration of a solid body producing waves in the air. The first essential property of a sound is the *frequency* of the waves which depends on the rate of vibration of the source. The human ear recognises frequency as the *pitch*, which is higher at greater frequencies. The frequency can be recorded by a cathode ray oscillograph as a number of waves, or cycles, per second. The principal frequencies of stridulation sounds produced by acridoids range from 2 to 12 kc/s but more common maximal frequencies are between 4 and 8 kc/s (Frings & Frings 1958).

Stridulation noise has a somewhat complex origin. It arises partly as a result of the rhythmical impacts of file and scraper, producing sound waves of maximum amplitude, but the tegminal veins and membranes continue to vibrate between the strokes at a lesser amplitude and at different frequencies partly caused by resonance; this sound may not be audible. An oscillogram will, accordingly, illustrate the frequency and structure of a complex of continuous sound waves, their amplitude and the frequency of *pulses* (i.e. the groups of waves arising at each stroke). Oscillograms of different songs of British grasshoppers are shown in fig. 112, and table 43 summarises their characteristics.

The second characteristic of a sound is its *intensity*, or loudness. This depends on the energy of vibration at the source and can be measured by a sound-level meter with microphone and amplifier, in decibels above the zero threshold value for the human ear (which corresponds to the pressure of

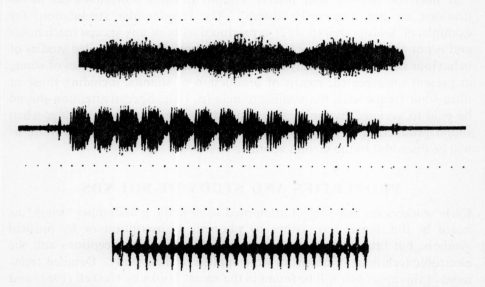

Fig. 112. Oscillograms of the calling song of the male of three species of British grass-hoppers: Bottom, *Omocestusviridulus*; top, *Stenobothrus lineatus*; middle, *Chorthippus parallelus*. Timing mark (dots) throughout $\frac{1}{10}$ sec. (From the original records by J. E. Moorhouse).

0·0002 dynes per sq. cm). Since sound energy decreases inversely as the square of the distance from the source, this distance should always be specified.

Direct study of sounds, especially in the field, is not recommended, and either a gramophone (Broughton 1952*a*, 1952*b*) or, better, a tape recorder, should be used, so that an analysis can be carried out afterwards, an additional advantage being that the record can be played at a reduced speed allowing for more detailed analysis. A special type of loudspeaker, the ionophone, permits reproduction of ultra-sonic frequencies (Klein 1955).

Since all sounds result from relative motions of body parts, some of their characteristics can be better understood by simultaneous studies of both sounds and movements. The stridulatory pegs of species with the femoro-tegminal type of sound production are usually more densely placed near the

Table 43. *Comparative song characteristics of males of British grasshoppers (after Haskell 1957b)*

	Song type	Frequency in kc/s		Pulse frequencies	Heard by human ear
		Mean spectrum	Principal		
Stenobothrus lineatus	Normal	0·4–8	4	1	Continuous warbling note
	Courtship	0·5–6	4	7	Series of repeated clicks
Omocestus viridulus	Normal	0·32–8	5	10–18	Continuous trill
	Courtship	0·4–6·4	3·2	5	Series of repeated clicks following normal song
Chorthippus brunneus	Normal	0·8–8	5	—	Single pulse at irregular intervals
	Courtship	2–6·4	4	5·8	Series of repeated clicks
Chorthippus parallelus	Normal	0·5–10	5	5	Phrases of 3–15 pulses repeated at intervals
	Courtship	—	—	5	Single pulse of sound

base than towards the apex of the femur (p. 178). The section of the file coming in contact with the scraper depends on the amplitude of the femoral movement; when it is small, only the basal, more densely placed, pegs are engaged and the frequency of tegminal vibration is greater than when sparsely

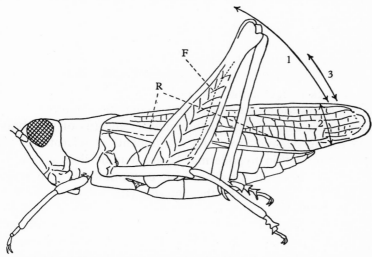

Fig. 113. *Eremogryllus hammadae*, male; stridulatory movements of hind femur (E. S. Brown 1951).
R, radial vein (scraper); F, position of the file on the inner face of the femur; 1, 2, 3, arcs of three types of femoral movement.

placed distal pegs are involved (fig. 113). Thus the frequency of the sound (i.e. its pitch) depends on the density of pegs and the angular deflexion of the femur (Faber 1929; E. S. Brown 1951; Marikovskii 1955). The rhythm and the sequence of pulses also depend on the types of femoral motions. Some of the latter are small and of high frequency which makes direct observations unreliable; therefore, synchronised recording of sounds and motions, the latter by a high-speed cine-camera, is essential, allowing subsequent analysis of their correlation at a reduced speed, but so far, no such simultaneous studies have been carried out. Indeed, although at least the most common stridulatory mechanisms have been studied and very good progress has been recently made in the study of sounds, there is an obvious gap in our knowledge of the working of the mechanisms and their control. It should be added that there are no instrumental studies of noises other than stridulation, except some records of flight noises (Pierce 1948; Haskell 1957a).

AUDITORY SENSE

The usual concept of sound is restricted to air vibration perceived through auditory organs. However, it does not appear possible to draw a line between specialised organs serving for the perception of airborne sounds and those which respond to soundless air movements and to the substrate vibration. Such unspecialised receptors are discussed separately (p. 194).

Tympanal organ

Most (but not all, see p. 190) of the acridoids have a pair of tympanal organs, one on each side of the first abdominal tergite. Detailed morphological descriptions of these organs were given by Graber (1876), Schwabe (1906), Eggers (1928), Hers (1938), Hsu, Liu & Shen (1952) and Liu Wei-Teh 1952). Viewed internally (fig. 114, A) a tympanum consists of an oval membrane framed by a thick integumental rim; in some species (e.g. *Locusta*) the membrane is sunk below the level of the tergite, so that most of it lies at the bottom of a cavity which corresponds to the auditory meatus of vertebrates. The membrane (being derived from the integument) is sclerotised, very thin, and underlaid by a thin hypodermal layer; it is in close contact with the external membrane of an air-sac, which communicates with the first abdominal spiracle lying close to the anterior edge of the tympanum. The tension of the tympanal membrane is controlled by a tensor muscle attached to a strongly sclerotised process of the rim. The surface of the membrane bears minute spinules and may be somewhat wrinkled in its lower portion. In the upper part of the membrane there is a visible thickening which corresponds to the point of attachment of the sensory mechanism on its inner surface.

The sensory mechanism (fig. 114, B) consists of a ganglion (usually called Müller's organ) innervated by a branch of a nerve of the first tergite arising from the third thoracic ganglion. To the tympanal ganglion are attached four, or less (see below), sensory elements: the *elevated process* with thick walls, the heavily sclerotised *folded body*, the *styliform body* joined apically to the membrane, and the *fusiform body* with its continuation, the *pyriform vesicle*. Inside this complex there are groups of sensilla. Recent electron microscope study of the auditory sensilla (Gray 1960) revealed their extremely complicated structure, with a hair-like cilium in the apical part of the scolopale; this type of sensilla is not yet known in other insects.

The structure of the tympanal organ is not uniform throughout the Acridoidea (Knetsch 1939). In its simplest form the membrane is on a level with the tergite surface and not at all covered by overhanging rims (fig. 115, 2); such an open tympanum is typical of Pamphagidae and Pyrgomorphidae.

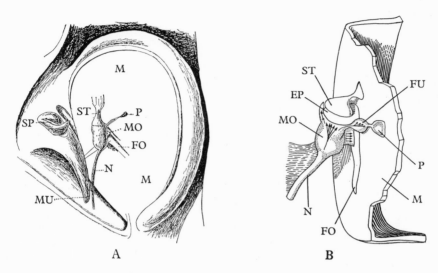

Fig. 114. A, *Mecostethus grossus*, internal view of the tympanal organ (after Schwabe 1906).
B, *Locusta*, sensory mechanism of tympanal organ (after Gray 1960).
M, membrane; MU, process to which tympanal muscle is attached; SP, spiracle; ST, styliform body; MO, ganglion (Müller's organ); EP, elevated process; FO, folded body; FU, fusiform body; P, pyriform vesicle; N, nerve; arrows, groups of sensilla.

A more specialised organ is provided by a shell-like extension of the posterior rim (fig. 115, 4–7) and also, or only, by a subtympanal lobe (fig. 115, 3); the membrane in this case is more or less deeply sunk in the tergite and lies within a cavity which sometimes has only a narrow slit to the outer air (fig. 115, 6). This arrangement must have a considerable effect on sound reception; a comparison of the hearing power of insects with the tympanal cover removed, with the normal ones, would be of interest.

The structure of the sensory elements as described above is that of the more specialised type. The Pamphagidae have a much simpler sensory complex, consisting only of the styliform body and the folded body, and in some of them (*Acinipe, Ocneridia*) only the latter can be distinguished. In Pyrgomorphidae there is also only a single, very much reduced structure (Knetsch, *t.c.*). Detailed studies of such less specialised organs might throw light on the evolution of the tympanum.

There is a considerable range of variation in the relative size of the tympanum, the ratio between vertical diameter of tympanum and length of body being from 0·1 to 0·02. As a rule the tympanum is larger and more enclosed by rims in males than in females.

The presence of a tympanum is, however, not universal. It is entirely absent in the families Lentulidae and Lathiceridae, all members of which are apterous. It tends to be reduced, or even becomes obsolete, in micropterous and brachypterous members of the groups in which it is normally well developed. This

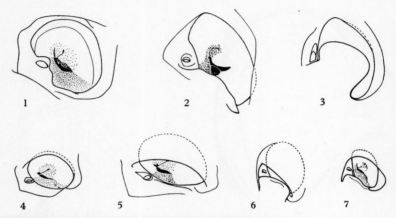

Fig. 115. External views of tympanal organs (original by J. Mason).
1, *Zoniopoda cruentata*, open membrane with a rim; 2, *Adephagus cristatus*, open membrane, without a rim; 3, *Tmethis cisti*, membrane partly covered by subtympanal lobe; 4, *Mesopsera filum*, membrane partly sunk; 5, *Sudanacris pallida*, membrane sunk and partly covered by shell-like rim; 6, *Chorthippus vagans*, membrane almost entirely covered by the rim; 7, *Chorthippus brunneus*, membrane partly covered. Covered portion of membrane shown by dotted line.

correlation between the development of wings and tympanum occurs independently in various groups. However, members of the family Trigonopterygidae, although fully winged, have no tympanum.

The tympanum as an organ of hearing

Some earlier workers attempted to investigate the sensitivity of a tympanal organ by observing the movement responses of an insect to artificial sounds. Thus Auger & Fessard (1928) found that *Anacridium aegyptium* failed to react to loud banging of wooden boards, but responded to the weak but high-pitched noise of rustling paper. By using a series of König's cylinders, reactions were observed to air vibrations of the frequencies of about 20,000 per second, which are inaudible to man. More recently, electrophysiological methods of recording impulses from the nerve of the tympanum stimulated by pure tone

Table 44. Sensitivity thresholds of tympanal organs

(All data are from nerve recordings, except those marked with † which are from reflex response of a leg. Some figures are derived from curves and are approximate. * means that no higher frequency was studied.)

Species	Total frequency range in cycles per second	Minimum stimulus intensity in decibels above human threshold	Frequency of maximum sensitivity in cycles per second	References
Arphia sulphurea	300–21,000	65	10,000	Wever 1935
Paroxya atlantica	100–15,000*	75	10,000	Wever & Vernon 1957
" " *paraoxyoides*	100–30,000	75	15,000	" " 1959
Locusta m. migratorioides	500–11,000*	20	3,000	Pumphrey & Rawdon-Smith 1936
" " "	200–50,000	40	c. 7,000	Horridge 1961
" " *manilensis*	150–40,000	80–100		M. Busnel & R. Busnel 1956
†*Nomadacris septemfasciata*	600–45,000	55	4,000–9,000	Suga 1960
†*Schistocerca gregaria*	100–17,000	80–100		M. Busnel & R. Busnel 1956
	100–17,000	90–110		
Oxya japonica " "	100–15,000*	30	15,000	Haskell 1957*a* " "
Chorthippus, Omocestus, Stenobothrus	600–30,000	50	4,000–10,000	Katsuki & Suga 1960
	100–20,000*	40	20,000	Haskell 1956*a*
Human ear	16–20,000		1,500	

sounds from an oscillator and loud-speaker have been applied; some of the results are presented in table 44 and illustrated in fig. 116. It will be seen that the tympanum responds to a very wide range of frequencies, extending well into the supersonic range, that is, beyond 20,000c/s, which is the upper threshold of human hearing. On the other hand, the human ear can hear sounds of much lower frequency than the tympanum. The maximum sensitivity of the tympanum is certainly within a much higher range than that of the human ear. As regards intensity, the tympanum is much less sensitive than the ear in the lower audio-frequency range, but approaches it at higher frequencies.

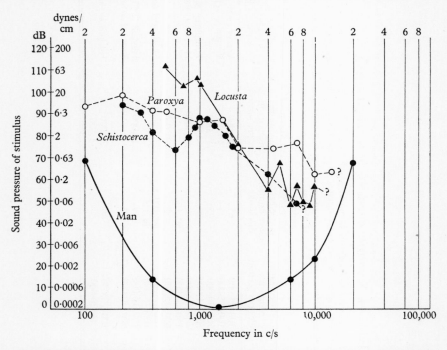

Fig. 116. Threshold intensities of tympanal organs of three acridoids, compared with that of man, for a pure tone stimulus (after Haskell 1961, modified).

The data for different species are difficult to compare, since the techniques were not the same in every case. It may be significant that such accomplished songsters as *Chorthippus* and related genera have their maximum sensitivity in a higher frequency range than the species which have no specialised sound-producing organs (e.g. *Schistocerca*, *Oxya* and *Paroxya*). Studies of various species under the same conditions and with identical techniques are obviously required.

Another important point is that reflex reactions (sudden leg movement, beating of wings) of a suspended locust are much more violent than those of one in contact with the ground (fig. 117). This means that tarsal contact inhibits the response (M. Busnel & R. Busnel 1956); nervous response of the leg probably results from the stimulation of the tympanum (Mazoué, M. Busnel & Chauchard 1957).

The question whether the tympanal organ is able to discriminate between different frequencies (i.e. to appreciate the pitch), has been a debatable one. Since a number of neurons is involved, it could be that they have a differential ability to distinguish frequencies (Horridge 1961), and Suga (1960), who at first came to an opposite conclusion, later considered this possible (Suga & Katsuki 1961).

A biologically important property of hearing organs is their directional sensitivity, that is, the ability to appreciate the direction from which sound vibrations reach them. This has been investigated in *Locusta* by Pumphrey (1940) and, in more detail, by Katsuki & Suga (1960) and by Autrum,

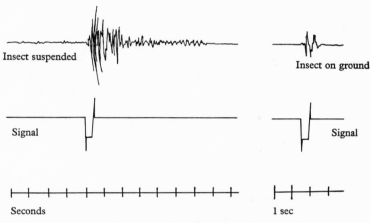

Fig. 117. *Locusta*, movement reactions of an adult, suspended or on the ground, to a sound signal (after M. & R. Busnel 1956).

Schwartzkopff & Swoboda (1961). The results (fig. 118) indicated that the sensitivity thresholds were highest when sounds came parallel to the locust's body and lowest for sounds coming perpendicularly to its sides. Moreover, if sounds were coming from the right, the tympanum on that side was more sensitive than that on the left, and the difference between the two was greater at higher frequencies. This should provide a mechanism for appreciating the direction from which the sound is coming, and it is likely to be particularly effective in the supersonic range.

The next important property of tympanal organs is their ability to recognise the rate of pulse repetition of sounds, even when the pulses are very close. Thus, *Stenobothrus lineatus* recognises pulses of 90 per second (Haskell 1961) and *Locusta* even 300 per second (Pumphrey & Rawdon-Smith 1939), but to the human ear such sounds would appear continuous.

This brief discussion of the tympanum is restricted to its function as an organ of hearing. However, although the tympanal organ is undoubtedly best developed in the most accomplished songsters, it is also present in the far more numerous members of the Pyrgomorphidae, Catantopinae, Calliptaminae, and others which are dumb or produce only somewhat indefinite occasional sounds. On the other hand, its tendency to degenerate parallel with the loss of flying ability (p. 190) suggests some function related to flight, such as echolocation which may help a flying insect to avoid obstacles as is known in night-flying moths. This finds further support in the fact that a

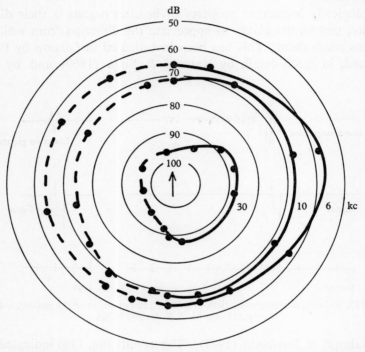

Fig. 118. *Locusta*, directional sensitivity of tympanal organ (after Katsuki & Suga 1960, modified).
  The circles represent sound intensities in decibels; solid curves—the thresholds of the right tympanum; broken curves—those of the left; position of the locust shown by the arrow; sound comes from the right; kc, kilocycles.

locust suspended in the air responds to acoustic signals much more violently than when its tarsi are in contact with the ground (p. 192), but there is no direct evidence yet that this is due to a change in the sensitivity of the tympanal organ.

Other organs of hearing

Long trichoid sensilla on the cerci, abdominal segments and sternum of *Locusta*, *Chorthippus*, *Omocestus* and *Stenobothrus* respond alike to gross air movements and to pure tone sounds of a frequency up to 300 c/s (Haskell 1956a,

1956*b*). The effective range of cercal hair sensilla in *Locusta* was 4–1700 c/s and in *Oxya japonica* 400–500 c/s (Katsuki & Suga 1960); in the latter species the response was only to sounds of great intensity (between 80–90 decibels above human threshold). Movement reactions of live locusts without abdomen to pure tone sounds of 5000 c/s and 100 decibels have been observed (M. Busnel & R. Busnel 1956; M. Busnel & Burkhardt 1962); this suggests that the reception of sounds is not restricted to the tympanum, and hair sensilla may also be responsible. Such sensilla on the ventral surface of the abdomen are capable of recording vibrations of the substrate (Haskell 1956*a*). Busnel & Burkhardt (*t.c.*) suggested that 'there exist receptors not yet described as such, or that the central nervous system could be stimulated directly, without peripheral receptors'.

The great variety and complexity of sound-producing and hearing organs is evidence of the great importance of sound in the biology of acridoids. Moreover, the production of sounds is the result of special movements which are only a part of behaviour. There is also much evidence on the reception of sounds from the behaviour responses to them, and the whole subject will be more fully discussed as an aspect of behaviour in the appropriate chapter of the next volume.

EYES AND VISION

The organs of vision are the compound eyes (Jörshke 1914), which are always present, and the ocelli, which may be absent. Apart from these, there is no evidence of any sensitivity to light that might be attributed to some unknown integumental sensilla (Medioni 1961).

COMPOUND EYES

Structure

Compound eyes are never absent in acridoids, but they vary in shape and in size. Generally speaking, species living on plants have relatively large elliptical eyes (fig. 2, M, AC), while in the ground-living ones, the eyes are smaller and approximately round (fig. 2, O).

Each eye consists of numerous *ommatidia* marked on the surface by hexagonal *facets*. The number of ommatidia and their dimensions are known only for *Schistocerca* (Bernard 1937), in which the number increases from 2470 in the Ist instar hopper to 9400 in the adult male; their size also increases (table 45). There are also differences between the sizes of ommatidia in different regions of the eye, but they have not been studied yet. A comparative study of ommatidial numbers and sizes in relation to taxonomy and habits should be of interest.

An ommatidium (fig. 119) ends distally in the colourless *cornea* which consists of a thinner outer, non-laminated cuticular layer, and a thicker inner, laminated one, the whole forming a bi-convex lens (Roonwal 1947*a*).

Table 45. *The growth changes in the compound eye of* Schistocerca *male; measurements in* μ *(Bernard 1937)*

	Hopper instars					Adult	Mean rate of increase
	I	II	III	IV	V		
Facet number	2470	3850	4675	6480	7685	9400	3·8
,, diameter	15·5–20	13·5–22·6	16–25·5	20–30·5	18·5–39	25·5–29·5	1·7–2·0
Retinula, basal diameter	6·5	5·5	8·5	9	5·8	6·5	1·7
Retinula, distal diameter	13	15	16	18	16·5	21·5	1·7
Retinula, height	114	154	201	306	405	456	4·0
Crystalline cone, height	30·5	40·5	53·5	72	98	115	3·7
Crystalline cone, diameter	10	13·5	19	23·5	19	20	2·0
Ommatidia, height	164	218	290	426	570	650	3·9

A few small hair sensilla are found on the cornea of *Anacridium* and *Callip-tamus* (Jörschke 1914; Friza 1929) but not on that of *Schistocerca* (Roonwal, *t.c.*). Under the cornea lies the distal end of a transparent *crystalline cone*,

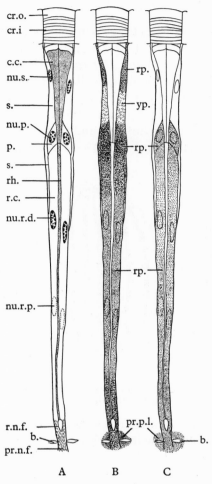

A   B   C

Fig. 119. *Schistocerca*, ommatidia of Vth instar hoppers. A, diagram of a bleached ommatidium; B, ommatidium of a gregarious hopper, showing distribution of pigment; C, ommatidium of a solitarious hopper, section through the interstripe (after Roonwal 1947 *a*).

cr.o., outer layer of cornea; cr.i, inner layer; c.c., crystalline cone; s., secondary pigment cells; nu.s., their nuclei; p., primary pigment cells; nu.p., their nuclei; rh., rhabdom; r.c., visual cells; nu.r.d., distal nuclei of visual cells; nu.r.p., their proximal nuclei; r.n.f., retinular nerve fibres; pr.n.f., post-retinular nerve fibres; b., basement membrane; rp., reddish-brown pigment; yp., yellow pigment; pr.p.1., post-retinular pigment layer.

which is surrounded by a sheath of pigment cells and extends inwards as a very long *rhabdom*; rhabdoms, together with the enveloping visual cells, form the *retinula* (for its fine structure see Fernandez-Moran 1958).

The visual nervous cells continue as fibres entering the optic lobe of the brain. Further nervous paths within the brain and leading from it to the central nerve cord are too complicated to be described here; it is to be noted that in *Locusta* some fibres cross over to the other side (Satija 1957, 1958; Burtt & Catton 1959*a*).

A noticeable external feature of the eyes in some genera is their pattern which often consists of parallel vertical dark stripes, for example in *Schistocerca* (fig. 120), *Calliptamus, Anacridium, Heteracris, Acrida* and others; in some Pyrgomorphidae, stripes are circular, while in *Oedipoda* and *Sphingonotus* they are replaced by round spots (Friza 1929; Volkonsky 1938*c*; Rao & Gupta 1939; Roonwal 1947*a*; Agrawal 1955). In the genus *Melanoplus* a variety of eye patterns occurs in hoppers and they may be used for differentiating between species (Handford 1946). In *Schistocerca*, stripes are well

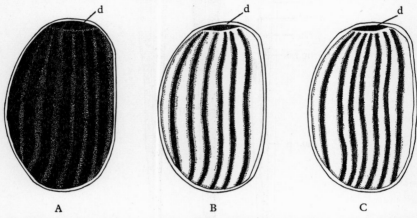

Fig. 120. *Schistocerca*, compound eyes. A, gregarious phase; B, solitarious phase, 6-striped form; C, ditto, 7-striped form; d, dorsal spot (after Roonwal 1947*a*).

separated by light-coloured interstripes, but only in the solitarious phase, while in the gregarious phase the interstripes are invaded by dark pigment and the pattern becomes obliterated. The number of stripes in this and other species is correlated with the number of hopper instars (p. 278). The striped pattern is due to the pigment cells in some groups of ommatidia being heavily loaded with dark-brown pigment, while in the alternating groups the cells contain only greyish-yellow pigment.

In addition to such patterns, each eye has a distinct *dorsal spot* (fig. 120), a uniformly coloured area at the upper end of the eye, separated from the rest by a pale line; this is the growth area of the eye during hopper development.

PHYSIOLOGY OF VISION

Electro-physiological work on vision should be an obvious basis for eventual understanding of those aspects of visual perception that have a bearing on behaviour, but it is still in its early stages. A dark-adapted eye of *Melanoplus* responds to brief flashes of light by a simple electroretinogram wave, consisting of a rapidly rising limb and a slowly descending one; a light-adapted eye responds by a wave of two distinct phases (Hartline 1928; Jahn & Crescitelli 1938, 1940; Jahn & Wulff 1942b; Taylor & Crescitelli 1944; E. T. Burtt & Catton 1956). In addition to these retinal responses, oscillatory electrical after-discharges occur under constant illumination; these are regarded as originating in the optic ganglion (Crescitelli & Jahn 1939a, 1942; Roeder 1939, 1940; Jahn & Wulff 1942b). The magnitude of the retinal response varies with temperature (Jahn & Wulff 1942a), oscillations occurring mainly in the range of 27–42°C (Crescitelli & Jahn 1939b). The response is affected by the intensity of light, but not by its wave-length, the effect of coloured lights depending only on their relative intensities (Crescitelli & Jahn 1939a; Weiss 1944). Some differences in response between species of grasshoppers were observed (Hartline 1928; Jahn & Wulff 1942a, 1942b; Taylor & Crescitelli 1944). Further investigations, concerned with the neurophysiology theory of vision (Wulff & Jahn 1947, 1948; Wulff, Fry & Linde 1955; Burtt & Catton 1954–1962c), cannot be discussed in detail here; conclusions from them are still largely theoretical.

Eye pigments which are likely to participate in photo-chemical reactions connected with electrical responses are very imperfectly known. The dark pigment is insectorubin (Goodwin & Srisukh 1950; Goodwin 1952a), belonging to the group of ommochrome pigments (p. 44) which change their colour on oxidation and reduction (Becker 1942; Butenandt, Biekert & Linzen 1958). In the eyes of *Locusta* and *Schistocerca*, β-carotene, astaxanthin (Goodwin & Srisukh 1950) and yellow pterin (Busnel & Drilhon 1942; Goodwin & Srisukh 1951b; Goodwin 1952a) were also found. All work on eye pigments was carried out in extracts from the whole eye, and no information exists on their distribution within the eye, which should be studied micro-chemically. In particular it would be essential to know whether morphologically stable dark regions of striped or spotted eyes and the diffused dark coloration are due to the same pigments.

Visual perception

Sensitivity to *intensity of illumination* undoubtedly exists, but it has been little studied. Flashes of light of different intensity produced distinguishable electrical responses in the retina of *Melanoplus femur-rubrum* (Hartline 1928). Some indication of the ability of *Locusta* to respond to changes in the intensity of light was given by Burtt & Catton (unpublished), who recorded responses from the ventral nerve cord and from the optic lobe to minimum changes of 8–20%, whereas the human eye detects changes of 0·6%. There is no doubt that there is an adaptation to continuous light or darkness (Crescitelli & Jahn 1939a; Taylor & Crescitelli 1944), but no evidence has been obtained of a regular diurnal rhythm in the responses of *Melanoplus differentialis*. However, no attention has been paid, so far, to the species in which diurnal movements of pigment in the ommatidia occur, as, for example, in *Chorthippus* (Stefanowska 1890; see p. 57) and *Dissosteira* (Fernandez-Moran 1958); a remark by the latter author that such pigment movements occur also in *Schistocerca* appears to be based on a misinterpretation of a statement by Wigglesworth (1953) who merely drew a parallel between moths where such

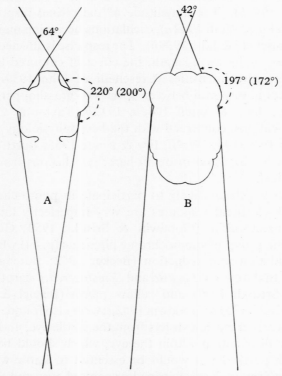

Fig. 121. *Schistocerca*, fields of vision of Vth instar hopper. A, in the horizontal plane; B, in the vertical plane (after Whittington 1951).

movements are known to occur and *Schistocerca* in which two colour types of the eye are known (p. 198), but did not mention pigment movements

Related to this problem is that of pigmented eye-stripes (p. 198). In the gregarious *Schistocerca* which is mainly diurnal the eye appears uniformly coloured, while it is striped in the solitarious phase of the same species which is particularly active at night, so that some connection may be expected between the eye pattern and visual sensitivity. The importance of eye stripes for vision has been discussed only theoretically (Friza 1929; Roonwal 1947a; Chauvin 1941b), the assumption being that dark stripes serve to isolate groups of ommatidia, thus shielding them from obliquely falling light; the result might be a brighter image than that formed in a uniformly coloured eye. Electro-physiological investigation is obviously needed.

A point of importance in the behaviour is the *field of vision* in various directions. This has been estimated for the Vth instar *Schistocerca* hoppers by Whittington (1951), as illustrated in fig. 121. Cornwell (1955) produced similar estimates for adult *Locusta*. In these two species the field of vision is very extensive, but it can be expected to vary in other species, with eyes of different relative size and shape.

Visual acuity (or resolving power) is the ability to see two contours as discrete. It is usually assumed that each ommatidium receives an impression of a light point separately, and the visual acuity depends on the number of

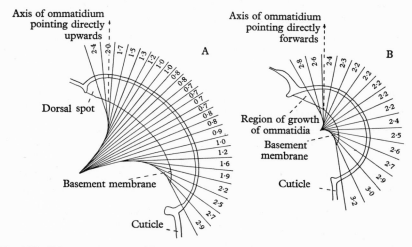

Fig. 122. *Schistocerca*, ommatidial angles of Vth instar hopper. A, vertical section; B, horizontal section (after Whittington 1951).

ommatidia and, particularly, on the angle between the ommatidial axes. The smaller that angle, the less light enters each facet and the image is less luminous, but sharper. Ommatidial angles in the *Schistocerca* hopper (fig. 122) vary from 0·7 to 3·2°, according to the position of facets on the eye and the plane of section. This means that the visual acuity in different directions may not be the same. In *Locusta* (Burtt & Catton 1954) the mean ommatidial angle in the vertical plane was determined as about 1°, but in the horizontal plane it averaged 2·4°. The angular thresholds for perception of movement of a bright light point determined by these authors are presented in table 46.

Later work by Burtt & Catton (1956, 1960 *b*, 1961 *a*, 1961 *b*, 1962 *a*) led these authors to question the assumption that each ommatidium receives light individually. Electrical responses from the optic lobe of *Locusta* to the angular movements of a light point as small as 0·1–0·3° were observed and they suggested that this was due to an extensive overlapping of the fields of adjoining ommatidia, which lowers the threshold of movement perception and increases the acuity of vision. Rainey (1958) concluded from this that an adult locust would fall within a 0·1° angle of vision of another locust at a distance of about thirty metres, but this does not necessarily imply that a locust would perceive a movement by another at this distance, since the angle value was obtained from responses to a stimulus of very high intensity (a tungsten-filament lamp at 0·5–1 metre from the eye).

While the available neurophysiological evidence on this point is inadequate, it nevertheless provides a basis for understanding the principle of the *perception of movement* (Burtt & Catton 1954). That the eyes are very sensitive to moving objects is well known to any collector of grasshoppers; they may be approached quite closely if one moves extremely slowly, but are disturbed by a brisk movement at a greater distance. The importance of movement perception is particularly great with regard to the co-ordination of behaviour in marching locust hoppers and in flying swarms and to the scanning movements of individuals (see below).

Table 46. *Acuity of movement perception in* Locusta *in relation to ommatidial angles, both in degrees of arc* (*Burtt & Catton* 1954)

	Vertical movement				Mean	Horizontal movement					Mean
Ommatidial angle	1·15	1·15	1·03	1·03	1·09	2·5	2·5	1·97	2·47	2·47	2·4
Movement threshold	0·22	0·16	0·33	0·38	0·27	0·32	0·45	0·32	0·25	0·16	0·30

Form perception by gregarious hoppers of *Schistocerca* has been studied by Wallace (1958, 1959; see also Burtt & Catton 1962a, 1962b), with results of considerable interest. He presented hoppers, released in a circular arena of two feet diameter, with pairs of black cards of different shapes and observed the numbers attracted to each shape. Figure 123 shows the results graphically. In A the preference was for a taller figure, and B and D suggest that this was not due to the difference in the size; this was confirmed by E and F, where the two figures were of the same area, but the taller one was preferred. Experiment C suggested that the important factor was the number of white-black vertical edges, and in G, where the whole circumference of the arena was half-black and half-white, the preference for the vertical edge was clear. Experiment H indicated a preference for a vertical edge as against an oblique one, while in I, J and K a straight vertical edge was chosen in preference to an irregular one; an apparent contradiction is seen in L, but here a taller figure was preferred. Experiments M and N showed a preference for complicated figures as against simple ones of the same size.

These results led Wallace to suggest that the hoppers were attracted to the figure whose contours produced the greatest number of impulses in the eye of a hopper walking on a horizontal surface; vertical contours, perpendicular to the motion, would have just such an effect and a number of vertical edges (as in C) would increase it. Figures of complicated contour (M and N) would also increase the number of stimulus changes per unit of time. The effect of vertical stripes need not necessarily involve actual marching of a hopper, since a stationary hopper tends to execute lateral swaying movements of the body, resulting in a *scanning* of the visual field and in a movement of images across it. Wallace's experimental data are supported by Chapman's

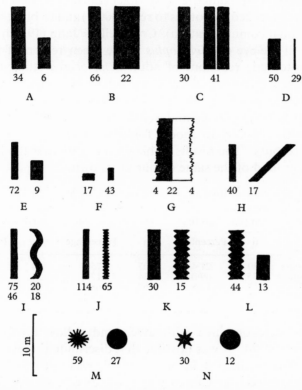

Fig. 123. *Schistocerca*, form perception by hoppers (after Wallace 1958). A to N, different shapes presented to hoppers; figures underneath, numbers of positive responses; see text.

(1955) finding that wandering hoppers of *Locusta* are frequently attracted to vertical sticks which they then climb; they also climb along black lines on a white vertical surface (L. H. Williams 1954).

Scanning movements are thought to be of importance also in the *estimation of the distance* to a visible object (Wallace 1959). It is commonly assumed that the visual estimation of distance is based on binocular vision, but Wallace has shown that *Schistocerca* hoppers with one eye completely blinded were still able to judge the distance and jumped towards the nearest of two objects, the choice being unaffected by the visual angles subtended by them. On the other hand, when an object was moved in the direction opposite to that of the scanning movement, the hopper jumped short of the object; this suggests that the distance is estimated by the extent of the movement of the object's image over the retina.

Data on *colour vision* are few and inconclusive. No electric response to red was obtained in the *Locusta* eye, that is wave-lengths exceeding 6250 Å have no effect; shorter wave-lengths produced responses up to violet (3900–4700 Å) and some were observed in the ultra-violet (Burtt & Catton, unpublished). G. A. Mazokhin recorded responses to red (6300Å) and to blue (450Å) in some acridoids (personal communication). Crescitelli & Jahn (1939a) recorded the greatest effect in the eye of *Melanoplus* in the green region of the spectrum (5300 Å). Phototactic reactions of adult *Schistocerca* studied by Chauvin (1941a, 1942) were weak to red light, but definite to yellow, green and blue. Vuillaume (1954) recorded similar results with *Zonocerus variegatus*.

Ergene (1950) studied green and yellow colour forms of *Acrida* (p. 54) with regard to their ability to choose for resting between two areas of cage floor of these colours. The results (table 47) indicate that the insects settled mostly on the ground of the same colour as its own.

Table 47. *Discrimination of ground colour by* Acrida (*Ergene* 1950)

	On yellow ground		On green ground		On cage sides	
	n	Percentage	n	Percentage	n	Percentage
Green hoppers	30	21·4	107	75·9	4	2·7
Yellow hoppers	135	69·0	34	17·4	26	13·6
Green adults	63	14·8	268	63·8	90	21·4
Yellow adults	205	66·6	25	8·1	78	25·3

Similar results were obtained with green and yellow forms of *Oedaleus decorus* (Ergene 1955b). It was possible that discrimination was not between colours, but between different intensities. This was tested by offering green *Acrida* a choice between green and grey grounds of the same intensity, and over 80% chose the green (Ergene 1952b). That the choice was a visual one was confirmed by blacking the eyes and ocelli, after which the insects settled randomly on ground of either colour. Similar experiments with *Oedipoda miniata*, the coloration of which being grey, reddish, yellowish or black, usually corresponds to that of the bare soil where it lives, have also shown preferences for a homochromous ground, that is, an ability to discriminate between these colours (Ergene 1953a, 1955c, 1957), which was lost on blacking the eyes.

This brief review of available data on vision reveals their inadequacy. Neurophysiologists are, naturally, mainly interested in the fundamental theory of vision and the mechanism of integration of responses and their work will be of great value to biologists. The latter, however, could obtain much useful information on most aspects of vision by carefully planned studies of behaviour responses to visual stimuli of various kinds. Vision plays an important part in behaviour and work of this kind is needed urgently.

OCELLI

The ocelli, or simple eyes, are normally three in number—an unpaired median, or frontal, ocellus situated on the frontal costa about its middle, and a pair of lateral ocelli, placed close to the inner margins of the compound eyes (Link 1909; Tümpel 1914).

The *frontal* (*median*) *ocellus* is usually smaller than the lateral and tends sometimes to be greatly reduced and even to disappear (see below). A double

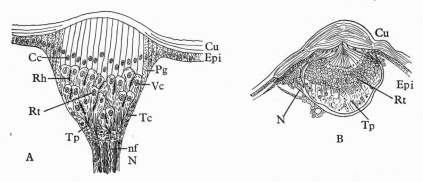

Fig. 124. A, *Psophus*, section of frontal ocellus (after Link 1909); B, *Anacridium*, section of lateral ocellus (after Tümpel 1914).
Cu, cuticle; Cc, corneagene cells; Epi, hypoderm; Pg, pigment; Rh, rhabdom; Rt, retinula; Vc, nucleus of a visual cell; Tp, tapetum; Tc, nucleus of a tapetum cell; nf, nerve bundle; N, nerve.

frontal ocellus occurs as an abnormality (Slifer 1960). The external part of an ocellus (fig. 124, A) is the *cornea*, which is a transparent portion of cuticle, forming a lens, the lower surface of which may be convex in the middle and concave near the periphery. The cells of the cornea (corneagene cells) are elongate and have nuclei near their lower ends. Below the cornea lies a *retinula*, composed of visual cells, arranged in groups of 405 or more, each group embracing optical rods or *rhabdoms*. Below the retinula there is the *tapetum*, a layer of pigmented cells, followed by nerve fibres, leading to the median ocellar nerve which arises from the protocerebrum (p. 152). The ocellus is surrounded by pigmented hypodermal cells.

The *lateral ocelli* are larger than the frontal and are very rarely reduced. Their structure is essentially the same, though the lower edge of the lens may be bi-convex (fig. 124, B). Moreover (at least in *Anacridium*), some corneagene cells are pigmented, and there is a group of nerve cells near the outer margin of the ocellus, connected with the ocellar and with the antennal nerves (Tümpel 1914).

The *function of ocelli* is still debatable (Parry 1947; Cornwell 1955; Hoyle 1955*c*; E. T. Burtt & Catton 1956; Ruck 1954, 1957). There appears to be a general view that although the lens of an ocellus can produce an image, its focal distance is so great that the image falls well beyond the retinula, and therefore cannot be perceived as an image. These conclusions, however, are based on theoretical optical considerations, and not enough attention has been paid to the differences between the median and the dorsal ocelli indicated by Tümpel, although Burtt & Catton and also Ruck recorded different electroretinograms of the frontal and lateral ocelli to 'on' or 'off' light stimulation, without discussing the implication. Another point raised by Tümpel was that in the ocelli of insects kept in the dark, the pigment is concentrated in some cells, while others become clear; this may have some bearing on Hoyle's (1955*c*) observations that there is a continuous discharge in the low light intensities.

The general opinion on the function of ocelli in insects is that they are efficient light collectors and respond to changes in light intensity, thus serving to augment impulses received through the compound eyes (Parry 1947; Dethier *in* Roeder 1953) and to provide stimuli for the orientation and movement of the insect (Cassier 1960, 1962). More detailed physiological work, however, is necessary, as well as more extensive behaviour observations. Attention should be paid, particularly, to their function and role in behaviour in weak light (at night).

Some suggestions on their possible function may be obtained from their occurrence in species with different habits. They are always present and well developed in active flyers, but tend to become smaller, sometimes clearly nonfunctional, in the micropterous and apterous species. In extreme cases, for example in representatives of the family Lathiceridae and in the small and completely apterous *Dysanema* from Mount Everest, there is no trace of ocelli. This suggests that they are of some special importance during flight, either by themselves or in conjunction with the compound eyes.

TEMPERATURE RELATIONS

Heat as a form of energy is expressed in calories, but the usual measure of its level is temperature and most investigations on heat economy of acridoids concern their temperature relations, though in some recent papers the quantitative aspects of heat balance have also been discussed (p. 220).

INTERNAL TEMPERATURE

The term body temperature is in general use for describing the insect's own temperature. However, the temperatures on the surface of the body and inside its different parts are not the same (p. 210); therefore, it is more exact to designate temperatures measured inside the body as *internal temperatures* (M. A. Volkonsky 1939; Uvarov 1948).

Measurements of internal temperatures are made with a fine thermocouple needle which is introduced either through the anus or into the thorax; in either case, some damage is inevitable and may cause physiological disturbance affecting the results. Precautions must also be taken to eliminate errors due to the effects of external conditions on the needles themselves; the latest laboratory technique is described by K. U. Clarke (1960) and Haskell, Paskin & Moorhouse (1962), and field techniques by Gunn, Perry *et al.* (1948), Smit (1960), and Stower & Griffiths (1965).

Internal temperature is positively affected by the temperature of the air, by radiant heat from the sun and from the ground and objects on it, and by the metabolic production of heat; while losses of heat may be due to convection and long-wave radiation from the body, as well as to the evaporation of water.

Air temperature

In the absence of any other factors, internal temperature is close to that of the surrounding air, but not necessarily identical with it. The equilibration of internal temperature with that of the air was studied by Bodenheimer *et al.* (1929) in *Schistocerca*, by transferring an insect from room temperature to a higher one. As can be seen in fig. 125, the internal temperature reached the level of that of the air within a few minutes. Moreover, the equilibration was achieved much more quickly, within less than three minutes, in the small Ist instar hopper than in the adult locust. Another factor affecting the rate of rise was air humidity, the rate being greater in the humid air than in the dry, in which even after twenty minutes equilibrium was not achieved, because of the cooling effect of evaporation (p. 217).

Koidsumi (1934–5) obtained similar data for *Gastrimargus* (table 48). Table 48 provides interesting data on the *rate of the temperature equilibration*.

On transference to a higher temperature, the rate of increase of the internal temperature at 60% RH was very high initially, 5·76, 2·44, 1·84 and 1·48° per minute during the first four minutes, but it slowed down at the higher temperatures, so that the mean rate for thirty minutes was only 0·65° per minute. The

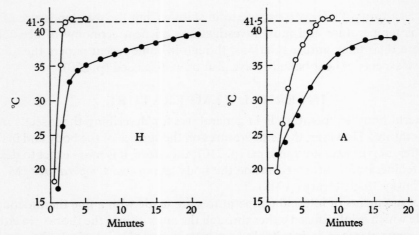

Fig. 125. *Schistocerca*, equilibration of internal temperature of Ist instar hopper (H) and adult (A) on transference to a higher air temperature in humid (open circles) and in dry (black circles) air (after Bodenheimer *et al.* 1929).

Table 48. *Equilibration of internal temperature of* Gastrimargus *on transference from room temperature (about 20°C) to 39·52° C and to 4° C*
(*after Koidsumi 1934–5*)

| Minutes | From about 20°C to 39·52°C | | | From about 20°C to 4°C | |
	R.H. 30%	R.H. 60%	R.H. 90%	Dry air	Humid air
0	19·04	19·44	20·52	19·84	20·36
1	21·36	25·20	27·84	15·06	14·54
2	23·08	27·64	31·40	13·92	11·48
3	24·12	31·16	33·76	12·56	8·68
4	25·96	33·00	36·08	10·60	6·20
5	27·36	34·48	37·16	10·08	5·44
6	29·36	35·64	38·00	9·04	5·12
7	31·00	35·96	38·64	8·16	4·80
8	32·24	37·32	39·08	7·00	4·64
9	33·00	37·84	39·20	6·64	4·56
10	33·72	38·36	39·32	6·32	4·48
15	36·36	38·88	39·48	4·76	4·44
20	37·52	38·80	39·12	4·52	4·52
25	37·92	38·92	39·32	4·92	4·20
30	37·80	38·98	39·38	4·76	4·24

situation was similar at 90% RH, at which the internal temperature rose by 7·32° during the first minute; at 30% RH the rise was gradual. In the cooling experiment, the initial rate of fall was similar in dry and in humid air, but the equilibrium was approached more rapidly in the latter.

More precise information on the equilibration of internal temperature was provided by K. U. Clarke (1960), who followed the effects of a slow rise of air temperature (0·18°C per minute) on the internal temperature of adult *Locusta*. The curves in fig. 126 show that the internal temperature initially lagged by about 1·4°C behind the air temperature, but after about fifteen minutes, both increased at about the same rate. When the change of the air temperature stopped above 35°C, the internal temperature continued to rise and reached about 0·5°C above that of the air. This latter fact suggests a metabolic effect,

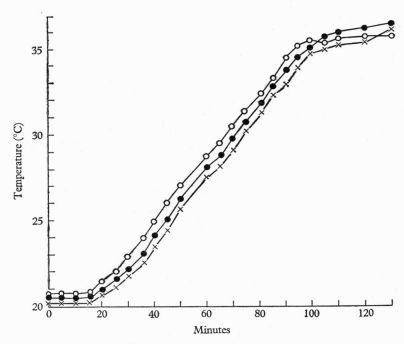

Fig. 126. *Locusta*, adult. Effects of a slow rise of air temperature on the internal temperature (after K. U. Clarke 1960).
Open circles, air temperature; black circles and crosses, internal temperature of two individuals.

and this is supported by the observation that no overshoot occurred in starved locusts or in those injected with a sublethal dose of potassium cyanide; on the other hand, an injection of a metabolic stimulant (2:4-dinitrophenol) accelerated increase of internal temperature and caused a greater final overshoot. Clarke's data indicate that even under most rigidly controlled experimental conditions, the internal temperature is not quite identical with that of the air, while in field conditions other factors introduce still greater divergence between the two.

The rate of change of internal temperature should have some connection with the *specific heat* (i.e. thermal capacity in calories per unit mass) of the insect; determinations made by Shinozaki (1957) for two species indicated that it increased with the water content of the tissues (table 49).

Table 49. *Specific heat of adults of two Japanese grasshoppers (Shinozaki 1957)*

	Cal/gm/°C	Water content
Oedaleus infernalis	0·76	65·7
Atractomorpha bedeli ♂	0·68	63·1
,, ,, ♀	0·74	65·9

Distribution of temperature in the body

Koidsumi (1934–5) compared temperatures inside the body and on the ventral surface of the abdomen, and table 50 shows the differences between these temperatures and that of the air.

The difference between the internal and external temperature is slight, but the latter is consistently lower, presumably because of the loss of heat by convection (p. 217).

Table 50. *Differences between air temperature and temperature inside and on the surface of adult Gastrimargus (Koidsumi 1934–5)*

Air		Difference in °C	
°C	R.H. %	Inside the body	On the surface
10	30	+0·47	+0·32
	60	+0·63	+0·49
	90	+1·28	+1·17
20	30	−0·38	−0·63
	60	+0·44	+0·36
	90	+0·47	+0·44
30	30	−1·52	−1·80
	60	−0·19	−0·35
	90	+0·87	+0·64

The distribution of temperatures within the body of *Schistocerca*, studied by Church (1960b) on freshly killed, electrically heated, specimens, is shown in table 51.

Measurements made on live locusts produced similar results, with the maximum excess in the pterothorax (even on its surface), with a fall towards the head and, particularly, in the abdomen; this is probably due to insulation by large air-sacs. In marching hoppers of *Locusta*, in which metabolic heat is produced in the thoracic muscles, the difference between thoracic and abdominal temperatures may be as great as 6·3°C (Strelnikov 1935). The temperature within the large thoracic air-sacs is always lower than the thoracic temperature outside the sacs, the difference in shade being 3·6°C and under solar radiation as much as 7·4°C, although it is always below the air temperature (Strelnikov 1936). Thus, the conduction of heat within the body is rather poor and the point where a measurement is taken should be indicated precisely.

Table 51. *Temperature excess distribution in*
dead male Desert Locust (Church 1960b)

	°C
Head	0·5
Prothorax	2·4
Pterothorax, centre	6·2
,, top, under cuticle	5·8
,, ,, cuticle surface	5·6
,, side, under cuticle	5·2
,, ,, cuticle surface	4·6
Abdomen, 2nd segment, centre	2·8
,, ,, ,, under cuticle	1·6
,, between segments 4 and 5	0·7
,, 8th segment, centre	0·3
,, ,, ,, under cuticle	0·2

Radiation

It is generally agreed that solar radiation is the most important source of heat gain.

Figure 127 shows the sudden rise of internal temperature in a *Locusta* hopper on exposure to the sun and its rapid fall on shading. It can be seen that during the first minute of exposure the temperature rose from 27·7° to 36°C, at the rate of 8·3° per minute; then the rate slowed down and the mean rate of rise, before the equilibrium temperature of 42·7° was reached after ten minutes, was only 1·04° per minute. The excess of the internal temperature over that of the air at the equilibrium was 15·1°C and it can be entirely attributed to the absorption of radiant heat.

Similar figures, illustrating the effects of radiation, have been recorded by other authors (Kennedy 1939; Franz 1930; Strelnikov 1932, 1934, 1935). Krüger (1931) observed a particularly striking initial rate of rise in *Gomphocerus sibiricus* in the Swiss Alps, when the internal temperature of an individual, at the air temperature of 22°C, rose by 13·7°C and reached the equilibrium during the first minute of exposure to direct sunlight. In adult *Schistocerca*, Volkonsky (1939) recorded excess temperatures up to 20·4°C and in *Locusta* up to 18·9°C above the air temperature, when that of the air was 19·8°C. The highest recorded excess is that for *Miramella alpina*, 26·7°C (Krüger & Duspiva 1933).

Figure 128 illustrates the course of rise of internal temperature of green *Schistocerca* hoppers exposed to solar radiation. The curve indicates a much more rapid initial rise in the small hopper than in the large one, but equilibrium was reached at a much higher level in the large hopper, excess temperature of which was about four times greater. This must be due to the loss of heat by convection which is inversely related to the size (p. 217).

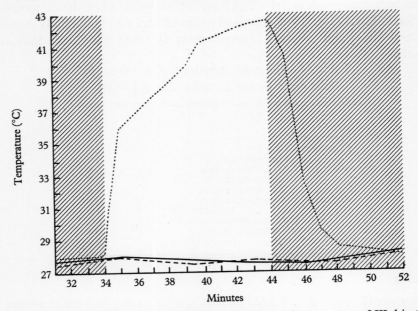

Fig. 127. *Locusta,* effects of solar radiation on the internal temperature of IIIrd instar gregarious hoppers (after Strelnikov 1936).
Solid line, air temperature; broken line, internal temperature of a hopper kept in shade throughout; dotted line, internal temperature of a hopper first shaded, then insolated and again shaded.

The quantitative effect of solar radiation is measurable in calories of heat received by one square centimetre of the surface in a minute. Detailed laboratory investigations (Digby 1955) have shown that the relation between the radiation intensity and internal temperature excess is practically linear.

Modifications of radiation effects are caused by several factors. One of them is the angle of incidence of heat rays. As shown in table 52 there can be a

Table 52. *Internal temperatures (°C) of Vth instar hoppers of* Schistocerca *with different orientation to sun rays* (Bodenheimer *et al.* 1929)

	Perpendicular	Parallel	Difference
	38·7	35·7	3·0
	42·1	38·2	3·9
	45·1	41·6	3·5
	38·9	36·0	2·9
	40·2	36·0	4·2
Means	41·7	38·7	3·4

substantial difference in the internal temperatures of two hoppers exposed to the same intensity of radiation, one orientated perpendicular to the sun rays, the other parallel.

Strelnikov (1936) observed differences in the internal temperatures of *Locusta* hoppers up to 6·7°C depending on the angle of incidence of sun rays. In adults

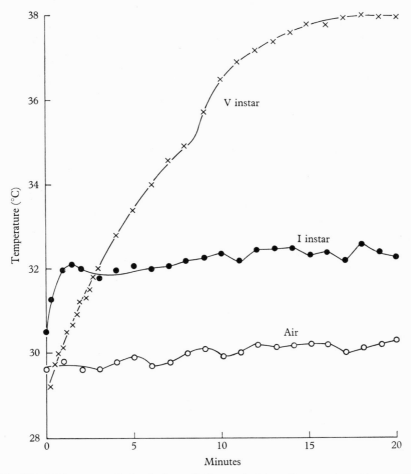

Fig. 128. *Schistocerca*, effects of solar radiation on the internal temperature of green solitarious hoppers of the Ist and the Vth instar (after Stower & Griffiths 1965).

of *Schistocerca* sitting parallel to sun rays the excess temperature was 5·9–7·8°C, and in those perpendicular to the sun rays it was 15·5–17·8°C, so that the orientation of the insect may change its internal temperature by as much as 10°C (Volkonsky 1939).

Since the absorption of radiant heat depends on the proportion of the rays, particularly of the infra-red part of the spectrum, which are reflected by a surface, the colour of the insect would be expected to be of importance. Buxton

(1924) and Bodenheimer (1934) recorded that the internal temperature of the black colour form of *Calliptamus coelesyriensis*, exposed to sunshine, had internal temperature 2·5°C higher than the buff form of the same species. Hill & Taylor (1933) determined the temperature under the pronotum of a black gregarious hopper of *Locusta*, kept under an arc lamp, as being 3–3·5°C higher than that of a green solitarious hopper. Strelnikov's (1936) field com-

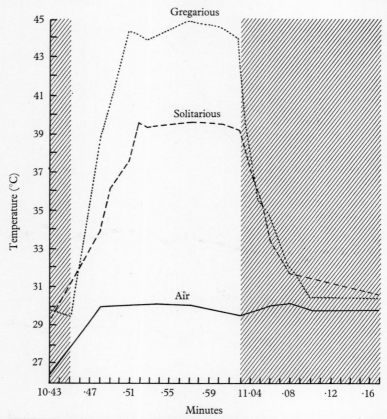

Fig. 129. *Locusta*, effects of solar radiation and shading on the solitarious (green) and the gregarious (black) hoppers (after Strelnikov 1936).

parisons of the two colour types of *Locusta* are illustrated in fig. 129. Detailed records of the course of temperature rise, made at ten-second intervals, on which the curves are based, have shown that in the first minute after exposure to the sun, the temperature of the green hopper rose by 3·4°, and that of the black by 8·6°C; their equilibrium temperatures also differed by 5°C. The temperature of a basking grey hopper of *Locustana pardalina* was about 5°C above that of a green one (Smit 1960, graph 9).

Pepper & Hastings (1952), on the other hand, found that the average equilibrium temperatures of the black and the yellow forms of *Melanoplus differentialis* did not differ significantly, although the black reached the equilibrium more rapidly; unfortunately, no detailed records of the rate of initial rise were published.

Stower & Griffiths (1965) also found no statistically significant differences between the mean internal temperature excesses and between the rates of its rise in black and in green *Schistocerca* hoppers exposed to solar radiation; there were differences in some individual cases, but none in others. This is in striking contrast with Strelnikov's data on *Locusta* quoted above and it remains to be seen whether the reason lies in the methods used, in the difference between the subspecies or in the air temperatures at the time of experiments, which may have been much higher on the Red Sea than in Central Asia.

Another related point requiring investigation is the effects of radiation reflected from the ground, vegetation and other objects, as distinct from direct insolation. Such radiation from bare ground may contribute up to 40% of the total radiant heat (Gunn, Perry *et al.* 1948), but its effects fall off extremely rapidly with the height above the ground. When the sand surface on the Red Sea coast at midday was over 56° C, the air temperature only 6 mm from the ground was 40° C, and *Schistocerca* adults in such situation adopted a 'stilting posture', rising on their legs to that height, with the result that their internal temperature was only 43° C; on the other hand, when the sand surface temperature was above that of the air, locusts tended to adopt a 'crouching' posture, with the ventral side pressed to the warm surface (Z. Waloff 1963). Observations on the temperature of *Oedipoda* on white and black backgrounds by Franz (1930) were also suggestive, but they were made in different conditions and the results are not comparable. The problem may be of importance for interpreting behaviour on differently coloured backgrounds.

Metabolic heat

Oxidation processes connected with respiration are a definite source of heat and quantitative estimations of the latter can be obtained by calculation from the metabolic rate (Weis-Fogh 1952). Prat (1954) studied the course of metabolic heat production in *Melanoplus* by micro-calorimetric analysis and obtained a variety of curves (fig. 130), but it is not possible to say, from single experiments, what caused the variation; more extensive work on these lines would be of value.

Muscular work also produces heat, but exact data on its effects on the internal temperature are few. Temperatures of marching and jumping *Locusta* hoppers are shown in table 53. The excess of thoracic temperature over that of the air was, of course, largely due to radiation, but its excess over that in the abdomen indicates that some contribution to the thoracic temperature results from muscular activity; this contribution is probably greater than the excess shown, because the thorax is well ventilated during movement and some heat

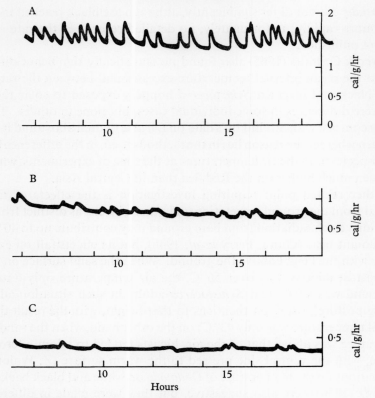

Fig. 130. *Melanoplus* spp. Metabolic heat production at 24·9°C.
A, *M. bivittatus*, female; B, *M. differentialis*, male; C, *M. sanguinipes*, male (after Prat 1954).

would be lost in this way. In the afternoon, and in cloudy conditions, the thoracic temperature excess over that of the air became less, partly because of reduced radiation and partly of slower movement; ventilation of the thorax was possibly responsible for the abdominal temperature becoming somewhat higher than the thoracic.

Table 53. *Internal temperatures of marching and jumping*
Locusta *hoppers (Strelnikov 1935)*

	Temperature °C					
Time	Air	Thorax	Abdomen	Difference thorax-air	Difference thorax-abdomen	Radiation in g/cal
10.35	31·0	43·9	37·6	+12·9	+6·3	1·24
12.13	33·3	44·2	41·2	+10·9	+3·0	1·18
12.20	32·6	44·8	41·5	+12·2	+3·3	1·18
16.12	30·9	42·0	41·0	+11·1	+1·0	1·18
16.58	27·9	31·8	32·0	+ 3·9	−0·2	Cloudy
17.2	27·9	33·8	33·9	+ 5·9	−0·1	,,
17.10	27·4	29·3	30·5	+ 1·9	−1·2	,,

Stower & Griffiths (1965) recorded that marching hoppers of *Schistocerca* at 31°C had a mean internal temperature of 35·3°C as compared with 32·1°C in the immobile ones.

Fanning (i.e. strong continuous vibration of the half-open wings), observed in many species, has a significant effect on the thoracic temperature. In *Nomadacris* the internal temperature of fanning individuals exceeded the air temperature of 9–11°C by 6–12° (Rainey, Waloff & Burnett 1957).

Metabolic heat production during flight must be very considerable, but its contribution to internal temperature is not easy to measure directly, since the level of that temperature is at the same time positively affected also by radiation and negatively by convection and by evaporation In laboratory conditions, in the absence of radiant heat, the thoracic temperature excess of flying *Schistocerca* was stated to be 6–7°C (Weis-Fogh 1956*a,b*); cooling effects of convection and evaporation were not estimated. In similar experiments with *Locusta m. manilensis* the internal temperature of males exceeded that of the air (25°C) by 5·3–6·9° and of females by 5·2–8·0° (Hwang Guan-Huei & Long Ching-cheng 1962). In a captive *Locusta* made to flutter its wings, the thoracic temperature rose after two minutes by 10°C above that of the air which was 27°C; the abdominal temperature was 30·5°C (Strelnikov 1935).

Loss of heat

Some indication of a loss of heat by *evaporation* can be seen in the data on the rates of equilibration of internal temperature with the air temperature at different air humidities (table 48); the less rapid rise in dry air must be due to the cooling effect of evaporation. In *Melanoplus differentialis* placed in a stream of dry air, the internal temperature was equal to the air temperature of 25°C, but at 39·1° it was 0·9°, at 49·4° it was 2°, and at 54·9° even 3·2° below the air temperature (Pepper & Hastings 1952); this suggests a significant moderating effect of evaporation only at very high air temperatures. Very exact determinations of the cooling effects of evaporation in flying *Schistocerca* have also shown that these effects are very small, since even in perfectly dry air at 30°C evaporation reduced the temperature excess of the pterothorax by about 0·5°C, or 10%, and even at 40°C the reduction was only 1·2°C (Church 1960*a*). Most of this heat loss is due to the evaporation from the spiracles, since cuticular transpiration which amounts only to about one-third of the total water loss (p. 229) may become relatively more important only at the temperatures above the melting point of cuticular wax (p. 33), but such temperatures are near the lethal limit (p. 222).

Loss of heat by *convection* from the surface occurs even in still air and it is known that its rate varies inversely with the size of the insect (Parry 1951; Digby 1955; Church 1960*b*). This is illustrated by fig. 125. The rate of loss is,

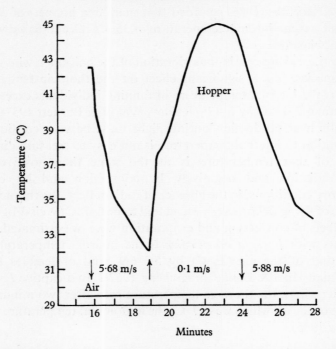

Fig. 131. *Locusta*, effects of wind velocity on the internal temperature of a gregarious IVth instar hopper (after Strelnikov 1936).

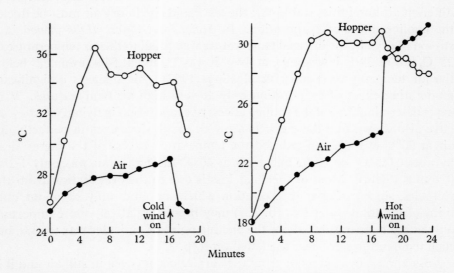

Fig. 132. *Schistocerca* hoppers facing into wind or away from it; changes in the prothoracic temperature caused by cold and hot wind (after Haskell, Paskin & Moorhouse 1962).

218

naturally, very much affected by air flow which may be caused by the wind or by the insect's movement, especially flight. The relation of the rate of loss to wind velocity is shown in fig. 131. The effects of convection are also well illustrated in fig. 132, showing that a drop in the prothoracic temperature of caged *Schistocerca* hoppers occurred when either a cold or a hot air stream was directed on them. It is of special interest that, in the case of hot wind, the pronotal temperature fell well below that of the air (Haskell, Paskin & Moorhouse 1962), possibly, due to the evaporation (p. 217).

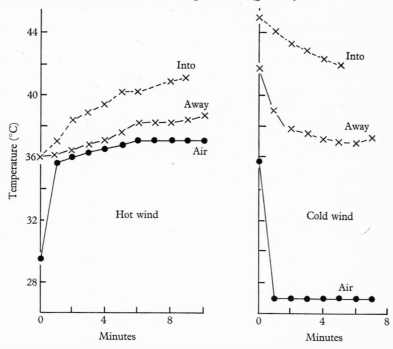

Fig. 133. *Schistocerca* hoppers, changes in the prothoracic temperature caused by their orientation to hot or cold wind (after Haskell, Paskin & Moorhouse 1962).

A curve of internal temperature of a *Locusta* hopper exposed to radiation showed a series of zigzags during a gust of wind lasting three minutes, with the amplitude of 0·9–2·7° per minute (Strelnikov 1936).

The orientation of the insect in relation to the air stream is also important: the temperature excess of a *Schistocerca* hopper at 90° to the wind was 88% of that when the hopper was facing it (Digby 1955). Changes in the pronotal temperature of *Schistocerca* hoppers facing into a hot or a cold wind or away from it (fig. 133) indicate that the behaviour in this case, as with radiation, serves to regulate the internal temperature.

Some loss of heat occurs by *long-wave radiation* from the body, which should be noticeable in the absence of solar radiation (i.e. at night). Strelnikov (1936) recorded that the temperature of black *Locusta* hoppers after sunset fell by

0·9°C below the air temperature. In adult *Nomadacris* internal temperatures before sunrise and after sunset were from half to one degree below those of the air (Rainey, Waloff & Burnett 1957). This effect appears to be relatively small.

Behaviour and temperature regulation

While the external physical factors affect the internal temperature in the ways discussed above, it is essential to remember that their impact on a living insect may be greatly modified by its behaviour. We have seen that the insect should be able to regulate its internal temperature by, for example, moving from sun to shade, or from a windy situation to a sheltered one; or changing its orientation to the source of heat or of wind; or even merely adopting a special posture. Such behaviour reactions often result in more significant changes of the internal temperature than do those caused by fluctuations in the physical factors; they will be discussed, as behaviour traits, in the next volume.

These reactions, moreover, are sometimes so instantaneous that they can hardly be accounted for by responses to changes in the internal temperature and suggest the existence of some *organs of thermal sense*, but no thermoreceptors have yet been discovered. Geist (1928) tested the heat sensitivity of *Melanoplus* and *Dissosteira* by bringing a hot wire near the different parts of the body and concluded that the antennae, palps, tarsal pulvilli and abdomen were sensitive; this was confirmed for *Locusta* (Harlow 1958; Makings 1964). Adult *Schistocerca* on very hot sand were observed from time to time to raise their front feet and to hold their tarsi exposed to the wind (Z. Waloff 1963).

Slifer (1951) thought that the special areas of thin integument at the base of the antennae and on the thorax and abdomen of *Locusta* and other species (Slifer's patches, p. 33) were heat-sensitive, but subsequent studies failed to show that electrical responses to heat from the nerves in such areas were different from the responses elsewhere (Weir 1957; Makings, *t.c.*). Dunham (1962), however, found that the patches transmit less, and absorb more, of the infra-red radiation than the normal cuticle. The whole problem of thermoreception remains unresolved.

Thermal balance

An attempt by Koidzumi (1935) to calculate the thermal balance of resting *Gastrimargus* in the absence of radiation, at 60% RH, produced the figures in table 54.

Calculations, based partly on field records of internal temperatures, but largely on metabolic and thermodynamic arguments, are available also for settled and for flying *Nomadacris* (table 55).

It is hardly possible to compare the two tables, as the conditions and the methods were so different. The relative importance of the factors of heat gain and loss in *Nomadacris* appears to be very reasonably expressed.

Much more elaborate calculations of the thermal balance of a resting

Table 54. *Thermal balance-sheet of* Gastrimargus, *in cal/kg/hr*
(after Koidzumi 1935 and Gunn 1942)

°C	Metabolic heat gain	Heat loss		Unexplained balance
		Evaporation	Convection	
10	3240	2410	170	+650
20	7490	7500	0	− 10
30	14720	14520	0	+200

Table 55. *Estimated thermal balance, in cal/min/locust, of adult*
Nomadacris (*Rainey, Waloff & Burnett* 1957)

	BASKING (8 a.m., 90° to sun-rays; air 20°C; wind 0·9 m/sec; vapour pressure 10 mm)		FLYING (3 p.m., sun; air 30°C; air speed 3·1/m/sec; vapour pressure 10 mm)	
	Heat gain	Heat loss	Heat gain	Heat loss
Radiation	2·2		1·6	
Metabolism	0·1		2·1	
	2·3		3·7	
Evaporation		0·002		0·25
Ventilation		<0·001		0·03
Convection		2·3		3·42
		2·3		3·7

Schistocerca hopper, with and without radiation, presented by Stower & Griffiths (1965) were based almost entirely on theoretical considerations and on the assumed values of the various factors derived from data relating to other insects. Their general conclusions were that, apart from the air temperature which is always the governing factor, the main source of heat gain is radiation, while convection causes the greatest loss; in a hopper shielded from radiation and wind, losses by convection were calculated as approximately equal to those by evaporation (cf. p. 217).

UPPER LETHAL LIMITS

In hoppers and adults, abnormally high temperatures cause, at first, a depression of activities, followed by stupor and then death. Some of the available data on the upper lethal temperature limits are presented in table 56.

The figures in the table must be regarded with many reservations, because of the different methods and conditions. Thus, Hussein's data were obtained by slow heating from room temperature at the rate of 11·1°C per hour, and maintaining the relative air humidity at about 70%, while Parker and Knipling & Sullivan exposed their insects to a high temperature for short periods and did not prevent a sharp fall in air humidity. Also, the mortality was estimated by Knipling and Sullivan after twenty-four hours, while other authors did not even specify the period.

Nevertheless, some useful suggestions can be extracted from the table. It would appear that, in spite of the wide range of species from very different climates, the upper fatal limit may lie at about 50°C. Secondly, there is clear evidence that the length of exposure has a serious effect on mortality. Indeed,

Table 56. *Effects of high temperatures on adults and hoppers*

Species and stage	°C	Minutes	Percentage mortality	Reference
Camnula pellucida, adult	54·5	5–10	Majority	Parker 1924
,, ,, ,,	57·7	5–10	Few survived	,,
Melanoplus sanguinipes, hoppers	54	10	100	Parker 1930
,, ,, adults	58	10	100	,,
American grasshoppers, 5 species, adults & hoppers	50	15	3±1	Knipling & Sullivan 1958
,, ,, ,,	50	30	16±8	,,
,, ,, ,,	50	45	55±9	,,
,, ,, ,,	50	60	88±4	,,
,, ,, ,,	55	15	78±8	,,
,, ,, ,,	55	30	100	,,
,, ,, ,,	60	15	100	,,
Siberian grasshoppers, 5 species, adults	c.50		Majority	Rubtzov 1935*b*
Eirenephilus longipennis, adults	51·08–54·82		100	Hukusima 1955
,, ,, hoppers	46·56–53·24		100	,,
Israel grasshoppers, 33 spp., adults	46·7–54·0		100	Bodenheimer 1935
Locusta m migratorioides, Ist instar	47·2–51·7		100	Hussein 1937
,, ,, ,, adult	51·1–55·6		100	,,
Schistocerca gregaria, Ist instar	47·2–52·2		100	,,
,, ,, adult	51·7–55·6		100	,,
Nomadacris septemfasciata, Ist instar	47·8–52·2		100	,,
,, ,, older hopper	52·2–55·6		100	,,

Hussein recorded that *Locusta* hoppers heated to 48·3° and immediately removed not only recovered, but developed into fertile adults, whereas those kept at that temperature for five to fifteen minutes died.

Another point of interest is that the lethal temperature appears to be lower for hoppers than for adults of the same species. The effect of the size can be further illustrated by a field observation of Nikolskiĭ (1918), in which Ist instar hoppers of *Locusta* on bare surface with a temperature of 62°C died in one minute, those of the IInd instar in one to two, IIIrd in three to seven, and IVth in four to eighteen minutes. The temperature, as specified, must have been augmented by intense radiation, increasing the internal temperature of larger hoppers more than that of the smaller (p. 207). Indeed, it is a serious fault of all previous experiments that only the ambient temperatures were recorded and not the internal temperatures, which are primarily concerned in the physiological disturbance leading to death. Future work on this subject must be based on internal temperatures, and such aspects as the rate of change from the normal to the high temperature, the length of exposure and the final, not only the immediate, mortality must be recorded. It will be essential also to obtain such data not only for each stage and each instar of a species, but also for the ages within them, since one may expect different effects of high temperature between recently moulted and older hoppers, and between fledglings and old adults. Since death, particularly during longer exposures, may be partly due to desiccation (p. 234), air humidity conditions must always be taken into account.

LOWER LETHAL LIMITS

Somewhat disjointed data on the lethal effects of very low temperature on hoppers and adults are presented in table 57.

Table 57. *Lower lethal temperatures of adults and hoppers*

Species and stage	°C	Time	Percentage mortality	References
Aeropedellus variegatus, Ist instar	−8	10m	Some	Rubtzov 1935*b*
,, ,, ,,	−13·5	10m	100	,, ,,
,, ,, IInd ,,	−12	10m	100	,, ,,
,, ,, IIIrd ,,	−10	10m	100	,, ,,
Gomphocerus sibiricus, Ist instar	−6·5	10m	Some	,, ,,
,, ,, ,, ,,	−13	10m	100	,, ,,
Arcyptera fusca	−7	10m	Some	,, ,,
Camnula pellucida, adults	−7	12h	Some	Parker 1924
,, ,, ,,	−8	12h	100	,, ,,
American grasshoppers, 5 spp., adults & hoppers	0	1h	7±2	Knipling & Sullivan 1957
,, ,, ,,	−5	1h	33±1	,, ,, ,,
,, ,, ,,	−10	1h	87±10	,, ,, ,,
,, ,, ,,	−15	1h	100	,, ,, ,,
Locusta m. migratoria Ist, instar	−2·9	3h	0	Sacharov 1930
,, ,, ,, ,, ,,	−2·9	6h	94	,, ,,
,, ,, ,, ,, ,,	−3·9	3h	88	,, ,,
,, ,, ,, ,, ,,	−5·75	2·5h	100	,, ,,
Schistocerca gregaria, adult	−2	1–18h	0	Rungs 1933
,, ,, ,,	−2·5	24h	66	,, ,,
,, ,, ,,	−3	48h	100	,, ,,
,, ,, ,,	−5	14·5h	100	,, ,,

The data are not directly comparable, but they suggest that the species of warmer climates (*Locusta*, *Schistocerca*) succumb at higher temperatures than the northern ones, hoppers of which are likely to experience freezing temperatures at least occasionally. However, adults of the tropical *Schistocerca*, frozen to become brittle (e.g. after twenty-four hours at −2·5°), could be revived and were subsequently able to lay eggs (Rungs 1933).

For the effects of temperature on eggs, see pp. 264–267.

As regards the theoretical basis of cold resistance, it is well known that when an insect is exposed to sub-zero temperatures the water in its body, being partly bound in the tissues (p. 108), becomes super-cooled and freezes only when a much lower temperature is reached. When this critical point is reached, the internal temperature suddenly rises to the freezing point of water and then falls gradually. It is the position of this critical point that determines the resistance, or cold-hardiness, of insects in different stages. General theories of the physiology of cold-hardiness have been discussed, for example by Uvarov (1931), Precht, Christophersen & Hensel (1955), Salt (1950, 1958, 1962), and Ushatinskaya (1955), but the data concerning acridoids, reviewed above, are too scanty to be regarded as serious contributions to the problem. Indeed, the physiology of cold resistance of northern grasshoppers has been a somewhat neglected subject; such empirical information as exists suggests that the problem is very complex and demands a serious physiological approach.

WATER RELATIONS

WATER CONTENT

The present chapter deals with water relations of adults and hoppers; those of eggs are dealt with on pp. 247, 256.

Determinations of water content are usually based on comparisons of fresh and dry weight. The fresh weight comprises the weight of all skeletal parts and organs, plus all water which is contained in the haemolymph, in body cells and in gut contents, and all these fractions are subject to variations owing to growth and the physiological state of the insect. The dry weight is also subject to changes due to growth and the state of reserve substances. Therefore, water content expressed as percentage of fresh weight can often be misleading; it is also not always known whether the methods of drying ensured that the tissue water, as well as that in the haemolymph, was accounted for. Hochrainer (1942) suggested that it would be more exact to determine the percentage of water to the fresh weight of the whole insect free from fat (ether extracted) and from chitin (NaOH extracted). His sets of figures (table 58) for the two kinds of percentage, however, show only such difference between them as might be expected because of the partial reduction of dry matter.

Table 58. *Percentage water content of grasshoppers*
(Hochrainer 1942)

Species	Percentage of total weight	Percentage of fat- and chitin-free weight
Oedipoda caerulescens	65·5–69·8	71·9–72·9
Psophus stridulus	69·7–70·0	72·9
Calliptamus italicus	68·6–73·3	73·0
Miramella alpina	69·6–71·1	72·4–73·4
Podisma pedestris	72·0	73·4
Arcyptera fusca	69·9–70·6	73·5
Chorthippus apricarius	70·2–72·9	72·4
,, biguttulus	69·1–70·2	73·1
Euthystira brachyptera	71·0–72·4	73·8

This table, based on randomly collected material, demonstrates merely that individual variation is no less, even if not more, important than the specific differences. The existence of the latter was suggested by Bodine (1921) in two species of *Melanoplus*, but the significance of his figures (table 59) is uncertain.

The same author (Bodine 1921, 1923) has shown that in *Chortophaga viridifasciata* hibernating in the adult stage, the water content fell from 72 to 65%; when the insect was transferred to 38°C, it rapidly increased to 75%.

15   225

Even more striking changes in water content were recorded by Millot & Fontaine (1937) in *Schistocerca* adults. Young adults, kept for six to eight weeks at 28°C and 40% RH, reduced their water content from the original 71–76 to 53% if they had fresh food; on dry food, their water content fell to 43%. In the locusts kept on dry food at 30°C and 30% RH, the water content fell to 37·4%, and after six days without food it reached the record low figure of 36·5% (i.e. approximately only half of the original). The authors claimed that the ability of *Schistocerca* to tolerate such wide variations in water content is an exceptional adaptation to desert conditions, but no comparable data are available for other species, except the mesophilous *Chortophaga viridifasciata* which is unable to survive if its water content falls below 56–58% (Ludwig 1937).

Table 59. *Percentage water content of adults of two species of* Melanoplus *(mean values in brackets) Bodine* (1921)

Species	Hoppers	Adults
M. femur-rubrum	73·9–78·5 (75·6)	70·3–76·0 (72·6)
M. differentialis	—	66·8–71·0 (68·0)

An important source of error in estimating water content as percentage of fresh weight is due to growth changes, even in an adult. Male fledglings of *Melanoplus differentialis* contained 76·4–77·7% of water and females 72·8–75·3%. During the first twelve days of adult life, there was a decrease to 65–70%, after which the percentage remained relatively constant in both sexes (Weed Pfeiffer 1945a). The initial drop in percentage, however, was due not to loss of water, since the absolute weight of water actually increased during the first few days, but to an increase in the dry matter. Female fledglings of *Locusta* contain 72–74% of water, and the figure falls to about 60% after a week (Phipps 1950) for the same reason. Similar changes in laboratory-bred *Schistocerca* adults are summarised in table 60.

Table 60. *Average live and dry weight and water content of* Schistocerca *adults* (Dudley 1961)

Days old	Weight in mg				Water in live			
	Live		Dry		mg		Percentage	
	♂	♀	♂	♀	♂	♀	♂	♀
1	1460	1875	409	502	1051	1374	72·0	73·3
5	1949	2455	660	827	1288	1628	66·2	66·5
10	2233	3060	909	1182	1324	1877	59·2	61·4
15	2080	3129	861	1263	1222	1866	58·7	59·6
20	2126	3580	828	1611	1298	2053	61·1	57·3
25	2120	3363	876	1221	1244	2142	58·9	63·7
30	1998	3626	782	1438	1216	2188	61·1	60·2
35	2315	3593	992	1592	1323	2001	57·0	55·6
50	2165		857		1309		60·4	

Similar results were obtained from analyses of swarming male adults of *Schistocerca* (Z. Waloff, personal communication). As shown in fig. 53, the mean water content was 700–800 mg per locust immediately after fledging but it rose to 1100–1200 mg in one to three days, thus increasing by some 50% of the initial amount and accounting for more than 50% increase in the total fresh weight. The percentage content of water, however, actually fell in the first few days from 73 to 65–60%, because of the simultaneous increase in the dry matter (p. 302). During the rest of the adult period, there was little change, but in old locusts the absolute and the percentage content increased again, the latter up to 66–68% of the fresh weight.

The most detailed analysis of water relations during the life of *Schistocerca* is that by R. M. Lee (1961) who studied not the total water content, but separately the haemolymph volume (expressed in relation to the unit weight) and the percentage water content of tissues in relation to dry weight; gut contents were removed, a precaution not always taken by other workers. His data are discussed on p. 108, but the main lesson of this work was the need to distinguish between water in the haemolymph and that in the tissue cells, the latter containing most of it. The balance between the two may well depend on the osmotic pressure of haemolymph (p. 113) which affects the rate of water absorption in the rectum (Phillips 1964).

The water content of locust hatchlings is considerably higher than that of adults, the mean values being 78·6% for *Nomadacris* and 79% for *Schistocerca*; in the latter, the female hatchlings had a higher content (81·15%) than the males (79·66%), but this was not the case in *Locusta* and *Nomadacris* (Blackith 1961). Extensive data on the moisture content of *Locusta*, *Nomadacris* and *Schistocerca* hatchlings of different phases were provided by Albrecht (1962b).

Delphin (1963a, 1963b) suggested that a hormone secreted by the thoracic and abdominal ganglia of *Schistocerca* is important in the conservation of water in locusts reared on dry bran.

GAIN OF WATER

An obvious source of water is food and the data of Millot & Fontaine (1937) on *Schistocerca* kept on fresh and on dry food (p. 226) illustrate its importance. R. M. Lee (1961) obtained somewhat similar results with the same locust kept on grass and on artificial dry diet (Howden & Hunter-Jones 1958), but the difference between the two groups was not striking, possibly because the locusts kept on dry diet were given water to drink. In locusts fed on dry grass the absolute percentage weight of haemolymph decreased, but that of the cellular and gut fluid did not, which suggests that the haemolymph may act as a reserve of water for tissues.

Direct *drinking* of water is frequently observed in laboratory, even in the presence of fresh food. Gangwere (1960b) doubted whether this occurs in nature, but Nikolskiĭ (1925) saw marching hopper bands of *Locusta* in Middle Asia stopping at pools of water and definitely drinking; the same was recorded by Bodenheimer (1944) for *Dociostaurus* adults in Iraq. Gangwere's statement was based on observations in Michigan where there could have been no shortage of food with high water content.

A possible internal source of water is *oxidation of fat* (100 g of fat produce 107 g of water) but *Schistocerca* starved for fourteen days in a dry atmosphere lost only 3 % of fat (Gueutal 1941) and starvation for seven days did not result in an increase of water content (Millot & Fontaine 1937) as would be expected if fat were metabolised. A different conclusion was obtained by Ludwig (1937) in whose experiments starving hoppers of *Chortophaga* kept at 12 % RH maintained a high water content, possibly as a result of production of metabolic water. The problem is obviously far from solved.

A theoretically possible source of water is *water vapour in the air*. Bodine (1921) and Lugwig (1937) obtained evidence of some initial increase in percentage water content of *Chortophaga* hoppers kept at 96 % RH (fig. 138). Buxton (1932) suggested that this may have been due to condensation of water vapour in the tracheoles and its diffusion into the haemolymph, but there may have been also some condensation of water on the surface of the insects, or on the walls of the container. Colosi (1933) concluded that there was no absorption of water vapour through the integument in *Anacridium*, but his experiments were few and not convincing.

LOSS OF WATER

Water can be lost in three ways: by excretion, expiration with the air through the spiracles and evaporation through the cuticle.

Faecal pellets are normally dry though their water content greatly depends on that of the food (p. 120), but the water eliminated with them depends not only on that contained in the food, but whether there is a relation between the amount of water excreted and that in the haemolymph and the tissues (Phillips 1964).

The losses of water through the spiracles and cuticle are not easy to separate and both are usually considered together as transpiration.

Total transpiration

Quantitative data on total transpiration were given by Koidsumi (1934–5; Uvarov 1948) for three Japanese species and by Jakovlev & Krüger (1953) for several German ones (table 61).

The table shows consistently higher total transpiration in females of the same species, but the rates per unit weight in the heavier females are only 43–58 % of the values for the corresponding males. The authors tried to relate the unit weight rate to the size, taking as index of the latter the body length,

Table 61. *Mean transpiration rates of grasshoppers at* 27–28° *C and* 45–53 % *RH*
(*Jakovlev & Krüger* 1953)

Species	Weight in mg		Transpiration rate			
			μg/minute		μg/g/minute	
	♂	♀	♂	♀	♂	♀
Chorthippus apricarius	63	165	16	20·0	260±6	122±6
„ parallelus	66	138	15·0	18·7	227±5	132±7
„ brunneus	74	178	10·6	13·0	144±2	71±3·5
Omocestus viridulus	95	251	17·5	24·5	184±6	92±3·5
Mecostethus grossus	180	510	23·8	46·1	129	83
Oedipoda caerulescens	133	532	15·6	32·0	118±7	71

which was obtained not by direct measurement but as a cubic root of weight;
this produced evidence that the rate was proportional to the length. However,
the assumption that the weight is a cube of body length cannot be
correct since, for example, an adult female nearly doubles its weight on
maturation (p. 300), with only a small increase in body length. The physiological age of the grasshoppers studied has not been considered, and this may
account for the results being in some respects contradictory.

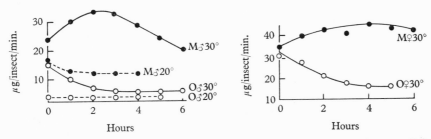

Fig. 134. Transpiration rates of *Oedipoda caerulescens* (O) and *Mecostethus grossus* (M)
in relation to temperature (after Jakovlev & Krüger 1953).

More informative were the results obtained by the same authors by comparing
the total transpiration rates of the two species with different ecology, *Oedipoda
caerulescens* and *Mecostethus grossus* (fig. 134). Comparing the same sexes at
45 % RH, the hygrophilous *Mecostethus* transpired at much greater rates both
at 20° and 30° C than the xerophilous *Oedipoda*, though at the lower temperature both species had a low rate which soon became stabilised. An important
difference was the initial rise in the transpiration rate in *Mecostethus* at 30° C,
while at 20° C the stabilisation was achieved by a fall in the rate, as it was
in *Oedipoda* at both temperatures. This suggests that 30° C is abnormally
high for *Mecostethus*, but not for *Oedipoda*.

Flying *Schistocerca* lost water at the rate of 21 mg/locust/hour at 30° C and
44 at 40° C (Church 1960 a).

The relation of transpiration rate to *temperature* is further illustrated by fig. 135 A in which several species of small, mainly mesophilous, grasshoppers are contrasted with the xerophilous *Oedipoda*. In the first group the transpiration rate tended to increase at temperatures above 15°C and rose sharply at 35°C, as it did also in *Oedipoda* in which it remained stable below that point. According to Koidsumi (*t.c.*), the transpiration rate of *Gastrimargus transversus* was trebled with rise of temperature from 10 to 20°C, and increased six times at 30°C (RH 60%).

The *relative humidity* of the air naturally also affects the transpiration rate, which, in general, is proportional to the relative humidity. However, at humidities between 27 and 76%, there is much irregularity, while at 96% RH there is in starving *Chortophaga* hoppers an initial absorption of water, followed by a loss (fig. 138). Effects of air humidity on the transpiration of hygrophilous and xerophilous species are illustrated in fig. 135

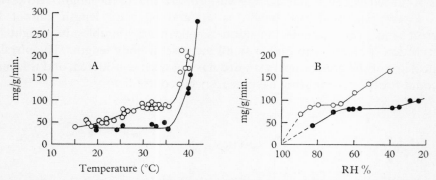

Fig. 135. A, Transpiration rates of mesophilous grasshoppers (open circles) and of xerophilous *Oedipoda caerulescens* (black circles) in relation to temperature. B, Transpiration rates of hygrophilous *Chorthippus montanus* (open circles) and xerophilous *Stenobothrus stigmaticus* (black circles) in relation to air humidity (after Jakovlev 1957).

An aspect of transpiration which, so far, has received only a mention, is the possible effect of the osmotic pressure of the blood depending on the concentration of water-soluble solids, particularly amino-acids (Blackith 1961). This concentration increased, for example, in hatchlings of *Nomadacris* subjected to evaporation by the abrasion of the cuticle (p. 233), from 24·3% to 28·9% of the dry weight; although the osmotic pressure was not measured, it presumably affected the retention of water.

It has been suggested (Buxton 1932) that the rate of transpiration is correlated not with the relative humidity, but with the saturation deficit of the air; this was not the case in *Chortophaga* (Ludwig 1937) and this correlation is not regarded as necessarily valid (Ramsay 1953; Edney 1957).

Cuticular transpiration

As already mentioned, it is extremely difficult to differentiate between water lost with the expired air and that evaporated through the cuticle. Koidsumi (*t.c.*) attempted to eliminate tracheal transpiration by sealing all spiracles of live *Gastrimargus* with vaseline and claimed that this reduced the rate to about one-fourth of the normal; this he considered to represent cuticular transpiration. As pointed out by Jakovlev (1959), insects with all spiracles sealed die promptly and if they did not in Koidsumi's experiments, this suggests imperfect sealing. Jakovlev himself, therefore, studied transpiration in *Locusta* by enclosing a live insect in an air-tight partition between two chambers so that its head and thorax were in one chamber and the abdomen in the other. When all spiracles in either half of the locust were sealed with special glue, the locust did not die, but the tracheal transpiration in the relevant chamber was excluded. He claimed that the amount of water vapour in the air of both chambers remained the same (not specified), thus proving that all transpiration in *Locusta* was cuticular and that respiration played no part in the loss of water. Jakovlev suggested that in *Locusta* and, possibly also in *Schistocerca*, which would be liable to lose much water during long flight, purely cuticular transpiration has been developed as a special adaptation. Unfortunately, no parallel experiments on other species, which he assumed to have no such adaptation, were mentioned and no detailed record of these experiments on *Locusta* has been published.

Church (1960 *a*) measured cuticular transpiration in flying *Schistocerca*, with the spiracles, anus and mouth sealed, and found that the average water loss was 7 ± 0.6 mg/hr/locust at 30°C and 17 ± 1 mg/hr/locust at 40°C; these values were roughly one-third of the total water loss by a normal flying locust under the same conditions. This ratio between cuticular and respiratory transpiration appears reasonably supported by facts.

Koidsumi (*t.c.*) studied cuticular transpiration of *Gastrimargus* by applying to the integument a thin film of collodion which becomes clouded by water vapour. He found that transpiration was most active, on the one hand, in such heavily sclerotised parts as frons, clypeus, occiput, pronotum and pleurae and, on the other, on the thin membrane of the neck and between abdominal segments. Eder (1940) carried out similar tests on several European grasshoppers, using collodion with cobalt chloride, which turns blue with water vapour, and found strong transpiration on the pronotum, the whole of the abdomen and the femora. She connected this with the existence in the cuticle of pore canals which were particularly well developed in the pronotum. It is generally held that the canals end in the epicuticle (p. 32) and have no outer openings, so that the transpiration should depend on the permeability of the thin outer layer of epicuticle and on the amphion containing lipoid and wax (p. 33). Exact studies of transpiration in freshly killed *Schistocerca* adults (thus eliminating respiration, though not evaporation from the spiracles) have shown a sudden increase in the rate when the temperature rose to about 50°C (Beament 1959); in hoppers, the rise was gradual below that temperature, but also rapid when it was reached (fig. 136). This suggested that the sudden rise occurred when the melting point of wax was reached; in fact, this point for hoppers lies at 50–54°C (Pradhan & Bindra 1956). In *Melanoplus bivittatus* hoppers, also, the rate rose more steeply at about 45°C (fig. 137), whereas the curve of

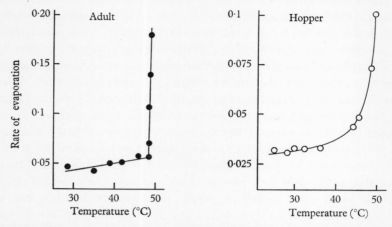

Fig. 136. *Schistocerca*, rates of evaporation (in mg/animal/mm. Hg/hr) from freshly killed adults and hoppers in relation to rising temperature (after Beament 1959).

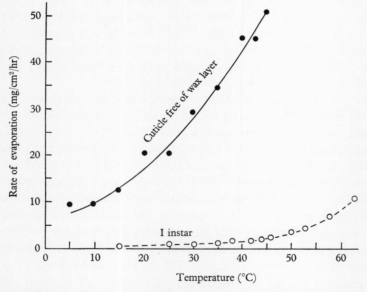

Fig. 137. *Melanoplus bivittatus*, rates of evaporation in Ist instar hoppers, normal (open circles) and with the cuticular wax layer removed (black circles), in relation to temperature (after Chefurka & Pepper 1955 b).

evaporation rate through cuticle free of wax layer followed a regular course (Chefurka & Pepper 1955 b). The shape of the transpiration curve in fig. 135, A, suggests a sudden rise in the rate at about 35°C in grasshoppers, while in *Locusta* this happens at 40°C (Jakovlev 1959), and these might be the melting points of wax in the species concerned. There are thus good reasons to suggest that the rate of cuticular transpiration, at least at high temperatures, is connected with the physical properties of the waxy covering, which appear to vary specifically, possibly in relation to the normal temperatures of the habitat.

The importance of the waxy covering was very strikingly shown by Blackith (1961) in the case of locust hatchlings. The amount of water lost after fifteen hours at 25°C and 65% RH was about ten times greater in hatchlings treated with abrasive siliceous dust than in the intact hatchlings (table 62).

It will be seen that the Desert Locust is very resistant to loss of water, even with the cuticle abraded; this may well be an adaptation to its dry and dusty environment.

Table 62. *Rates of water loss from hatchling locusts with intact or abraded cuticle* (*Blackith* 1961)

| Species and phase | Mean Weight mg | Water loss | | | |
| | | Intact | | Abraded | |
		mg/hr/insect	Percentage per hour	mg/hr/insect	Percentage per hour
Locusta, solitarious	12·4	0·004	0·40	0·637	6·37
,, gregarious	17·4	0·056	0·41	0·699	5·00
Nomadacris, gregarious	18·9	0·076	0·51	0·882	5·88
Schistocerca, gregarious	20·2	0·060	0·38	0·507	3·13

Spiracular transpiration

The data on cuticular transpiration, however inadequate, suggest that it plays a substantial part in the rate of water loss, particularly at higher temperatures. The evidence for water loss through the spiracles is even less satisfactory, and while there is no reason to exclude it as Jakovlev did (p. 231), quantitative data are lacking, the only exception being Koidsumi's (*t.c.*) statement that some 70% of transpiration in *Gastrimargus* was through the spiracles; his technique, however, leaves the results open to serious doubts.

The inadequacy of the available data on water economy of acridoids is particularly regrettable, since in their ecology they exhibit strong dependence on the humidity of the environment. Most of the experimental work in the past has been done on mesophilous species and it would be of value to carry out investigations on those from habitats with extreme dry or humid conditions. Such studies should comprise, on the one hand, the structure and properties of the integument and, on the other, detailed experimental investigations of water economy and its regulating mechanisms, always taking into account not only possible specific differences, but also those due to the stage and the physiological state of the insects. A possible distinction between the behaviour

233

of the haemolymph water and that bound in the tissues (p. 108) should also be borne in mind.

FATAL LIMITS OF DESICCATION

Desiccation as a sole lethal factor has hardly been studied, most of the few available data recording the combined effects of desiccation and starvation. Ludwig (1937) found that hoppers and adults of *Chortophaga viridifasciata*, kept at 0–5% RH, died when their water content fell to 56·1–58·8%, regardless of the original content. The latter was lower in hibernating hoppers than in active ones which had more reserve water and were able to survive a loss of 40% of the original total weight, while hibernating hoppers died on losing 28%, regardless of the original content (table 63).

Table 63. *Relation between the original water content and total weight and their values at death in* Chortophaga *kept at 0–5% RH* (*Ludwig* 1937)

Stage	Percentage water		Weight at death as percentage of the original
	Original	At death	
Hibernating hoppers	65·6–68·1	56·1–58·8	72·4–72·5
Active hoppers	70·7	56·3	61·1
,, ,, and adults	73·6–75·9	57·9–58·8	54·8–56·2

Ludwig's data on the length of life of *Chortophaga* hoppers starved at humidities ranging from 0 to 96% have shown (fig. 138) that they all died within 5·2–6·6 days regardless of humidity, although those at the lower humidities lost relatively much more weight; this suggests that their death was due to starvation, not desiccation alone.

Blackith (1961) recorded that hatchlings of *Locusta*, *Schistocerca* and *Nomadacris* died when their water content dropped to about 63%, regardless of the initial content. The latter, in the case of *Schistocerca*, varied from 74 to 84%, larger hatchlings having relatively more reserve water and, therefore, being able to survive longer. The latter point was illustrated by Albrecht & Blackith (1960) in the case of starving *Schistocerca* hatchlings (p. 334); gregarious hoppers weighing 19–23 mg survived for 70–100 hours, while the solitarious ones weighing 10·5–13·5 mg died in 43–50 hours. However, the length of survival was appreciably higher at 35% than at 100% RH in the case of gregarious hatchlings, while the solitarious ones showed a reverse relation which possibly suggests different osmoregulation in the two; the starvation effects could not be separated. The rate of water loss was greatly increased if the waxy waterproof covering of the cuticle was abraded (p. 233). In a more recent and extensive paper, Albrecht (1962*b*) has shown that hatchlings of

Locusta and *Nomadacris* survived longer at high air humidity, while those of *Schistocerca* were more resistant to desiccation. He has also found (1964) that solitarious adults of *Locusta* survived at 30 % RH and 30° C for 140 hours,

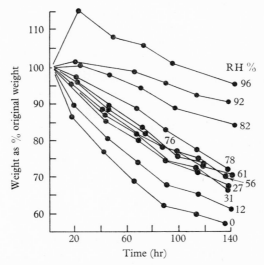

Fig. 138. Length of life of starved *Chortophaga* hoppers at different relative humidities
(after Ludwig 1937).

if they were green, but the brown-coloured lived for 185 hours; brown gregarious adults were still most resistant, surviving for 210 hours.

The high resistance of adult *Schistocerca* to desiccation was suggested by Millot & Fontaine (1937) whose data will be found on p. 226.

THE EGG AND EMBRYONIC
DEVELOPMENT

EXTERNAL APPEARANCE OF EGGS

An egg (fig. 139) is a slightly curved cylinder, tapering to roundly blunted apices; its length is usually about four to five times its diameter, though in *Euthystira* the ratio is about three, while the egg of *Acrida* is about eight times as long as wide (Hafez & Ibrahim 1958).

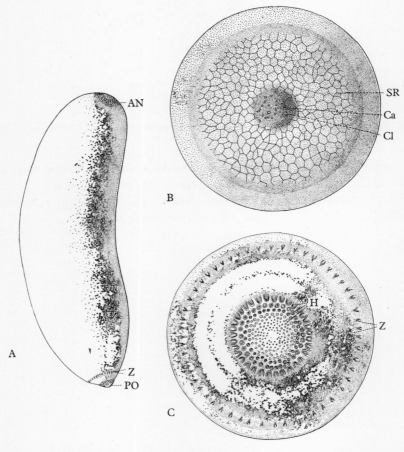

Fig. 139. *Dociostaurus* egg. A, side view; B, anterior (cephalic) end; C, posterior (caudal) end (Jannone 1939*b*).

AN, anterior end; PO, posterior end; Z, micropylar zone; SR, surface of the anterior end; Cl, cap of the anterior end; Ca, opening of 'false aeriferous canals'; H, hydropyle.

Although the size of the newly laid egg depends to some extent on the size of the species, its length in small species is greater in relation to the female body length than in large. Thus, the female of *Parepistaurus* is 15·3 mm long, but its egg is 4·18–4·34 mm, the ratio being nearly a quarter, while the female of *Ornithacris*, 60 mm long, has the egg 6·25 mm long, that is almost one-tenth (Phipps 1959). Considerable individual variation in egg-size occurs, particularly in the swarming species, in which the gregarious phase has larger eggs than the solitarious (p. 353). Moreover, a substantial increase in size of eggs occurs in the course of incubation (p. 246).

The coloration of eggs is fairly constant for a species, but it is also subject to some change with development. The more common shades are yellow, grey, pink and brown, darker colours being apparently associated with thicker chorion; for example, very hard eggs of *Sauracris* are deep brown (Popov 1959). The eggs of *Schistocerca obscura* and of *S. lineata* (Tuck & Smith 1940; Duck 1944) are of unusual red colour.

EGG COVERINGS

Studies on the finer structure of eggs have been considered technically difficult, their sectioning being hampered by abundant yolk and by very resistant membranes. However, treatment of eggs by cupric phenol and subsequent soaking in water renders them easy to section (Slifer & King 1933; Roonwal 1936).

The literature dealing with egg coverings is extensive, but very confused as regards the interpretation and the nomenclature of their different layers (McNabb 1928; Kulagin 1932; Roonwal 1936 a, 1954 a, 1954 b; Slifer 1938 a, 1949 a, 1949 b; Slifer & Sekhon 1963; Matthée 1951; Salt 1952; Shutts 1949). Slifer (1937) has introduced order into chaos and her system, with a few later additions (Hartley 1961), is followed below.

A point of both theoretical and practical importance is that egg coverings are formed gradually, beginning during development in the ovary and still continuing after oviposition (fig. 140).

The first to make its appearance is the delicate *vitelline membrane* (fig. 140, A, VM) developing on the surface of the yolk mass shortly before the egg is ready for laying. Simultaneously, or a little earlier, the follicular cells of the ovariole secrete the inner layers of the chorion (CH). When two layers of the chorion have been secreted, the egg passes into the oviduct where it acquires a thin extrachorion (ECH), probably of mucous secretion, not of the same origin as the chorion proper. A newly laid egg (fig. 140, B) has a distinct vitelline membrane, a substantial chorion and a thin outer extrachorion. The vitelline membrane disappears very soon. After about a week's incubation, when the embryo begins to develop (fig. 140, C), there appears a new membrane, the *serosa* (SE) which has a cellular structure and envelops the yolk and the embryo.

The serosa then secretes on its outer surface two further membranes, the *yellow cuticle* (YC) which is very thin, and the thick, fibrous *white cuticle* (fig. 140, D, WC). The white cuticle later (fig. 140, E) becomes very thick; it has

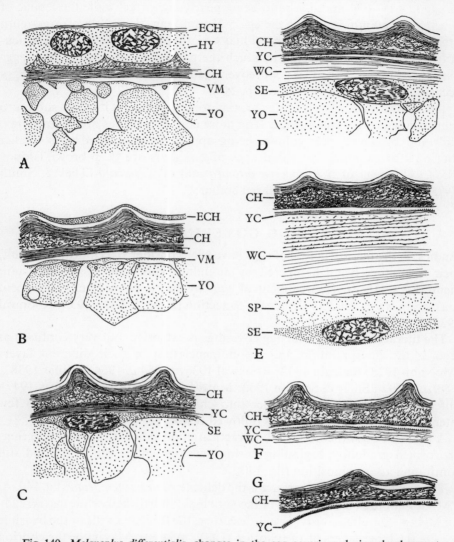

Fig. 140. *Melanoplus differentialis*, changes in the egg coverings during development (after Slifer 1937, modified).

ECH, extrachorion; HY, hypoderm; CH, chorion; VM, vitelline membrane; YO, yolk; SE, serosa; YC, yellow cuticle; WC, white cuticle; SP, space filled with liquid.

been miscalled in the past the vitelline membrane (Uvarov 1928) or oölemma (Kulagin 1932). Still later, the embryo secretes a provisional *embryonic cuticle* enveloping it (Sharan 1958). Shortly before hatching (fig. 140, F), the white cuticle decreases in thickness and then almost disappears (fig. 140, G); by this time, the extrachorion may become cracked and peel off as a result of drying, though in eggs kept moist it is preserved intact to the end. Thus, the egg surface may present a different appearance depending on the age of the egg, and this must be borne in mind in all studies.

As regards more detailed data on each type of egg covering, the thin yellow cuticle is chemically related to the cuticulin of the exoskeleton containing no chitin, but the white cuticle consists mainly of chitin, has fibrous structure and is traversed by fine pore canals not penetrating into the yellow cuticle (F. L. Campbell 1929; Slifer 1949a; Matthée 1951). The chorion is soluble in NaOCl except for a very fine membrane at its inner surface, which also has a thin wax

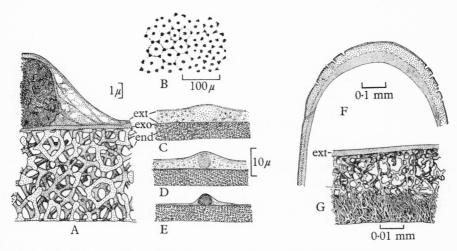

Fig. 141. A–E, *Locusta*, egg coverings. A, enlarged section, showing fibrous structure of endochorion; B, surface sculpturing; C, D, E, reduction of extrachorion and formation of tubercles. F and G, *Chorthippus parallelus*, egg coverings (Hartley 1961).

covering (Slifer 1948, 1958b; Matthée 1951). Chemically, the two layers of chorion are probably composed of two kinds of protein (Jahn 1935b).

The fine structure of the chorion has been much in dispute but the latest investigation by Hartley (1961) has helped to clarify it (fig. 141). The innermost layer is the endochorion which in the *Locusta* egg consists of a meshwork of fine fibres, with spaces between them filled with air or liquid; outside it lies the thin *exochorion*, the surface of which shows faint hexagonal pattern, which corresponds to the shape of the follicular cells with an indistinct central spot in each of the hexagons. The outermost layer, added when the egg is in the oviduct, is the *extrachorion*; it contains granules and its thickness decreases while the egg is still in the common oviduct; as it shrinks, the granules condense in the corners of the hexagons and in the central spots (fig. 141, C, D). When the egg is laid, the extrachorion shrinks further and the condensed granules form tubercles (fig. 141, E) which may be connected by raised lines in a more or less clear hexagonal pattern (fig. 141, B). The extrachorion may eventually crack and peel off.

The chorion of the few other species so far studied shows the same general features, but with modifications. In the *Schistocerca* egg, there is no clear differentiation between the exochorion and the endochorion; the extrachorion when it shrinks lies over the tops of the ridges, leaving spaces between it and the chorion proper. In *Chorthippus parallelus* the endochorion has a denser mesh in the inner zone (fig. 141, F, G), the exochorion is very thin and the extrachorion is relatively thick and continuous.

These descriptions suggest, firstly, a need for studies of chorionic coverings in many species, before their significance in egg biology can be understood. The fibrous nature of the endochorion is probably of importance in maintaining the water balance of the egg and, possibly, in its respiration. The presence of air spaces under the extrachorion may also have some functional consequences, but much more information is needed on these fine structures and on the changes in them during egg development under different conditions.

The surface sculpturing of the extrachorion is of importance in practice, since its pattern, although essentially hexagonal, offers considerable variation in different species and makes possible the identification of eggs. Tuck & Smith (1940) provided descriptions, figures and a key to eggs of forty-four North American species, largely based on surface sculpturing, and Hilliard (1959) and Onsager & Mulkern (1963) added further data. Zimin (1938) has supplied descriptions and a key to egg-pods and eggs of sixty-five Russian species while Chapman & Robertson (1958) have done the same for forty-eight species from Central Africa, Chapman (1961) for forty-eight West African, and Katiyar (1960) for fourteen Indian species.

Chapman & Robertson suggested a classification of types of sculpturing, which is offered here in a modified form (fig. 142).

(1) Surface smooth.
(2) Irregular tubercles. (A,K,L)
(3) Tubercles arranged in hexagons. (B,C,D)
(4) Hexagonal, pentagonal or oval cells, without tubercles. (E,F,I)
(5) Cells with corner tubercles. (C,D,J)
(6) Cells with corner and central tubercles.

It would appear that the basic pattern is a cellular one, with raised ridges which separate the cells and may be reinforced by tubercles at the corners and in the middle, and a gradation from a smooth surface, through an irregularly tuberculated one, to the cellular pattern conveys an impression of a regular series. Extreme developments also occur, for example, when the ridges are very thick and there are central tubercles or when the corner tubercles become spine-like.

The taxonomic distribution of the types of sculpturing is not clear. It appears, however, that the eggs of Pamphagidae, Pyrgomorphidae, Catantopinae, Calliptaminae and Cyrtacanthacridinae usually have a well-developed cellular pattern, whereas those of Oedipodinae have an irregularly tuberculate surface, and in Gomphocerinae the surface is frequently smooth, or with a weak cellular pattern. Since the latter is the most advanced group, it is possible to speculate that the evolution of the pattern has been by its gradual simplification, from heavily sculptured to smooth. However, only a few representatives of each group have been studied.

No obvious relation can be found between the surface sculpturing and the ecology of eggs, nor is there enough evidence on the possible variation within the species, but there are good specific differences (compare fig. 142, F and J).

In future studies, the possibility should be kept in mind that there may be

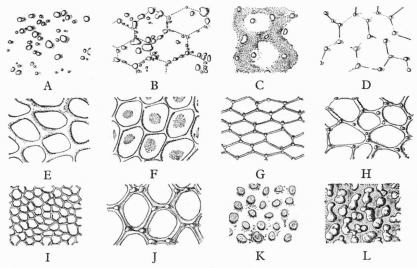

Fig. 142. Surface sculpturing of eggs (after Zimin 1938).
A, *Sphingonotus coerulipes*; B, *Angaracris barabensis*; C, *Epacromius coerulipes*; D, *Thisoecetrinus pterostichus*; E, *Asiotmethis muricatus*; F, *Celes skalozubovi*; G, *Podisma pedestris*; H, *Calliptamus italicus*; I, *Dericorys albidula*; J, *Celes variabilis*; K, *Pyrgodera armata*, near posterior end of egg; L, ditto, middle of egg.

some differences in the surface pattern between an egg still in the ovary and one that has been in an egg-pod for a long time. In most of the descriptions, the source and age of the eggs were not stated.

The above descriptions apply only to sculpturing on the main body of the egg, and it may be substantially different near its ends, particularly posteriorly, where often a differently coloured and sculptured 'cap' may be distinguished (fig. 142, K and L). Within this cap lie two specialised structures, the hydropyle and the micropyle.

HYDROPYLE

Since water is essential for the development of the embryo, the problem arises how water is able to reach it and a solution was offered by Slifer (1938a; Slifer & Sekhon 1963).

At the posterior end of the egg there can be seen a round area without external sculpturing and with its surface riddled, like a sieve (fig. 139, *c*), by minute pores leading into canals which traverse the exochorion and the endochorion (Slifer 1938*a*, 1949*a*, 1950*b*; Jannone 1939*b*; Matthée 1951). The yellow and the white cuticle under this area are thinner and modified in structure, and the serosal cells are enlarged and specialised (fig. 143). Jannone thought these canals might supply air to the egg, but Slifer has showed that sealing them artificially prevents the intake of water by the egg, and she called this structure the hydropyle (water-gate). Sealing also occurs naturally during a diapause (p. 257) when wax is deposited in the hydropyle of *Melanoplus* (Slifer, *tt.cc.*), while in *Locustana* the sealing material is protein (Matthée, *t.c.*). According to

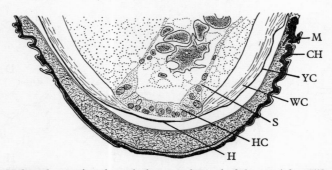

Fig. 143. *Melanoplus*, section through the posterior end of the egg (after Slifer 1938 *a*). M, micropyle; CH, chorion; YC, yellow cuticle; WC, white cuticle; S, serosa; H, hydropyle; HC, hydropyle cells.

Hartley (1961), the egg of *Chorthippus parallelus* also has a hydropyle, but in other species of the genus the whole egg can take up water, though no evidence of this was provided.

MICROPYLE

The penetration of the sperm into the egg is ensured by the micropyle, a ring of easily visible pores round the posterior end of the egg containing the hydropyle (fig. 139). The detailed structure of the micropyle, as described for *Schistocerca* and some other Indian species (Husain & Roonwal 1933; Roonwal 1954*b*), *Locusta* (Roonwal 1954*a*) and *Dociostaurus* (Jannone 1939*b*) is essentially the same in all cases (fig. 144). Outer openings of micropylar canals are thirty-five to forty-three in number in *Locusta*, forty-four to sixty-five in *Schistocerca*, fifty to sixty in *Dociostaurus*. The opening of each canal appears as a shallow depression of the chorion and the funnel-shaped canal continues obliquely downwards through the exochorion and endochorion. No substantial differences were found between the micropylar structures of representatives of Acridinae, Gomphocerinae, Oedipodinae, Catantopinae and Pyrgomorphidae.

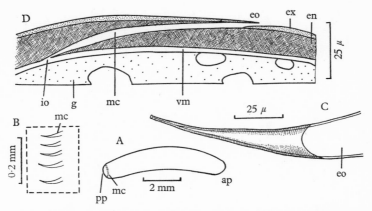

Fig. 144. *Locusta*, micropylar apparatus. A, whole egg; B, openings of micropylar canals; C, a canal enlarged; D, longitudinal section of egg-wall in the micropylar zone (after Roonwal 1954*a*).

ap, anterior end of egg; pp, posterior end; ex, exochorion; en, endochorion; vm, vitelline membrane; g, yolk; mc, micropylar canal; eo, external opening of a canal; io, internal opening.

RESPIRATORY (?) CANALS

Jannone (1939*b*) described in *Dociostaurus* a circular area at the anterior pole of the egg, with a score of minute openings of canals which penetrate the exochorion (fig. 139, B). He did not think the canals reached the endochorion and therefore called them 'false aeriferous canals'. However, the existence in the endochorion of air spaces, in at least some species (p. 239), makes it essential to investigate whether these canals lead to the air spaces, in which case they might be regarded as an aeropyle.

As Shumakov & Yakhimovich (1950) pointed out, embryos in diapausing eggs of *Locusta* placed in water at 25° C are able to complete their development almost to hatching, which suggests that they can obtain oxygen without having access to free air. This is not surprising since the embryo is, in any case, surrounded by a liquid (Jones 1958), but the mechanism of penetration of air through the egg coverings and the significance of the chorionic air spaces are still obscure. Wigglesworth & Beament (1950) suggested that in *Locusta* there is a diffusion of gases through egg-coverings but this has not been supported by convincing evidence.

THE EMBRYO

Embryonic development begins with the differentiation of germ cells near the posterior (micropylar) end of the egg, followed by the development of the embryo on its concave side (fig. 145) and its gradual growth and movement downwards; on reaching the posterior end of the egg, the embryo bends

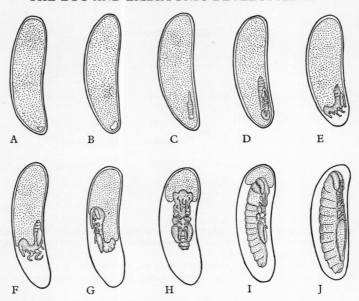

Fig. 145. *Dociostaurus*, main stages in the embryonic development.
A–D, anatrepsis; E–G, blastokinesis; H–J, katatrepsis (after Bodenheimer & Shulov 1951).

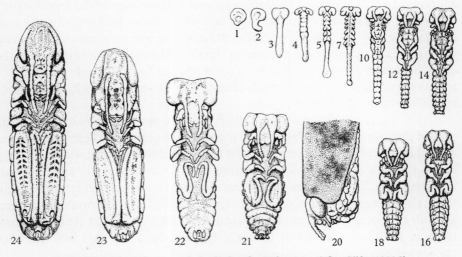

Fig. 146. *Melanoplus*, morphological embryonic stages (after Slifer 1932 b).

round inside it and begins an upward movement along the convex side, at the same time rotating on its long axis, while continuing to grow and to develop segmentation of body and appendages. As a result, the fully developed embryo lies with its head at the upper end of the egg in its normal position in the soil, facing its concave side. The movement of the embryo inside the egg is called *blastokinesis* (or revolution), the period before turning is termed

244

anatrepsis and that after it *katatrepsis*, though there is no sharp division between the two periods. Development of a normal embryo may occasionally occur without blastokinesis (Slifer 1932 *a*).

In detailed studies on the course and the rate of embryonic development it is useful to designate the exact morphological stages reached, in order to make comparisons between species, or to study the effect of various factors on the development of the same species. Sequences of morphological stages in embryonic development have been established for several species, for example, *Melanoplus* spp. (Nelsen 1931 *b*; Slifer 1932*a*, 1932*b*; Moore 1948; Salt 1949*a*; Riegert 1961), *Locusta* (Roonwal 1936*b*, 1937; Shumakov & Yakhimovich 1950; Shulov & Pener 1959), *Schistocerca* (Jhingran 1947; Shulov & Pener 1961, 1963), *Austroicetes* (Steele 1941), *Dociostaurus* (Jannone 1939*b*; Bodenheimer & Shulov 1951) and *Locustana* (Matthée 1951).

The following scheme of embryonic stages, illustrated in fig. 146, has been prepared by Slifer (1932*b*) and Moore (*t.c.*) assigned to it the percentages of development.

(1) A tiny cap of cells at posterior end of egg.
(2) Differentiation into 'head' and 'tail' (10%).
(3) Tail elongates.
(4–5) Rudiments of antennae and labrum; segmentation of anterior part of 'tail' into paired protuberances; the first three pairs are rudiments of mandibles, maxillae and labrum; the other three those of the thorax and its appendages (20%).
(6–7) Segmentation of abdomen (30%).
(8–9) Segmentation of mouth parts begins; a furrow along thorax and abdomen.
(10) Rudimentary legs turn inwards; notch on posterior border of labrum.
(11–14) Differentiation of all appendages continues (40%).
(15) Pleuropodia (ventral abdominal appendages, see p. 269) clearly visible; posterior legs curved (50%).
(16–18) Very little further change (if embryo in diapause).
(20) Embryo turning—blastokinesis (60%).
(21–22) Antennae and legs show segmentation (70%).
(23) Legs well differentiated (80%).
(24) Spines of posterior tibiae clearly pigmented. Embryo ready to hatch (100%).

Other authors distinguished somewhat different numbers of stages: twenty-three for *Locusta* (Shulov & Pener, *t.c.*), sixteen for *Austroicetes cruciata* (Steele, *t.c.*), eighteen (Jhingran, *t.c.*) or twenty-three for *Schistocerca* (Shulov & Pener, *t.c.*), seventeen for *Melanoplus sanguinipes* (Moore *t.c.*) and twenty for *Dociostaurus* (Jannone, *t.c.*; Bodenheimer & Shulov 1951) and twenty-two for *Calliptamus palaestinensis* (Pener & Shulov 1960).

It would appear desirable, if possible, to establish some uniform criteria for classifying the embryonic stages, in order to facilitate comparisons between species. It is somewhat odd to see that stage 14 of *Locusta* differs substantially from stage 14 of *Dociostaurus*.

The relation of the morphological development of the embryo to incubation time is illustrated by fig. 147.

Parallel with the external morphology of the embryo, there occurs the differentiation and development of its internal organs. Development of all systems was described for *Locusta* by Kulagin (1923), Shumakov & Yakhimovich (1950) and, in more detail, by Roonwal (1936b, 1937); other authors dealt with different tissues and organs, for example eyes (Bernard 1937), digestive tract (Stuart 1935b), heart (Walker 1935; Thompson 1937, 1938), nervous system (Baden 1936, 1938; Tahmisian 1943; Shafiq 1954, 1955), chordotonal organs (Slifer 1935), terminal abdominal structures (Karandikar 1942), reproductive and copulatory organs (Nel 1929; Else 1934; Nelsen 1931a, 1931b, 1934; Qadri 1940; Snodgrass 1937; Colombo & Bassato 1957),

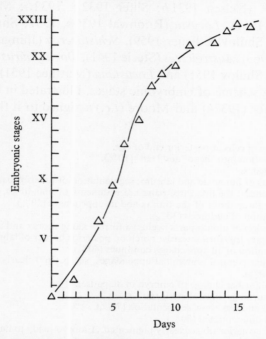

Fig. 147. *Locusta*, relation of the embryonic stages to the incubation time (Shulov & Pener 1959).

Malpighian tubes (Savage 1956), endocrine glands (Jones 1956a, 1956b), suboesophageal ganglion and pericardial cells (Kessel 1961).

EGG SIZE AND WEIGHT

Embryonic development is accompanied by changes in the size of the egg. A freshly laid egg of *Locusta* averages 5.68×1.18 mm; at the middle of development it measures 6.92×1.82 and when ready to hatch 7.85×1.99 mm (Roonwal 1936a). Similar increases have been recorded for other species, with the exception of the highly xerophilous *Tmethis*, the egg of which does not change in size (Shulov 1952d). Daily weight changes during the whole development were studied in *Schistocerca* by Shulov & Pener (1963). Since in *Locusta* and other species there is no increase, and even a decrease, in the dry weight

Table 64. *Changes in wet and (in brackets) dry weight, and percentage increases in wet weight during development of an egg*

	Weight in mg				
Species	Freshly laid	Half developed	Fully developed	Increase percentage	Reference
Locusta m. migratorioides	6·3(3·0)	13·5(3·0)	14·0(2·4)	122	Roonwal 1936 *b*
,, ,,	7·1(3·3)	12·3(2·9)	15·4(2·9)	118	Shulov & Pener 1959
Schistocerca gregaria	10·5	19·1	23·5	122	Shulov 1952 *b*
,, ,,	9·0(4·8)	—	17·4(4·6)	93	Roonwal 1954 *b*
,, ,,	—	—	—	104–159	Hunter-Jones 1964
Anacridium aegyptium	6·6	13·5	14·6	110	Shulov 1952 *b*
Dociostaurus maroccanus	6·7	5·5	9·4	70	Bodenheimer & Shulov 1951
Tmethis pulchripennis	13·4	13·1	8–13	0	Shulov 1952 *d*

(Salzen 1960), the total weight increase is probably due to the absorption of water by the developing egg. In fact, table 64 and fig. 148 show that the water content of eggs of most species is more than doubled during development and the role of water in developing eggs is discussed below (p. 256).

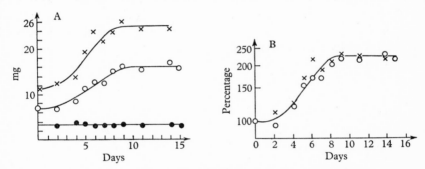

Fig. 148. A, increase in weight of developing eggs (upper curve, *Schistocerca*; middle curve, *Locusta*; lower line, dehydrated *Locusta* eggs). B, percentage increase in weight of *Locusta* and *Schistocerca* eggs (Shulov & Pener 1959).

RESPIRATION OF EGG

The mechanism of egg respiration remains unstudied, the assumption being that egg covers and embryonic membranes are permeable to gases (Wigglesworth & Beament 1950). The fact that eggs of *Melanoplus* (Bodine 1933; Boell 1935) and of *Locusta* (Shumakov & Yakhimovich 1957) can develop also under water suggests that the embryo can obtain oxygen from water and that carbon dioxide is eliminated also by diffusion into water; this is not surprising, since the embryo inside the egg is always surrounded by a liquid. Moreover, the existence in the egg-shell of air-filled spaces (p. 239) has not yet been considered in relation to respiration; these spaces may well be regarded as a *plastron* (Hinton 1962).

Since the rate of respiration provides an index to the rate of general metabolism, a considerable amount of work has been done on the respiration of eggs,

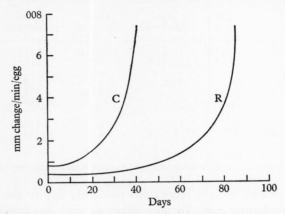

Fig. 149. Oxygen consumption of developing non-diapause eggs of *Chortophaga* (C) and *Romalea* (R) (after Bodine 1932).

particularly by the late Dr J. H. Bodine and his many collaborators at the Iowa University. However, the main emphasis in that work was on the metabolic phenomena connected with the diapause, and the respiration of non-diapausing eggs received less attention.

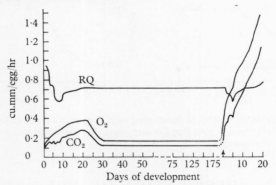

Fig. 150. Changes in the oxygen consumption (O_2), carbon dioxide production (CO_2) and respiratory quotient (RQ) of *Melanoplus* eggs developing with a diapause (after Boell 1935).

The rate of oxygen consumption by eggs of *Chortophaga* and *Romalea* developing without a diapause shows a regular gradual increase (Bodine 1929, 1932; fig. 149). In the eggs of *Melanoplus differentialis* subject to diapause, both the oxygen consumption and carbon dioxide output rise steadily during the early development and reach their maximum at about the twentieth day (fig. 150), when the embryo, still in the anatrepsis stage, enters the diapause and the respiration rate falls to a low level, at which it remains until the development is resumed, when it rises very steeply (Burkholder 1934; Boell 1935).

An important point to consider is the respiratory quotient (RQ), that is, the volume ratio of carbon dioxide produced to oxygen consumed, since the value of the quotient indicates which chemical substances are oxidised in each stage of development. The initial value of the quotient in *Melanoplus* is fairly high (0·87 to 1·05) suggesting the utilisation of carbohydrates, but on the fourth day it falls to 0·71, and it remains near that level throughout the major part of the development, indicating that fat (egg-yolk) is the chief source of energy. This is supported by the evidence on the great reduction in the amounts of fatty acids in eggs during the course of development (table 65). The initial

Table 65. *Utilisation of fat for respiration of developing eggs of* Melanoplus differentialis (*after Boell* 1935)

Period of development	Number of days	Total fatty acid lost from eggs during each period (from Slifer 1930)		Total O$_2$ consumption during each period		O$_2$ required to oxidise total fat (cu.mm)	Percentage of O$_2$ uptake of each period on basis of fat
		mg	Percentage	cu.mm	Percentage		
Pre-diapause	21	0·034	14·4	140·7	21·0	69·4	49·5
1st and 2nd weeks	14	0·013	5·5	79·2	11·8	26·4	33·4
3rd week	7	0·021	8·9	61·5	9·2	43·0	70·0
Diapause	28	0·025	10·5	116·0	17·3	52·6	45·3
1st week	7	0·009	3·8	29·0	4·3	18·4	63·5
4th week	7	0·014	5·9	29·0	4·3	28·8	99·3
Post-diapause	18	0·178	75·0	415·0	62·0	364·0	87·8
Whole development	67	0·237	100·0	671·7	100·0	486·0	72·5

fat content of the *Melanoplus* egg is 17–22% of the dry weight, but eventually less than half of it remains (Slifer 1930). In *Locusta* eggs the initial percentage of fat is 18·81, falling to 15·33 before hatching (Zambin 1939; see also table 70). Salzen (1960) found that an egg of *Locusta* loses some 20% of its dry weight and he ascribes this to fat combustion for respiration. Some further data on fat in eggs will be found on p. 267.

CHEMISTRY OF EGG

Carbohydrates

Carbohydrates (particularly reducing sugars) are considered the main energy source in the first few days of the development of the *Melanoplus* egg; later they are utilised for the embryo growth and, to a lesser degree, for the formation of the embryonic cuticles (D. L. Hill 1945) but their total quantity increases; thus the percentage of glucose to dry weight in the *Locusta* egg increases from 1·85 in the early post-diapause egg to 3·57 before hatching

(Zambin 1939; see p. 266). The changes in the relative carbohydrate content of the embryo and the yolk suggest that this increase in the total egg carbohydrate occurs at the expense of the yolk, as well as by the conversion of protein (Bodine & West 1953).

Proteins

Proteins constitute a high percentage of the dry matter of eggs, for example up to 54·3 % in eggs of *Locusta* (Cheu 1952). While the total nitrogen content of the *Melanoplus* egg remains constant throughout embryonic development, the embryo nitrogen increases at the expense of the yolk nitrogen; shell

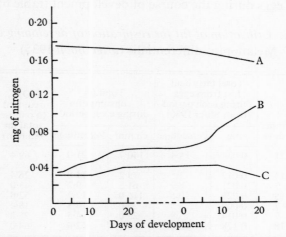

Fig. 151. Changes in the nitrogen content of *Melanoplus* eggs developing with a diapause (after Trowbridge & Bodine 1940; modified).
A, total nitrogen; B, shell and embryo nitrogen; C, shell nitrogen; vertical distance between B and C represents embryo nitrogen; that between A and B represents the yolk nitrogen.

nitrogen at first increases slightly owing to the formation of the white cuticle, then decreases with its digestion (fig. 151). Determinations of the uric acid in developing eggs of the same insect suggest that approximately 6·6% of the initial total protein is broken down (Bodine 1946).

A large number of amino-acids involved in egg metabolism, including those containing sulphur, have been determined (Shaw 1955; Fu 1957; Teppert 1958). Studies of changes in the amino-acid content of developing *Schisto-cerca* eggs (Colombo, Benassi *et al.* 1962) have shown that the quantities of the twenty acids identified were low during the earliest embryonic states, but a great increase occurred at stages 8–9, when the embryo was still poorly formed. The spectra of the free acids in the yolk and in the embryo were different, and it appeared that some acids were degraded, or synthetised mainly in the yolk, others mainly in the embryo. The high content of the glutamic acid in the earlier development stages indicated metabolic activity of the yolk, which also contained beta-alanine and aspartic acid, whereas glycine, proline and tyrosine were thought to be involved mainly in the metabolism of the embryo.

Still in the initial stages are studies on egg nucleoproteins, very complicated compounds of phosphorus-containing nucleic acids with proteins, regarded as important chemical constituents of chromosomes. The total egg phosphorus remains constant during development, but the lipid phosphorus declines rapidly in its early stages, while phosphorus in ribonucleic (RNA) and desoxyribonucleic (DNA) acids increases with the growth of the embryo; it was suggested that DNA is almost entirely confined to the cell nuclei of the embryo, while RNA is found mainly in the cytoplasm (Thompson & Bodine 1938; Lu & Bodine 1953).

Enzymes

The information on the enzymes concerned with the various metabolic processes in the developing egg is very scattered and table 66 presents an incomplete summary of it.

Table 66. *Enzymes in developing* Melanoplus *egg*
(*after Fitzgerald* 1949; *modified*)

Enzyme	Location	First appearance	Author
Cytochrome oxidase	Embryo	14 days	Allen 1940
Cholinesterase	Embryo	6 days	Tahmisian 1943
Esterases	Yolk	At laying	Carlson 1941
Tyrosinase	Extra-embryonic fluid	10 days	Bodine & Allen 1941; Jones 1956a
Catalase	Yolk (?)	9 days	M. E. Williams 1936
Alkaline phosphatase	Extra-embryonic fluid	12–14 days	Fitzgerald 1949
Indophenol oxidase	Yolk	At laying	Bodine & Boell 1935

Proteases of *Dociostaurus* eggs were discussed by Lichtenstein, Bodenheimer & Shulov (1949), and those of *Locusta* eggs by Shulov, Pener *et al.* (1957); enzyme systems in the eggs of *Dociostaurus* and *Schistocerca* proved to contain at least two lipolytic enzymes with somewhat different properties (Fodor 1949).

Vitamins

Substances giving fluorescence in ultra-violet light and determined as riboflavin (vitamin B_2) have been found in eggs of *Schistocerca* (Busnel & Chauvin 1942; Busnel & Drilhon 1942; Goodwin & Srisukh 1951 a), *Melanoplus* (Bodine & Fitzgerald 1947a, 1947b, 1948b) and *Locusta* (De Lerma 1951 b, 1952). Pterin, which also has some vitamin properties, was found in *Melanoplus* eggs (Bodine & Fitzgerald, *t.c.*; Burgess 1949). Carotenoids, in particular β-carotene (vitamin A), occurs in eggs of *Schistocerca* and *Locusta* (Goodwin & Srisukh

1949). The presence of vitamin D in eggs of *Schistocerca* recorded by Brodskis & Rungs (1944) needs confirmation.

TEMPERATURE REQUIREMENTS

While a certain range of favourable conditions is essential for the development of eggs of all species, in some of them the development is not continuous and the growth of the embryo ceases on reaching a particular stage, regardless of the conditions, and is only resumed after an inactive period, or diapause. The diapause type of development is discussed separately (p. 259) and the simpler conditions for continuous development are reviewed first.

The incubation time of non-diapause eggs is affected by the temperature in the same way as all biological processes. The relation between constant temperature and the duration of incubation can be represented by an empirical curve, approaching a hyperbola, the reciprocal of which is a straight line along most of its course; along this line lie the values of the daily percentage rates of development at the respective temperatures, obtained by dividing 100 (= complete development) by the number of days at the given temperature (fig. 152).

Theoretically, the intersection of the straight line with the temperature axis should denote the point at which all development ceases, that is the *development zero* or the *threshold of development*. Detailed studies on other insects (Uvarov 1931; Lin, Hodson & Richards 1954) has shown, however, that the reciprocal line diverges from the straight at its ends and that the empirical value for the threshold is somewhat higher than the theoretical. This empirical value is not easy to establish, because it should be that below which no development (i.e. cell division) occurs; it may, however, proceed at a rate too slow to be observed. In fact, Church & Salt (1952) have found that some development of embryos of *Melanoplus bivittatus* may occur at a temperature as low as 5°C, although the threshold for normal development was about 12°C. Thus, the conception of the threshold of development remains somewhat theoretical and its biological significance is not clear.

In all experimental work the total length of the incubation period is determined by the time elapsed between oviposition and hatching, which is assumed to occur as soon as the embryo is fully grown. It is, however, commonly observed in the field that fully developed eggs begin to hatch immediately they are dug out and exposed to a higher temperature than in the soil. This is understandable because the completion of embryonic development depends on the amount of heat needed for the metabolic processes and cell division, while the hatching process is one of movement (p. 271) and some additional stimulus may be required to initiate it. Exact observations are needed to establish how long a fully developed embryo may be prevented from hatching by the lack of a stimulus for movement. In the absence of such data the *hatching threshold*, which is easily observable, cannot be regarded as the terminal point of embryonic development, which may be somewhat lower.

A further point is the effects of the incubation temperature on the *percentage of hatching*. Figure 152 shows clearly sudden reductions of the percentage at the extreme temperatures. Since the best percentage obtained was eighty, some 40% hatch may be regarded as satisfactory, in which case the temperature range 23–37° should be regarded as giving a reasonable hatch in *Schistocerca*. In

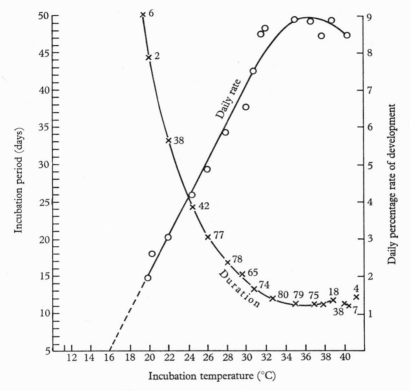

Fig. 152. *Schistocerca* eggs, duration of incubation, rates of development and percentage hatch (figures along the curve) in relation to temperature (original by P. Hunter-Jones).

Locusta, hatches over 40% were obtained by Ahmad (1936) within the range of 27–37°C and possibly below, because the hatch at the next lower temperature of 23° was 37%. The hatching percentage is of great practical value, and it may be useful to introduce this conception into the evaluation of experimental results. By analogy with the 50% mortality level from insecticides, conventionally accepted as the measure of their comparative toxicity (the lethal dose being designated as LD50), it is suggested that H40 be regarded as an index to the *hatchability threshold*.

In other insects (e.g. the bug *Oncopeltus*), it was found that some high hatching percentages of eggs incubated at favourable temperatures produced nymphs

253

with very poor survival (Lin, Hodson & Richards, *t.c.*; Hodson & Al Rawy 1958). This suggested the need for determining the *viability threshold*, defined as the lowest temperature producing a reasonably high percentage of hoppers which are able to reach the adult stage if kept under favourable conditions, for example V40. This aspect, admittedly very important for population studies, has not been investigated in any acridoid insect.

Since eggs in nature are not incubated in constant conditions, there is a need for some means of comparing the incubation periods at constant and fluctuating temperatures. In theory, it may be assumed that complete development would be achieved when the embryo received, throughout the incubation period, the requisite amount of heat. This amount can be expressed by multiplying the effective temperature (i.e. the number of degrees above the hatching threshold) by the number of days of exposure to a constant temperature, thus obtaining the *thermal constant*, or the sum of temperatures required to complete incubation, expressed in degree-days. The assumption is that this sum is the same whatever the constant temperature, and in the case of fluctuating temperatures the same value should be expected when the sums for each period at a given temperature are added together. In *Locusta m. gallica*, if the effective temperatures were calculated above the theoretical threshold of 14·4°C, the thermal constant was found to keep at about 240 degree-days at constant temperatures ranging from 16 to 40°, and also when the temperature fluctuated between 30° and 20° and 30° and 0° (Le Berre 1953). However, if 18°C was accepted as the empirical threshold, the thermal constant became more variable, with the mean value about 189 degree-days. In the case of *Schistocerca*, the sum of temperatures, calculated from the data on which fig. 152 is based, varied within the range of 24–35°C from 151 to 216 degree-days; such variation makes the value of temperature summation uncertain, even for constant temperatures. However, more exact experimental work, using degree-hours instead of degree-days, may throw more light on this point; should it become possible to establish some reasonable time-temperature relation, this would be of great value for estimating incubation periods and for forecasting hatching in the field.

In table 67 a number of scattered data on the length of incubation periods of various species are assembled. They are obviously of very unequal value, but provide some points of interest. Even if only the cases of development at the reasonable range of about 30–32°C are compared, it appears that the incubation periods of many species tend to be, on the whole, fairly uniform, at about fourteen to twenty days. However, the eggs of most of the Cyrtacanthacridinae require generally longer, with the exception of the two swarming *Schistocerca* species which have a notably shorter incubation period. It is noteworthy that, amongst Oedipodinae, again the swarming species of *Chortoicetes*, *Locusta* and *Locustana* have shorter incubation periods than other members of the subfamily under the same conditions. These considerations apply, however, only to the

Table 67. *Incubation periods of eggs developing without a diapause.* (*Lab.,* *unspecified laboratory conditions; ALRC, data from the laboratory of the Anti-Locust Research Centre*)

	°C	Days	Reference
PAMPHAGIDAE			
Tmethis pulchripennis	25	100–149	Shulov 1952*d*
PYRGOMORPHIDAE			
Pyrgomorpha kraussi	32	24–27	ALRC
,, ,,	28	34	,,
,, *cognata*	32	14–16	,,
Atractomorpha crenulata	Lab.	20–27	P. Srivastava 1957
Poekilocerus hieroglyphicus	32	40–42	ALRC
CYRTACANTHACRIDINAE			
Cyrtacanthacris tatarica	29	25–29	M. T. Volkonsky 1953
Ornithacris turbida	32–33	40–77	ALRC
Patanga succincta	Lab.	40–42	Pagden 1959
Anacridium aegyptium	32	20–25	ALRC
,, ,,	29	20–45	M. A. Volkonsky 1937
,, ,,	28–30	29	Colombo & Mocellini 1956
,, *melanorhodon*	29	39–40	M. T. Volkonsky 1953
Schistocerca gregaria	32	11–13	ALRC
,, *paranensis*	32	16–20	,,
,, *pallens*	23·9	46–55	Gonçalves 1957
,, *obscura*	20	63–105	Duck 1944
Nomadacris septemfasciata	32	19–24	ALRC
,, ,,	27	27–40	Shulov & Pener 1961
OXYINAE			
Oxya vicina	27–35	14–20	Kumashiro 1935
,, *velox*	27–35	13–19	,, ,,
CALLIPTAMINAE			
Pareuprepocnemis syriaca	27	42–57	Shulov & Pener 1961
EYPREPOCNEMIDINAE			
Eyprepocnemis plorans ornatipes	32	17–19	ALRC
,, ,, *meridionalis*	32	17–20	,,
MELANOPLINI			
Melanoplus differentialis	25	38	Slifer 1932*b*
,, *femur-rubrum*	23	45	Bodine 1925*a*
,, ,,	36	14	,, ,,
,, *sanguinipes*	25	24	Riegert 1961
,, ,,	35	15	,, ,,
ACRIDINAE			
Acrida pellucida	28	40–49	Hafez & Ibrahim 1958
,, ,,	35	27–32	,, ,, ,,
,, ,,	40	22–24	,, ,, ,,
OEDIPODINAE			
Aiolopus thalassinus	28	18–22	Khalifa 1957
Chortoicetes terminifera	30	13	Davidson 1936
Gastrimargus africanus	28	18–26	Hunter-Jones & Ward 1959
Humbe tenuicornis	30	22–26	Hunter-Jones & Lambert 1961
Chortophaga viridifasciata	23	53	Bodine 1925*a*
,, ,,	36	19	,, ,,
Arphia xanthoptera	36	17	,, ,,
Encoptolophus sordidus	23	33	,, ,,
,, ,,	22–25	43	Carothers 1923
Locustana pardalina	35	10	Matthée 1951
Locusta m. migratorioides	32	9–13	ALRC
,, ,, *capito*	27–33	20–46	Frappa 1938
,, ,, *gallica*	30	15	Le Berre 1953
,, ,, *migratoria*	Lab.	16–30	Plotnikov 1915
,, ,,	Lab.	20–29	Yakhimovich 1952
,, ,, *manilensis*	Lab.	14–24	Gonzales 1932
Acrotylus insubricus	27	22–26	Shulov & Pener 1961

gregarious phases of these locusts, the solitarious ones having longer incubation periods (p. 356).

There are some striking specific differences, for example between the two species of *Pyrgomorpha*, both from tropical Africa. *Acrida pellucida*, an Egyptian species, has a rather long period, but there are no data on other members of the subfamily.

WATER REQUIREMENTS

In earlier work on the role of water in egg development it has been assumed that eggs are able to absorb water from the air and the effects of exposing eggs to air of various relative humidities on the rate of their development were studied, for example, by Parker (1930), whose results were further analysed by Buxton (1932) and Johnson (1942) from the point of view of saturation deficit. However, A. G. Hamilton (1936) showed that an egg suspended in saturated air does not absorb water from it and contact with liquid water is essential. This has been confirmed by Shulov (1952*b*), Shulov & Pener (1963) and Salt (1949*b*), though the latter suggested that a negligible quantity of water may be absorbed from the air. Some aberrant results by other authors may be due to condensation of water vapour on the egg surface, which is difficult to prevent, particularly if there is even a slight variation in temperature. Therefore, a reliable basis for experimentation is to compare the effects of abundant contact water with those of the absence of it; in the latter case, eggs should be guarded against losing water by evaporation (Salt 1952; Shulov 1952*b*; Shulov & Pener 1961, 1963) by suspending them in saturated air and taking precautions against condensation of moisture. Studies of this kind have shown that the most important factor in egg development is the exact timing of the contact with water in relation to the stage of the embryo. In *Schistocerca*, the embryo can commence its development without access to water, probably utilising water available within the egg, and it may reach the stage just before the end of anatrepsis, when its further development is suspended; it may remain in such a quiescent condition for about two weeks, when it either dies or, if contact water is provided, undergoes katatrepsis and completes its development (Shulov 1952*b*). An egg in contact with water during the first days of incubation absorbs enough of it for the embryo to undergo katatrepsis and to complete development, provided evaporation is excluded. Thus, the eggs of *Schistocerca* incubated for three days in wet sand and then transferred to saturated air where they could neither gain nor lose any water, were still able to hatch if returned to wet sand after ninety-eight days; although the percentage hatch was low, the experiment has shown a possibility of a great extension of the incubation period due to the deficiency of water (Shulov & Pener 1961, 1963; Husain, Ahmad & Mathur 1940). In eggs of *Anacridium aegyptium* normally developing in about thirty days, the incubation period may be extended for more than two months by water deficiency (Shulov 1956).

Schistocerca eggs incubated in sand with different percentages of water in it did not hatch in either waterlogged (25 cc water per 100 gm of sand) or almost dry sand (0·6 cc of water per 100 gm of sand), but otherwise the amount of water in the sand made no difference (Hunter-Jones 1964).

The access of water to the embryo, however, cannot depend entirely on the availability of contact water, which has to penetrate egg coverings. The permeability of egg membranes has been studied by treatment with dye solutions (Slifer 1949*a*, 1949*b*; Matthée 1951) and by determining their electrical conductivity and resistance (Jahn 1935*a*, 1935*b*, 1936; Cole & Jahn 1937). The dye

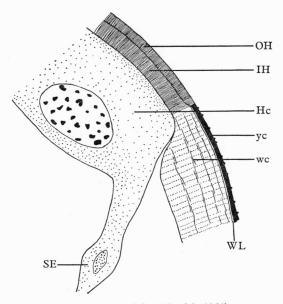

Fig. 153. Hydropyle of the *Locustana* egg (after Matthée 1951).
OH, outer layer of the hydropyle; IH, inner layer; yc, yellow cuticle; wc, white cuticle; WL, secondary wax layer; Hc, hydropyle cell; SE, serosa.

method established the importance of the wax layers (see below), while the electronic techniques suggested, in particular, that the egg coverings become practically impermeable after the yellow cuticle is formed; this may be connected with the deposition of the secondary wax layer, which is known in *Locustana* (fig. 153) and possibly occurs in other species also. With this impermeable layer enveloping the whole egg, except the hydropyle area (p. 241), the access of water becomes possible only through the latter. The hydropyle at this stage assumes the role of a mechanism regulating water intake and, at least partly, its loss by evaporation. This regulation is achieved in *Locustana* by the secretion from the specialised serosal cells (hydropyle cells) of a proteinaceous substance which is permeable to water and even soluble in it, but in dry conditions becomes impermeable and prevents evaporation from the egg (Matthée, *t.c.*). In

Melanoplus differentialis, the hydropyle is waterproofed by a wax-like material, which seals the egg during the diapause, but breaks down chemically at the end of the latter (Slifer 1946; Slifer & Sekhon 1963); it has also been suggested that at a low temperature, which helps to terminate diapause (p. 261), the wax becomes brittle and water passes through cracks in it (Matthée 1951).

The importance of the hydropyle mechanism in water regulation has been decisively demonstrated by Slifer (1946) by treating eggs with xylol, toluol, carbon tetrachloride and other solvents, which dissolve the waxy layer of the hydropyle; this allows the intake of water and terminates the diapause. This procedure has been criticised, without supporting evidence, as likely to injure the embryo (Andrewartha 1952; Hinton 1957), but Slifer (1958b, 1959) has shown that a treatment with mineral oil, which also dissolves wax and permits the entry of water, was quite harmless to the embryo.

Hartley (1961) stated, though without quoting experimental evidence, that egg coverings of *Chorthippus brunneus* and some other species are permeable to water.

The above conclusions regarding the mechanism of water regulation in a developing egg were essentially based on studies of only two species, and the problem appears to be much more complicated. Thus, eggs of *Schistocerca* suspended in air of 0–50% RH rapidly lose weight through evaporation (Shulov & Pener 1963); Salt (1952) also stated that the eggs of *Melanoplus bivittatus* lost water by evaporation at 40°C and 0% relative humidity, even if their hydropyle ends were sealed, the loss being due to evaporation through the cuticle. The possibility that such a loss may be due to res- piration has not been considered, and it has been shown by Matthée (1951) that *Locustana* eggs kept in nitrogen failed to absorb water, although they remained alive, which suggests that the water regulation may be, to some extent, dependent on respiration.

An indication that the absorption of contact water and its loss have a physiological basis was obtained by keeping eggs of *Locusta m. migratoria* in contact with NaCl solutions; the eggs gained weight in 1–5% solution, but lost it in 10%, presumably as a result of the difference in the osmotic pressure between the egg fluid and the solution (Lozina-Lozinskiĭ & Sokolov 1938). Eggs of *Schistocerca* kept up to ten days in saline sand and then transferred to normal moist sand were able to hatch (Shulov & Pener 1963).

Although some need for external water is clear in most of the cases studied, it would be unwise to assume that it is universal. Indeed, the eggs of *Tmethis*, a desert species, do not require any absorption of water and do not increase in weight throughout their full development (table 64), and even fail to develop in contact with water (Shulov 1952d); the embryos are, presumably, able to complete growth with only the original water in the egg.

The need for more extensive, as well as more precise, studies on the physiology of water balance in eggs has been rightly stressed by Salt (1949b, 1952).

Even in the case of eggs normally developing without interruption, the effects of external conditions are still not clear, and the problem becomes even more confused when the phenomena of diapause and quiescence are considered.

DIAPAUSE AND QUIESCENCE

As is well known, the eggs of species living in temperate climates with a cold winter and in semi-arid hot climates with a pronounced dry season usually pass the unfavourable season without developing and many of such eggs cannot be made to develop by ensuring uninterrupted suitable conditions. This suspension of development, without an apparent external reason, has been termed *diapause*. Such a definition is unsatisfactory, since, on the one

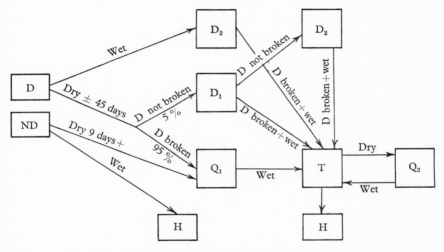

Fig. 154. *Locustana*, a scheme of the various types of egg development, with and without a diapause, or quiescence; explanation in the text (after Matthée 1951, modified).

hand, it allows invoking a diapause in all cases when no reason for the suspension of development has yet been found or suggested; on the other hand, it assumes the existence of a clear-cut distinction between a diapause state and a temporary suspension of development, proved to be caused by unfavourable environmental conditions, which is then termed *quiescence* (or dormancy). Before discussing the validity and the usefulness of these conceptions, a review of factual evidence on non-continuous embryonic development is essential.

The scheme of development in eggs of *Locustana*, very thoroughly elaborated by Matthée (1951), is of particular interest because it shows how complex the course of development can be (fig. 154). This species lays both diapause and non-diapause eggs, which may even be in the same egg-pod. Non-diapause eggs (ND) kept moist from laying hatch (H) on about the tenth day, but if kept dry for that period, they become quiescent (Q_1) with the embryos in stage 15 (p. 245) until moistened, when they absorb water and become turgid (T); if turgid eggs are kept dry, their embryos advance to stage 19 and lose a little water, becoming quiescent again (Q_2), in which state they may remain for many months, but on wetting they become turgid and hatch (H). If diapause eggs (D) are moistened after laying, their embryos develop to stage 19 and remain in diapause (D_2) quite regardless of conditions. The diapause can be eliminated (broken) by keeping newly laid eggs dry for about forty-five days, when the embryos reach stage 15 and eggs become quiescent (Q_1), after which they follow the same course as non-diapause eggs. The elimination of the diapause, however, may not occur in all such eggs and some 5% of the embryos on reaching stage 15 enter a diapause (D_1), which may continue for a long period (over three-and-a-half years) and can be broken in the usual way with the sequence as before (i.e. through turgid egg to hatching); if the diapause is not broken, the embryo advances a little, reaching stage 19; this advanced diapause (D_2) can again be broken by the usual dry treatment. It should be stressed that the quiescent (Q_1, Q_2) and the diapausing (D_1, D_2) embryos are morphologically identical and their nature can only be discovered by their response to moistening. A simpler case is offered by *Melanoplus differentialis*, the eggs of which, if kept at 25°C and moistened normally, develop to stage 15–16 and then enter a diapause which may last for several months, regardless of conditions; finally, growth recommences, blastokinesis occurs and hatching follows; such a diapause is common for species from temperate climates and can be terminated by a temporary exposure to low temperature.

Another type of diapause is illustrated by the case of *Calliptamus palaestinensis*, which lays its eggs in dry soil, where they develop slowly and reach the late anatrepsis stage in some fifty days; the same rate was observed in moist soil. After that, all eggs, regardless of conditions, become dormant and may remain so for a long period; this dormancy may finally be interrupted by moistening and by low temperature treatment. The total period of incubation may extend for as long as 257 days (Pener & Shulov 1960).

In the species just discussed the diapause occurs at the end of anatrepsis (stage 14–16 or 19), and this is also the case in *Austroicetes cruciata* (Birch 1942; Andrewartha 1943, 1944, 1952), *Locusta m. migratoria* (Shumakov & Yakhimovich 1950), *Dociostaurus maroccanus* (Bodenheimer & Shulov 1951), *Camnula pellucida* (Moore 1948), *Hesperotettix* spp., *Chloealtis conspersa*, *Circotettix verruculata*, *Melanoplus femur-rubrum* (Carothers 1923), *M. scudderi* and *M. luridus* (Slifer 1958b). This list can be extended, but a similar list by Andrewartha (1952) includes at least two erroneous records: *Gomphocerus sibiricus* credited to Bei-Bienko (1928) who did not even discuss diapause in the paper quoted (although this species has a diapause), and *Chortophaga viridifasciata* on the authority of Carothers (1923) who clearly stated that this species has no diapause. On the other hand, diapause in *Melanoplus bivittatus* occurs just before hatching at stage 23 (80% development; Moore 1948), and the same applies to *M. sanguinipes* (Parker 1930; Salt 1949*a*), *M. flavidus*, *M. foedus* (Slifer 1958*b*) and *M. packardi* (Salt 1949*a*).

The case of *Austroicetes cruciata* is complicated (Andrewartha 1943, 1952; Birch & Andrewartha 1942; Andrewartha & Birch 1954), since in this species one diapause occurs a few days after the egg was laid when the embryo is in stage 1–2; if incubated at 25–30° C the eggs eventually die. However, an exposure for 100–150 days to 16–25° C enables the embryo to grow; also, intermittent exposure to high and to low temperature stimulates growth to the stage of late anatrepsis (it is to be noted that this kind of 'diapause' appears not to inhibit development, only to prolong it); a second diapause occurs at late anatrepsis, as in other species, and can be terminated by low temperature treatment. In *Dociostaurus maroccanus* also, there is either a quiescent or a diapause period at the very early embryonic period, as well as a diapause before katatrepsis (Bodenheimer & Shulov 1951). These examples show that prolonged development, quiescence (or dormancy) and diapause are known to occur at different embryonic stages and may or may not be influenced by temperature or humidity. Shulov & Pener (1961), in a review of the problem, listed six types of interrupted development, although the range of the species sufficiently studied in this respect is still limited mainly to those of temperate climates. It should be added that cases of arrested development lasting for more than one year are known. Thus, two to three years' dormancy was observed in several species of *Melanoplus* and in *Chorthippus curtipennis*, amongst populations of mountainous areas of North America (Putnam & Handford 1958; Kreasky 1960). Eggs of *Locustana* may remain dormant for over three-and-a-half years (Lounsbury 1915).

In some species with eggs that normally undergo a diapause, development may also occur without it. Thus, although the majority of eggs of *M. differentialis* undergo a diapause, some do not and it is possible to select a non-diapause strain (Slifer & King 1961); the same applies to *M. sanguinipes* (Riegert 1961). This indicates some genetic control of diapause, but the mechanism of its inheritance is assumed to be polygenic which may 'make an exact genetic analysis impossible in the present state of our knowledge' (Slifer & King, *t.c.*). In *M. bivittatus* both diapause and non-diapause eggs exist and the proportion of the latter varied from nil to 43%, apparently increasing as the season advanced (Church & Salt 1952). In *Locustana*, on the other hand, the percentage of diapause eggs increased with the age of the female (Matthée 1951). In *Locusta m. gallica* three kinds of eggs were distinguished (Le Berre 1953): some had an obligatory diapause, others had none and still others developed with a more or less long period of either quiescence or diapause. The diapause and the non-diapause strains could be selected; but breeding in the laboratory for several generations, without any selection, produced all three types of eggs, those of the intermediate type gradually disappearing and the non-diapause type increasing to 100% in the sixth generation; the embryonic stage at which diapause occurred has not been established. Verdier (1962) suggested that in another sub-species of *Locusta* the incidence of diapause depended on the photoperiod.

It would appear from the above examples that a distinction between the diapause and non-diapause types of development, which may be clear in extreme cases, often becomes blurred. Further evidence that the distinction may be somewhat artificial is provided by data on the course of embryonic development in some species assumed to have no egg diapause. Occasional absence of egg diapause has been found in *Locusta m. migratoria* (Plotnikov 1927; Shumakov & Yakhimovich 1950; Lozina-Lozinskiĭ & Sokolov 1938) and *Dociostaurus maroccanus* (Plotnikov 1912), although eggs of these species normally hibernate in diapause. In fact, so far, no conclusive evidence is available with regard to any species having only an obligatory egg diapause, that is, whose eggs never, even exceptionally, develop without a diapause. Moreover, as demonstrated in *Locustana* (p. 259), the difference between quiescence and diapause is not easy to establish and many cases of assumed diapause are open to doubt. In particular, it is quite wrong to classify as species with an obligatory egg diapause all those which in the field pass the winter, or the dry season, in the egg stage, without any experimental evidence that their dormancy is not directly due to environmental conditions. As an example, eggs of *Encoptolophus sordidus* normally hibernate, but they complete their development without any diapause and six successive generations in a year can be produced in the laboratory if kept at 22–25° C (Carothers 1923). Similarly, *Humbe tenuicornis*, an African species, normally has one generation a year, the eggs remaining in the soil during the long dry season. In the laboratory, however, eggs incubated at 30° C, in contact with water hatched in about twenty-three days (Hunter-Jones & Lambert 1961). Eggs incubated for four to six days in moist conditions and then transferred to the dry, rapidly lost their water, as did eggs kept moist for thirteen days and then subjected to dry conditions (fig. 155, A). Pre-incubated eggs kept dry for ten days and then given water rapidly regained their full weight and hatched in thirty days (fig. 155, B). Other examples of such quiescence, induced by dryness, have been mentioned above (p. 256); if sufficiently prolonged, it could be interpreted as a diapause, were it not for the experimental evidence.

It is significant that a quiescent period may intervene in non-diapause eggs with insufficient water reserve at the same anatreptic embryonic stage at which diapause usually occurs in other species; this supports Slifer's (1946) view that the anatrepsis stage 'is a difficult and critical time in embryonic development'. Her own work and that of Matthée (1951) has shown that in some species diapause is connected with the closure of the hydropyle and is terminated when water intake again becomes possible through changes in the covering of the hydropyle (pp. 257–8). This theory has been well presented and accepted by Lees (1955), though it does not account for the diapause occurring, for example, in *Melanoplus bivittatus*, at the end of katatrepsis. It should be remembered, however, that the hydropyle mechanism and its functions during embryonic development have been studied only in *M. differentialis* by Slifer and in *Locustana* by Matthée, not in *M. bivittatus*, nor, indeed, in any other species.

While the present evidence favours strongly the importance of water in the control of diapause, this cannot be the full explanation. A point which deserves attention is that in many species of temperate climate, with hibernating eggs, diapause can be eliminated by a relatively short exposure to low temperature. There has been a considerable amount of experimental work on this theme (e.g. Burdick 1937; Parker 1930; Church & Salt 1952; Richards & Waloff 1954; etc.), but in all such work only temperature has been studied as a factor directly affecting embryonic development and no attempt has been made to link it up with water metabolism which must be affected by temperature. It is,

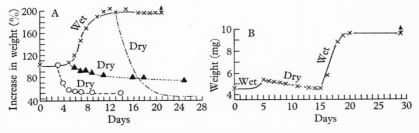

Fig. 155. *Humbe tenuicornis*, egg development in relation to moisture; explanation in the text (after Hunter-Jones & Lambert 1961).

indeed, surprising that, for example in eggs of *Austroicetes cruciata*, water relations have been thoroughly studied with reference only to egg survival (Birch & Andrewartha 1942, 1944), while the diapause in the same species was experimentally studied only with regard to temperature (Andrewartha 1943, 1944, 1952), although both the physiological and the ecological interpretations results should be based on considering both factors.

In view of the obviously unsatisfactory state of evidence concerning the physiology of continuous embryonic development, quiescence and diapause, it appears premature to formulate any definite hypotheses on the nature of these phenomena and their regulation. The main lesson so far learned is that while a purely experimental approach is essential for establishing the facts, it is unlikely to throw much light on the essence of the problem and detailed studies of the physiological and morphogenetic processes are needed. Only when enough of such detailed knowledge, relating to a wide range of species with different ecology, has been accumulated, will it be possible to begin looking for the principles regulating the course of embryonic development. The connection between the cause and the effect is certainly not a direct one. For instance, the known fact that diapause can be prevented, or eliminated, by exposure to cold, is not necessarily a proof of direct effect of low temperature on embryonic development, since in other insects (e.g. the *Cecropia* moth, C. M. Williams 1956) in which the pupal diapause is also terminated by exposure to low temperature, this effect is mediated by the neurosecretory action of the brain which is stimulated by it and inhibited by high temperature, the hormone secreted by the secretory brain cells catalysing biochemical processes involved in the resumption of development. Japanese work on the silkworm has further shown that the production of diapause eggs by a female depends on a hormone secreted by the suboesophageal ganglion (Schneiderman 1957). No work on these lines has yet been carried out on acridoids, though there is some evidence that the secretion of the prothoracic gland has no effect on termination of the egg diapause in *Locustana* (Jones 1956*a*, 1956*b*), but serves to initiate the intermediate moult (p. 272).

EGG MORTALITY

Extremes of both temperature and humidity can be important factors of egg mortality.

The effects of *high temperature* are presented in table 68. These data are of somewhat uncertain value since death at a longer exposure may be due to excessive evaporation and not to temperature. Also, eggs in these experiments were exposed in the air, while normally they would be at a certain depth in the soil where such high temperatures are unlikely to occur and where evaporation would be moderated.

Table 68. *Effects of high temperature on eggs*

Species	°C	Minutes	Percentage mortality	Reference
Gomphocerus sibiricus ready to hatch	30–35	20	10	Rubtzov 1935*b*
,, ,,	38–40	15	30	,, ,,
,, ,,	48–52	30	100	,, ,,
,, ,,	56–60	15	100	,, ,,
Melanoplus sanguinipes & *Camnula pellucida*	45	180	28–44	Parker 1930
,, ,,	50	120	100	,, ,,
,, ,,	60	20	100	,, ,,
,, ,,	70	10	100	,, ,,
Schistocerca gregaria	46	120	100	Husain & Ahmad 1936*a*

Resistance of eggs to *low temperature* has been somewhat better investigated, because of the interest attached to the survival of eggs of northern species, which normally hibernate in that stage (table 69).

A comparison of tables 69 and 57 leaves no doubt that eggs of the species of cold and temperate climates are much more resistant to cold than hoppers and adults. It would be of interest to carry out a comparative study of the

264

geographical races of the same species from widely different climates, for example those of the tropical *Locusta m. migratorioides* and the central European *L. m. rossica*.

Table 69. *Effect of low temperature on eggs*

Species	°C	Duration	Percentage mortality	Reference
Melanoplus sanguinipes	−20	16 hr	16–20	Parker 1930
and *Camnula pellucida*	−25	16 hr	44–76	,, ,,
	−30	16 hr	100	,, ,,
Siberian grasshoppers	−4	10 min	4	Rubtzov 1935*b*
	−10	10 min	27	,, ,,
	−20	10 min	30–50	,, ,,
Locusta m. migratoria	−5·75	24 hr	8	Sacharov 1930
	−11·1	24 hr	76	,, ,,
	−17·35	24 hr	100	,, ,,

The tabulated data represent, however, only somewhat generalised empirical findings, and more detailed experimental work on eggs of *Locusta m. migratoria* by Zambin (1939) revealed the complexity of the problem of cold resistance of eggs. This author was able to establish that the degree of resistance depends on the stage in the development of the embryo, of which only five major stages were distinguished, as follows:

   I. A distinct germ band.
   II. Before blastokinesis; eyes and legs differentiated.
   III. After blastokinesis; embryo occupies ⅓–½ of the yolk.
   IV. Embryo occupies ¾ of yolk.
   V. Ready to emerge.

As can be seen from fig. 156, four-hour exposure to temperatures ranging from −1 to −20°C caused in eggs of the stages I–III only a low mortality, which corresponded to that in the control batches of eggs not subjected to

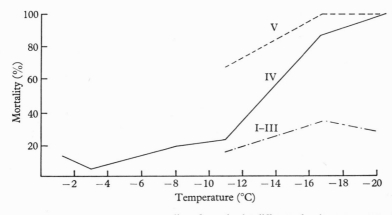

Fig. 156. *Locusta m. migratoria*, mortality of eggs in the different development stages (see text) exposed for four hours to a range of low temperatures (after Zambin 1939, modified).

freezing, so that, in fact, there was no mortality due to cold. On the other hand, in eggs of stage IV, mortality increased at $-11°$, reached 85% at $-17°$ and was total at $-20°$; eggs of stage V were all killed already at $-14°$C. A longer exposure, for twenty-four hours, resulted in all eggs of stage III being killed at $-20°$, and all of stage V at $-11°$. The importance of time is also illustrated by fig. 157.

In another series of Zambin's experiments, *Locusta* eggs were exposed to cold for two hours, thawed out and frozen again for two hours. Although the total cold period was again four hours, stage III eggs were all killed at $-20°$C. Thus, repeated freezing and thawing lowered the resistance of eggs to cold.

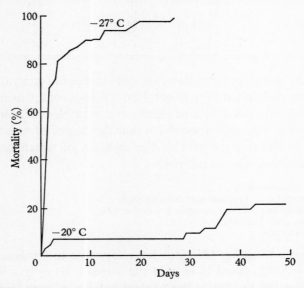

Fig. 157. *Melanoplus bivittatus,* mortality of eggs at two low temperatures in relation to the length of exposure (after Salt 1950).

Cold resistance was also reduced in the presence of contact moisture; when eggs absorbed water to the extent of 10–20% of the original weight, they froze at $-21°$, but when the increase was 30% they were killed at $-11°$C, whereas eggs in dry soil survived cooling to $-30°$C without any ill effects. Since salts in water changes the osmotic balance between it and the fluid in eggs (p. 258), cold resistance of eggs in contact with water containing more than 6% NaCl was increased (Lozina-Lozinskiĭ & Sokolov 1938).

Zambin (*t.c.*) has provided evidence that the resistance of eggs decreases during the embryonic development as their percentage content of water increases that of the fat content decreases, and that of glucose increases (table 70).

Zambin's findings with regard to the importance of the quantity of fat for cold resistance are of obvious interest and indicate the need for comparative

Table 70. *Changes in the percentages of water, fat and glucose in eggs of* L. m. migratoria *during embryonic development (Zambin 1939)*

Embryonic stage	Water	Fat		Glucose	
		Live weight	Dry weight	Live weight	Dry weight
I	72·12	5·25	18·81	0·50	1·85
II	71·84	5·55	19·70	0·65	2·31
III	73·48	4·56	17·21	0·59	2·21
IV	75·40	4·24	17·29	0·87	3·55
V	76·36	3·62	15·33	0·84	3·57

studies of eggs from different climates. In this connection, Slifer (1932 c) has found a qualitative difference between fats in hibernating eggs of American grasshoppers and those that are laid and hatch in summer; the former contain fat with a low melting point, while in the summer eggs this point is considerably higher. Such differences are observed even between species of the same genus (*Arphia, Hippiscus*), with a different seasonal cycle (table 71).

Table 71. *Properties of the fatty acids of one-day-old eggs (Slifer 1932 c)*

	Complete melting °C	Iodine number
Hibernating Eggs		
Melanoplus bivittatus	25·5	—
Melanoplus differentialis	26·2	—
Melanoplus femur-rubrum	26·6	133·8
Melanoplus walshii	—	151·2
Encoptolophus sordidus	26·2	—
Dissosteira carolina	28·4	128·4
Arphia xanthoptera	28·5	—
Hippiscus rugosus	29·0	—
Spharagemon bolli	30·5	—
Summer Eggs		
Hippiscus apiculatus	37·0	142·0
Chortophaga viridifasciata	39·4	134·0
Arphia sulphurea	39·5	166·9

The iodine numbers of the fatty acids from different species also differed considerably, but they were all high, indicating that the acids are highly unsaturated; the fat of *Dociostaurus* eggs, however, had the iodine number as low as 95·5 (Fickendey 1918). No significant change in the degree of saturation during the development has been found. Some additional data on the subject are given by Allen, Boyd & Bodine (1942). It is relevant to mention that Salt (1962) has recently indicated the importance for cold resistance of the glycerol content of hibernating insects; glycerol is involved in the synthesis of fatty acids, but its presence in hibernating grasshopper eggs has not been investigated.

Data on the *resistance of eggs to desiccation* are neither numerous nor exact. The changes in the water balance of a developing egg are complicated and its ability to retain, or lose, water must vary according to the embryonic stage. Salt (1952) found that the rate of water loss of *Melanoplus bivittatus* eggs exposed to 0% RH at 40°C for one hour was higher in the early stages than later; no lethal limit was established and only partial mortality observed.

Eggs of *Melanoplus differentialis* which on drying lost less than 2 mg, or 33% of their weight, recovered, but those losing 2·5 mg (46%) all died (Thompson & Bodine 1936). Eggs of *Camnula pellucida* were killed when they lost 64–68% of the original water but those of *Locustana pardalina*, which are able to survive drought for several years, remained alive when their water content fell below 40% (Matthée 1951). Eggs of *Austroicetes cruciata*, also a species of very dry habitat, survived when the ratio water/dry weight was reduced from 3·2 to 0·6, and their resistance to drying depended on the embryonic stage (Birch & Andrewartha 1942, 1944).

One-day-old *Schistocerca* eggs exposed to air of 40–80% RH all died within six days, but those allowed to absorb contact water for a few days were able to continue development without contact water (Shulov 1952b). However, such eggs exposed to 0% humidity died from water loss (Shulov & Pener 1963). Eggs in dry sand die within two days (Hunter-Jones 1964).

Excessive water may also be a cause of egg mortality, particularly in species laying eggs in dry soil (e.g. *Dociostaurus* and *Tmethis*); their eggs are killed if moistened soon after laying and up to the end of anatrepsis (Shulov & Pener 1961b). Eggs of *Locusta m. migratoria* are killed if submerged in water when the embryo is ready to hatch (Shumakov & Yakhimovich 1950).

Shulov & Pener (1963) stressed that the whole problem of water regulation in eggs, as far as it has been studied, reveals a complicated relationship between the embryonic stages and the ability of eggs to absorb, or to lose, water. It must be even more complicated in the case of eggs laid in the field, where the physical properties of different soil in relation to the dynamics of water in it will have to be considered. Moreover, eggs of many species are inside egg-pods with envelopes of different structure, but with unknown properties as regards the transmission of water through them; this aspect will be discussed in the second volume.

HATCHING AND DEVELOPMENT
OF HOPPERS

HATCHING

Changes in the embryo

After the embryo has reached its full morphological development, including the formation of the provisional cuticle (p. 238), it is still enclosed in thin yellow cuticle and thick, tough white cuticle. The latter would be difficult to rupture at hatching, but a few days before hatching it becomes dissolved by an enzyme secreted by the *pleuropodia*, a pair of small projections on the sides

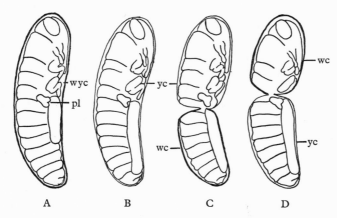

Fig. 158. *Melanoplus differentialis* egg and embryo, illustrating the function of pleuropodia. A, one week before hatching, with both yellow and white cuticle; B, at hatching, with only yellow cuticle present; C, ligatured below pleuropodia; D, ditto, above them (after Slifer 1937).
wyc, white and yellow cuticle; yc, yellow cuticle; wc, white cuticle; pl, pleuropodia.

of the first abdominal segment of the embryo. These peculiar organs have been described in *Locusta* by Kulagin (1923) who suggested that they may have an excretory function, but Slifer (1937, 1938*b*) established their secretory nature in *Melanoplus*, and Jones (1956*a*, 1956*b*) confirmed this for *Locusta* and *Locustana*. Slifer showed by ligaturing an isolated embryo just below the pleuropodia, that the white cuticle disappeared above the ligature, but when the ligature was applied just above them, it was dissolved only in the posterior part of the embryo (fig. 158). Jones (*tt.cc.*) has further established that the secretory activity of pleuropodia is stimulated by a hormone produced by the prothoracic gland (p. 159). As hatching approaches, pleuropodia cease to function and degenerate.

As a result of the dissolution of white cuticle, the provisional cuticle of the embryo becomes separated from the epidermis, thus signifying the beginning of the intermediate moult (Sharan 1958) which is completed after hatching (p. 272). It is, therefore, correct to regard the secretion of pleuropodia as a hatching enzyme, and its properties, including the ability to digest white cuticle, have been studied, although very incompletely, by Shutts (1952).

Mechanism of hatching

Detailed descriptions of hatching have been provided for *Schistocerca* by Vosseler (1905), for *Locusta* by Mikhelson (1922), for *Dociostaurus* by Künkel d'Herculais (1890*a*, 1890*b*, 1893–1905) and others. The chorion of an egg quite ready to hatch often cracks and the hatching larva has to break mainly the thin yellow cuticle. Hatching begins with active wriggling movements of the larva. The thin membrane between the head and pronotum begins to swell, forming a paired *cervical ampulla* (fig. 159, B), pulsations of which exert pressure on the cuticle and cause its transverse rupture; the anterior portion may remain on the head of the larva, like a skull-cap, even after emergence of the larva from the soil. The mechanism of inflation of the ampulla is not clear. Künkel d'Herculais believed it to be due to the larva swallowing air which causes an increase in the volume of the alimentary canal and this forces blood into the anterior portion of the body cavity; Nikolskiï (1925) observed that the alimentary canal of a freshly hatched larva may be full of air. On the other hand, Slifer (1937) noted that the larva just before hatching swallows some of the fluid that surrounds it within the egg, although she did not connect this with the hatching mechanism. The pulsation of blood in the neck may be due to peristaltic movements in the abdomen (Roonwal 1937).

The vermiform larva

A larva which has just emerged from the egg is not quite like the ordinary hopper. Indeed, it scarcely differs from the fully developed embryo still in the egg (fig. 159, C). Its head is bent downwards, its antennae and legs lie close to the body and the whole insect is enclosed in a thin transparent membrane which envelops the whole body like a sac, but with separate 'sleeves' for the legs, the distal part of the antennae and the cerci. This membrane was regarded in the past as the amnion (i.e. one of egg membranes), but it is actually a true cuticle, being chitinous, without cellular structure, and is called the *provisional cuticle* (p. 238). Its formation in the embryo was described by Sharan (1958). The vermiform larva is, therefore, the real first instar, but it is distinguished from the later instars by a special name in order to avoid confusion in numbering the free hopper instars (Uvarov 1928).

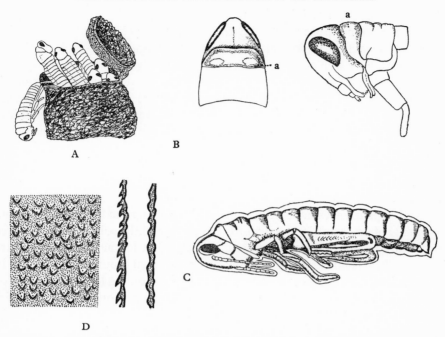

Fig. 159. *Dociostaurus*. A, vermiform larvae emerging from an egg-pod; B, head and thorax of a larva showing the cervical ampulla (a) (after Künckel d'Herculais 1893–1905); C, vermiform larva (after La Baume 1918); D, *Locusta*, surface of the provisional thoracic cuticle of the vermiform larva (Roonwal 1937).

Emergence

Owing to the presence of the enveloping cuticle, the larva is unable to make use of its legs during its progress to the surface of the soil and its upward movement is mainly executed by wriggling of the abdomen which has particularly well developed muscles (Wiesend 1957). These vermiform movements are assisted by energetic pulsation of the cervical ampulla which alternatively collapses, enabling the larva to push its anterior portion into a narrow space, and inflates, forming a support for the abdomen to be drawn up. The movement may be further facilitated by the numerous tubercles on the surface of the cuticle, which are particularly strong in the thoracic region where they are hook-like, with pointed ends directed backwards (fig. 159, D). It is possible that the provisional cuticle has also an important function of protecting the final cuticle of the hatchling, during its laborious progress, from abrasion which would increase the danger of excessive water loss by transpiration after the emergence (Blackith 1961).

Since it is commonly observed in the field that hatching occurs simultaneously from a number of egg-pods, a great deal has been written on the immediate stimuli causing fully developed larvae to emerge; temperature, moisture and light have been invoked. However, the emergence is a result of locomotory activity of the larvae, and it is natural to expect such activity to occur when, for example, the temperature at that depth in the soil reaches the limit at which muscular contraction is possible, and a rise in temperature, or in moisture (due to rain), may well act as a trigger. As regards light, earlier observations that eggs kept in a dark box did not hatch, but that hatching started immediately it was opened (Künckel d'Herculais 1893–1905), probably mean merely that light also provided a trigger for activity; if light were essential for hatching, the latter could not commence as long as eggs were in the soil. The often quoted fact that eggs may begin to hatch as soon as they are dug out of the soil is also reasonably explained as an activation of larvae by disturbance or by a change of temperature since even fully developed larvae cannot emerge without a locomotory stimulus.

Very divergent views have been expressed regarding the factors orientating movements of emerging larvae towards the surface of the soil. The simplest of such factors has been usually ignored, namely, that larvae in an egg-pod are lying with their heads upwards, so that any movement would be inevitably in that direction, which is also that of least resistance owing to the structure of the egg-pod. Experiments with eggs in the reversed position, or with artificial obstructions, designed to prove or disprove the existence of geotaxis (Husain & Bhatia 1936; Remaudiére 1954) produced contradictory results; in any case, such situations do not arise in nature. Of more practical value in relation to agricultural practices would be studies of the emergence of larvae through layers of soil of various thicknesses and physical properties, but exact experimental data are lacking.

Intermediate moult

As mentioned above, the moulting of the vermiform larva is initiated while it is still in the egg (p. 270) and the shedding of the provisional cuticle begins as soon as the head of the larva has emerged on the surface of the soil. While the larva is still lying on the ground, the cuticle is burst by vigorous pulsations of the cervical ampulla, and wriggling movements of the body, assisted by the legs as soon as they are free, help the larva to get out of its first skin. The shed cuticle shrivels into a whitish lump and the ground near the exit is strewn with such lumps. The moult is, perhaps, stimulated by the cessation of pressure on the larva, since it sometimes commences moulting when a cavity in the soil is reached (Mikhelson 1922; Shapinskiĭ 1923).

The vermiform larva enables the insect to emerge on the surface, but it also exists in acridoids laying eggs in the stems of plants, on leaves and so on, as well as in other orthopteroids and related insects (mantids, blattids), regardless of their oviposition habits; it therefore cannot be regarded as a special adaptation to egg-laying in soil.

It has been suggested that air humidity may affect the success of the intermediate moult, but information on this point is scanty. A successful moult was observed in saturated air (Husain, Ahmad & Mathur 1941), but not in very dry air (Shulov & Pener 1963).

HOPPER DEVELOPMENT

The young insect appearing after the intermediate moult resembles an adult in its general appearance, and is usually called a hopper. This term may be regarded as a colloquial one, but it is less liable to mislead than such terms as nymph, or larva, which have different meanings in other insect groups. In

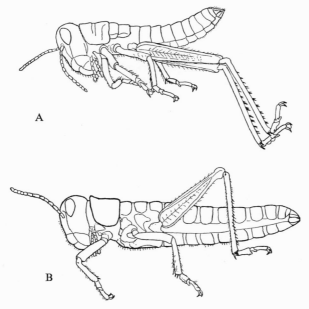

Fig. 160. *Schistocerca*, Ist instar hoppers. A, hatchling; B, at the end of the instar (after Vosseler 1905).

acridoids, some authors apply the term larva to the hopper instars preceding the reversal of wing rudiments (p. 280) and call the later instars the nymphs. The American abbreviation 'hopper' (for grasshopper) is applied regardless of the developmental stage and is apt to be confusing, for example when swarms and flights of 'hoppers' are mentioned.

The development of hoppers consists in growth associated with periodic moults.

The first instar hopper, immediately after the intermediate moult, is called a *hatchling*. Its colour is very pale and any darker pattern, proper to the species or phase, appears gradually after a few minutes. It has a relatively short and compressed abdomen, but this extends eventually, so that the hopper at the end of the instar has a somewhat altered appearance (fig. 160). Its body is now larger and thicker, and the head no longer appears abnormally large as it does at hatching. Similar changes in the appearance of the hopper occur during each successive instar. The changes in size are, however, due not to growth, but to the expansion of the intersegmental membranes, while the more strongly sclerotised parts do not grow at all during an instar, their measurements increasing suddenly after each moult.

Total growth

The total growth of hoppers can be estimated by measuring the increases in the total body length and in weight at the beginning of each instar. Care should be taken to execute the measurements in newly moulted hoppers before they take any food.

Table 72. *Mean net weight in mg of* Locusta *hoppers, and rates of increase by instars (after Duarte 1938, modified)*

Instar	Males		Females	
	Weight	Rate of increase	Weight	Rate of increase
I	14·3	—	14·3	—
II	33·2	2·32	37·6	2·63
III	71·8	2·16	77·4	2·06
IV	173·7	2·42	207·5	2·68
V	408·5	2·35	487·0	2·35
Adult	904·0	2·21	1250·7	2·56
Total	—	63·2	—	87·5

Earlier workers attempted to establish empirical laws of growth and to produce formulae expressing the rate of growth. Thus Bodenheimer *et al.* (1929) suggested that in *Schistocerca* the body length increases 1·26 times and the weight is doubled from instar to instar; but a recalculation from their figures for the rates of weight increase shows a range from 1·9 to 2·8. Considerable and irregular deviations from such postulated rates were found by other workers, for example by P. M. Davey (1954) and Pradhan & Bindra (1956) for *Schistocerca*, by Key (1936), K. U. Clarke (1957b) and Duarte (1938) for *Locusta* (table 72), by Hodge (1933) for *Melanoplus differentialis*, by Shpet (1934) for *Dociostaurus* and other species, and by Putnam & Peters (1960) for five Canadian species.

Table 72 shows that the rates of weight increase from instar to instar in *Locusta* and the total weight increase is higher in females than in males. In *Schistocerca*, a similar picture is obtained (fig. 161) and the total weight becomes seventy-nine times that of the first instar hopper in fledgling male and 109 times in the female (P. M. Davey 1954). In *Dociostaurus* an adult weighs sixty-five times as much as a Ist instar hopper (Shpet 1934).

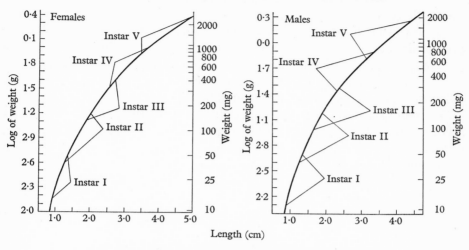

Fig. 161. *Schistocerca*, hopper growth in length and in weight
(after P. M. Davey 1954, modified).

The growth of parts

One of the reasons for the irregularity of growth rates throughout the instars may be to the different rates of growth between the various body parts and between instars in the same part (fig. 162). Thus, the rate of growth of the pronotum is higher than that of other parts during the first four instars, but

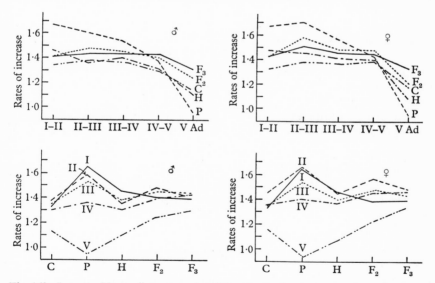

Fig. 162. *Locusta*. Upper diagrams, rates of increase in the size of different body parts; lower diagrams, variation in the rates of increase of parts between instars (after Duarte 1938).

I, II, III, IV, V, instars; Ad, adult; C, head width; P, pronotal length; H, pronotal height; F_2, length of second femur; F_3, length of third femur.

then falls sharply; the adult pronotum becomes actually shorter than that of the last instar hopper; the hind femur (F_3) grows at a steady rate, but the rate declines after the fourth moult. Wiesend (1957) produced data for the growth of wings and hind femur in several European grasshoppers.

The growth in weight is also unequal for different body parts and for different instars (Shpet 1934) as shown in table 73.

Differential growth of body parts in different populations of the same species accounts for intraspecific variation depending on conditions of rearing, particularly density (phase polymorphism, p. 338), geographical distribution (Petersen & Weber 1949), and possibly other factors.

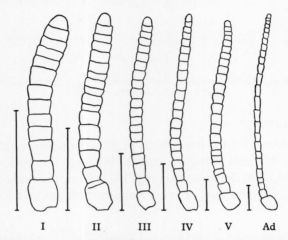

I II III IV V Ad

Fig. 163. *Dociostaurus maroccanus*, growth of the antenna from the Ist instar to the adult; line = 0·8 mm (after Paoli 1937*b*, modified).

The actual mode of growth has been studied for only a few parts and organs.

As regards the integument, Neville's (1963*b*, 1963*c*, 1963*d*) discovery that the age of an adult locust can be ascertained by counting the discrete layers of cuticle deposited daily (p. 32) opens a way to a similar investigation of the growth of hopper integument during each instar and in the different parts of body.

The growth of the *antenna* occurs, apart from the increase in the size of individual segments, also by their successive divisions, particularly of those in the basal half (except the scape and the pedicel) (Paoli 1937*b*), and fig. 163 illustrates changes in the general shape of the antenna in *Dociostaurus maroccanus*, which becomes relatively more slender as it grows. Similar data on the increase in the number of segments are available for several other species (e.g. Takahashi 1925; Lebedeva 1925; Coleman 1911; Coleman & Kannan 1911; Katiyar 1953; O. W. Richards & N. Waloff 1954; Remaudière 1954; Zolessi 1958) and a list for twenty-three species was compiled by Roonwal (1952*b*). The number of segments added at each moult varies from nil to six. There are, of course, some individual variations within

Table 73. *Weight in mg of body parts of hoppers of Dociostaurus maroccanus and rates of increase by instars* (Shpet 1934)

	I	II/I	II	III/II	III	IV/III	IV	V/IV	V	Ad/V	Adult	Mean
Head width	2·446	2·42	5·908	2·21	13·040	2·53	33·03	2·14	70·56	1·35	94·936	2·13
Antenna	0·044	1·91	0·084	2·20	0·185	1·94	0·359	1·80	0·646	1·27	0·819	1·82
Prothorax	0·571	2·09	1·192	3·00	3·575	2·01	7·192	2·68	19·258	1·49	28·752	2·25
First leg	0·199	2·71	0·323	2·39	0·771	2·39	2·158	2·27	4·902	1·45	7·122	2·24
Third femur	0·696	2·37	1·650	3·07	5·073	1·93	9·783	2·16	21·090	2·33	49·044	2·37
Third tibia	0·138	2·69	0·371	2·64	0·978	2·51	2·453	2·28	5·598	1·48	8·306	2·32
Third tarsus	0·021	3·19	0·067	2·27	0·152	1·68	0·408	2·17	0·886	1·39	1·228	2·34
Meso- and meta-thorax and abdomen	5·520	2·40	13·240	3·10	40·980	1·78	72·929	2·33	170·056	2·49	424·08	2·42
Mean rate	—	2·47	—	2·61	—	2·22	—	2·23	—	2·10	—	2·32
Total weight	9·555	2·39	22·835	2·84	64·754	1·98	128·310	2·28	292·996	—	614·255	—

a species, as well as differences due to sex (as in adults, see p. 9) and to the number of instars. Some asymmetry between the two antennae of an individual also occurs (Katiyar, *t.c.*; Roonwal, *t.c.*). There are no studies of antennal growth in species with highly modified antennae (p. 10).

The general shape of the *head* in most Ist instar hoppers tends to be globular, even in the species in which it becomes more elongated later. In species with a conical head (e.g. *Colemania*; Coleman 1911), the head becomes relatively longer, but no hoppers of species with highly modified heads (p. 4) have been described in detail.

There are some changes in the shape of the *compound eye* during hopper growth in *Nomadacris* in which its horizontal diameter increases faster than the vertical (fig. 164). Substantial changes occurring in the component parts of the eye during growth (Bernard 1937) have been recorded (p. 196).

A feature of eye development, which is of importance for the determination of instars, is the change in their pigmentation, known so far only for the few species with a striped eye pattern (p. 198). Studies on *Schistocerca* (Mukerji

I   II   III   IV   V   VI   VII   Ad

Fig. 164. *Nomadacris*, growth of compound eye; line = 1 mm (Burnett 1951).

& Batra 1938; M. A. Volkonsky 1938*c*; Roonwal 1947*a*), *Anacridium aegyptium*, *A. melanorhodon* (Volkonsky, *t.c.*) and *Nomadacris* (Burnett 1951; Albrecht 1955) have shown that the first dark stripe appears near the upper end of the eye in the Ist instar and grows downwards; at each successive moult, a new stripe appears at the anterior edge of the eye, the earlier stripe moving backwards (fig. 164). Since one stripe is added at every moult, the total number of stripes in the adult indicates the total number of instars. Although occasional disagreement between the number of instars and of stripes has been recorded (almost certainly in error), this correlation is of great value in establishing development cycles, particularly when the number of instars is subject to variation, as for example in phases of the same species (p. 337). No work has been done on developmental changes in eyes with other than striped pigment patterns.

Of special value for distinguishing between hopper instars is the course of *development of tegmina and wings* (Albrecht 1955; Dovnar-Zapolskiï 1926; Michelmore & Allan 1934; Burnett 1951; Coleman 1911; Coleman & Kannan 1911; Karandikar 1945). In the Ist instar, the lower posterior angles of the mesonotum and metanotum do not show any differentiation (fig. 165) but already in the second they become somewhat extended and punctured, or rugulose;

in the subsequent instars they appear as rounded-triangular lobes directed obliquely downwards, with distinct traces of raised longitudinal ridges, which are tracheae, later to become axillary veins; their number in the hindwings of *Locusta* increases at each moult (Remaudière 1954), though this has not been studied throughout the development. The number of instars with alar rudiments in this condition varies according to species (p. 280), but after either the second instar or a later one, a striking change occurs: both pairs of rudiments turn on their axes, so that the outer surfaces become the inner and the

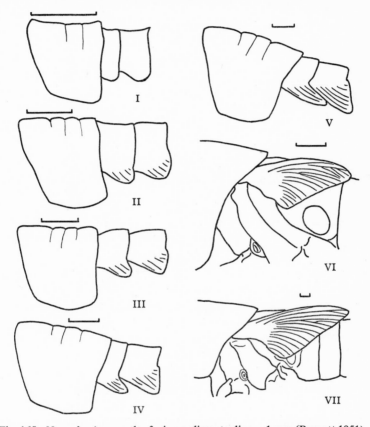

Fig. 165. *Nomadacris*, growth of wing rudiments; line = 1 mm (Burnett 1951).

rudiments of the tegmina (attached to the mesonotum) become covered by those of the wings, both lying dorsally and directed obliquely upwards. The mechanism of the reversal is based on the lower layer of hypodermal cells of the rudiment growing at a greater rate than the upper, thus pushing the rudiment upwards (T. S. Ivanova 1947). The tracheation of the rudimentary tegmina and wings is more clearly discernible after the reversal and reflects their final venation (Ragge 1955). Further development consists only in growth of the rudiments.

279

The *reversal of the alar rudiments* thus divides the hopper instars into two distinct groups. The instar in which the reversal occurs varies according to the total number of instars and may differ in two sexes of the same species (fig. 166), if they pass through different numbers of instars (p. 288). The cases so far known are illustrated by examples in table 74.

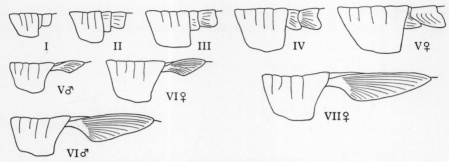

Fig. 166. *Hieroglyphus banian*, growth of wing rudiments in the two sexes (after Coleman & Kannan 1911).

Table 74. *Hopper instars in which the reversal of alar rudiments occurs*

(L, rudiments lateral; R, rudiments reversed; Ad, adult)

Species	I	II	III	IV	V	VI	VII	Ad
Chorthippus spp. ♂♀	L	L	R	R	Ad			
Dociostaurus kraussi ♂	L	L	R	R	Ad			
" " ♀	L	L	L	R	R	Ad		
" *maroccanus* ♂♀	L	L	L	R	R	Ad		
Locusta ♂♀	L	L	L	R	R	Ad		
Calliptamus italicus ♂	L	L	L	R	R	Ad		
" " ♀	L	L	L	L	R	R	Ad	
Hieroglyphus banian ♂	L	L	L	L	R	R	Ad	
" " ♀	L	L	L	L	L	R	R	Ad
Patanga succincta	L	L	L	L	L	R	R	Ad

A similar tabulation, but not including species from the temperate zone (e.g. *Chorthippus*) which pass through four instars, led Roonwal (1946, 1952 a) to formulate a 'rule' according to which the reversal occurs usually during the moult from the IIIrd to the IVth instar and to attach special physiological importance to the IIIrd instar. Table 74 shows, however, that the reversal may occur at the moult from the IInd, IIIrd, IVth or Vth instars to the next. The only regularity so far apparent is that the reversal precedes the final moult by two instars. The course of alar development in wingless acridoids is of interest. In *Lamarckiana* (Pamphagidae) in which the male is fully winged, the course follows the usual pattern, but in the adult female, which is completely apterous, there are small rudiments of both tegmina and wings up to the Vth instar; at that instar, the rudiments in the male reverse, but in the female disappear altogether (Thomas 1954 *a*).

The sexual differentiation of the *terminal abdominal segments* and of the external genitalia begins already in the embryo (Nelsen 1931*b*; Else 1934) and the different instars, as well as the two sexes, can be distinguished in hoppers without difficulty, which is important for experimental work. The changes

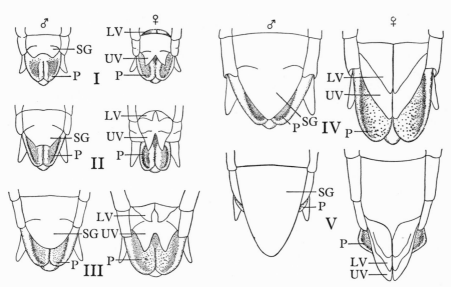

Fig. 167. *Locusta*, growth of external genitalia in the two sexes, from below (after Dirsh 1950).

SG, subgenital plate; LV, lower ovipositor valve; UV, upper ovipositor valve; P, paraproct.

during the development of *Locusta* (Dirsh 1950) are shown in fig. 167 and described below:

Instar	Male	Female
I	Subgenital plate semi-circularly excised at apex, with short obtuse lobes covering only base of paraprocts.	Upper ovipositor valves short, triangular, subacute, separated by a deep rectangular excision. Lower valves represented by a transverse fold (distinct only towards end of the instar) at bases of upper valves.
II	Subgenital plate narrowed to apex which has a shallow excision and reaches middle of paraprocts.	Upper ovipositor valves longer, acute, separated by deep and acute excision. Lower valves broadly triangular, separated by acutangular excision.
III	Subgenital plate with broadly parabolic apex, reaching beyond middle of paraprocts.	Upper ovipositor valves broader, separated by a broader excision. Lower valves almost as long as upper.

281

IV	Subgenital plate with narrowly para-bolic apex, reaching almost to apex of paraprocts.	Left and right ovipositor valves separated along the middle line. Upper valve shorter than paraprocts.
V	Subgenital plate elongate-parabolic, much longer than paraprocts.	Both upper and lower valves longer than paraprocts.

Descriptions and figures of the course of development of the terminal abdominal segments are available also for *Schistocerca* (Karandikar 1952; Albrecht 1955), *Nomadacris* (Burnett 1951; Albrecht 1955), *Dociostaurus* (Jannone 1939*b*), *Locustana* (Nel 1929), *Melanoplus marginatus* (C. C. Wilson & Keifer 1941), *M. bivittatus* (Shotwell 1941), *Chorthippus* (Shpet 1930), *Podisma* (Pichler 1957) and *Scotussa* (Zolessi 1958); the development of the ovipositor and its musculature in *Locusta* has been described by Agarwala (1952). In the male of *Calliptamus*, which differs from the female by having very large, pincer-like cerci (p. 19), the latter grow at a much greater rate than in the female, particularly during the last two instars (Pichler 1956).

The *development of the internal organs* has received less attention from authors, except Jannone (1939*b*) who described the rudiments of the digestive, respiratory and reproductive systems in the first instar of *Dociostaurus*, as well as some changes in gonads and their ducts in later instars. The rudiments of the testis in *Melanoplus* can be seen already in the embryo (Nelsen 1931*b*). Ovaries are also formed in the embryo (Nelsen 1931*a*); and in hatchlings, although small, they show the final number of ovarioles (Albrecht & Verdier 1956; see p. 353). The development of female genital ducts in *Locusta* and *Colemania* was described by Nel (1929). The Malpighian tubes in *Schistocerca* number eighteen in the late embryo and in the hatchling, but their number increases during instars from forty-three in the Ist instar to ninety-four in the IInd and to 182 in the IIIrd, finally reaching the mean figure of 251 (Savage 1956). The development of the central nervous system in *Locusta* was described by Afifi (1960) and that of the tympanal organ by Liu Weih-Teh (1952).

As regards the *musculature*, several muscles in the thorax and abdomen are present only in hoppers, and degenerate in adults a few days after the final moult (Ewer 1954*b*, 1954*c*, 1957*c*; Wiesend 1957). For example, in *Locusta* four pairs of tergo-pleural muscles are present in hoppers, but not in older adults, and it has been suggested that they may assist in moulting. On the other hand, some muscles (e.g. those serving in flight) are histologically different in hoppers and the adults and appear to be non-functional in the former (Thomas 1954*b*).

Blood-cell counts in *Locusta* (Webley 1951) have shown that the average was about 7,000 cells per cu. mm for hoppers of all instars, with a spectacular increase (up to 14,000) in the third instar, followed by a fall in the later instars (p. 116). Substantial increases occur towards the end of each instar (i.e. just preceding a moult); they were ascribed by Webley to a decrease in blood volume, but R. M. Lee (1961) showed that the volume also increases at this period, and suggested that higher cell counts were due to a full mobilisation of blood cells, many of which become sedentary after the moult and cause a fall in the count, although the blood volume remains constant. The special tissue producing blood cells (p .117), found in the coxae of hoppers, disappears in adults (Ögel 1960).

Descriptions of hoppers

Apart from the descriptions of hopper instars of individual species, the following papers deal with numbers of species from various countries, and

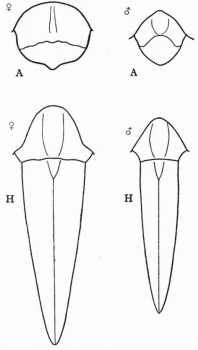

Fig. 168. *Acrida*, supra-anal plates (epiprocts) of last instar hoppers (H) and adults (A) of both sexes (original by J. Mason).

some of them include keys for determination: England (O. W. Richards & Waloff 1954), Germany (Pichler 1956, 1957), Ukraine (Dovnar-Zapolskiĭ 1926), Siberia (Bei-Bienko 1928; Rubtzov 1932), Canada (Criddle 1926, 1931; Handford 1946), United States (Carothers 1923; Shotwell 1930), South Africa (Chesler 1938).

Most of the available descriptions (a notable exception is the paper by Richards & Waloff *t.c.*) are based on the colour and pattern of hoppers, while their detailed morphology and anatomy are neglected. Reliable descriptions and identification keys for hoppers are particularly needed for ecological studies in which it is essential to distinguish between species in mixed populations from their earliest instars. Such studies would also be of value for taxonomists, since there are already some cases known where hoppers possess morphological features disappearing in adults. Thus, hoppers of *Acrida* (in both sexes), have the supra-anal plate strongly elongated (fig. 168), whereas in the adult it is normal (Chesler 1938; Dovnar-Zapolskiĭ 1926; Hafez & Ibrahim 1958). Another interesting case is that of the closely related *Gastrimargus nigericus* and *Locusta*, in which Ist instar hoppers differ very strongly but the differences gradually disappear during the development, the adults being very similar; the difference in the first instar is especially striking, since *Gastrimargus* has a large, shiny-black hemispherical tubercle on the side of the pronotum, of which there is no trace in *Locusta* (Dirsh 1959). This example, incidentally, suggests that the old conception of ontogeny reflecting phylogenetic affinity cannot always be sustained, there being no doubt that the two genera are close relations, but they differ more in the early instars than in the adult stage.

MOULTS

A moult (or ecdysis) from one hopper instar to the next is essentially a repetition of the intermediate moult (p. 272). The main difference is that, while the vermiform larva moults on the ground, the hopper, when ready to moult, climbs a plant and hangs head downwards, thus utilising gravity to help in the process. The abdomen distends and the cervical ampulla (p. 270) becomes active. The distention of the abdomen due to gravity is increased by the swallowing of air, and also by the expansion of abdominal air-sacs which occurs during a moult; it was suggested even that the main function of the abdominal sacs was to facilitate moulting (K. U. Clarke 1957c). The initial splitting of the cuticle occurs along the middle line of the pronotum where the cuticle is particularly thin; the split extends forwards on to the head and backwards to the first tergite. Vigorous contracting and expanding movements of the thorax and abdomen cause the split to widen, and the head and thorax come out of the old cuticle. When the legs also become free, the hopper remains connected with the support by the claws of the shed skin. Finally, it curves its abdomen, reaches with its legs for support and leaves the shed skin (exuvium) hanging.

Histological preparations for a moult (fig. 169) commence some days before (Duarte 1939; Malek 1958a, 1958b), and consist mainly in the formation of a new integument under the old one. Already by the middle of an instar (fig. 169, D), there begins a separation of the old cuticle from the epidermis and a day later a new epicuticle appears on the outside of the new epidermis, while on the innermost layer of the old cuticle a thin ecdysial membrane is deposited, and the space between the new and the old cuticle widens. This is followed by separation of the ecdysial membrane from the old endocuticle and by the development of the new endocuticle under the new epicuticle. The laminated old endocuticle then becomes digested by the secretion of the moulting glands of the epidermis, but the ecdysial membrane, although extremely thin, is not soluble in the moulting fluid and is shed during the moult together with the old cuticle. Some part in the production of new cuticle may be played by oeno-

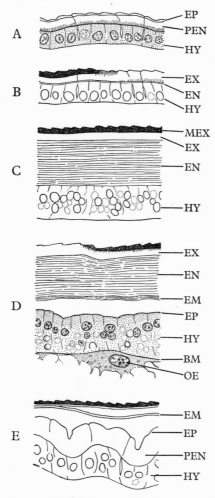

Fig. 169. *Schistocerca*, changes in the integument during preparations for the last moult. A, newly moulted hopper; B, hopper two hours old; C, 3–4 days old; D, 5–6 days old; E, shortly before moulting to adult (after Malek 1958 *b*).
EP, epicuticle; PEN, pre-exuvial endocuticle; HY, hypoderm; EM, ecdysial membrane; EX, exocuticle; MEX, melanised exocuticle; EN, endocuticle; BM, basement membrane; OE, oenocyte.

cytes (p. 104) which become vacuolated before a moult and return to their normal condition after it (Duarte 1939).

Physiological changes occurring at moulting time consist in a hopper ceasing to feed and becoming less active a few hours before the moult and again after it. This depression of neuro-muscular activity appears to be connected with a change in neurosecretory activity (pp. 159, 289) and with a rise in the potassium concentration of the haemolymph (p. 66); a rise in that of sodium also occurs at the moult (Hoyle 1956).

After a moult a hopper has a soft integument and its colour is very light, but in a matter of hours it hardens and darkens (p. 43).

It has now been established that the moulting process is under hormonal control. Since the evidence for this is largely based on variation in the number of hopper instars, the information on this subject will be reviewed first.

NUMBER OF INSTARS

A rapid glance at table 75 is sufficient to show the variation in the number of hopper instars between species. The table is not complete and further scattered data might be added to it, but it includes only the more reliable records, particularly those based on rearing. In view of purely incidental representation of taxonomic and geographical groups in the table, it would be unwise to suggest the prevalent number of instars; Roonwal's (1946, 1952b) statement that most species pass through five instars was based on very incomplete data. A number of families are either absent from the table, or represented by few records, and only occasional data are available for the tropical species. Nevertheless, a few suggestions may be made. Thus, it appears that

Table 75. *The usual number of hopper instars in grasshopper species*

Species	♂	♀	Reference
PAMPHAGIDAE			
Pamphagus elephas	5		Roubaud 1953
Tmethis pulchripennis	5		Shulov 1952d
Lamarckiana sp.	6		Thomas 1954a
PYRGOMORPHIDAE			
Chrotogonus robertsi	5–6	5–7	Latif & Haq 1951
Colemania sphenarioides		5–6	Coleman 1911
Zonocerus elegans	5	5	Chesler 1938
Poekilocerus pictus		6	Pruthi & Nigam 1939
,, bufonius	5	5	Fishelson 1960
,, hieroglyphicus	7	8	A. Antoniou (unpublished)
Pyrgomorpha kraussi	5	6–7	,, ,,
Phymateus viridipes		7	De Lotto 1951
Aularches punctatus		6	Katiyar 1955
ROMALEINAE			
Romalea microptera	5	5	P. Hunter-Jones (unpublished)
EYPREPOCNEMIDINAE			
Eyprepocnemis plorans			
meridionalis		6–8	Antoniou & Hunter-Jones 1956
,, ,, ornatipes			
,, roseus	5	6	Katiyar 1953
,, hokutensis	6	7	Tinkham 1940
Choroedocus capensis	6	7	Tinkham 1940
TROPIDOPOLINAE			
Oxyrrhepes cantonensis	6	7	Tinkham 1940

Table 75—*continued*

	♂	♀	Reference
HEMIACRIDINAE			
Parahieroglyphus bilineatus	6	6	Katiyar 1953
Hieroglyphus banian	6	7	Coleman & Kannan 1911
,, *nigrorepletus*		6	Roonwal 1952*b*
OXYINAE			
Oxya spp.	6	6–7	Kumashiro 1935; Tinkham 1940
CATANTOPINAE			
Podisma pedestris		5	Pichler 1957
Miramella alpina		5	,, ,,
Odontopodisma decipiens		5	,, ,,
Melanoplus differentialis	6	6	Shotwell 1941
,, *sanguinipes*	5–6		,, ,,
,, *marginatus*	5–6		C. C. Wilson & Keifer 1941
Scotussa cliens	7		Liebermann 1951; Zolessi 1958
Cornops aquaticum	6		Zolessi 1958
Pezotettix giornai	6	6	Dovnar-Zapolskiĭ 1926
CALLIPTAMINAE			
Calliptamus italicus	5	6	Pichler 1956
CYRTACANTHACRIDINAE			
Schistocerca obscura		5	Duck 1944
,, *flavofasciata*	5	6	Kevan 1943
Anacridium aegyptium	5	5	Colombo & Mocellinĭ 1956
,, ,,	5	6	M. A. Volkonsky 1937
,, *melanorhodon*	5–6		,, 1938*c*
Acanthacris ruficornis	7		Chesler 1938
Ornithacris turbida	6	8	A. Antoniou (unpublished)
Patanga succincta	7–9		Pagden 1959
OEDIPODINAE			
Camnula pellucida	5	5–6	Shotwell 1941
Oedaleus nigrofasciatus	5	5	Chesler 1938
,, *decorus*	5		Berezhkov 1956
Gastrimargus musicus	5	5	Common 1948
,, *nigericus*	5	5	Dirsh 1959
,, *africanus*	4–6	5–6	Hunter-Jones & Ward 1959
Psophus stridulus	4	4	Bei-Bienko 1928
Aiolopus thalassinus	5	5	Dovnar-Zapolskiĭ 1926; Chesler 1938
Epacromius tergestinus	4	4	,, ,, ,,
Oedipoda caerulescens	4	4	,, ,, ,, ; Shpet 1935
Bryodema tuberculatum		5	Berezhkov 1956
Dissosteira longipennis		5	Wakeland 1958
,, *carolina*	5–6	5–6	Shotwell 1941
Acrotylus angulatus	5	5	Chesler 1938
Trilophidia conturbata	5	5	,, ,,
Parapleurus alliaceus	5	5	Dovnar-Zapolskiĭ 1926
ACRIDINAE			
Acrida sp. (Ukraine)	5	5	Dovnar-Zapolskiĭ 1926
,, ,, (South Africa)	6	7	Chesler 1938
,, *pellucida*	6	7–8	Hafez & Ibrahim 1958
GOMPHOCERINAE			
Euthystira brachyptera	4	4	Bei-Bienko 1928
Neopodismopsis abdominalis	4	4	Criddle 1930
Chorthippus spp.	4	4	Shpet 1930, 1931; Kadzevich 1935; Richards & Waloff 1954; Karelina 1957
Euchorthippus pulvinatus	5	5	Dovnar-Zapolskiĭ 1926
Stenobothrus spp.	4	4	Bei-Bienko 1928; Richards & Waloff 1954
Omocestus spp.	4	4	Richards & Waloff 1954
Gomphocerippus rufus	4	4	Bei-Bienko 1928
Gomphocerus sibiricus	4	4	Il'enko 1930
Pararcyptera microptera	5	5	Berezkhov 1956
Dociostaurus maroccanus	5	5	Various authors
,, *brevicollis*	5	5	Bei-Bienko 1928
,, *kraussi*	4	5	Plotnikov 1926

the majority of species in the most advanced group (Gomphocerinae) pass through only four instars, while in the more primitive groups (e.g. Catantopinae, Pamphagidae, Pyrgomorphidae) the number is five or more. This might suggest an evolutionary trend towards a reduction in the number of instars, but it may be due also to the fact that all the Gomphocerinae in the list are of small size, while the others are mostly larger. That the adult size may be of importance is suggested by the list of Cyrtacanthacridinae, which are all large and in which the number never falls below five (and that only in the smaller males) and may be as high as nine (this record for *Patanga* requires confirmation). Another indication of the importance of size is that in many species with notable sexual size dimorphism, the larger female normally has one instar more than the male. This may be a general phenomenon,

Table 76. *Variation in the number of instars in
laboratory populations (after Shotwell 1941)*

Species	Number	Percentage 5 instars	Percentage 6 instars
Melanoplus bivittatus ♂	214	93	7
" " ♀	241	59·3	40·7
" *sanguinipes* ♂	18	77·8	22·2
" " ♀	15	60·0	40·0
" *femur-rubrum* (Montana) ♂	78	97·4	2·6
" " " ♀	95	96·8	3·2
" *femur-rubrum* (Tennessee) ♂	27	0·0	100·0
" " " ♀	20	10·0	90·0
" *packardi* ♂	77	92·2	7·8
" " ♀	57	71·9	28·1
" *gladstoni* ♂	1	100·0	0·0
" " ♀	9	77·8	22·2
Dissosteira carolina ♂	119	96·6	3·4
" " ♀	115	78·3	21·7
Camnula pellucida ♂	28	100·0	0·0
" " ♀	35	97·1	2·9

many records in the table being based on rearing the two sexes together, or on field observations.

Variation in the instar number within the same species (apart from that due to sex) is of particular interest. Incidental records of this kind are very numerous but are usually regarded as abnormalities. However, such variations were found in practically every species which has been under close observation, as illustrated by table 76, summarising results of controlled cage rearings of several species.

The data in this table suggest some geographical variation in the number of instars, since individuals of *Melanoplus femur-rubrum* from Montana had mostly five instars, while those from the more southern locality (Tennessee), reared in the same conditions, nearly all passed through six.

An indication that food may have an effect on the course of development was obtained by rearing *Schistocerca* on lucerne (Telenga 1930). This food generally slowed the development down, but four out of fifty hoppers became adult eight days earlier than others, passing through only four instars, instead of the normal five. The resulting adults were much smaller than normal, and their tegmina were only half the normal length, not reaching the end of the abdomen. They, however, matured normally, copulated and laid eggs. A somewhat similar case was reported for *Melanoplus sanguinipes*, small and definitely brachypterous individuals (fig. 50) having been obtained amongst those reared on lucerne at low temperature and high humidity (Brett 1947); although the number of instars was not recorded and the effects of food were not separated from those of other factors, the parallelism with *Schistocerca* may not be accidental. Strangely enough, in *Melanoplus sanguinipes*, 85 per cent of individuals reared on oats, a diet on which high mortality occurs (p. 83), developed an extra instar. Thus, untritionally deficient food may upset the development cycle by either increasing or decreasing the number of instars. The variation in the number of hopper instars is important in relation to phase phenomena in locusts, where the solitarious phase often has more instars than the gregarious (p. 337).

Hormonal control of the instar number

It was suggested long ago that moults and the instar number in locusts may be under hormonal control (Key & Edney 1936). Recently great advances have been made in this field relating to other insects (Wigglesworth 1954; C. M. Williams 1958), but experimental data on locusts are less definite (Strich 1955; Strich-Halbwachs 1959; P. Joly 1958; L. Joly 1955, 1958, 1960). It has been deduced that hopper moults in *Locusta* are stimulated by a *moulting hormone* (*ecdysone*) secreted by the prothoracic gland. When an extra gland was implanted in the Ist or IInd instar hopper, the number of subsequent instars was reduced (Staal 1961). Implantation of an extra gland in the IVth instar shortened the mean duration of the instar from 8·11 to 6·25 days, but, paradoxically, the subsequent instar was prolonged by about one day; implantation in the Vth instar reduced its duration. Extirpation of the gland from the IVth instar either prolonged it, or caused the hopper to remain longer than normal without moulting; such individuals were called 'permanent larvae' (Strich-Halbwachs, *t.c.*), although they died within eighteen to twenty-two days.

The moulting hormone is not restricted to hoppers, as Stamm (1959) claimed to have isolated, in crystallised form, from adults of *Dociostaurus* two kinds of ecdysone which he identified by chromatographic tests and by the effects on the pupation of a fly; their presence in adults suggests some function other than that in moulting.

The secretion of the corpora allata in other insects is supposed to contain a *juvenile hormone*. *Locusta* hoppers of the fourth instar from which corpora allata have been removed became, after a moult, not fifth instar hoppers, but 'precocious adults', described as typical in all respects but with tegmina and wings shorter than the body (L. Joly 1960). If, however, additional corpora allata were implanted into fourth instar hoppers, they moulted into what has been called 'adultoids', described as essentially hopper-like, but with tegmina and wings longer than in hoppers. It was suggested that the transformation into adult was inhibited by the surplus juvenile hormone and the resulting insects were regarded as hoppers. However, my examination of such 'adultoids', kindly sent by Mme. Joly, showed that the females had ovipositors as fully developed as in adults and the tegmina and wings had adult venation, although they were shorter than normal and not fully expanded; there was certainly a disturbance of the moulting process, but it apparently affected only the length of the eventual adult flight organs.

The latest hypothesis relating to the cyclical processes of growth and moulting in *Locusta* hoppers (K. U. Clarke & Langley 1962, 1963*a*, 1963*b*, 1963*c*, 1963*d*) postulates that there is a constant production of neurosecretory material in the medial cells of the brain and constant release of it from the corpora cardiaca. Its production and release are dependent upon impulses arising in the stretch receptors of the pharynx associated with the intake of food during an instar and with the swallowing of air into the gut during the moult. This can give rise to a cyclical stimulation of the prothoracic gland in the following manner: during an instar the neurosecretory material is used in growth and metabolism, but before a moult, when there is no feeding, the material could accumulate in the haemolymph and this would stimulate the prothoracic gland to produce ecdysone and thus initiate a moult. The whole problem obviously requires much more extensive and precise investigations. The situation is likely to be complicated, since the prothoracic gland is large and active in younger hoppers, but tends to cease functioning in the older ones, and disappears in the adult locusts (but only if they are crowded; see p. 377). The corpora allata also vary in their activity during the hopper and the adult life and the effects of their secretion cannot be assumed to be always the same. The functions of the corpora cardiaca in hoppers are very imperfectly known. Moreover, examples of the effects of climate (p. 288), food (p. 289) and phase (p. 337) on the instar number suggest that the normal course of development may be disturbed by environmental influences and much remains to be done to clarify the mode of action of the various hormones that have been postulated, the probable importance of their balance, and their effects on metabolism and growth. In the meantime it is certainly premature to speculate on the primary causes of variation in the instar number.

ENVIRONMENTAL FACTORS

Effects of temperature and *humidity* on hopper development must be discussed together, because it is extremely difficult in experimental work to separate the two factors. On the one hand, the relative humidity of the same air varies with temperature, and on the other, hopper metabolism is possibly more affected by the water content of food than by air humidity, both of which may influence the quantity of food consumed and, therefore, the rate of growth.

Nevertheless, some evidence of temperature effects should be briefly mentioned. Parker's (1930) extensive experiments with several American grasshoppers clearly indicated a shortening of the hopper period and an accelerated rate of development (percentage of total development per day) with rising temperatures (table 77).

Table 77. *Effects of temperature on the mean length of the hopper period in days and (in brackets) the mean daily rate of development (after Parker 1930)*

Species	22°	27°	32°	37°
Melanoplus sanguinipes	79·2(1·26)	41·9(2·38)	27·3(3·66)	23·1(4·32)
„ *femur-rubrum*	65·2(1·53)	34·7(2·88)	30·8(3·24)	
„ *packardi*		45·1(2·21)	27·5(3·63)	22·0(4·58)
Camnula pellucida		43·3(2·29)	25·0(4·00)	20·6(4·85)

Dudley's (1961) summary of data from various authors on the effects of temperature on the development rate of *Schistocerca* hoppers is illustrated by fig. 170.

In very detailed and extensive experimental studies on locusts by A. G. Hamilton (1936, 1950), the effects of a series of combinations of temperatures and relative humidities were studied. He chose to use relative humidity rather than the saturation deficit (p. 230) because the experimental data have shown, for example, that *Schistocerca* hoppers could complete their development at 26·7°, with the saturation deficit varying within wide limits, from 0·155 to 0·672; at 26·7°C and 25% R.H. no development occurred, while it proceeded at 32·2°C and 45% R.H., although the deficit values were practically identical (0·775 in the first case and 0·783 in the second). The curves summarising the results for *Locusta* (fig. 171), while indicating a decrease in the length of hopper period with rising temperature, show also that the effects of humidity substantially modify those of temperature, particularly in the higher range of the latter. The shortest hopper period might be considered as reflecting the optimum for development, but such a view cannot be accepted, without taking into consideration the percentage of hoppers reaching the adult stage. As can be seen, the effects of humidity on survival again combine with those of temperature. The optimum conditions for the rate of development and for survival do not coincide, since *Locusta* hoppers develop fastest at 42·2°, while the lowest mortality occurs at 34·4°; for *Schistocerca*, the respective optimum values are 38·3° and 32·2°.

The graphs in fig. 172 show the combined effects of temperature and humidity on the length of the hopper period and on the percentage reaching the adult stage. A comparison of the graphs for *Locusta* with those for *Schistocerca* shows the different requirements and ranges of limiting conditions of the two species. Hamilton's findings were criticised by Husain, Ahmad & Mathur (1940), whose experiments with *Schistocerca* 'proved

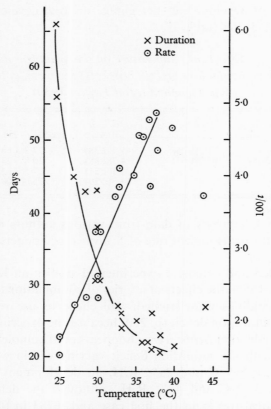

Fig. 170. *Schistocerca*, the duration and the rates of development of hoppers in relation to temperature (Dudley 1961).

beyond doubt' that relative humidity had no effect on hopper development. Apart from the fact that their conclusion was based on very few experiments, these authors provided hoppers with unlimited green food, thus counteracting the effects of low air humidity, while Hamilton used food plants partly wilted to approximately the same water content. Dudley (1961) also found no difference in the rate of development of *Schistocerca* hoppers at air humidities ranging from 30 to 90%, but they had access to drinking water. Chauvin (1941*b*) claimed that, contrary to Hamilton's findings, *Schistocerca* hoppers develop best at a relative humidity very close to zero. It was not mentioned

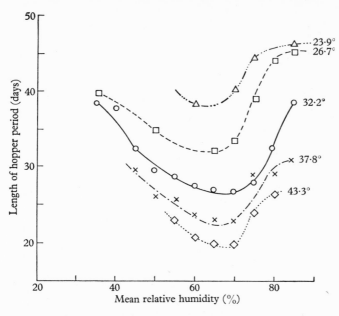

Fig. 171. *Locusta*, length of hopper period in relation to temperature
and humidity (A. G. Hamilton 1950).

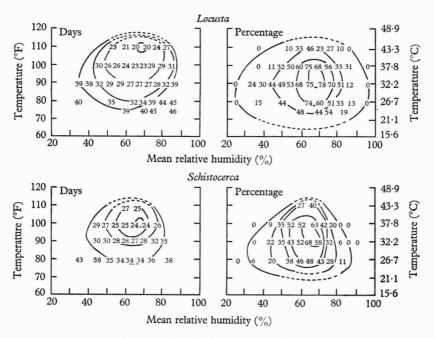

Fig. 172. *Locusta* and *Schistocerca*, length of hopper period and the percentage of hoppers
reaching the adult stage, in relation to temperature and humidity (Hamilton 1936).

293

whether such a low value was measured, and it could hardly be achieved in a cage with one side covered by wire net admitting the outside air, while the food provided was fresh grass or lettuce with the stalks (outside the cage) in water.

Since in nature neither the temperature nor the air humidity remain constant, it is essential to know the effects of fluctuating conditions on development. In experiments designed to investigate this problem (A. G. Hamilton 1950), hoppers of *Locusta* and *Schistocerca* were kept at different combinations of temperature and humidity during the day and during the night; knowing the time spent in each set of conditions, it was possible to calculate their mean values, weighted by the time, and to compare them with the results obtained at the same constant temperatures and humidities. The results showed that the rate of development and the survival were practically the same. This suggests that, as regards temperatures, the ruling factor may have been the number of degree-hours above the developmental threshold, which was calculated as 11·7° for *Locusta* and 17·2° for *Schistocerca*. However, Parker's (1930) experiments with *Melanoplus sanguinipes* indicated that an effective temperature, alternating with a low one (12°), had a marked accelerating effect on hopper development. Further work is clearly needed.

Effects of food on the development and the mortality of hoppers and adults are discussed above (p. 289) and in the chapter on the alimentary system (p. 82).

Fig. 173. *Locusta*, final moult. A, adult half emerged; B, *ditto*, almost fully emerged; C, the exuvium; D, adult, free of exuvium, in the process of expanding its wings (original photos by E. Yatsentkovskii).

facing p. 295

THE ADULT

The adult life begins with the completion of the final moult.

FINAL MOULT

This moult is essentially similar to those separating hopper instars, except after the new adult is free from the exuvium (fig. 173). It then hangs on the first two pairs of legs, and the tegmina and wings assume their normal position (i.e. with the tegmina covering the wings). Both are at first quite soft and crumpled, but vigorous movements of the abdomen apparently serve to pump haemolymph into them and they gradually expand, begin to harden and are eventually folded on the dorsum.

ANATOMICAL CHANGES

A newly emerged adult, called a *fledgling*, has at first soft, weakly pigmented integument, but in a few hours it hardens and acquires the coloration and pattern of the species. The processes of hardening (sclerotisation) and of the development of dark pigmentation (melanisation) have been regarded in the past as intimately connected, but this view is no longer held (p. 43). In fact, many very light-coloured cuticles are as hard as the dark ones; in particular, there is no obvious difference in this respect between the normal black, heavily pigmented gregarious hoppers of *Schistocerca* and the albino ones (p. 43).

The melanisation process has been already discussed and the chemistry of the sclerotisation is still under dispute (Goodwin 1952a; Malek 1957, 1958b, 1961; Jones & Sinclair 1958). The essential substances are thought to be polyphenols and quinones, and various schemes were proposed to describe the processes involved, but the most recent review by a biochemist concludes that 'much that has been written on the hardening of the insect cuticle is of a speculative nature' (Gilmour 1961).

From the morphological point of view, the integument of a young hardened adult (no longer a fledgling but not yet sexually mature), is characterised by a thin epidermal layer consisting of flat cells with relatively large nuclei (fig. 174), whereas the epidermal cells of a mature male are greatly enlarged in height, with vacuoles and nuclei of two kinds, some large and some small (Loher 1960, 1961). The cuticle also increases in thickness with age (Chauvin 1939b, 1941b, *Schistocerca*; Strich-Halbwachs 1959, *Locusta*); the increase is due to the deposition, every 24 hours, of a pair of layers which are distinguishable by the intensity of fluorescence in the ultra-violet light, so that an examination of cuticle sections provides an exact measure of the age of an adult in days (Neville 1963*b*, 1963*c*, 1963*d*).

Structural changes occurring on the transition from hopper to adult are not restricted to the obvious sudden transformation of wing-pads to fully developed

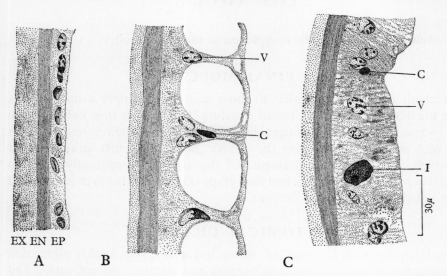

EX EN EP

A   B   C

Fig. 174. *Schistocerca* integument. A, an immature male; B, mature male; C, mature male, with corpora allata removed (original by W. Loher).
    EX, exocuticle; EN, endocuticle; EP, epidermis; V, large nucleus; C, small nucleus; I, inclusion.

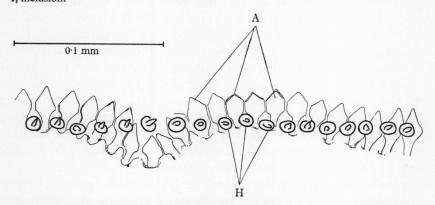

0·1 mm

Fig. 175. Male of *Stenobothrus lineatus*, change in the size of femoral stridulatory pegs from the last instar hopper (H) to the adult (A) (Roscow 1963).

tegmina and wings, and detailed morphological comparisons will certainly reveal more of them than are known at present. Externally, there is a marked change in the terminal abdominal structures; the ovipositor valves of the adult female, for instance, are quite distinct from that of the last instar hopper by their hard, acute, black tips (compare figs. 18 and 167). In the male of

Calliptamus, considerable changes occur during the final moult in the structure of the last abdominal segments and the cercus, as well as in their musculature (Pichler 1952). The disintegration in the adult of some other muscles present in the hopper has been mentioned elsewhere (p. 282), while the definitive adult muscles take several days to become fully functional.

Roscow (1961, 1963) recorded a remarkable change occurs in the size of the femoral stridulatory pegs of *Stenobothrus lineatus*, which are quite small and imperfectly formed in the last instar male hopper, but suddenly increase in size after the final moult (fig. 175).

COLOUR CHANGES

An adult immediately after the final moult is very weakly pigmented, but definite background coloration appears after a few hours, parallel with hardening of the cuticle, and black, or dark, patterns due to melanin also develop.

Further colour changes during the adult life are particularly noticeable in gregarious *Schistocerca*, in which the young adults are pink, while the old ones are bright yellow (coloured illustrations given by Künckel d'Herculais 1893–1905; Vosseler 1905; etc.). The difference is so striking, that some doubts were expressed whether the two forms belonged to the same species, until Künckel d'Herculais clarified the matter. A detailed description of colour changes in cage-bred gregarious *Schistocerca* based mainly on that by Chauvin (1941*b*) and Norris (1954) follows:

(1) Young hardened fledgling. Overall colour pink. Head with a purplish postocular spot. Pronotum pink, with small paler dots and faint traces of the dark pattern which is black in hoppers; median line clear pink. All legs pink. Tegmina greyish-pink, with dark-red spots. Wing veins pink.
(2) General colour becoming bluish or greyish-pink, particularly on sides of thorax and abdomen.
(3) General colour changing to brownish; the pink gradually disappearing, its last remnants seen at end of hind tibia.
(4) Yellow tinge appears, first at base of wings.
(5) General yellowing. In male end of abdomen becomes yellow first, coinciding with readiness to copulate; in female this is marked by the disappearance of pink colour from hind tibia.
(6) Fully mature. Overall yellow, brilliant in males, less so in females. Dark pattern obsolete on pronotum and abdomen, only tegmina with small dark spots.

Colour changes in wild populations of this species have not been sufficiently well described, but they seem to follow the same general course, although the overall pink and yellow colours are usually much brighter than in cage populations. Also there may be modifications, possibly due to environmental effects; for example young adults may be brick-red in the stage corresponding to the brown stage 3 in the above scheme; this appears to happen in wild adults with long-delayed maturation (Pasquier 1946). The scheme applies only to the ph. *gregaria*, while in the ph. *solitaria* the pink colour of fledglings and the yellow of mature adults are absent (p. 341); and in populations of the ph. *transiens* various intermediate colour schemes actually occur.

Since the change from general pink coloration to yellow in *Schistocerca* coincides approximately with the beginning of copulation, it has been assumed in the past that it is closely correlated with the maturation of the gonads, although some authors (e.g. Boldyrev 1946) maintained that yellow coloration is merely a sign of ageing and not of maturation. Careful experimental work by Norris (1954, 1964c) has shown that the yellowing of the integument, the maturation of the gonads and readiness to copulate are all influenced by the presence of a mature yellow male; by introducing such a male into a cage of immature ones it is possible to produce very rapid yellowing in the latter. Thus, *Schistocerca* males became mature in about twenty-seven days when kept with females only, but similar males matured in seventeen days when stimulated by a single yellow male; *Locusta* males copulated in 17–25 days after emergence, but in the presence of mature males they were ready to copulate after 13–14 days. The stimulus to maturation proved to be an olfactory one and Loher (1960) demonstrated that yellow males of *Schistocerca* secrete an oil-soluble hormonal substance, the smell of which perceived by immature males through sensilla (probably antennal) induces activity in the corpora allata; the secretion of the latter, in its turn, stimulates secretory activity of hypodermal cells of the abdominal tergites (fig. 174, B), the secretion being deposited on their cuticle, where it can be collected by wiping the surface with cotton-wool. The secretion thus collected can be used for stimulating immature males even at some distance. Such hormones, in distinction from those released in the blood, are known as *pheromones*. Some indication of the chemical nature of the male pheromone of *Schistocerca* was obtained by Carlisle & Ellis (1964) from applying to females a 10% solution of 2-chloro-ethanol in ethanol, which resulted in a colour change and oöcyte growth; it is of interest that this substance is related to ethylene which is known to accelerate the ripening of stored apples. Although the effect of such stimulation on the development of the male gonads has not yet been studied, the fact that it induces readiness to copulate suggests that it may exist, although most of the spermatogenesis occurs in hoppers (p. 303). In practice, the coincidence of the yellowing with mating is sufficiently close to provide a useful guide for judging the onset of the reproductive period in wild locust populations.

Similar colour changes occur in the gregarious phases of most other locusts, although with modifications. In *Schistocerca paranensis*, the ground colour of fledglings is reddish, with well marked black pattern, and the wings are hyaline; later, dull-reddish colour spreads, obliterating the dark pattern and the wings become pink basally; at mating, the yellowish colour appears over the body and the wings (Bruner 1898). In *Nomadacris*, fledglings have some pink ground colour, and very distinct black pattern, but the wings are hyaline, with dark veins; in older adults a red suffusion gradually develops so that the black pattern becomes less distinct, and the wings become red (first at the base); during the mating period the bright red gives way to brownish-yellow or yellow, except on the wings which remain crimson (Michelmore & Allan 1934). Colour changes in *Patanga* follow a similar sequence (Maxwell-Lefroy 1906). In *Locusta*, there is no pink colour in fledglings, but yellowing at the reproductive period is well pronounced, especially in males (Vinokurov 1916). In *Locustana*, there is also no pink colour in fledglings, but yellowing of the abdomen and hind legs at reproduction is very pronounced (Faure 1923). In *Dociostaurus maroccanus*, fledglings show some brownish-pink tinge, turning yellowish at mating, the dark pattern becomes obsolete, and the hind tibia turn from pink to carmine-red (La Baume 1918; Waterston 1951; Merton 1959). Yellowing at the mating period was also described in two species of *Austroicetes* (Key 1954).

It needs to be emphasised that all these examples refer to the gregarious phase, but no general yellowing coincident with mating is known to occur in the solitarious phase. Thus, even in *Schistocerca gregaria*, in which the adult colour changes are particularly striking in the gregarious phase, solitarious fledglings develop no pink coloration and no yellowing occurs at mating time. This became understandable only when it was established (Loher 1960) that

Fig. 176. *Mesopsis laticornis*, changes in wing coloration during adult life (E. D. Burtt & Uvarov 1944).

the yellowing depends on olfactory perception and the resulting neuro-secretion, which also affects maturation of gonads. It is not known yet what controls the pink of fledglings, which is, indeed, absent (or obscured) in some of the locusts (*Locusta, Locustana*). Again, the reddening of wings in mature *Nomadacris* and *Patanga* may be of a somewhat different nature, since it occurs in both phases of these species. (For a biochemical discussion of the pigments involved see p. 52; for the phase aspects p. 341.)

Changes in adult coloration are now known not only in gregarious locusts, but also in some grasshoppers. In the African *Mesopsis laticornis*, the hyaline wings gradually develop a large black patch (fig. 176; E. D. Burtt & Uvarov 1944); this may be connected with the onset of reproductive activity, but direct observations are needed. Detailed studies on British grasshoppers revealed changes in adult coloration, in most cases parallel with maturation of the gonads (O. W. Richards & N. Waloff 1954). As can be seen from table 78, in species of group A, there was a change in the colour of the ventral side of the abdomen from grey or green in young adults to yellow in mature ones, parallel with the ovariole development; in group B, the ventral colour in both sexes changed to a shade of red, again parallel with sexual maturation and the hind tibiae also became red. A further group C, including *Omocestus ventralis* and *Chorthippus vagans*, was distinguished, in which the development of reddish or red colour occurred without apparent relation to the state of the gonads. This study is of particular interest, since it was carried out on the commonest grasshoppers, in which such colour variations have been known, but considered as individual and not developmental. The need for careful studies of such phenomena is obvious.

Table 78. *Colour changes in adult grasshoppers in relation to maturation (after Richards & Waloff 1954)*

Species	Mean weight (mg)	Colour of abdomen below	Gonads	
			♂ testes	♀ ovarioles
GROUP A				
Chorthippus parallelus ♂	60·2	Grey to greenish		
,, ,, ♂	68·9	Green to yellow		
,, ,, ♀	110·1	Grey to pale green		Thread-like
,, ,, ♀	190·1	Yellow		Mature
Omocestus viridulus ♂	82·5	Green to grey		
,, ,, ♂	98·9	Green to yellow		
,, ,, ♀	159·4	Green to grey		Thread-like
,, ,, ♀	277·2	Green to yellow		Egg 1 full-grown
GROUP B				
Chorthippus brunneus ♂	63·9	Yellowish	3·79 mm	
,, ,, ♂	79·2	Orange-red	4·47 mm	
,, ,, ♀	142	Yellowish		Thread-like
,, ,, ♀	223	Orange-red		Egg 1 full-grown
Stenobothrus lineatus ♂	85	Green	White	
,, ,, ♂	102	Yellow, tip red	Yellow	
,, ,, ♀	161	No red		Thread-like
,, ,, ♀	240	Red		Egg 1 full-grown
Myrmeleotettix maculatus ♂	47	No red	3·0 mm	
,, ,, ♂	58	Orange-pink	3·5 mm	

WEIGHT CHANGES

For a few hours following the final moult the young fledgling does not feed and loses some weight, but this loss is rapidly regained. From the age of two days, the weight of adults increases steadily until what is called the *basic weight* is reached (fig 177). The increase is considerable as can be seen in table 79.

For *Schistocerca*, Norris (1954) regarded as the basic weight the value reached in thirteen to seventeen days, when the rate of feeding decreases and

Table 79. *Changes in weight in adult females of grasshoppers (Richards & Waloff 1954)*

Species	Percentage increase from emergence to maturity	Mean mature weight (mg)	Mean drop in weight at oviposition	
			mg	Percentage
Chorthippus brunneus	72·8	188·7	31·1	16·5
,, parallelus	95·2	160·3	32·9	20·6
Omocestus viridulus	82·7	276·3	41·1	16·7
Stenobothrus lineatus	94·5	234·5	29·8	12·7
Myrmeleotettix maculatus	49·0	131·1	17·6	13·4

the weight becomes almost stationary; this corresponds to an average increase of 78% over the emergence weight in the case of females and 55% in males. In the female, a further sharp increase follows the first copulation, until a

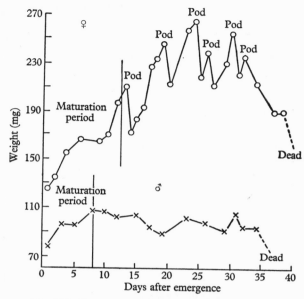

Fig. 177. *Omocestus viridulus*, weight changes during adult life (Richards & Waloff 1954).

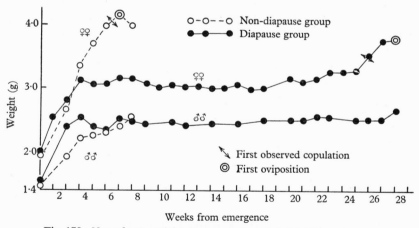

Fig. 178. *Nomadacris*, weight changes during adult life (Norris 1959a).

maximum (i.e. the *mature weight*) is reached at the first oviposition, after which there is a sharp drop to the basic value, followed by fluctuations above and below that value corresponding to successive ovipositions. Similar weight changes occur in *Nomadacris* (fig. 178; Norris 1959a) and *Locusta* (Phipps 1950).

THE ADULT

The initial increase in weight is associated with the growth of the exo-skeleton, particularly the increase in thickness of the cuticle (p. 295) and the development of muscles. The relative contributions to this increase from the body cuticle and the developing wing muscles are shown in fig. 179;

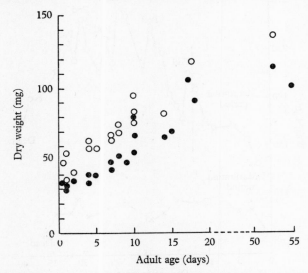

Fig. 179. *Schistocerca*, increase in the weight of body cuticle (black circles) and of the wing muscles (open circles) during adult life (after Weis-Fogh 1952).

other muscles presumably make further substantial contributions (Weis-Fogh 1952). This is reflected in the increase in the dry weight as shown by Dudley (1961) for *Schistocerca* (table 80).

Table 80. *Changes in the mean fresh weight and water content of adult* Schistocerca (*Dudley* 1961)

Age (days)	Fresh weight, mg ♂	Fresh weight, mg ♀	Dry weight, mg ♂	Dry weight, mg ♀	Water, mg ♂	Water, mg ♀	Water, Percentage ♂	Water, Percentage ♀
1	1460	1875	409	502	1051	1374	72·0	73·3
5	1979	2455	660	827	1288	1628	66·2	66·5
10	2233	3060	909	1182	1324	1877	59·2	61·4
15	2080	3129	861	1263	1222	1866	58·7	59·6
20	2126	3580	828	1611	1298	1969	61·1	50·0
25	2120	3363	876	1221	1244	2142	58·9	63·7
30	1998	3626	782	1438	1216	2188	61·1	60·2
35	2315	3593	992	1592	1323	2001	57·0	55·6
50	2165		857		1309		60·4	

The main increases in the female are dependent on the maturation of eggs, as illustrated by table 81 which shows a steady increase in weight during the first three ovarial maturation stages (p. 304), then a drop at stage IV when the first eggs are laid.

302

Table 81. *Ovarial maturation stages
and weights of* Locusta *females*
(*Phipps* 1950)

Stages	No. of locusts	Mean weight, mg
I	40	1·837
II	24	1·966
III	24	2·486
IV	45	2·310

Such correlation between weight and maturation may be of value in determining the readiness of females in a wild population to oviposit, without dissecting them, though the latter method is admittedly simpler and more direct (O. W. Richards & N. Waloff 1954).

A substantial proportion of the weight of a live insect is water and fat reserves; changes in these respects related to growth are discussed elsewhere (p. 226).

MATURATION OF GONADS

Male

Rudiments of the testes can be seen already in young hoppers and much of the spermatogenesis is completed before the final moult when active sperma-

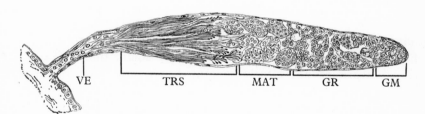

Fig. 180. *Locusta*, a testis follicle (after Liu & Leo 1959).
GM, zone of primordial spermatogonia (germarium); GR, zone of spermatogonial divisions and of spermatocyte formation; MAT, zone of maturation of spermatids; TRS, zone of transformation of spermatids into spermatozoa; VE, duct.

tozoa may be already present or are produced soon after it (p. 306). In a follicle of the testis several regions can be distinguished according to the stage in the development of the germ cells (fig. 180). The free apex of a follicle includes the *apical cell* and a number of primordial spermatogonia; below it lies the zone of growth, within which successive spermatogonial divisions occur, resulting in spermatocytes; the latter undergo two divisions and transform into spermatids which give rise to spermatozoa; for histological details, see Davis (1908); McClung (1914); Depdolla (1917); Nelsen (1931*b*); Malan

& Malan (1925); White (1935, 1951 a, 1954); Liu & Leo (1959); Gatenby & Thamisian (1959); Gupta, Gupta & Nath (1960); R. S. Mathur (1960). The number of spermatogonial divisions varies in acridoids from five to eight; the variation does not appear to be of taxonomic significance, since it is not quite constant even within a species. A greater number of divisions, resulting in a larger number of spermatozoa per bundle (see below) does not, however, mean a greater sperm production, which is more affected by the number of follicles. It has been suggested that more primitive groups (e.g. Pyrgomorphidae) produce more sperm than more advanced ones, but more data are needed (White 1955).

The apical cell, which has been regarded as a supporting structure, appears to have more important functions. It was suggested that it produces some substance which passes into spermatogonia thus conveying the influence of somatic cells to chromosomes (McClung 1939), but this view was not supported by Carson (1945) who suggested that the apical cell influences the mitochondrial mechanism of germ cells. The secretion of the apical cell appears to induce degeneration of some spermatogonia, the end product being very rich in ribonucleic acid (RNA) (Battaglia 1950; Battaglia & Sara 1951).

The spermatozoa of acridoids have not been studied extensively, but they appear not to differ much from those of other insects, consisting of a spindle-shaped head and a long tail. They are collected in bundles, called *spermatodesms*, ending in a hyaline apical knob (fig. 188, C). The transfer of the sperm from male to female is discussed below (p. 316).

Female

Rudiments of ovaries can be seen in the earliest hopper instars, but after the final moult the ovaries are still relatively small, thread-like, with the individual ovarioles not clearly separated. A fully developed ovariole (fig. 181) consists of three parts: the slender terminal filament; the broader germarium, where division of germ cells occurs; and the vitellarium containing oöcytes (developing eggs) in different stages of growth. Each oöcyte is enclosed in a follicle, the cells of which secrete the egg chorion. The egg nearest to the oviduct is termed egg 1; it is the largest and grows at a higher rate than the egg behind it, and the whole ovariole also gradually increases in length (Colombo 1953, 1955; Strich-Halbwachs 1958; L. Joly 1960). The whole process of ovarian maturation can be conveniently divided into four stages (Phipps 1949, 1950; Quo Fu 1956; Lusis 1963), as follows:

    I. Immature. Ovary small and white; oöcytes very small. Walls of oviduct not thickened (fig. 181, A).
    II. Pre-reproductive. Ovary larger; fat body well developed. Egg 1 yellow (fig. 181, B).
    III. Reproductive. Ovary very large; fat body large early in the stage, but becomes reduced later. Egg 1 almost full size and very much larger than others. Oviduct swollen with secretion (fig. 181, C, D).
    IV. Ovulation has occurred, that is egg 1 passed into oviduct, or even already laid.

The process of ovulation is still insufficiently studied, particularly as regards the releasing stimulus. All ovarioles pass their egg 1 into the oviducts at the same time, thus providing the first *clutch* of eggs deposited as an egg-pod. The eggs remaining in the ovariole then advance in their rank and a new egg 1 begins to grow faster than the others while new öocytes are produced at the other end. This is repeated as many times as the total number of clutches eventually produced.

When ovulation occurs the wall of the follicle of the egg 1 contracts, its epithelium degenerates and the whole shrinks to form a ring-like structure, which is usually not pigmented and was formerly called *corpus luteum*;

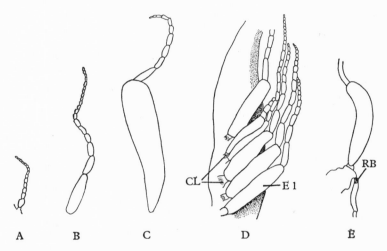

Fig. 181. *Locusta*, development of ovarioles. A, stage I; B, stage II; C, stage III; D, group of ovarioles in stage III; E, two ovarioles in stage IV, in one of which an öocyte has been resorbed (after Phipps 1950, modified).
CL, corpus luteum; E 1, first egg; RB, resorption body.

its presence denotes that an egg has passed into the oviduct; as subsequent ovulations occur, several such bodies may be found. Their name led to confusion with the orange-yellow structures at the base of ovarioles (Dufour 1841; Roonwal 1949, *Schistocerca*, *Hieroglyphus*; Yakhimovich 1952, *Locusta*), the presence of which has been assumed to indicate definitely that the female has oviposited (Vel'tischev 1941). However, Boldyrev (1946) and Phipps (1949, 1950) suggested and Singh (1958) and Descamps & Wintrebert (1962) confirmed that these yellow, or reddish-orange, structures are *resorption bodies*, formed occasionally when an öocyte fails to develop and is resorbed, whereas the true corpora lutea are normally colourless, although some of them may also resorb the adjacent öocyte and become pigmented. Lusis (1963) described the histology and histochemistry of both kinds of bodies and proposed to call them the *white* and the *yellow follicles*. The pigments in the resorption bodies contain carotene, a fluorescent substance and cholesterol (De Lerma 1951 b, *Locusta*), though Lusis (*t.c.*) found no evidence for the last named substance in *Schistocerca*.

The degeneration and resorption of egg-rudiments in ovarioles, as well as the failure of some ovarioles to grow ('small ovarioles', Phipps *tt.cc.*) and to produce eggs is an important factor affecting fecundity. As an example, Singh (*t.c.*) found that some 18% of the total ninety-five ovarioles in isolated *Locusta* females were subnormal, or partly or fully degenerate.

In developing oöcytes, nucleic acids (RNA and DNA) were found (Colombo 1953, *Anacridium*; Swift & Kleinfeldt 1953, *Melanoplus*; Lusis, *t.c.*, *Schistocerca*).

RATE AND CONDITIONS OF MATURATION

Much of the spermatogenesis occurs in hoppers (p. 303), but the stage in the formation of the sperm reached when the adult male emerges may vary according to the conditions experienced during the hopper life (A. G. Hamilton 1936). Thus, fledglings of *Locusta*, emerging from hoppers reared at 26·7°–32·2°C, had no sperm bundles in the follicles, but if hoppers were kept at 37·8°C sperm bundles were found already in the fifth instar hoppers, that is, they were more mature sexually than the adults raised at lower temperatures. In *Schistocerca*, on the other hand, sperm bundles were not found in newly-emerged adults, regardless of the temperature at which they were reared. The effects of temperature on the subsequent production of sperm bundles were noticeable in *Locusta*, in which the rate of their production rose more steeply at the higher temperature (fig. 182); a horizontal line drawn at the level of 64% of the follicular length occupied by sperm bundles intersected the curves for each temperature at points corresponding to nine, nineteen and thirty-two days, which was in good agreement with the dates of the first copulation at the respective temperatures.

The effects of air humidity on sperm production are not clear. Some delay in sperm development may be caused by rearing hoppers, or keeping adults, at an otherwise suitable temperature if the humidity is reduced to 30% (Hamilton 1936), but no detailed experimental data are available with regard to such marginal combinations of temperature and humidity which would inhibit or delay the production of sperm, without causing death; Boldyrev (1946) recorded that males of *Locusta m. migratoria* kept for nearly three months at 20–25°C produced spermatozoa which failed to reach the seminal vesicles; these males copulated, but their spermatophores were without sperm; even at 25–30°C males did not become fully mature.

The female gonads at adult emergence are not as advanced as those of the male, and females lag considerably behind males in their maturation. Unfortunately, no studies have been made on the time and conditions required for the ovary to reach the reproductive stage III (p. 304), and in all experimental work the time from emergence to the first oviposition is designated as the *maturation period*, although it comprises the general growth and the ovarian maturation. Moreover, most of the work has been done on groups of both sexes kept together, and this exerts a special influence on the rate of maturation (p. 359).

An important point was raised by Dudley (1961), who found that crowded *Schistocerca* kept at rigidly controlled constant temperature of 35° C, with all other conditions also kept constant, failed to mature for as long as seven to eight months and then died. Males developed normal pink coloration, but when it disappeared, they did not become yellow; sperm appeared in the seminal vesicles somewhat later than in normal stocks. Dissections of females showed that yolk appeared in the ovarioles much later than normally and its

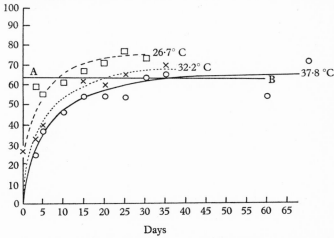

Fig. 182. *Locusta*, the maturation of sperm in relation to temperature (after A. G. Hamilton 1936).
Vertical scale—percentage of the follicle length occupied by sperm bundles.

quantity was deficient. It was suggested that in such rigidly constant conditions there is a deficiency in the functioning of corpora allata which stimulate yolk production (p. 312). Whatever the reason, these very careful experiments indicate that constant environmental conditions affect locust physiology very unfavourably.

The available data on the temperature effects alone cannot be considered very reliable, because of the modifying effects of air humidity. However, Pospelov (1926a) recorded a suppression of egg-laying, in *Locusta m. migratoria* kept at 20° C, though at 35°C eggs were laid after some forty days.

Extensive experiments with various combinations of temperature and humidity by A. G. Hamilton (1936, 1950) enabled him to construct diagrams showing environmental effects on maturation periods of *Locusta* and *Schistocerca* females (fig. 183). The shortest period for *Locusta* was about twelve days at 70% RH and about 40°C, whereas for *Schistocerca* it averaged seventeen days at the same humidity and 36·7°C; these highest rates of maturation, however, resulted in the shortest adult life (p. 321). These data were obtained with approximately constant conditions, but when the temperatures and humidities were made to fluctuate with similar mean values (weighted by the times of exposure) there was no appreciable difference in the length of the maturation period, which suggested that its length, at favourable humidity, depends on the accumulated degree-hours.

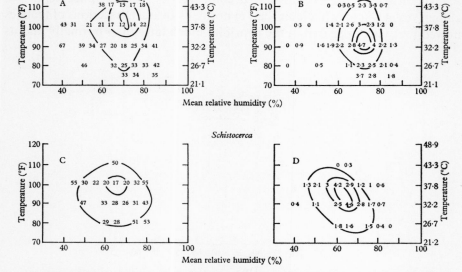

Fig. 183. Females of *Locusta* and *Schistocerca*, maturation periods (days) and number of pods per female, in relation to temperature and humidity (after A. G. Hamilton 1950).

The quality of food also affects the rate of maturation of females. *Schistocerca* females laid the first pod after 33·50–37·00 days if fed on lush *Heliotropium* and in 43·10–54·50 days on the same plant in dry conditions (Rao 1942, 1960).

ADULT DIAPAUSE

It is well known that many acridoids living in subtropical countries with a long dry period remain as non-reproductive adults for several months, and it is assumed that such species exhibit an obligatory adult diapause, that is the development of their gonads is suspended, regardless of the environmental conditions.

The Red Locust (*Nomadacris*) offers a striking example of such a life-cycle, with a single generation per year, the adults living about eight months, and becoming sexually mature only with the advent of the next rainy season, during which the egg and hopper stages are passed. Experimental work with this species has shown, however, that its adult's diapause is not obligatory, and rapid maturation of adults can be induced in the laboratory by suitable temperature and humidity (Uvarov 1933; A. G. Hamilton 1936; Norris 1959a). On the other hand, continuous laboratory breeding under the same conditions in London has shown a variation in the length of the maturation period (measured as the time between emergence and the first laying) according to the season (Norris 1959a, 1959b, 1962c, 1964a, 1964b). Adults

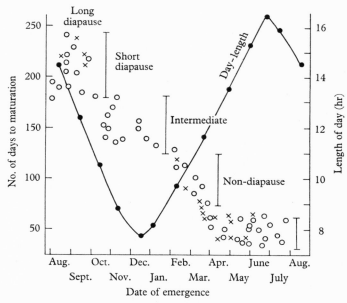

Fig. 184. *Nomadacris*, adult diapause in relation to photoperiod (after Norris 1959b; with the curve of day-length in London added).
Circles, adults emerging in laboratory, in normal day-length; crosses, those emerging in artificial day-length periods.

emerging during the English spring and early summer became mature within two months, while those emerging in late summer and autumn did not copulate or oviposit until seven to eight months later and their weight became stationary at the basic value (fig. 178). Such extreme non-diapause and long-diapause groups were connected by groups with transitional cycles, emerging during late autumn and winter (fig. 184). As other treatment of all groups was identical, it was suggested that the occurrence of diapause may depend on the day-length, which in London is decreasing in the autumn. Experiments with artificial photoperiods during adult life tended to confirm this suggestion, while no effect was observed if only hoppers received such treatment. A long diapause was induced by photoperiods of about twelve to thirteen hours, such as normally occur in the autumn in London and throughout the year in the normal habitat of *Nomadacris* (at 7°S latitude) where the annual range of day-length fluctuation is only fifty-five minutes, but even this slight shortening at the time of adult emergence was considered a possible factor inducing diapause, whereas an increase of the photoperiod from 12 to 13 hours resulted in maturation without a diapause. However, adults emerging in the field at that time and subjected to artificial very humid conditions in outdoor cages reproduced without a diapause (Albrecht 1955).

Experimental evidence suggesting an effect of artificial photoperiod on adult diapause in *Schistocerca* in a London laboratory was also obtained (Norris 1957), but in this case the diapause was induced by long, not short, days, adults maturing in the English summer in about fifty-five days, while in winter the average period was thirty-three days. Thus, the effects of photoperiod on the two species were opposite.

Adult diapause was studied experimentally also in *Anacridium aegyptium*, a Mediterranean species in which the adults hibernate, eggs are laid in spring and hatch in one to two months and new adults emerge in summer (M. A. Volkonsky 1937; Colombo 1953, 1955; Colombo & Mocellin 1956). The male has mature sperm soon after the last moult and copulation may occur in the autumn, the sperm surviving in female spermatheca until the next spring; however, only a few oöcytes develop yolk before winter, and the first eggs are formed only after hibernation; thus, in this species only the female can be said to have an adult diapause. In laboratory, at 28–30°C and 40–60% relative humidity, the majority of females matured in about 200 days, but some laid eggs in twenty to seventy days after emergence (i.e. practically without a diapause). This was explained as a possible cause of genetical variability (Colombo *tt.cc.*), although direct effects of temperature on ovarian maturation were also recorded; for example, females collected in Italy in autumn and kept in the laboratory at the conditions indicated above, oviposited in December–January, whereas those collected in January–February matured in a month, and those taken in April–May laid very promptly. A rapid maturation could also be obtained in winter, if females were fed on fresh twigs of *Ligustrum* standing in water. These observations suggest that there is no obligatory diapause in *Anacridium*, but only a very slow ovarian development, which can be accelerated by suitable temperature, as well as by food; Norris (1964*a*) found that the diapause can be averted by exposing hoppers and young adults to an increasing day-length. This tendency to slow development may be specific since the egg incubation period (see table 67) and the hopper period in *Anacridium* are also relatively long.

Females of *Melanoplus devastator* become normally adult in California by mid-July, but begin to lay eggs only after 2–4 months; this has been ascribed to the onset of cool and wet weather, but the latter may not occur until December, and dissections of females revealed mature ovaries well before rains, suggesting that the delay was not due to the temperature or humidity. Laboratory experiments showed that females kept in the normal day-length had the oöcytes much less advanced than those subjected to a short photoperiod of 9·5 hours; females in constant day-light also matured much more slowly than those kept continuously in darkness (Middlekauff 1964).

Studies of adult diapause, reviewed above, can hardly be regarded as conclusive even as regards the existence of a true diapause (i.e. one quite independent of environmental conditions). As Norris (1962c) concluded, the reproductive diapause is usually less firmly established than diapause in other stages and can be prevented, or interrupted, by a variety of environmental factors, such as temperature, humidity and the day-length; it may be added that changes in the intensity of the factors are possibly of greater importance than the intensity itself. As regards the physiological processes involved, no attention has yet been paid to the possible role played by the endocrine organs in the maturation delays which are sufficiently long to be regarded as a diapause, though their short-term effects on maturation are known, as discussed below.

HORMONAL CONTROL OF MATURATION

Norris (1952, 1954) observed that an immature female *Schistocerca* kept with a male of its own age became sexually mature, on average, in forty-eight days, but one kept with an already mature male did so in twenty-seven days and in a crowded stock of both sexes, females matured in twenty-two days. This suggested an influence of the presence of a mature male on the rate of female maturation. Similarly, immature males (still pink in colour and refusing to copulate with mature females) turned yellow in three days when caged with other mature males. When kept in groups, some males matured more quickly than others and this had a rapid effect on other locusts of both sexes in the group. The mechanism of this stimulation was further investigated by Loher (1960, 1961) who found that the yellowing of males coincided with the production by the epidermal cells of a pheromone (p. 298) which is volatile and can stimulate other locusts even at a distance, presumably through the olfactory sense; when locusts came in contact with each other, the stimulation was improved. Recent work (Highnam 1961–2c 1964; Highnam & Lusis 1962; Highnam, Lusis & Hill 1963a, 1963b; Highnam & Haskell 1964; L. Hill 1962, 1963; Lusis 1963; Delphin 1963a, 1963b) has thrown much light on the neurosecretory processes during the maturation of the female gonads in *Schistocerca*, and the sequence of events is illustrated diagrammatically in fig. 185. When an immature female is kept with mature males (A), the neurosecretory cells of the brain (ns. cells) and the corpora cardiaca (c.c.) contain few stainable inclusions; but the oöcytes (ooc.) grow fast (B). After some fourteen days when the first eggs pass into the oviducts (C), the amount of the inclusions increases greatly; this suggests that the neurosecretory cells and corpora cardiaca are active during the growth of oöcytes, but that once the growth is completed, their secretion is no longer used and is accumulated. In the females kept without males the oöcytes grow much more slowly (D) and by the fourteenth day the histological picture (E) shows that the secretions are produced, but not utilised for oöcyte growth. If, however, such a female is given a male, the inclusions are rapidly used and the

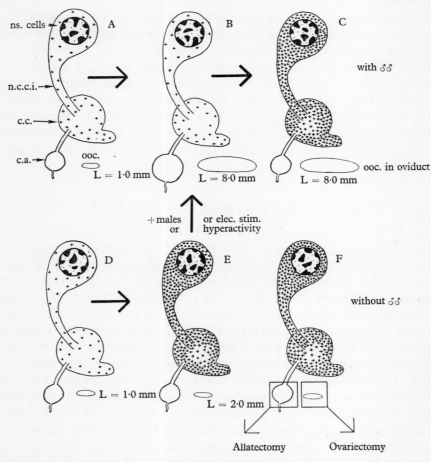

Fig. 185. *Schistocerca*, diagram illustrating the effects of neurosecretion on the oöcyte growth; explanation in the text (Highnam 1962 *a*).

oöcyte growth is stimulated (E to B). The results have been confirmed by the removal and implantation of the corpora cardiaca.

The removal of corpora allata (c.a.) results in an accumulation of the secretory material and an inhibition of the oöcyte growth (F). The importance of corpora allata for sexual maturation has been shown by Weed Pfeiffer (1939, 1945 *b*), who found that in *Melanoplus differentialis* the removal of corpora allata inhibited the growth of oöcytes when they reached the stage of yolk deposition, while the size of the fat body increased greatly (p. 99); this suggested that the corpora allata hormone facilitates the mobilisation of the stored fat and its utilisation for egg-yolk formation. Similar conclusions were reached by L. Joly (1955, 1960) in her work on *Locusta* (p. 103).

The removal of the ovaries prevents the increase of corpora allata and causes an accumulation of secretion in the system (fig. 185, F); this replaces an early suggestion (Mestscherskaya 1931; Iwanoff & Mestscherskaya 1935) that ovaries may exert a hormonal action.

As regards the pheromonal effects, Highnam and his collaborators (*tt.cc.*) have shown that electrical stimulation of the central nervous system and enforced activity, such as rotation in a flask for forty-five minutes, stimulated neurosecretion in isolated females in the same way as the presence of males

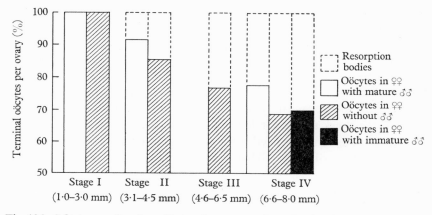

Fig. 186. *Schistocerca* females, effects of neurosecretion stimulated by males, on the growth and resorption of oöcytes (after Highnam & Lusis 1962).

(fig. 185, E). The stimulating effect of wounding (Norris 1954) probably has the same basis. The action of the male pheromone may, therefore, be not direct but through the increased activity of the female. The importance of one type of activity, namely, flight, was demonstrated (Haskell 1962; Highnam & Haskell 1964) in *Schistocerca Land Locusta* females flown daily on a roundabout; this accelerated the production of the neurosecretory material and the growth of oöcytes; flight, however, also results in a rise of internal temperature (p. 217).

An important aspect of hormonal control of reproduction is the effects of the secretion on the resorption of developing oöcytes (p. 305). In the absence of males, that is, without the hormonal stimulation, ovaries in some females failed to develop, or the rate of oöcyte development was very slow, and the proportion of resorbed oöcytes increased with their development, so that the final number of fully developed eggs decreased; this also happened in females kept with immature males (fig. 186; Highnam, Lusis & Hill 1963 b).

Strich-Halbwachs (1958, 1959) produced experimental evidence that the removal of the prothoracic gland in *Locusta* also had an effect on ovarial maturation. If the hoppers have moulted into adults after the operation, maturation was merely somewhat retarded, but if they remained as 'permanent larvae'(p. 289), the growth of the ovaries was completely inhibited.

Delphin (1963 a, 1963 b) has, further, shown that the last abdominal ganglion also plays a part in the stimulation of maturation, in conjunction with the neurosecretory activity of the brain.

Lusis (1963), in attempting to summarise the physiological aspects of the problem, suggested that the oöcyte development in *Schistocerca* is controlled by the combination of the neurosecretion from the pars intercerebralis of the brain and of the corpus allatum hormone, the first affecting the synthesis of proteins in the fat body, and the second facilitating their transport from haemolymph to the oöcytes to be used in yolk formation. Thus, an insufficient stimulation of neurosecretory activity would lead to protein deficiency and reduced ability of oöcytes to absorb it from the haemolymph. One may add that the factors stimulating neurosecretion include the male pheromon, as well as the raised activity level which depends both on the sensory stimulation and the general physiological state.

This very brief account of the hormonal control of sexual maturation is certainly incomplete, as the research on these lines is rapidly progressing. Moreover, the work so far carried out has concerned only the maturation of the female gonads, and the need for parallel work on the hormonal control of spermatogenesis is obvious. Also, most of the findings refer to two species only.

COPULATION AND SPERM TRANSFER

The act of copulation is usually preceded by a more or less elaborate courtship behaviour which will be discussed in the appropriate chapter of the next volume. Here we are concerned only with copulation and the transfer of the sperm from male to female.

Copulation

The most common method of copulation is that illustrated by fig. 187, A, where the male sits on the back of the female, clasping her firmly by the first two pairs of legs, the third pair playing no direct part during the whole process. The male abdomen is curved down, its tip is brought under that of the female abdomen, the penis is extruded and the hooks of the epiphallus grasp the female subgenital plate; the male cerci also assist in gripping the female abdomen. The penis is then introduced between the ventral ovipositor valves of the female into the vagina and its tip reaches the spermathecal duct (Fedorov 1927, *Anacridium*; Boldyrev 1929, *Locusta*; Kyl 1938, *Melanoplus*; Gregory 1961, *Locusta*). Randell (1963) stressed the importance of the inter-locking mechanism of the male epiphallus and the female subgenital plate (p. 20).

In other species, the copulating postures may differ. Katiyar (1952, 1956 b) distinguished two other types of postures, in addition to that described above, which he called 'riding' and which occur, according to him, in the species with the two sexes of similar size. If the male is smaller than the female and is unable to reach the tip of her abdomen with his own, a 'dorso-lateral' posture is adopted, the male sitting somewhat on the flank of the female (*Phlaeoba*), or even by its side without holding it (*Choroedocus*; see also Jhingran 1944); the latter posture is called 'lateral'. Finally, when the ratio of the female

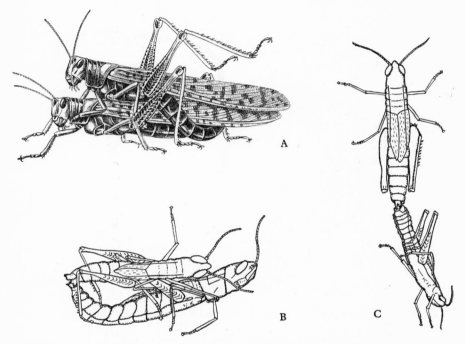

Fig. 187. Copulation postures. A, *Schistocerca* (Künckel 1893–1905); B, *Parahieroglyphus bilineatus*, beginning of copulation; C, ditto, final 'hanging' posture (after Katiyar 1952).

length to that of the male is very high (1·72), the male attaches itself to the female in a 'hanging' posture (fig. 187, C) which may be also assumed at the end of copulation in another position. There are, of course, full transitions between these types and such classification is somewhat artificial.

A female with a male on its back may continue feeding and crawling; in fact, regular marching of copulating pairs of *Schistocerca* is known (Popov 1958). In some species with strong sexual dimorphism in size, a female may even fly with the male attached (*Spaniacris*; Hebard 1937a). Remembering the great variety in the structure of the cerci (p. 19), epiprocts (p. 18) and epiphalli (p. 142) of males, one should expect an even greater variety of copulation postures, when a wider range of species is studied.

The duration of copulation varies; thus, in *Anacridium*, the pairs remained united for eighteen to sixty hours (Fedorov 1927), but one should distinguish in such observations between the pairing and the actual copulation, that is the process of sperm transmission, the length of which depends largely on the rate of spermatophore formation.

The spermatophore

The sperm is transmitted from male to female not directly, but through a complicated temporary structure, the spermatophore. The existence of this

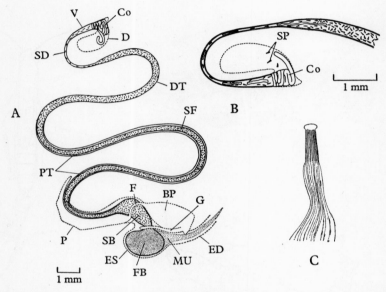

Fig. 188. *Locusta*. A, spermatophore; B, apical end of spermatophore and the spermatheca (Gregory 1965a); C, spermatodesm (Boldyrev *in* Uvarov 1928).
V, vestibule of spermatheca; D, diverticulum of spermatheca; SD, spermathecal duct; SP, spermatodesms; Co, coils of spermatophore; DT, distal tube; SF, seminal fluid; PT, proximal tube; P, penis (outline dotted); F, flexure of penis; BP, basal valve of penis; G, gonopore process; FB, first bladder of spermatophore; SB, second bladder of spermatophore; ES, ejaculatory sac; MU, mucilaginous secretion; ED, ejaculatory duct.

mode of transmission in acridoids was suspected by Boldyrev (1915, p. 228, footnote), confirmed by S. A. Ivanova (1925, 1926) and Sokolow (1926a, 1926b), and described in some detail for *Locusta* by Boldyrev (1929). Recently, the formation of the spermatophore and the transfer of sperm in *Locusta* were thoroughly investigated by Gregory (1965a, b), on whose work the following account is based.

A fully formed spermatophore (fig. 188, A), which can be found only after several hours from the beginning of copulation, consists of a thin-walled reservoir, one part of which (first bladder) lies in the ejaculatory sac and the other (second bladder) in the spermatophore sac of the male. At its posterior end, the reservoir passes into the thick-walled spermatophore tube extending through the canal of the penis and through the whole length of the female spermathecal duct. The proximal part of the tube has thick hyaline walls and a narrow lumen; in the distal part it has thin, opalescent walls and wider lumen, and at its end, the tube becomes coiled and enters the preapical diverticulum of the female spermatheca.

Gregory's investigations have shown that the spermatophore begins to be formed, from the secretions of the male accessory glands, one-and-a-half to two minutes after the beginning of copulation. At first, the secretion entering the upper ejaculatory duct is viscous and milky, then it is replaced by hyaline material; in passing through the narrow gonopore, the secretions become converted into a cylindrical structure, with hyaline walls and milky

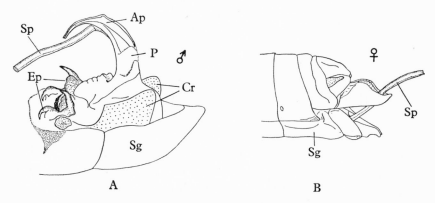

Fig. 189. *Locusta*, ejection of spermatophore (after Boldyrev 1929).
Sp, spermatophore; Ap, apical valves of penis; P, penis; Cr, rami of cingulum; Sg, subgenital plate; Ep, epiphallus.

central part. In the ejaculatory sac this cylinder expands into an oval reservoir, which becomes filled with the seminal fluid with spermatodesms in it. The secretions continue to be pushed by contractions of muscles at the base of the penis along the canal of the penis and enter the spermathecal duct, forming the proximal and then the distal spermatophore tubes, along which the seminal fluid reaches the spermatheca through the coiled end of the tube. The spermatodesms fall apart soon afterwards and the spermatozoids become free. It has been established that, while the material for all parts of the spermatophore is secreted by the various accessory glands, the seminal fluid is produced in the seminal vesicle. The whole process of spermatophore formation is very complicated, this being the reason for the length of the copulation period.

Spermatophores have been studied in only a few species and they vary considerably. Thus, in *Calliptamus* a spermatophore measures only about 2 mm, in *Acrida* in spite of the very long body it is 4 mm long (Boldyrev 1929), and in *Locusta* 35–45 mm; detailed comparisons of the structure in different species are lacking and there is a vast field open for study.

At the end of copulation, the separation of male from female causes a rupture of the spermatophore tube, one part of which remains within the penis of the male, and the other within the spermathecal duct of the female. The male now ejects the tube, while the tube in the female is gradually dissolved and the proximal part is ejected (fig. 189). The ejected spermatophores shrink and, in some cases, form a small lump between the lower ovipositor valves, which later hardens, becomes brittle and crumples into small bits; the presence of this lump makes it possible to recognise a fertilised female, for example in *Acrida*, for as long as ten to twenty-five days (Boldyrev 1929).

Repeated copulation

Boldyrev (*t.c.*) regarded the presence of more than one spermatophore in a fertilised female as unusual, although Ivanova (*tt.cc.*) recorded finding three to four tubes in a *Locusta* female, and Fedorov (1927) found up to thirty spermatophores in an *Anacridium*. Careful experiments by Gregory have shown that in a *Locusta* female two to six ejected spermatophores could be found, indicating that it allowed copulation to be repeated as many times. The ejection of spermatophores occurred always some twelve to twenty-four hours before oviposition. Boldyrev suggested that the ejection is essential to open the way for the sperm to pass down the spermathecal duct and fertilise the eggs, but Gregory could not obtain any evidence of the presence of sperm in the female genital tract and the site of fertilisation remains problematical. The occurrence of repeated copulations before each oviposition leads to the question whether it is only the first one that is effective in fertilisation. Hunter-Jones (1960) by crossing the albino *Schistocerca* female with the normal male obtained normal progeny from the first two egg-pods; when the same female was then crossed with an albino male, the progeny was entirely albino, suggesting that the latest fertilisation was the effective one.

Another point of substantial interest is that a single copulation is sufficient to fertilise a number of successive egg-pods, as shown by Norris (1954) in *Schistocerca*, and the sperm in the female spermatheca may remain viable for a very long period, for example in *Anacridium* the sperm in females fertilised in the autumn remains in the spermatheca until the next spring (Grassé 1922).

Control of copulation

A long series of experiments by Gregory (*t.c.*) has shown that in *Locusta* the preliminary approach and pairing behaviour were under nervous control of some sensory receptors on the head and of the brain. On the other hand, if the male cerci were removed, cauterised, or waxed, the pairing occurred normally, but copulation did not take place. This means that the sensory equipment of the cercus must be effective and, moreover, the cercus must be

318

in communication with the last abdominal ganglion; if the connecting nerve was severed, no copulation occurred. Therefore, the male cercus, with its various and little studied sensilla, is not a mere grasping organ, and the great variation in its shape (p. 19) tends to confirm its importance in reproduction.

Gregory obtained no evidence that copulation is under hormonal control, which, however, may be of importance for the physiological readiness for copulation.

PARTHENOGENESIS

Fertilisation is not an absolute condition for egg development and occasional parthenogenesis has been recorded in as many species as have been tested (table 82); no records of complete failure of such experiments are known.

Table 82. *Recorded cases of parthenogenesis*

(+ indicates the stage attained by the progeny)

Species	Eggs	Hoppers	Adults	Eggs	References
PYRGOMORPHIDAE					
Poekilocerus pictus	+				Pruthi & Nigam 1939
ROMALEINAE					
Romalea microptera	+				King & Slifer 1934; Swann & Mickey 1947
CATANTOPINAE					
Melanoplus differentialis	+	+	+	+	King & Slifer 1934
CALLIPTAMINAE					
Calliptamus italicus	+				Plotnikov 1921
CYRTACANTHACRIDINAE					
Schistocerca gregaria	+				Telenga 1930
,, ,,	+	+	+	+	Husain & Mathur 1946
,, ,,	+	+	+	+	Norris 1954
,, ,,	+	+	+	+	Hamilton 1955
,, *paranensis*	+				Del Carril 1938
,, *flavofasciata*	+	+			Kevan 1943
OEDIPODINAE					
Locusta m. migratorioides	+	+	+	+	Bergerard & Seugé 1959
,, *m. migratoria*	+	+			Plotnikov 1921
,, *m. manilensis*	+	+			Quo Fu 1956; Leo & Quo Fu 1962
Oedaleus decorus	+				Plotnikov 1921
Locustana pardalina	+	+	+		Potgieter 1929
,, ,,	+	+			Faure 1923
Arphia sulphurea	+				King & Slifer 1934
Hippiscus apiculatus	+				,, ,, ,,
Dissosteira carolina	+				,, ,, ,,
Trimerotropis maritima	+				,, ,, ,,
TRUXALINAE					
Chorthippus curtipennis	+	+			Creighton & Robertson 1941
Dociostaurus maroccanus	+				Plotnikov 1921
,, ,,	+				Sviridenko 1924

In most of these cases, only egg-laying was recorded, and high mortality of eggs and hoppers discouraged the majority of experimenters. However, in *Schistocerca*, parthenogenetic reproduction can be successful, since A. G. Hamilton (1955) has kept a culture going for six generations. All the progeny were females. (Husain & Mathur (1946) claimed obtaining parthenogenetically both male and female progeny, but no details were given.) The average numbers of egg-pods and of eggs per pod were the same as in normal stocks, but the average hatch was only about one-third of that of the controls. Hoppers developed at the normal rate, adults took longer to mature, their oviposition rate was slower, and they lived much longer as shown in table 83. In *Locusta m. manilensis* the percentage hatch from parthenogenetic eggs was 8·5, but rose to 19·2 in eggs laid by females paired with the males deprived of the whole phallic complex (Leo & Quo Fu 1962).

Table 83. *Reproduction of parthenogenetic and normal*
Schistocerca (*after A. G. Hamilton* 1955)

	Parthenogenetic Stock						Normal stock
	F	F_1	F_2	F_3	F_4	F_4 mated	
Hopper period (days)	29·3	32·7	28·7	29·5	28·5	—	28·6
Percentage reaching adult stage	—	—	—	—	34·7	48·5	52·2
Days to first egg-pod	35	37	31	30	41	23	21
Adult life (days)	182·1	130·5	91·4	161·1	136·4	69·2	68·3
Days to last egg-pod	320	211	157	200	144	76	107
Egg-pods per female	5·4	3·1	2·4	2·3	2·9	2·6	4·6
Eggs per pod	42·8	40·1	47·0	41·3	42·5	40·5	40·0
Percentage hatch	23·6	26·3	25·5	27·8	23·8	83·9	80·4
Incubation period (days)	14·2	14·7	14·8	14·5	14·7	13·5	14·7

Similar results were obtained with *Schistocerca* by Hunter-Jones (1958), except that he noticed not only a greatly reduced percentage of hatching, but also a tendency for unfertilised females not to lay compact egg-pods in the ground, but to scatter their eggs on the surface; this tendency was particularly strong in females kept singly. The main effect of parthenogenesis was a reduction in the fertility of eggs and in the viability of hoppers, but both were restored by mating (table 83).

Parthenogenetically produced embryos of *Schistocerca* (Hamilton, *t.c.*), *Locusta* (Bergerard & Seugé, 1959) and *Melanoplus differentialis* (King & Slifer 1934) had the diploid (normal) or haploid (half the normal) number of chromosomes, as well as some supernumerary chromosomes. Many embryos of *Locusta* were malformed (Bergerard & Seugé, *t.c.*; Verdier 1960).

LENGTH OF ADULT LIFE

If the adult period of a species in nature overlaps the unfavourable (cold or dry) season, the longevity of adults depends primarily on their ability to survive the extreme conditions. For example, the mean longevity of *Chorthippus brunneus* females in the field in Britain was 36·5 days, but in the laboratory they lived up to seventy-three days (O. W. Richards & Waloff 1954). Adult *Dociostaurus maroccanus* in Cyprus during the dry summer period survived for sixty-three days in the field and for up to 114 days if kept in cages and given fresh grass (Waterston 1951).

This last example suggests the importance of the availability of food, and there is also evidence regarding the quality of food as illustrated by table 84.

The table suggests that cotton was the most favourable food for the survival of females, but the fecundity of those fed on it was the lowest (p. 329). This adverse effect of the reproductive activity on female survival was confirmed in *Eyprepocnemis plorans meridionalis*, of which the length of life in the laboratory varied from 31 to 337 days and the females that were slowest to mature lived longest (Antoniou & Hunter-Jones 1956). The parthenogenetic females of *Schistocerca* matured only a little more slowly than normal ones, but their adult life was, on the average, three times as long, with the maximum of 320 days and their fecundity was lower (p. 320).

Table 84. *Longevity in days of* Melanoplus differentialis *females on three food plants (Sanderson 1939)*

Plant	Variation	Mean
Wheat	24–64	38·80
Soya beans	21–92	47·14
Cotton	64–160	100·00

Since the males are much less liable to expend their reserves in reproduction, one would expect them to be generally longer lived than females. Unfortunately, little attention has, so far, been paid to this point and the few available data are contradictory. Thus, adult males of *Atractomorpha crenulata* lived in cages for twenty-five to thirty-six days, and females for thirty to sixty-eight (Agrawal 1955). Isolated *Nomadacris* males in the laboratory live generally much longer than females, the maximum period recorded being 310 days as against 137 for the female (Norris 1959). On the other hand, males of *Anacridium* in the laboratory lived for seventy-eight to ninety-nine days while females survived for 202 to 308 days (El-Zoheiry 1937); the record longevity for a female of this species was 600 days after hatching or over 500 days of adult life (Colombo & Mocellin 1956). Such great longevity may be accounted for by the delayed ovarian maturation common in *Anacridium* (p. 310). The differential survival of the sexes may have a striking effect on the adult sex ratios in field populations, as was pointed out by Popov (1954) who recorded that in immature swarms of *Schistocerca* the sexes are approximately equal in numbers, but towards the end of the oviposition period females die off before males, with the result that swarms come to consist almost entirely of males. Field records of the sex ratio in populations of uncertain age are, therefore, of little value.

21

OVIPOSITION

The oviposition behaviour, including movements of the female before the actual egg-laying, is connected with searching and probing for suitable conditions and it will be more appropriately discussed in the section dealing with ecology. Here we are concerned mainly with the mechanisms involved in the process of oviposition. These have been discussed by several authors (Künckel d'Herculais 1893–1905; Giardina 1901; Coleman 1911; Grassé 1922; Fedorov 1927; Paoli 1937*a*, 1937*b*) and their data were reviewed, in the light of original observations on *Locusta*, by Agarwala (1952–4), whose work is largely used in the following description.

Digging

Since most acridoids lay their eggs in the soil, the digging of a hole is an essential part of the oviposition process. The actual working of the ovipositor during digging is conveniently observed in a cage with a horizontal partition, the upper part serving to keep the insects and the lower filled with soil, or material representing soil (e.g. very small transparent glass balls to facilitate visual observations); the partition has a narrow slit close to a glass side of the cage and this slit is the only surface available to the female for digging and oviposition, which can be observed through the glass wall of the cage.

A female beginning to dig raises its body on the first two pairs of legs and arches the abdomen so that it is approximately vertical. The ovipositor valves become extruded and the abdomen is pressed into the substrate by a series of jerks coinciding with the alternate opening and closing of the dorsal and ventral valves. As the closed valves are pushed in and then opened widely (fig. 190, C) they force the particles of soil sideways and somewhat upwards; this is followed by closing of the valves and a new thrust of the ovipositor. When the hole is still shallow, the abdomen retracts slightly and the valves continue opening, but less widely, while the posterior end of the abdomen rotates on its long axis, first one way, then the other, through a semi-circle; these movements serve to pack soil particles and to smooth the walls of the hole. This is followed by another spell of digging and the process continues until the hole is sufficiently deep.

The depth of the oviposition hole is usually such that the female abdomen finally becomes greatly extended, for example in *Anacridium* from 3·5 to 9–10 cm, and in *Acrida*, with a very slender body, from 4·5 to 15–17 cm (Hafez & Ibrahim 1958). Such extension is possible because the abdominal intersegmental membranes in the female are folded (fig. 191, C) and very much more elastic than in the male (fig. 191, B). The extent to which the membranes are stretched during oviposition is illustrated by figs. 190, B and 191, A, and table 85 provides numerical values.

There must be some change in the elasticity of the membranes during adult

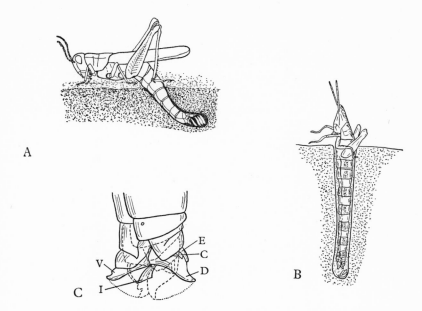

Fig. 190. Oviposition. A, *Melanoplus* sp. (Uvarov 1928); B, *Colemania sphenarioides*;
C, ditto, end of female abdomen during digging (Coleman 1911).

E, epiproct; C, cercus; D, dorsal ovipositor valve; V, ventral valve; I, inner valve.
Broken line shows the position of parts when the valves are closed; dotted line, range of
movement of valves.

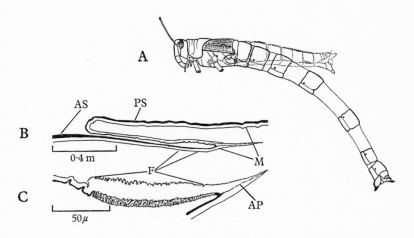

Fig. 191. A, *Schistocerca*, showing the extension of the female abdomen during oviposition;
dotted outline shows the normal size (after Vosseler 1905); B, longitudinal section
through the dorsal abdominal cuticle of male; C, ditto, of female (after Malek
1958 *b*).

AS, anterior end of a tergite; PS, posterior end of a preceding tergite; M, intersegmental
membrane; AP, apodeme; F, corresponding areas of the membrane in male and female.

life, since the abdomen of the immature *Schistocerca* female cannot be extended for more than 5 mm without rupture, while that of a mature one can be forcibly stretched by 36 mm without damage (Vosseler 1905). Such stretching of the whole abdomen must affect most of the internal organs and Thomas (1965) pointed out that the ventral nerve chain and the intestine have bends which permit this.

Table 85. *Length (in mm) of extended intersegmental membranes in ovipositing females of* Locusta *(Agarwala t.c.) and* Acrida *(Hafez & Ibrahim 1958)*

Between segments	*Locusta*	*Acrida*
3–4	1	1
4–5	10	16
5–6	12	55
6–7	10	40
7–8	1	23
Total extension	34	135

The mechanism of abdominal extension has been given various explanations and several theories were tested by Agarwala. The main factor is believed to be an increase in internal blood pressure in the abdomen through vigorous rhythmic pumping movements; such movements have been observed by other authors and led to the theory that the extension of the abdomen is due either to increased intake of air into the tracheae and air-sacs or to swallowing air into the digestive tract. Pumping of air into the body cavity and into the gut of *Locusta* produced an extension of abdomen by 22 and 14 mm, respectively, but when water was pumped into the body cavity, the abdomen extended by 34 mm, as during oviposition. An objection to the blood pressure theory raised by Grassé (1922) was that the total quantity of blood is insufficient to cause the increase in the volume of the abdomen caused by the extension, but a comparison by Agarwala of the volumes of the normal and of the extended abdomen immersed in water showed only a slight increase in volume since the abdomen becomes narrower as it is elongated. Woodrow (1963) found that the volume of tracheae and air-sacs in an ovipositing *Locusta* female increased by 117% and the gut was also distended by air, indicating that this was the main reason for the extension of the abdomen.

However, when egg-laying occurs elsewhere than in a hole in the soil, as sometimes happens, the abdomen extends much less. This suggests that the full elongation is assisted by the pull on the abdomen during the repeated opening of the ovipositor valves, and by the friction between the abdomen and the walls of the hole.

The direction and the shape of the oviposition hole depend on the physical properties of the soil. At the beginning of the digging the direction is near vertical, but deeper down the increasing compactness of the soil may cause bending of the abdomen, usually in the posterior direction (fig. 190, A).

Oviposition

When the hole is completed, the female retracts its abdomen slightly and the frothy secretion of the accessory glands is emitted; this is partly absorbed by

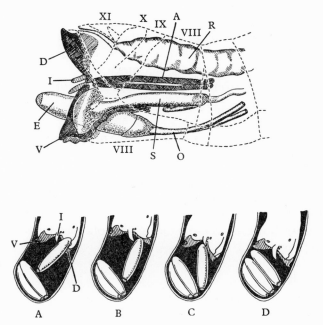

Fig. 192. *Dociostaurus*. Above, diagram of female abdomen during oviposition; below, four stages in the emission of eggs (after Paoli 1937 a, 1937 b).
VIII–XI, abdominal segments; R, rectum; S, spermatheca; O, oviduct; D, dorsal ovipositor valve; A, its apodeme; V, ventral valve; I, inner valve; E, egg.

the soil and it hardens to form the walls of the egg-pod. At the same time, eggs are propelled by pulsating movements of the VIIIth and VIIth sternites; when an egg approaches the exit, the ovipositor valves open widely and the egg comes out between the ventral and the inner valves (fig. 192). The egg appears with the micropylar end first, the other end being held between the dorsal valves; as the ovipositor closes, the egg slips out and rotates in the bottom of the hole, so that finally it lies in the position ensuring that the head of the future embryo will point upwards. Pulsating movements of the terminal segments are then resumed, more frothy secretion emitted, and the second egg laid. The process continues with the abdomen gradually contracting and the walls of the hole being smeared with frothy secretion. When all

325

the eggs are laid, the upper portion of the hole in some species is filled with froth, forming a 'plug' of the egg-pod. There is considerable variation in this respect between species, as will be seen when different types of egg-pods are described in the second volume. There are also differences in the arrangement of eggs within the egg-pod, which must be due to some variation in the movements of the ovipositor during the emission of the eggs.

Some divergence from the oviposition process as described above is to be expected in species which oviposit not in the soil, but amongst blades of grass, or on the surface of leaves, but the oviposition mechanism in them has not been studied.

Nervous control of the digging and of the emission of glandular secretion and eggs remains unstudied. The presence of the various sensilla on the different terminal sclerites of the abdomen (Thomas 1965) suggests that they play a part in the stimulation and regulation of the sequence of the processes involved.

FECUNDITY AND FERTILITY

The terms fecundity and fertility are often used as synonyms, but a clear distinction between them is essential. The term *fecundity* should be restricted to the ability to produce offspring and its value (or birth-rate) is represented by the total number of eggs laid by a female, regardless of their subsequent fate. The *fertility*, however, is estimated as the total production of viable eggs giving rise to hoppers.

Potential fecundity

The first attempt to estimate and to compare the potential fecundity of different species was based on the number of ovarioles multiplied by the number of oöcytes per ovariole. The resulting figures, however, showed no correspondence with the abundance of a species, the highest values being associated with the relatively rare species; the figures were considered to provide merely an indication of potential fecundity (Rubtzov 1934), but even this is not justified, because of continuous production of new oöcytes after each ovulation (p. 305). The potential fecundity clearly depends both on the number of eggs laid at one time and the maximum number of successive layings.

The number of eggs in an egg-pod or a *clutch* can never exceed the total number of ovarioles, and usually there is good agreement between the mean number of ovarioles and of eggs in a clutch (O. W. Richards & Waloff 1954). The actual range of egg numbers per clutch is naturally as wide as that of ovariole numbers. Data on numbers of eggs in pods are available for eighteen species from Canada (Criddle 1935), sixty from the western United States (Hilliard 1959), sixty-seven from Russia (Zimin 1938), forty-eight from Central Africa (Chapman & Robertson 1958; I. A. D. Robertson &

Chapman 1962), forty-eight from West Africa (Chapman 1961) and fourteen from India (Katiyar 1960), apart from scattered records for individual species. The lowest mean number for a species is four and most of the small-size Gomphocerinae and Acridinae have low egg numbers while large Cyrtacanthacridinae have clutches of 150 and more eggs (e.g. 229 in a pod of the African *Orthacanthacris humilicrus*). The record high numbers are 417 in a pod of *Pamphagus elephas* (Cros 1929) and 282 in a pod of *Phymateus viridipes* (Chapman 1961). Clutch size is of little taxonomic value, since closely related species may have very different numbers, for example five to thirteen in *Dociostaurus brevicollis* and nineteen to twenty-four in *D. tartarus*. Nor is the number correlated with the size of the insect, small *Eyprepocnemis* laying thirty to eighty eggs in a pod, while the closely related *Tropidiopsis*, which is about twice the size, lays only twenty-four to thirty-eight.

The variation in the clutch size in the same species probably mainly depends on the number of fully functional ovarioles, a reduction of which may occur as a result of unfavourable external conditions, for example deficient feeding. A reduction in the size of successive clutches laid by the same female, which may have a similar explanation, can be substantial (table 86).

Table 86. *Average number of eggs per pod by weeks through the oviposition period of* Melanoplus differentialis (*after Drake, Decker & Tauber 1945*)

Weeks	Cages indoors		Cages outdoors
	1938	1939	1939
1st	162	120	106
2nd	124·3	104·5	79·9
3rd	106·7	160·4	93·9
4th	100	88·1	85·3
5th	104·5	90·6	71·5
6th	106·7	89	69·2
7th	95	81	69·3
8th	—	66	63
9th	—	51	68·5
10th	—	—	63

Similar data were recorded for individual females of *Anacridium aegyptium* (Colombo & Mocellin 1956), *Aularches miliaris* (Katiyar 1955), *Locusta* (Norris 1950; Albrecht, Verdier & Blackith 1959) and *Schistocerca* (Norris 1952; Papillon 1960). This effect was less noticeable in British grasshoppers (O. W. Richards & Waloff 1954) possibly because of the small total number of ovarioles.

The changes in the total ovariole number and therefore in clutch size, and in percentage of non-functional ovarioles, as an important phase effect is discussed on p. 353.

The next factor of fecundity is the *number of pods* laid by a female during her life. Abundant evidence is available to show that the potential maximum number may be very high, but its realisation depends on how long the female survives in a reproductive state under given conditions. This is shown particularly clearly by data for the same species in the laboratory and in the field. *Eyprepocnemis plorans meridionalis* is supposed to lay only twice in the Rukwa Valley, Tanganyika (Chapman & Robertson 1958), but females from that population kept in the laboratory lived up to 337 days and laid an average of 13·9 pods per female, with thirty-three as the maximum, achieving mean fecundity of over one thousand eggs per female (Antoniou & Hunter-Jones 1956), which is a very high number for any acridoid. Criddle (1935) recorded that two females of *Mecostethus gracilis* laid 2592 eggs (i.e. 1296 per female); figures of the same order are known for the solitarious *Locusta* (p. 356).

Table 87. *Egg production by* 100 *females of three species of* Melanoplus (*averages for* 3 *years*)

Species	Total eggs	Total pods	Pods per female	Eggs per pod	Eggs per female
M. bivittatus	12888	185·3	1·9	69·7	128·9
M. differentialis	12788	144·0	1·4	88·8	127·9
M. sanguinipes	11726	597·3	6·0	19·6	117·2

Data on the comparative fecundity of three species of the same genus kept under similar conditions (Drake, Decker & Tauber 1945), summarised in table 87 suggest that in *M. sanguinipes* clutches are small, but their number is greater than in the other two species, which lay fewer pods with more eggs in each. The resulting total fecundity is approximately the same in all three though Barnes (1955) obtained 874 eggs per female of *M. sanguinipes*.

Factors affecting fecundity and fertility

The total number of layings by a female primarily depends on the length of the period during which the female continued its reproductive activities. The male need not be considered, since a single copulation is sufficient to ensure repeated fertilisation of successive clutches of eggs (p. 318).

The length of adult life and of the reproductive period are affected by external conditions in a similar way but their effects on fecundity are different. *Camnula pellucida* survived at 37°C for only 15·8 days, but 4·2 egg pods per female were laid during that time, whereas at 27°C the length of life was doubled (32·6 days), but only 1·0 egg pod per female was laid (Parker 1930). In *Locusta* the maximum number of eggs per pod and of viable eggs was obtained at a constant temperature of 26·7°C and in *Schistocerca* at 32·2°C. In the case of fluctuating temperatures, however, these optima are at a considerably

328

lower mean temperature, namely, 25·1°C for *Locusta* and 23·5°C for *Schisto-cerca* (A. G. Hamilton 1950). Since such fluctuations are normal under field conditions, the values obtained at constant laboratory conditions have to be regarded with caution, and the available experimental data on the effects of temperature and humidity on fecundity and fertility are very inadequate.

Food is another factor that would be expected to exert influence on reproduction, and experimental studies have shown striking differences in the fecundity of the same species fed on different plants (Tauber, Drake & Decker 1945; Pfadt 1949; Kozanchikov 1950; Barnes 1955; Pickford 1958; Karelina 1960). An example is given in table 88.

Table 88. *Effects of food plants on oviposition period and fecundity of* Melanoplus sanguinipes (*after Pfadt* 1949)

Plant	Oviposition period in days	Pods per female	Eggs per pod	Eggs per female	Eggs per female per week
Taraxacum officinale	60·5	9·8	21·0	206	23·9
Wheat	63·3	8·8	21·3	188	21·2
Descurainia sophia	52·5	7·5	21·4	160	20·9
Medicago sativa	65·0	7·6	20·7	157	18·4
Cirsium plattense	42·7	3·9	18·4	71	10·0
Poa pratensis	35·0	3·5	18·6	65	10·4
Agropyron smithii	28·8	2·5	17·9	45	7·0

The table shows that the number of eggs per pod is not greatly affected by food, but the number of pods per female is clearly dependent on the length of the oviposition period as well as on the oviposition rate. The latter can be judged by the number of eggs per female per week, which reflects the rate at which new eggs are produced after each laying. Thus, the total fecundity appears to depend on the relative value of a food plant both for the survival of the female and for the reproductive metabolic activity. The two effects may be very different, since *Locusta m. migratoria* lives much longer on *Agropyron repens* than on other grasses, but its fecundity is very much reduced (table 89). Females of *Melanoplus differentialis* live longest if fed on cotton (p. 321) but their fecundity is then the lowest.

There are definite indications that the food value of different plants for reproduction is not the same for different species.

As can be seen from table 89, the fecundity of *Locusta* is particularly high when it is fed on grasses, while its reproduction is completely suppressed by feeding on Compositae, Cruciferae and Leguminosae, all of which have more satisfactory effects than grasses on the fecundity of *Melanoplus sanguinipes*; according to Barnes (1955) the latter species when fed on *Sisymbrium irio* (Cruciferae) produced an average of 196 eggs per female, while only eighty-nine were laid by females fed on a grass (*Sorghum halepense*). The most intriguing result of that author's work was that fecundity on a mixed plant diet was higher than the highest on individual plants. This was confirmed by Pickford (1958), in whose experiments *Melanoplus sanguinipes* produced an average of 243 eggs when fed on wheat, 467 on wild mustard (*Brassica*

Table 89. *Effects of food plants on oviposition period in days and fecundity of* Melanoplus sanguinipes *(M) and* Locusta m. migratoria *(L) (data extracted from Pickford 1958 and Kozhanchikov 1950)*

(The number of eggs per pod in *Locusta* is average for this species)

	Oviposition period		Pods per female		Eggs per pod		Eggs per female	
	M	L	M	L	M	L	M	L
GRAMINACEAE								
Bromus inermis	48		9·0		19·5		175	
Wheat	53		11·9		20·4		243	
Phragmites communis		26·5		5·2		80		416
Calamagrostis epigeios				5·0		80		400
Dactylis glomerata		27		2·5		80		200
Agropyron repens		45		0·8		80		64
COMPOSITAE								
Taraxacum officinale	55	0	17·0	0	19·5	0	231	0
CRUCIFERAE								
Descurainia sophia	45		12·7		19·6		249	
Brassica caber	66		20·5		21·0		430	
Raphanus raphanistrum		0		0		0		0
LEGUMINOSAE								
Trifolium pratense				0		0		0

caber) and 579 on a mixed diet of the two plants. *Chorthippus albomarginodus* laid more eggs when fed on a mixture of four grasses, than on one of them (Karelina 1960). Reasons for such an effect are obscure, since the plant most favourable for reproduction presumably contains some essential

Table 90. *Effects of nitrogen content of wheat on fecundity and fertility of* Melanoplus sanguinipes *(after D. S. Smith & Northcott 1951)*

Nutrient	Percentage N content of wheat	Eggs per female	Percentage hatch
High N	6·16	57·6	44·8
Low N	4·29	34·7	46·8

chemical materials and a dilution by less valuable food can hardly be beneficial. It might be suggested that the admixture of less valuable food stimulates the feeding activity and more food is taken, but possible effects of the quantity of food on fecundity have not been studied.

The chemical factors in food affecting fecundity are very little known. *Melanoplus sanguinipes* fed on wheat grown in nutrient solution of high nitrogen content laid more eggs than on wheat with low nitrogen content, but the percentage hatch was approximately the same in both cases (table 90).

Similar work with nutrient solutions containing phosphorus (D. S. Smith 1960 a) has shown that fecundity was greater on wheat with 0·17% dry-weight phosphorus content, than on that with 1·86%.

The available data on fertility are very scanty. In *Locusta*, the percentage of sterile pods and sterile eggs in otherwise viable pods increased with the age of the female (table 91).

Table 91. *Non-viability of* Locusta *eggs in pods laid in six successive two-week periods (after Norris 1950)*

	weeks				
	1	2	3	4	5–6
Percentage of sterile pods	5	5	14	34	49
Percentage of sterile eggs in fertile pods	12	15	25	38	62

In *Schistocerca*, on the average, 7% of all pods and 21% of eggs in fertile pods were sterile and it was calculated that out of an average of 317 eggs per female 231 hoppers hatched, so that the fertility was 72% of the fecundity (Norris 1952). The reasons for sterility are little known. In locusts there is a noticeable effect of higher density on sterility (p. 355).

The sterility increases greatly in parthenogenetic eggs of *Schistocerca*, only some 23·8% of which hatch, as compared with 80·4% in the parallel normal stock (A. G. Hamilton 1955; see table 82).

It is clear that fecundity and fertility of acridoids are very imperfectly studied and there is a wide field open even for simple experimental work, as well as for physiological investigations closely linked with nutritional research based on synthetic diets (p. 85). These problems are of fundamental importance for population dynamics and should receive special attention.

PHASE POLYMORPHISM

Keppen (1870), nearly a hundred years ago, expressed the view that the two morphologically distinct forms of *Locusta* were 'merely varieties of the same species, which are, moreover, not constant, but changing one into another'. Since morphological polymorphism in locusts, related to their swarming, was established some 40 years ago (Uvarov 1921; Faure 1932) there has appeared a vast number of publications on the subject. The following review is intended to bring together the factual information on the various aspects of phase polymorphism, to assess the evidence critically, to attempt its synthesis and to discuss the nature of the phenomena and the more promising lines of further investigations.

The present chapter is based essentially on laboratory data, while a discussion of phase variation in wild locusts in relation to ecology, behaviour, population dynamics and control is reserved for the next volume of the work.

Phase polymorphism comprises a whole complex of responses of an insect to the population density and it appears best not to anticipate the conclusions of this review as to the nature of these phenomena by the use of formal designations of the phases. Instead, the terms crowded (or gregarious) and isolated (or solitarious, a term to replace the ambiguous word solitary) will be used throughout. The degree of crowding is usually indicated, while isolation means, in the case of hoppers and adult males, that the insect was kept in a container by itself throughout its life, and, in the case of reproducing females, that they also were kept singly, except for a short period (usually twenty-four hours) when a male was introduced for fertilisation.

CHARACTERISTICS OF THE EXTREME PHASES

Although the extreme phases are merely the terminal expressions of a continuous polymorphic series (Kennedy 1956, 1961), it is convenient to begin by discussing such differences between them as have so far been established, before considering the intermediate (or transient) forms and the processes involved in phase changes. It should be stressed that laboratory populations of locusts may approach in their characteristics the extreme phases as found in wild populations, but usually do not reach them (Gunn & Hunter-Jones 1952); possible reasons for this will be mentioned later. Moreover, crowded locusts are easily maintained in the laboratory through many successive generations, while much space and labour are needed to keep large continuous cultures of isolated locusts requiring individual attention. As a result, most comparisons are made between locusts from continuously crowded stocks and locusts derived from crowded parents and isolated for only one, or very few, generations. As will be seen later, some responses to density are immediate, while others are cumulative in the course of several generations and the above practice does not allow a fair comparison of the effects of extreme densities maintained for an equal number of generations in the same conditions. Therefore, most of the comparisons indicate merely the trends of density responses rather than their amplitude.

Hatchlings

Crowded females lay eggs which produce larger hatchlings than those from eggs laid by isolated females (table 92). Additional data were provided by Albrecht (1962b).

In *Locusta* and *Schistocerca* there is also a small sexual dimorphism in the hatchling weight, females being heavier by about 2%, but this is not affected by density.

Table 92. *Mean weight and ovariole number of hatchlings from isolated and crowded parents*

	Weight in mg		Ovariole number		
	Isolated	Crowded	Isolated	Crowded	Reference
Locusta	12·7	19·7	—	—	Hunter-Jones 1958
,,	13·3	16·8	103	83	Albrecht, Verdier & Blackith 1959
Schistocerca	14·5	21·3	129	112	Papillon 1960
Nomadacris	10·2	17·7	196	153	Albrecht 1959

The heavier hatchlings from crowded parents are, as a rule, of darker and even almost black colour, while isolated females produce hatchlings in which light weight is associated with reduction or loss of black pigmentation and their usual colour is light-grey, fawn, or green (the latter particularly in *Nomadacris* and *Schistocerca*). In *Locusta* and *Nomadacris* hatchlings from the same egg-pod are all of the same colour type, but *Schistocerca* often produces hatchlings of more than one type from the same egg-pod (Chauvin 1941b; Hunter-Jones 1958). Papillon (1960) confirmed this for *Schistocerca*, but pointed out that in no case had an egg-pod laid by an isolated female produced only black hatchlings, nor had one laid by a crowded female produced only green ones.

The weight difference between hatchlings of different colour is largely attributable to higher water content of the heavier ones (Blackith 1961; Albrecht 1962b), which, therefore, are better protected against desiccation (p. 334).

Quantitative differences in the chemical composition of different hatchlings are substantial. Large black hatchlings have a higher initial content of fat (p. 89, table 17) and their haemolymph contains more amino-acids, more ascorbic acid and more of a substance supposed to be vitamin C (Blackith & Howden 1961). While fat is of little importance as a reserve food during starvation, the other substances are important and their higher content in black hatchlings contributes to the greater ability to survive starvation. Figure 193 illustrates the comparative viability of starved *Schistocerca* hatchlings from isolated and grouped parents; gregarious hatchlings survived considerably longer than solitarious, particularly at low humidity (Albrecht & Blackith 1960), but hatchlings of *Locusta* and *Nomadacris* survive longer in higher humidity, with little phase difference (Blackith & Albrecht 1960; Albrecht 1962*b*).

A very important anatomical difference between hatchlings from crowded and isolated parents is the higher number of ovarioles in the latter (table 92). This has a bearing on the fecundity of the two phases (p. 353).

Hopper coloration

In general, solitarious locust hoppers are of uniform (frequently green) coloration, while gregarious ones have a heavy black pattern typical of their

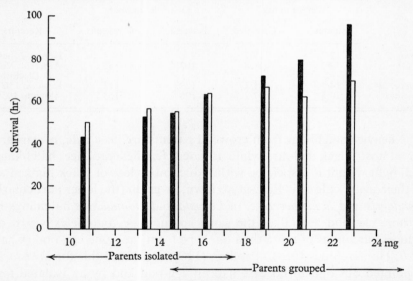

Fig. 193. *Schistocerca*, survival of starved hatchlings in relation to parentage and humidity (black 35% R.H.; white 100% R.H.) (after Albrecht & Blackith 1960).

species, on a yellow or orange background (see frontispiece). The pigments responsible for coloration have already been reviewed (p. 42ff.) and the two types of hopper present striking biochemical differences (table 93). The basic green colour of isolated hoppers is due to a mixture of yellow chromoproteins with blue mesobiliverdin, which is absent from crowded hoppers. The latter are

Table 93. *Main pigments and colours of isolated and crowded locusts*
(Goodwin 1952, modified)

	INSECTORUBIN		MELANIN		MESOBILIVERDIN		CAROTENOIDS	
	Isolated	Crowded	Isolated	Crowded	Isolated	Crowded	Isolated	Crowded
Schistocerca								
Vth instar	Absent	Present	Absent	Present in the black areas	Blue component of green	Absent	Yellow component of green	Yellow areas
Fledgling	As above	Present; pink colour	Grey tegminal spots; black tips of mandibles and leg spines	As above	As above	As above	As above	Present
Mature adult	As above	Present, but masked by yellow carotenoid	As above		As above	As above	No external yellowing	Yellow colour
Locusta								
Vth instar	As above	Present	Absent	Present in black and orange areas	As above	As above	Yellow component	Present, without affecting colour
Fledgling	As above	Present in dark areas	Grey tegminal spots; black tips of mandibles and leg spines	As above	As above	As above	As above	As above
Mature adult	As above	Present but masked by yellow carotenoid in male	As above		As above	As above	Yellow colour of male	As above

particularly characterised by the presence, or greater development, of insecto-rubin and melanin, both responsible for the dark and black pattern, which is absent or greatly reduced in isolated hoppers.

It is to be noted that carotenoids and chromo-proteins play important, but different, parts in the coloration. Thus, they are present in both types of *Schistocerca* hoppers, but in crowded ones they alone are responsible for the yellow ground colour, whereas in the isolated ones they combine with bilin pigments in producing green colour. It is also of interest that the yellow ground colour of crowded *Schistocerca* hoppers and the orange of crowded *Locusta* hoppers are due to quite different pigments, although their overall distribution pattern is somewhat similar. It may be added that yellow ground coloration is found also in crowded hoppers of *Nomadacris* (Faure 1932) and *Schistocerca paranensis* (L. Bruner 1898), whereas it is replaced by orange in *Gastrimargus musicus* (Common 1948), *Locustana*, *Melanoplus sanguinipes* (Faure 1923, 1932) and *Dociostaurus* (Künckel d'Herculais 1893–1905; Pasquier 1934). Although the black pattern is normally associated with crowding, the development of dark pigmentation is not closely linked with other phase changes, since Pener (1963) has shown that crowded hoppers of the albino strain of *Schistocerca* (p. 47) had no black pattern, although their respiratory rate was higher than in the isolated hoppers and they produced morphometrically gregarious adults.

An essential feature of the gregarious coloration pattern is that it is not subject to changes in response to the colour of the environment, whereas isolated hoppers readily adjust their coloration to it (p. 52).

Hopper physiology

Differences in the respiratory rates of isolated and crowded locusts found by several authors are summarised in table 94, and illustrated in fig. 194.

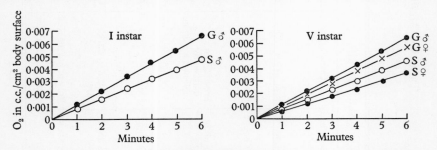

Fig. 194. *Locusta*, respiratory metabolism of solitarious (S) and gregarious (G) hoppers (after Butler & Innes 1936).

Although most of the figures in table 94 suggest a lower rate in isolated locusts, Blackith & Howden (1961) found great individual variation and variation between different stocks which could mask phase differences found by other investigators.

Table 94. *Mean oxygen uptake, in ml/mg/hour,*
by isolated and crowded locusts

	°C	Hatchling Is.	Hatchling Cr.	Late hopper Is.	Late hopper Cr.	Adult Is.	Adult Cr.	Reference
Locusta	25	—	—	0·68	0·77	0·66	0·48	Krüger & Bishai 1957
„	27	0·75	0·75	0·19	0·24	0·24	0·34	Butler & Innes 1936
„	30	2·02	1·23	1·08	1·38	0·95	1·17	Blackith & Howden 1961
Schistocerca	29	0·58	0·90	—	—	—	—	Gardiner 1958
„	30	1·71	1·65	—	—	—	—	Blackith & Howden 1961
„ ♂	33	—	—	0·57	0·61	0·48	0·51	Pener 1963
„ ♀	33	—	—	0·50	0·61	0·49	0·54	

Some biochemical differences between isolated and crowded hoppers were indicated by Matthée (1945), but their physiological significance is not clear (table 95).

Table 95. *Biochemical differences between isolated and*
crowded Vth instar hoppers (Matthée 1945)

	Lactic acid mg/g wet weight Is.	Lactic acid mg/g wet weight Cr.	Uric acid mg per cent Is.	Uric acid mg per cent Cr.	Fat per cent dry weight Is.	Fat per cent dry weight Cr.	Blood pH Is.	Blood pH Cr.
Locusta	0·3036	0·3018	21·22	14·36	11·11	14·02	6·814	6·776
Locustana	0·5602	0·5450	20·31	13·78	12·79	14·63	—	—

Hopper development

In several species of locusts there is a reduction in the number of hopper instars in crowded cultures as compared with isolated hoppers. Owing to the difficulty of rearing isolated hoppers in sufficient numbers, exact experimental data are few, but the correlation between the eye-stripes of adults and the number of hopper instars (p. 278) is sufficiently reliable for the evidence from field material to be also taken into account. Table 96 presents some of the available information.

Table 96. *Number of hopper instars in locusts*

	Isolated	Crowded	References
Schistocerca	6	5	Roonwal *in* Rao 1937; Rao 1960; Albrecht 1955
Nomadacris	7	6	Mossop 1933; Burnett 1951; Albrecht 1955
Anacridium aegyptium	6	5–6	Volkonsky 1937

Although the greater number of instars of isolated hoppers might suggest a slower development rate, this may not always be the case. Male *Locusta* hoppers (reared isolated in humid conditions) developed, on the average, in 24·88 days, as against 28·17 days for crowded ones (Staal 1961). Isolated *Schistocerca* hoppers developed on the average in thirty days, while crowded ones required 33·5 days (P. Hunter-Jones, personal communication).

This suggests that the crowded hoppers expend a higher proportion of energy on movement than on growth. Since isolated hatchlings are much smaller, the extra instar enables them eventually to reach the same adult size as the crowded ones which have an initial advantage of size (p. 333). This induced Albrecht (1955) to regard the extra moult as one of 'adjustment', but this conception cannot hold good because in some species an isolated adult is even larger than a crowded one of the same sex (p. 348). Also, it may be that the greater number of instars in isolated locusts is normal for the species, while high density causes a reduction in the number.

Hopper growth

The only attempt to carry out a study of growth in isolated and crowded *Locusta* hoppers by comparing relative growth rates of body parts was made by Duarte (1938; see also p. 275). Unfortunately, his material was hardly suitable for the purpose, since he used hoppers produced by crowded females, isolated only after hatching. His figures for the weight of first instar hoppers do not show the difference that should be expected between gregarious and solitarious hoppers, suggesting that his two groups were both of intermediate kind, which makes the results of his work indecisive.

Table 97. *Morphometrics of* Dociostaurus *hoppers of III–V instar, reared isolated and crowded, and of the resulting adults*
(*after Gradojevič 1960*)

		Males				Females			
		III	IV	V	AD	III	IV	V	AD
F	Is.	5·33	7·26	10·20	12·70	5·68	7·79	11·41	14·71
	Cr.	5·81	7·89	11·27	14·47	5·97	8·36	12·27	15·71
C	Is.	2·10	2·55	3·38	3·85	2·22	2·86	4·02	4·82
	Cr.	2·41	3·10	4·14	4·86	2·45	3·36	4·71	5·50
P	Is.	1·65	2·55	3·62		1·88	2·82	4·33	
	Cr.	2·26	3·18	4·72		2·31	3·47	5·19	
F/C	Is.	2·49	2·82	3·16	3·30	2·58	2·78	2·82	3·03
	Cr.	2·41	2·53	2·71	2·96	2·47	2·49	2·60	2·82
F/P	Is.	3·17	2·83	2·82		3·01	2·84	2·62	
	Cr.	2·59	2·45	2·39		2·43	2·40	2·36	

This type of work, if carried out with well established gregarious and solitarious lines, should throw light on the relative growth of the body parts leading to eventual differences in adult morphometrics. In fact, Ellis (1951) compared the ratios of length of hind femur to width of head (F/C, p. 345) in crowded and isolated fourth instar hoppers of *Locusta* and found significant differences, which depended on the density at which the hoppers were reared and also on their parentage. Gradojevič (1960) also produced valuable data on the increase of hind femur length (F), head width (C) and pronotum length (P) of *Dociostaurus* hoppers (table 97).

Hopper activity

An essential difference between solitarious and gregarious hoppers is indicated by the name of the latter which implies their tendency to form

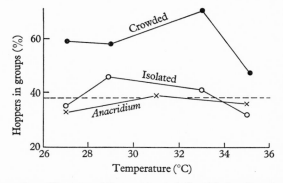

Fig. 195. Aggregation of hoppers of *Locusta* (crowded and isolated) and *Anacridium* in a circular cage; broken line, percentage that could be expected through aggregation by chance (after Ellis 1962).

groups. This type of behaviour was called social aggregation by Ellis (1953, 1956) but the adjective may be omitted provided the term is restricted to the grouping of hoppers due to their own movements towards each other and the maintenance of groups. The tendency of *Locusta* hoppers to aggregate was tested (Ellis 1953, 1959 a, 1962, 1963 a, b) by introducing numbers of hoppers of the same phase in a foodless circular cage, the floor of which was divided into thirty equal radial sectors; conditions within the cage were quite uniform and its shape prevented accumulation in corners. Records were kept of the number of hoppers in each division of the cage every half-hour; two or more hoppers within less than 2 cm of each other in a sector were regarded as a group; for the final evaluation, the number of groups which might have been due to random distribution was calculated and taken into account. The results were that very few of the solitarious hoppers were in groups, whereas up to 70% of gregarious ones were grouped (fig. 195). This happened regardless of their parentage, suggesting that the tendency to aggregate is acquired individually during the hopper life (p. 360).

339

A striking and well-known difference in the behaviour of solitarious and gregarious hoppers in the field is a greater activity of the latter; this is, no doubt, partly due to their mutual stimulation but there is also an intrinsic difference in this respect between the two types of hoppers. A characteristic form of behaviour of gregarious hoppers in the field is their concerted *marching* in bands. Ellis (1951, 1964, 1964 a) was able to induce marching in a cage with a glass top over the centre of which there was suspended an electric bulb, isolated by a water screen to reduce radiant heat; the floor of the cage was flat and free of obstructions. Hoppers placed in such a cage marched round the floor in a circle with its centre under the lamp, sometimes for hours; this activity was particularly pronounced if the hoppers were starved for several hours, but occurred also if food was present in the cage. The marching of hoppers was interrupted by periods of rest and feeding and the proportion of time spent in marching and the marching speed served as quantitative indices of activity.

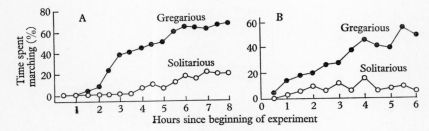

Fig. 196. *Locusta*, marching activity of gregarious and solitarious hoppers in cage (after Ellis 1951). A, without grass; B, with grass.

Figure 196, which illustrates the results of experiments with five marked hoppers placed in a group of twenty of the same kind and kept under close observation, shows that gregarious hoppers, during an eight-hour test, rapidly increased their activity and finally spent over 60% of the time in marching, while the solitarious remained inactive longer and never marched for more than 20% of the time. In the presence of food in the cage, both kinds of hoppers showed reduced marching, but the quantitative difference between them remained. There was also a difference in the average marching speed, which was 3·27 cm per second in gregarious hoppers and 1·33 in the solitarious.

Marching is mainly accomplished by walking, but also by some hopping, the hops being low and short, unlike the jumps made by disturbed hoppers. Plotnikov (*in* Predtechenskiĭ 1935) recorded that green solitarious hoppers of *Schistocerca* made forced jumps which averaged 36 cm in length, while the black gregarious hoppers jumped for only 23 cm; this, however, may be due to the lighter weight and the relatively longer femur of the solitarious hoppers, and not to their greater activity.

Movements of single hoppers of different phase in a cage, recorded by Ellis

340

& Pearce (1962) in connection with experiments on aggregation, also showed considerable differences (table 98).

Table 98. *Comparison of walking activities of gregarious and solitarious hoppers of fourth instar. Means are based on results for 20 individual hoppers during 20–minutes tests (Ellis & Pearce 1962)*

Mean measure of activity	Locusta		Schistocerca	
	Sol.	Greg.	Sol.	Greg.
Distance walked in cm	90·4	377·4	265·5	772·6
Time spent walking in minutes	3·28	7·57	6·21	11·25
Speed of walking in cm per minute	23·02	35·09	31·90	62·58

Adult coloration

A tendency of solitarious *Locusta* hoppers to be green more or less persists in the resulting adults, but this is not the case in *Schistocerca* and *Nomadacris*

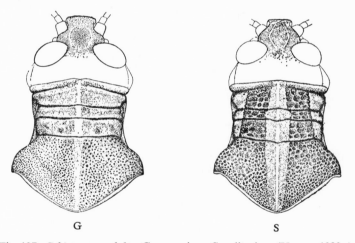

G   S

Fig. 197. *Schistocerca* adults; G, gregarious, S, solitarious (Uvarov 1923 *a*).

in which there is no green colour after the final moult (though in recently moulted solitarious *Schistocerca* it is retained for a short time). A general feature of adult coloration of solitarious adults is their more pronounced dark pattern as compared with gregarious ones (fig. 197); this is, to some extent, a reversal of the situation observed in hoppers (p. 334). More important, however, are changes in the integumental colours during the life of gregarious adults (p. 297 and table 93) which do not occur in solitarious ones; these indicate qualitative metabolic differences.

A particular feature of coloration of some species is the striped eye pattern, reflecting the number of hopper instars (p. 278), which is clear in solitarious locusts, but obscured in gregarious; this may well have a bearing on their respective visual powers (p. 200) and, consequently, on behaviour.

Adult morphology

Morphological differences between adults from crowded and isolated cultures are entirely quantitative, being investigated mainly by comparative measurements of various body parts. As such, they are best studied by

Solitarious   Gregarious

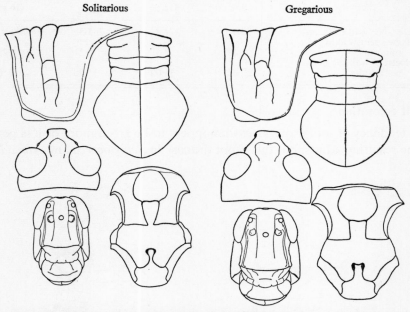

Fig. 198. *Schistocerca*. The main morphological differences between the extreme solitarious and extreme gregarious individuals (Dirsh 1953).

morphometrical methods (p. 344), but a brief survey of the main features involved may form a useful introduction.

Figure 198 illustrates some of the main differences between the two extreme phases of adult *Schistocerca* (Dirsh 1953). The more obvious ones are as follows. In crowded locusts, the head is wider; the pronotum is shorter and more constricted with its crest somewhat depressed; the whole sternal plate is shorter and broader and the mesosternal interspace shorter, broader and not narrowed behind. Additional features are larger compound eyes, which are also more widely separated on the vertex, shorter hind femur and longer tegmen. Some of these differences recur, in a varying degree, in other locust species. In *Locusta*, for example, the pronotal crest varies very strikingly, that of the solitarious type being high and arched in profile, whereas in the gregarious it is quite low and straight or concave in profile (fig. 199).

The shorter hind femur of the gregarious *Schistocerca* has only a few minute denticles along its upper edge, while in the solitarious adults there are about seven to nine larger spinules, in addition to small denticles (Roonwal & Bhanotar 1959). Similar differences in the armature of the hind femur were noted in *Locusta migratoria* from South India (Mukerji & Chatterjee 1956). The number of posterior tibial spines is also slightly, but not significantly, less in gregarious individuals of *Schistocerca* than in solitarious (Roonwal 1947*b*). Such slight morphological differences may be due to the shorter leg of gregarious locusts.

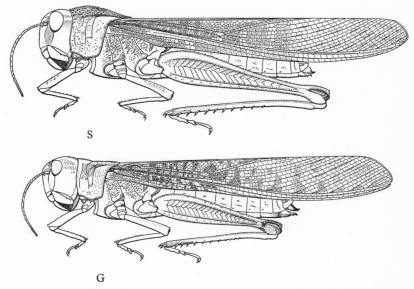

Fig. 199. *Locusta*, solitarious (S) and gregarious (G) female (original). × 1·5

Roehrich & Moutous (1955; Obolensky 1955) have found that the mean number of tubercles on the stridulatory tegminal vein of solitarious *Locusta m. gallica* was 175 in the male and 136 in the female, while in the gregarious the number was 124 in the male and ninety-five in the female, although the tegmen is shorter in the solitarious locust. This difference in the file should have an effect on the song pattern and, possibly, on the acoustic behaviour. In *Locustana*, there is a substantial difference in tegminal venation (Uvarov 1921); the tegmen of the gregarious locust is relatively broader and the medial area which includes the stridulatory vein is expanded (fig. 200); the tubercles of its file have not been studied but the whole arrangement should have some effect on stridulation.

The difference in the number of antennal segments reflecting the number of hopper instars has already been mentioned, and this applies also to the number of eye-stripes.

Baranov (1925) and Jannone (1939*b*) noted some differences in the epiphalli of gregarious and solitarious *Dociostaurus*, but Tarbinskiĭ (1932) did not confirm this and they may be due merely to the larger size of gregarious males.

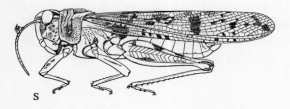

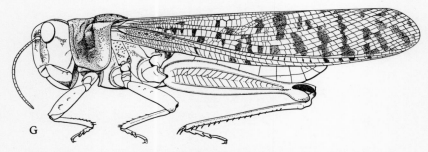

Fig. 200. *Locustana*, solitarious (S) and gregarious (G) male (original).　× 2.

Adult morphometrics

Most of the morphological differences between polymorphic adults are quantitative and can best be appreciated by the application of exact measurements and statistical analysis.

This approach helped in the initial attempt (Uvarov 1921) to clarify the interrelations of the two forms of *Locusta*, at that time usually regarded as distinct species. Only four measurements were made: length of tegmen, pronotum and hind femur, and maximum width of pronotum at the shoulders. The measurements were converted into ratios between the parts which appeared to vary in the two extreme types in opposite directions, namely femur/tegmen and pronotal width/length. Subsequently Plotnikov (1927) proposed to use the ratio tegmen/femur as more convenient. Recommendations for a series of standard measurements, defining the exact points between which they should be taken, were produced by the Fourth International Locust Conference in 1936 at Cairo (International 1937). A more extensive scheme of twenty measurements carried out by Dirsh (1953) is illustrated in fig. 201. He has stressed an important point, neglected by some earlier authors, namely the need for treating the two sexes separately, since the variation in

344

measurements, and in their ratios, was found not to be the same in male and female. When the measurements of the two extreme forms were examined statistically, it was found that the differences between the mean values of seven measurements in males were non-significant. In other cases, the sexes varied in opposite directions, the females of the two extreme types having on

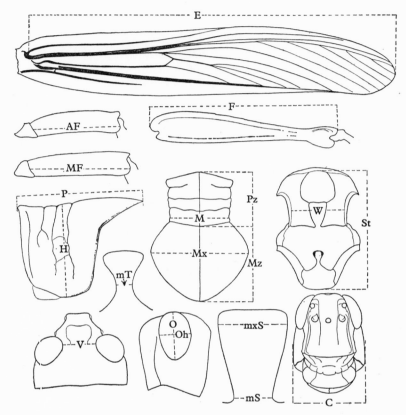

Fig. 201. *Schistocerca*, standard scheme of morphometric measurements (Dirsh 1953).
E, tegmen (elytron) length; F, posterior femur length; AF, anterior femur length; MF, middle femur length; P, pronotum length; H, pronotum height; Pz, length of the prozona of pronotum; Mz, ditto of its metazona; M, minimum width of pronotum; Mx, maximum ditto; W, width of mesosternum; Sr, length of sternum; mS, mimimum width of mesosternal interspace; mxS, maximum ditto; mT, minimum width of metasternal interspace; V, width of vertex between eyes; O, vertical diameter of eye; Oh, horizontal ditto; C, maximum width of head.

the whole more discriminating characters than the males. For these reasons, only eight measurements were finally selected as the more reliable, namely height of pronotum (H), minimum width of mesosternal insterspace (mS), minimum width of metasternal interspace (mT), length of posterior femur (F), width of vertex between eyes (V), vertical diameter of eye (O) and maximum width of head (C). The significance of the differences of means in these eight cases was high, but frequency distribution curves of the measurements showed considerable overlapping; this led to the conclusion that simple measurements are unsuitable for discriminating between phases, but possibly useful for comparisons between populations.

Several ratios were, therefore, examined and seven of them were found promising, namely O/V, O/mS, O/mT, F/mS, F/mT, F/V and F/C, but out of these only F/V and F/C showed no overlap of frequency distribution curves for the two sexes. It was argued that V (width of the vertex between the eyes) could be measured only under a binocular microscope with a micrometer eye-piece, while the others were measured by callipers and therefore the F/C ratio was recommended for general use 'as a reliable and convenient practical index of the phase'. While the detailed analysis described above was published only for *Schistocerca*, the F/C ratio proved to be equally useful for *Nomadacris*

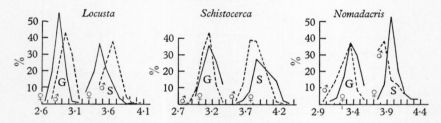

Fig. 202. Frequency distribution curves of the F/C ratio in the two sexes of the extreme phases of three locust species (Dirsh 1951).

and *Locusta* (fig. 202). A special value of the F/C ratio is that it can also be applied to hoppers (p. 338). It needs stressing that the measurement of the maximum width of the head (C) requires special care. Dirsh (1953) recommended measuring it by applying a calliper with parallel arms from the front; the arms should be passed over the genae backwards and forwards, while the calliper screw is adjusted, and the reading taken when the arms just fail to pass; an alternative method of taking the reading when the arms just pass the genae was claimed to reduce the chance of personal error (Rainey, Waloff & Burnett 1959), but this error would be negligible compared with the variability within a sample (Stower, Davies & Jones 1960). A spring-loaded calliper dial (fig. 203) makes this (and other) measurements more precise (Blackith & Albrecht 1961), provided that the spring loading is reduced to avoid pressure on the part measured.

The E/F ratio, which has been much favoured by earlier workers and is still used widely, was found unreliable by Dirsh because the tegmen length (E) varied between extreme types in different directions in males and females, while the femur length (F) varied in the same direction; moreover, the E/F frequency distribution curves showed considerable overlap. It should be noted that the C measurement, although reliable in the case of extreme phases, tends to be less so in the intermediate forms (D. E. Davies, personal communication).

Taking the extreme mean ratios for the available material, and dividing their range by 100, Dirsh constructed two tables in which the intermediate ratio values were ranked as 'percentages of gregarisation'; this term should be understood merely as an abbreviation for a shift in the F/C or E/F ratio from one of the extremes adopted by him to another.

A ratio which has been little used is that between the minimum width of the pronotum (M) and the maximum width of the head (C); it is particularly

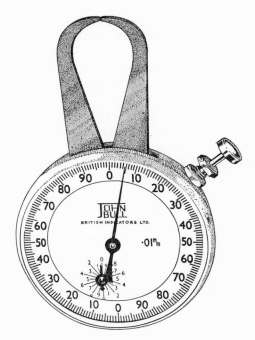

Fig. 203. Spring-loaded calliper dial (original supplied by British Indicators Ltd.).

valuable in the case of *Locusta*, in which the median construction of the pronotum in the gregarious phase is very striking and its degree varies subspecifically (p. 372). In taking this measurement, the calliper ends on each side should be applied to the point midway down the middle furrow of the pronotum (fig. 19, A, furrow *gd*), where it meets the short longitudinal furrow (*k*).

Blackith & Verdier (1961) found some differences in the maximum vertical diameter of the anterior femur between solitarious and gregarious adults of the same sex; similar measurement of the hind femur proved to be even better for phase discrimination. Beingolea Guerrero (1958) found this latter measurement (designated by him as A) useful for separating extreme phases of *Schistocerca paranensis* when compounded with the tegmen length into E/A ratio. Staal (1961) found that the length of hairs on the sternum of *Locusta* is greater in crowded individuals.

The need to treat separately the two sexes of the same species and phase, which has already been mentioned, arises from the sexual differences between measurements of the same characters. As a rule, there is a clear sexual dimorphism in size in the solitarious adults, the male being smaller, while in the gregarious the sexes tend to approximate in size. This led to adopting the sexual dimorphism ratio as one of the morphometric characters of phase. An illustration is provided by *Locustana*, in which the dimorphism is particularly striking (table 99) and has been used for phase discrimination.

Recently, more elaborate methods of statistical treatment of morphometric indices have been introduced, namely those of discriminant functions and generalised distances. Their application requires either a considerable knowledge of higher mathematics or the assistance of a statistician; only the principles of these methods can be outlined here and more detailed information on them

Table 99. *Mean length of tegmen (E) and of hind femur (F) and the sexual dimorphism ratios in the extreme phases of* Locustana *(du Plessis 1939)*

	E			F		
	Female	Male	Ratio	Female	Male	Ratio
Solitarious	36·68	27·14	1·35	18·17	13·90	1·31
Gregarious	43·25	41·87	1·03	20·21	19·92	1·02

will be found in the following acridological papers: Misra, Nair & Roonwal 1952; Nair 1953; Blackith 1957, 1962; Albrecht & Blackith 1957; Stower, Davies & Jones 1960; they include references to purely statistical books where the methods are described.

The basis of the methods is not to compare directly either the morphometric indices, or their ratios, in the two groups of locusts, but to utilise their differences from each other taking also into account their variabilities and co-variabilities. Using the past experience that E, F and C measurements appear to differentiate gregarious and solitarious locusts, the differences between the arithmetic mean values for each index in each group are calculated; after introducing corrections required by rigorous statistics, the differences are expressed as shown below for *Schistocerca* (Stower, Davies & Jones 1960):

	E	F	C
Gregarious males	52·267	23·703	7·488
Solitarious males	49·877	24·635	6·405
Difference	+2·390	−0·932	+1·083

The values of the differences are then multiplied by special coefficients and all three added up (bearing in mind plus and minus signs), and this gives a total

348

difference between the two groups; in this case it is 12·61342644, and a square root of this figure (3·552) represents the final discriminant between the gregarious and the solitarious males. Similar calculations produce discriminants between both sexes of both groups of locusts, as follows:

G male — S male	3·552
G female — S female	3·904
G male — G female	2·741
S male — S female	6·227
S male — G female	5·222
S female — G male	5·780

These values are pure figures and can be plotted on any convenient scale. The base line may represent the distance, in the terms of the unit selected, between the two sexes of the solitarious locusts; the values of the distances between the solitarious and the gregarious male and between the latter and the

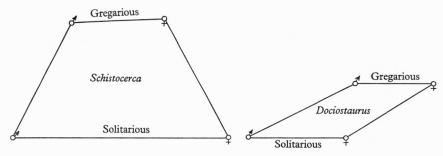

Fig. 204. Compound discriminant diagrams of the phases and sexes of *Schistocerca* (after Stower, Davies & Jones 1960) and *Dociostaurus* (original by D. Davies).

solitarious female make it possible to construct a triangle defining the position of the gregarious female; the latter should agree with the known distances between the solitarious male and the gregarious female as known from the table. The result, in the case of the two field populations of *Schistocerca*, one definitely swarming, and the other bred as hoppers in scattered formation from non-swarming parents, is shown in fig. 204, which, of course, applies only to these two populations; the actual distances between the sexes and groups do not represent extreme phase differences which could be taken as standards. Nevertheless, the resulting diagram shows clearly, for example, that there is greater sexual size dimorphism in the solitarious than in the gregarious *Schistocerca*, while it also gives a visual impression of the distances between the same sexes of the different phase. Diagrams of similar shape are obtainable for *Nomadacris*, *Locusta* and *Schistocerca paranensis* (D. E. Davies, personal communication).

A corresponding diagram for *Dociostaurus*, based on non-swarming specimens and specimens from a swarm, all from Cyprus, is strikingly different (fig. 204), showing that in this species gregarious locusts of both sexes are

349

very much larger than solitarious; the same situation is found in *Locustana* (Fig. 200).

It should be clear that the ability to discriminate populations by this method will depend on a careful selection of such body parts as present the most characteristic metrical differences. Some statisticians advocate using as many measurements as possible (Nair 1953), but it is more reasonable to suggest that, while this is needed in exploratory investigations with a view to selecting the measurements which reflect most faithfully the mode of growth of body parts, one should aim eventually to reduce their number to the minimum for practical reasons.

It should not be assumed that phase variation in all species results in metrical changes of the same parts of the body, and the selection of measurements must be essentially on a species basis, rather than on any uniform system. It will be essential to establish, for each sex of each species, or subspecies (p. 370), the two extreme phase standards, deriving them from well documented field samples of swarming and non-swarming populations, in both cases with the history of *several* previous generations known for certain. This is admittedly not easy because of the mobility of locusts, but it must be aimed at in all studies.

Although laboratory cultures may not result in the production of morphological extremes (p. 332), it is still advisable to establish the standards for the extreme densities that can be achieved under specified breeding and rearing conditions. The latter point is important, because morphometric characters of locusts are affected not only by their density, but also by other environmental factors (p. 367).

The method of discriminant functions is the latest to be used in locust morphometrics, but this does not necessarily make it the best. It appears to offer a very precise technique for discriminating between population samples, but the advantages of simpler statistical methods cannot be dismissed lightly. Acridologists need some means for comparing populations which superficially appear very similar, so as to follow even minor qualitative changes in populations, both in the field and in the laboratory. An essential requirement is that the methods used should produce reliable comparisons, without involving an excessive amount of labour, some of which demands special knowledge. A very precise, but laborious, method may restrict the number of cases analysed by it and thus limit the amount of factual information obtained, which is still very inadequate.

Finally, it should be remembered that morphometric differences between adults depend on the unequal growth rates of body parts and these rates are not all affected by density in the same way (p. 275). The use of ratios and of compounded discriminant functions may well conceal some of these effects, while neither method can claim that it reflects differences between the total morphometric patterns of populations. In particular, discriminant functions serve only to evaluate some of the differences, not to characterise each population separately, as the ratios do.

Such differences may be better shown by comparing not the absolute measurements of body parts which reflect the sizes of individuals, but by adopting one type of population as standard and expressing the changes in measurements (and in ratios) induced by an experimental treatment as a percentage of that standard. Staal (1961) was the only author to use this method and he adopted gregarious individuals as standards; but the density responses in his cultures were poorly pronounced, possibly because his isolated locusts were the immediate progeny of crowded parents. In any case it would be advisable in future to take for a standard, locusts from a stock isolated for several generations, and not from the crowded stock, the morphometrics of which depend too much on the degree and the length of crowding.

Adult physiology

The growth changes in weight and in fat (p. 98) and chitin (p. 92) content of isolated and crowded locusts have already been discussed (p. 97). The main point is that, although sexually immature crowded females of *Locusta* have initially more fat than the isolated ones, this excess disappears before the first egg-pod is laid, suggesting a higher utilisation of fat by crowded locusts for activity (Cheu 1952). Phase differences in pigment metabolism have been mentioned above (p. 341), and those in the rate of sexual maturation are discussed below (p. 352). Crowded males of *Schistocerca* absorb less water from their food than isolated ones (Norris 1961).

Adult activity

The most typical activity of adult locusts is flight, but this aspect has not been studied experimentally in relation to phase. The only pertinent observation is that of M. T. Volkonsky (1943) who recorded that isolated *Schistocerca* adults in cages displayed little activity at 35°C, when crowded ones flew about their cages. This suggests that the thresholds of responses to external stimuli may be different in the two, and this needs more precise studies. General activity of crowded *Schistocerca* adults in cages is greater than that of the isolated ones, particularly during the pre-maturation period (Norris 1962a, 1962b). The tendency to aggregate is as characteristic of gregarious adults as it is of hoppers. Norris (1963, 1964b) established experimentally that gregarious females of *Schistocerca* ready to lay eggs are strongly attracted to other locusts of either sex and in any state of maturity; the attraction and the cohesion of the groups may be partly visual and tactile, but the olfaction also plays a part, since even paper rubbed on other locusts is effective; it was suggested that some chemical substance on the cuticle is the active agent.

Some experimental evidence on adult activity refers to feeding by *Schistocerca* (Norris 1961). Crowded young males ate and excreted more than males of the same stock kept in isolation; the effect was already seen with five males in a 9-litre cage (fig. 205) and also with only two males, but the proportion of food utilised was not affected by the density. Bearing in mind that the isolated males were also reared at high density and were isolated only as adults, it appears probable that the difference in the feeding activity between extreme gregarious and solitarious adults would be even greater.

The difference in eye pigmentation (p. 198) should be expected to affect vision and visual responses, but only theoretical suggestions have been made in this respect (Chauvin 1941 *b*; Roonwal 1947*a*) although it is known that wild solitarious locusts fly mostly at night, while swarms do so in daytime.

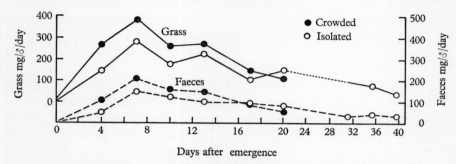

Fig. 205. *Schistocerca*, rates of feeding and excretion by crowded and isolated adult males (after Norris 1961).

Sexual maturation

The effect of density on the rate of sexual maturation is not the same in *Locusta* as in *Schistocerca* and *Nomadacris* (table 100). A female *Locusta* isolated with a male matured much faster than one in a crowd of both sexes, but in *Schistocerca* and *Nomadacris* a reverse effect was observed (p. 298). Subsequent experimental work (Norris 1954, 1964*c*) has shown that this was due to the accelerating effect on female maturation in *Schistocerca* of the most quickly maturing males in a crowd by means of a volatile secretory substance (pheromone) which is, apparently, also produced by males of *Locusta*, but the effect of which is masked by that of a postulated inhibiting pheromone (Haskell 1962; Norris 1964*c*).

Table 100. *Rate of sexual maturation of locust females*
isolated with a male, or crowded

Species	Mean number of days before first laying		Reference
	Isolated	Crowded	
Locusta	10·6	22·5	Norris 1950
Schistocerca	34	26	Norris 1952
Nomadacris	58·1	44·5	Norris 1959*a*

Adult longevity

Crowding of *Locusta* adults increases the length of their life, but has an opposite effect on *Nomadacris* and *Schistocerca* (table 101); this may be connected with some differences in neurosecretory activity between *Locusta* and the other two species.

Table 101. *Duration of adult life in days in relation to density (after Norris, 1950, 1952, 1959 a)*

Species	Isolated		Crowded	
	Mean	Max.	Mean	Max.
Locusta ♀	30	65	45	82
Schistocerca ♀	65	119	48	96
Nomadacris ♀	108 ± 29	137	69 ± 23	92
„ ♂	198 ± 70	310	94 ± 62	277

Reproductive potential

The upper limit of the total number of eggs which may be laid by a female is determined by the number of successive egg-pods and by the number of eggs per pod (p. 326). The latter depends theoretically on the total number of ovarioles, which is determined already in the embryo (p. 282), and is different according to the phase of the mother. Direct evidence on this point was produced by Albrecht, Verdier & Blackith (1959) and fig. 206 shows an ovary of a hatchling from a solitarious female, with 113 small ovarioles, and another from a gregarious one, with seventy-four larger ovarioles.

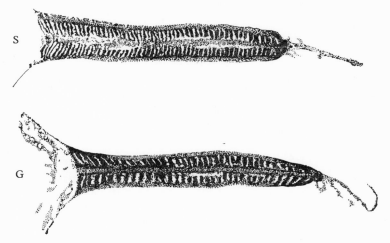

Fig. 206. *Locusta*, ovarioles of hatchlings. S, solitarious; G, gregarious (Albrecht, Verdier & Blackith 1959).

23

In *Schistocerca*, Papillon (1960; Tchelebi-Papillon 1962) found a similar relation of the ovariole number in hatchlings to the parental density (fig. 207).

The first indication that the ovariole number in adult females may vary according to their phase was that by Viado (1950) who recorded a mean of

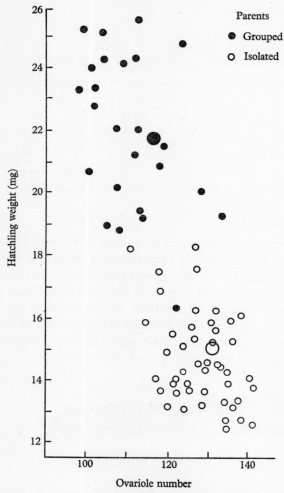

Fig. 207. *Schistocerca*, weights and ovariole numbers of hatchlings from crowded and isolated parents; large circles, mean values (after Papillon 1960).

sixty-five ovarioles in *Locusta m. manilensis* in a 'plague year' and 79·4 when there was no plague. Similar field data from wild populations of known phase status have never been collected; they are greatly needed for all locust species, as well as for grasshoppers. They should include both the total counts of ovarioles and information on the percentage of the non-functional ones, particularly in recently fledged females, since this percentage may increase with the ageing of a female.

Parallel with the collection of such field data, it is essential to investigate in the laboratory the direct effects of density (and other conditions) on the percentage of subnormal and partly, or fully, degenerating ovarioles. T. Singh (1958) found that in isolated *Locusta* females some 18% of ovarioles

Table 102. *Fecundity of locusts crowded and in isolated pairs*

	Pods per female, mean		Eggs per pod, mean		Total eggs		Percentage sterility		
	Is.	Cr.	Is.	Cr.	Is.	Cr.	Is.	Cr.	Reference
Locusta	7·0	5·6	71	59	497	330	19	34	Norris 1950
,,	15	8	79	68	1185	544	7·25	20·5	Albrecht, Verdier & Blackith 1959
Schistocerca	5·3	3·8	66	69	350	262	7	10·5	Norris 1952
,,	9·3	7	75	65	697	455	4·31	6·72	Papillon 1960
Nomadacris	6·6	5·9	121	84·8	802	500			Albrecht 1959
,,	6	4	107	97	642	388			Norris 1959 *a*

were non-functional, but produced no comparable data for crowded females. Some laboratory studies of the immediate effects of crowding on ovogenesis in *Schistocerca* have been already discussed (p. 311), but most of the evidence on the deleterious effects of crowding is based on the number of eggs per pod,

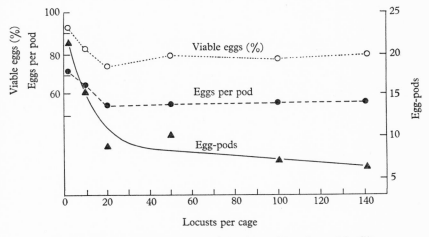

Fig. 208. *Locusta*, effects of parental density on fecundity and fertility (after Albrecht, Verdier & Blackith 1959).

their viability and the number of pods per female in relation to density. Some data bearing on these points are presented in table 102, and fig. 208 provides an illustration.

This table shows a falling off of the reproductive potential with crowding in all three species, but particularly in *Locusta*, in which in an extreme case a total of 1447 viable eggs per isolated female as against 299 per crowded one was recorded (Albrecht, Verdier & Blackith, *t.c.*). Field data on *Nomadacris* summarised by I. A. D. Robertson (1954) showed that in non-swarming field populations the mean number of eggs per pod was ninety-two, as against sixty-four in swarms, a reduction of some 30%, which agrees reasonably well with the laboratory data for this species. Average figures for *Schistocerca* are higher for both types of field populations than the laboratory ones, non-swarming females averaging 95–128 eggs per pod, while the mean figures from swarms were all below eighty (Ashall & Ellis 1962); the difference again supports laboratory evidence.

The situation appears to be reversed in two other locusts in which gregarious adults are much larger than solitarious (fig. 200). In *Locustana* Faure (1923) obtained an average of 27·6 eggs per pod from isolated caged females, while the mean number in pods from swarms in the field was 47·5, but there are no reliable data on the number of pods per female. In *Dociostaurus*, Boden-heimer (1944) found the average number of eggs per pod laid by a swarm in Iraq to be 31·37, while in a less dense population the mean number was 25·13. Merton (1958) obtained somewhat fewer eggs per pod but about twice as many pods per female from a cage population of low density (but not isolated females) than from one more dense; this suggests a higher total potential fecundity of solitarious *Dociostaurus*, but detailed experimental studies of fecundity in this species and in *Locustana* are obviously needed. Another little studied case is that of the Australian *Chortoicetes terminifera*, in which the gregarious female is scarcely larger than the solitarious, while the male size increases considerably with density (Key 1954); the egg number is about fifty in non-swarming females and forty in swarms (L. R. Clark 1947).

Another factor affecting not merely the potential fecundity but the actual fertility of locusts is the increase in the proportion of sterile eggs with increased density (table 102).

Egg development

The incubation period of the eggs of three locust species is definitely, if only slightly, accelerated by crowding the females (table 103).

Table 103. *Mean incubation periods (in days) of locust eggs from isolated and crowded females*

Species	°C	Isolated	Crowded	References
Nomadacris	30	25	23	F. O. Albrecht unpublished
Locusta	35	10	9	M. Verdier unpublished
,,	31	12·5	11·3	,, ,,
Schistocerca	30	15	14·5	Tchelebi-Papillon unpublished
,,	24	26·5	25	,, ,,

356

Egg diapause

It was believed in the past (Plotnikov 1927; Uvarov 1928) that eggs of solitarious *Locusta* develop without a diapause, whereas those laid by gregarious females have an obligatory diapause, but the latter statement can no longer be supported. In *Locustana*, on the other hand, solitarious females produced 100% diapause eggs, while in a dense, but not extreme, gregarious population only 42·31% of eggs underwent a diapause (Matthée 1951).

Total effects of density

In table 104 the main effects of high density as revealed by laboratory work are summarised for convenience.

Table 104. *Main effects of increased density on locusts*

(>, increase; <, decrease; =, no effect)

	Locusta	Schisto-cerca	Nomad-acris	Locus-tana	Docios-taurus	Chor-toicetes
HATCHLINGS						
Size and weight	>	>	>			
Water content	=	>	>			
Food reserves	>	>	>			
Vitality	>	>	>			
HOPPERS						
Melanin	>	>	>	>		
Insectorubin	>	>	>	?		
Respiratory metabolism	>	>				
Activity	>	>				
Rate of development	>	>	>			
Instar number	=	<	<			
ADULTS						
Size, male	<	<	<	>	>	>
„ female	<	<	<	>	>	>
Activity	>	>		>		
Maturation rate	>	>	>			
Ovariole number	<	<	<			
Eggs per pod	<	<	<	>	>	<
Pods per female	<	<	<			
Total eggs	<	<	<			
Viable eggs	<	<	<			

CHANGE OF PHASE

Having reviewed the main characteristics of the extreme types of locusts induced by density, we may now attempt to clarify the changes by which transitions between them are achieved.

The data in table 104 summarise the total effects of high density throughout the life-cycle of each species, and the first step in analysing the dynamics of the change is to evaluate separately the effects of crowding and isolation during each stage in the cycle.

Immediate effects of hopper density

Response to changes in density of hoppers by changes in their coloration is well known and will be discussed here only in relation to the degree of crowding.

An illustration is provided by table 105, summarising the results of rearing *Locusta* hoppers, all produced by gregarious parents but reared at different concentrations (Gunn & Hunter-Jones 1952). The grading of the types of hopper coloration adopted in that work was somewhat arbitrary, but it can be assumed that the categories A and B represented the typical solitarious type, while H and I can be regarded as representative of the gregarious. The relation between the number per cage and the degree of change in colour and pattern was unmistakable, and even with two hoppers per cage there was already evidence of a considerable trend away from the solitarious type.

Table 105. *Percentage distribution of colour types in Vth instar*
Locusta *hoppers in relation to their number per 12-litre cage*
(*Gunn & Hunter-Jones* 1952)

No. per cage	TYPES OF COLOUR PATTERN								
	A	B	C	D	E	F	G	H	I
1	75	25	—	—	—	—	—	—	—
2	23	33	17	—	17	6	—	—	—
4	16	20	32	—	16	8	8	—	—
8	10	10	23	7	33	3	13	—	—
16	6	12	14	5	23	8	26	—	—
32	—	2	—	3	9	12	63	12	—
64	—	1	—	1	7	4	48	40	—
128	—	—	—	—	1	4	37	46	12
256	—	—	—	—	—	1	11	52	36

From similar experiments with *Locustana*, Faure (1932) concluded that the extreme solitarious type of coloration can be maintained only when a hopper is kept in complete isolation throughout its life.

A related problem is that of the duration of isolation. The gregarious hoppers of *Locusta*, when isolated, lost the orange component of the pattern in the next instar; after two moults, the dark component also disappeared and hoppers acquired the solitarious type of coloration. Even two gregarious hoppers kept together until the fourth instar and then isolated changed their colour to pure green in the next instar (Gunn & Hunter-Jones 1952). Nickerson (1956) observed that solitarious hoppers of *Schistocerca*, after being crowded, acquired the full gregarious type of coloration much sooner than those crowded lost their coloration on isolation.

Changes in colour in response to density change are usually noticed only after a moult, but some effects become apparent even within an instar. Thus, pure green fourth instar hoppers of *Schistocerca* placed in a crowd of gregarious hoppers acquired in two to three days a grey pattern on the posterior part of the pronotum and abdominal tergites, which became darker in seven days (P. Hunter-Jones, personal communication). Stower (1959) put together fifty first instar *Schistocerca* hoppers of the extreme green solitarious type, and many of them developed dark speckling (probably insectorubin) after only two days, while most acquired black (melanin) pattern before the next moult.

These chromatic effects of density reflect changes in pigment metabolism and are more important as indicators of such changes than in themselves. Much more significant biologically are the immediate effects of density on the behaviour of hoppers, a problem not easy to study experimentally, but considerable light has recently been thrown on it in a series of valuable papers by Ellis.

The aggregation which is regarded as the most characteristic feature of the behaviour of gregarious hoppers proved to be a result of individual experience of a hopper, whatever its initial phase status. Experiments on aggregation (p. 339) showed that *Locusta* hoppers isolated during the first instar and crowded in the second exhibited a rise in tendency to aggregate after twenty-four hours; after four days, they aggregated as well as hoppers kept crowded from hatching. On the other hand, when formerly crowded hoppers were isolated, even after eight days there was only a small reduction in the numbers aggregating when tested, suggesting that hoppers are easily conditioned to aggregate, but that such conditioning is less easily lost. Comparing the aggregation ability of *Locusta* and *Schistocerca*, Ellis (1956) found that the first instar hoppers of *Locusta* did not aggregate until they were three days old, while *Schistocerca* hoppers showed signs of aggregation only six hours after hatching, and one day was sufficient to achieve the maximum aggregation. The greater tendency of *Schistocerca* to aggregate is illustrated by fig. 214.

Aggregation implies some kind of interaction between hoppers. Visual inter-attraction was postulated long ago (Uvarov 1928, 1937), but keeping a hopper in a mirrored jar had no effect on its subsequent tendency to aggregate. Crowded hoppers tested in darkness aggregated to some extent but this may have been due to tactile stimuli. The importance of the latter was demonstrated (Ellis 1959a, 1962) by placing a single hopper in a jar, in which several very fine suspended wires rotated mechanically, frequently touching the hopper, for seven hours with short intervals for rest. The result was that the hoppers individually conditioned to being touched, and then placed together, aggregated almost as well as crowded hoppers.

This last finding led to a more detailed study of the reactions of hoppers to each other by observing a hopper in a cage with live, but tethered, single decoy hoppers and groups of them (Ellis 1962; Ellis & Pearce 1962). The free test hopper walked about, stopped from time to time and executed scanning movements (p. 203); coming to a decoy the hopper examined it with antennae and palps. If the decoy moved, the test hoppers exhibited several kinds of reaction, classified, as follows:

A. Jumping away at the sight of the decoy.
B. Swaying the body away with the legs stationary.
C. Jumping or running away after being touched by the decoy.
D. Retreating a few steps, then returning.
E. Showing no reaction to being touched by the decoy.
F. Waving the antennae, or kicking with the hind legs, after being touched by the decoy which does the same.

By repeating many such tests with a number of hoppers which had different previous individual experiences, the percentages of different reactions were

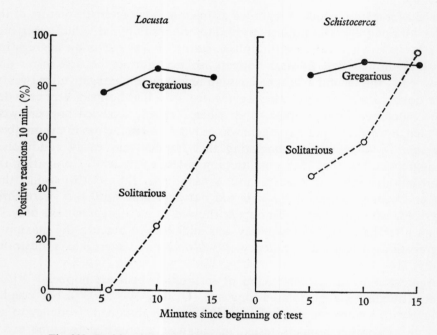

Fig. 209. Positive reactions of hoppers to decoys; explanation in the text
(based on data of Ellis & Pearce 1962).

calculated. Figure 209 represents the results diagrammatically, the A, B and C reactions being regarded as negative, D as indefinite and E and F as positive. As can be seen, there was a striking difference in the percentage of positive reactions between continually isolated and continually crowded hoppers of both *Locusta* and *Schistocerca*. Experimental hoppers from the isolated stock were then 'trained' for different periods, by placing them in a cage with one small part of the floor heated, where they assembled in response to the heat (see also Ellis 1963*a*, 1963*b*); they were isolated again and then tested in the

IVth instar. The results showed that grouping during training for only forty-eight hours of the Ist instar resulted in a great increase of positive reactions in *Locusta* hoppers of the IVth instar, while in *Schistocerca* the percentage of the reactions almost reached the level of the continually crowded stock after only twenty-four hours' training. Crowding throughout the whole Ist instar had the same result in *Schistocerca* and did not increase positive reactions in *Locusta*. When training was done in the IVth instar, four hours were sufficient to bring isolated *Schistocerca* to the level of crowded stock, but in *Locusta* this was not quite achieved even after forty-eight hours of training. Even only thirty minutes of training of *Schistocerca* hoppers had a striking result.

The same experiments provided data on the number of visits paid to decoys and the time spent with them, and statistical analysis largely confirmed the above deductions, which show the lasting effects of even short periods of induced grouping and indicate that *Schistocerca* hoppers form the aggregation habit much more quickly, and lose it less rapidly when isolated again, than those of *Locusta*. Similar experiments by Lea (1962) with *Locustana* hoppers indicated considerable individual variation in their ability to acquire the aggregation habit.

These experiments confirmed an early suggestion (Uvarov 1934, 1937) that any environmental factors bringing solitarious hoppers together, even for a short period, would induce their habituation to each other and result in a habit of aggregation, retained subsequently even in a uniform environment. In nature, temporary concentrations of hoppers occur, for example, during basking on sunny patches or feeding on isolated bushes, and this would lead to social aggregation and band formation, as has been suggested (Kennedy 1939; M. A. Volkonsky 1942). Some part in aggregation may be due to the olfaction. Volkonsky (*t.c.*) provided some evidence of olfactory attraction of *Schistocerca* hoppers to each other in the field, but without sufficient detail, and experimental work on this topic is needed.

The marching activity of hoppers is partly inborn (p. 340) but a change in its rate from one extreme to another can be obtained in about two weeks' experience, the amount of change depending on the length of experience. The optomotor reaction which makes one hopper walk parallel to another so as to compensate for the movement of the image of the other across the eye (Uvarov 1923*b*, 1928; Kennedy 1939) is a learned one. An isolated hopper placed in a small transparent cage, outside which crowded hoppers march round, does not learn to march, but if it is confined in a ring-like cage, it begins to march, although the full rate of marching activity is developed only when the hopper is not separated from others, suggesting that visual reactions must be supplemented by contacts (Ellis 1951, 1962).

Crowding during hopper life affects the morphometrics of the resulting adults, the extent of the change increasing with hopper density (Gunn & Hunter-Jones 1952); if some of the crowded hoppers are isolated during the successive instars, the adult morphometrics reflect the duration of crowding (Hunter-Jones 1958).

The important influence of hopper crowding on the reproductive potential of adults is discussed below.

Immediate effects of adult density

A visible effect of crowding on adults with non-swarming history was first noticed by Volkonsky (1938b) in wild solitarious *Schistocerca*, which, when grouped, acquired yellow coloration typical of mature gregarious locusts. Norris (1952) obtained experimental evidence that when only two, almost mature (but not yet yellow), males of *Schistocerca* were put together, they turned yellow; and a yellow male placed in a cage of immature males accelerated their maturation and yellowing. When adults were kept in groups, as soon as one or two males changed colour, others also did. The hormonal background of this phenomenon is discussed elsewhere (p. 311).

Table 106. *Effects on fecundity in* Locusta *of different density treatments during hopper and adult life* (*Albrecht, Verdier & Blackith* 1959)

Hoppers	Adults	Pods per female	Eggs per pod	Eggs per female
Crowded	Crowded	8	68	544
Isolated	Crowded	4	77	308
Crowded	Isolated	15	79	1185
Isolated	Isolated	12	77	924

Norris (*t.c.*) further recorded that the hopper density in *Schistocerca* had no effect on the maturation time of adults, but the higher their own density was, the more rapidly they matured. No definite effect of adult density on fecundity and viability of eggs was observed in this study, but this may be due to the heterogeneity of *Schistocerca* eggs within the same egg-pod (p. 333).

The effects of adult density were more evidence in *Locusta* (Norris 1950; Albrecht, Verdier & Blackith 1959) and table 106 presents the results of one series of experiments.

The table shows that the depressing effects of crowding on fecundity are partly due to high density of hoppers, but they may be entirely overcome if the resulting adults are at a low density. Similar results were reported for *Nomadacris* (Albrecht 1959), though quantitative changes were not so striking, mainly because of the lesser range of phase variability in this species and in the stock used.

The increase in the proportion of non-viable eggs due to crowding of parents (table 102 and fig. 208) is probably also attributable mainly to the effect of high density on adult females. The percentage of sterile eggs produced by isolated pairs of *Locusta* was only nineteen, as against thirty-four in those kept in larger groups both as hoppers and adults (Norris 1950).

It is reasonably clear that the fecundity and fertility of locusts is affected more by the density conditions of adult females than by those during their hopper life. A complication, however, is introduced by the fact that in *Schisto-cerca*, the presence of a mature male reduces the percentage of resorbed ovarioles (p. 313).

The effects of density in successive generations

Since the differences in the weight and colour of hatchlings in high and low density populations are clearly discernible soon after hatching (p. 333), they must be determined by the conditions experienced by the parents. Hunter-Jones (1958) has found that, in both *Locusta* and *Schistocerca*, the density of parents as hoppers did not affect the colour or weight of the

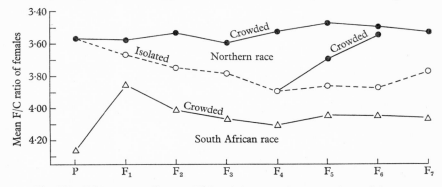

Fig. 210. *Schistocerca*, effects on F/C ratio in successive generations of the two geographical races (original by P. Hunter-Jones).

hatchlings of the next generation, but the density of parents during their adult life affected them significantly. Moreover, if the same density treatment was applied to the next generation, the following one had a further accentuation of characteristics corresponding to the density; in other words, the effect was cumulative for two generations. Ellis (1959 *b*) also provided evidence of the accumulation of density effects on hopper coloration in three successive generations of *Locusta* bred in isolation, by submitting some of the hoppers of each generation to contrasting density conditions, and stressed the point that the first change in density treatment caused a greater change in colour than did the continuation of the new treatment in the following generations. This last conclusion applies also to the F/C ratio of the resulting adults in Ellis's experiments on *Locusta* and it was supported by findings of P. Hunter-Jones, to whom I am obliged for the graph (fig. 210) illustrating the effects of two different density treatments on adult morphometrics in seven successive generations of *Schistocerca*, starting from a stock kept crowded in the laboratory for many generations. The graph (for the northern race, see p. 274) shows a change in the F/C ratio after the first isolation treatment, and a reverse change when crowding was applied to the fourth generation of the isolated line. In both lines, a stabilisation was achieved in three generations, after which the two curves became almost straight and parallel, with only slight, probably incidental, deviations.

In the series of experiments on *Locusta* already mentioned, Ellis (1959*b*, 1962) compared also the effects of parental densities on the marching rates of the progeny. The work started with the normal laboratory stock kept crowded for many generations. Figure 211 illustrates a sudden reduction in marching

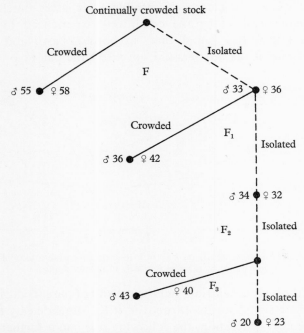

Fig. 211. *Locusta*, percentages of time spent in marching by IVth instar hoppers in successive generations, in relation to density (after Ellis 1962, modified).

activity in the F generation when hoppers with a long crowded ancestry were isolated for the first time. Crowding after one (F_1) or three (F_2) generations of isolation provided evidence of a rise in activity, but it still did not reach the original level of activity in the crowded stock, suggesting a residual effect of isolation during only one previous generation. The very low activity level of the F_3 hoppers of the isolated line suggests an accumulation of the effects of isolation from one generation to another.

Further evidence of transmission of density effects to successive generations concerns fecundity. As already mentioned (p. 364), the weight of hatchlings and the ovariole number of female hatchlings are different in the gregarious and the solitarious stocks, and they are determined by the conditions to which the parent locusts were subjected during adult life. Figure 212 shows the results of an experiment in which hatchlings from a single pod produced by a gregarious female *Locusta* were divided into two lots; the hatchlings of one were kept crowded throughout their life, the others were isolated. The ovariole number in the F_1 generation hatchlings remained low (83), while that in the isolated line rose to 103·5; repetition of this treatment in two more generations showed immediate reducing effects of crowding on the ovariole number of the progeny, whilst their number in the isolated line remained stable. The weight of hatchlings (in brackets) was also affected, crowding in each generation resulting in heavier hatchlings of the next. Similar effects for *Nomadacris* but starting from an isolated female are shown in the same fig. 212. In both

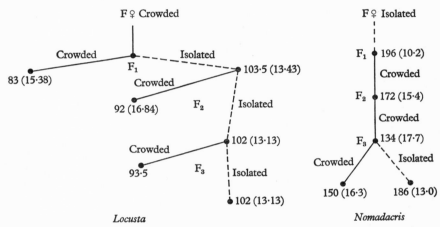

Fig. 212. *Locusta* and *Nomadacris*, ovariole numbers and weights (in brackets) of hatchlings in successive generations in relation to density (after Albrecht, Verdier & Blackith 1959, modified).

species the effects of density were cumulative for three generations, after which the response became more or less stabilised. On the other hand, reversals of density conditions did not result in complete return to the original indices, suggesting a residual effect of the earlier density conditions.

Thus, the coloration and marching activity of the hoppers, and the reproductive potential of adults, induced by density treatment during individual life, are then transmitted to the next generation. Chauvin (1941 *b*) called this phenomenon 'residual gregarism'.

Factors other than density affecting the expression of phase characters

As far as an individual is concerned, population density is one of many environmental factors and its true contribution to phase polymorphism can only be assessed when it is known whether any other factors can produce comparable changes in the various characteristics of the phases, or, at least, modify responses to density.

365

Hopper coloration offers examples of the modifying effects of temperature on phase characters, particularly as regards the dark pattern of gregarious hoppers which is greatly increased by low temperature and may be almost eliminated by high.

Schistocerca hoppers reared at 24°C were predominantly black, but at 44°C melanin pattern was practically absent (Husain & Ahmad 1936*b*); similar observations on field populations were recorded by Stower (1959). This is understandable since the production of both insectorubin and melanin is inhibited by high temperature and enhanced by low (p. 44). The same explanation may apply to eye-stripes which are normally not visible in crowded hoppers, but become visible if they are reared at 40°C, when the dark pigment (possibly insectorubin) disappears from interstripes.

The general darkening of the integument at low temperature is known also in non-swarming species; for example, hoppers of *Schistocerca obscura* are normally green, but when reared at 21°C develop black spots (Duck 1944). The extreme temperatures have no effect on the background colour, but they certainly affect the dark pattern in a way similar to density (Dudley 1961, 1964); this, of course, does not invalidate the fact that crowded and isolated hoppers reared at the same temperatures differ characteristically in the degree of melanisation.

L. Joly (1960) suggested that reduction of the dark pattern in *Locusta* may be associated with extreme low humidity (not specified), but Dudley (1961) found no effects of humidities ranging from 30 to 90%; however his hoppers had access to drinking water and further experimental work is needed to clarify possible humidity effects.

Dark colours of hoppers may also be partly influenced by food, since, for example, carotenes and vitamins may be needed for melanin formation (p. 43).

Much attention has been paid in the past to the green coloration of isolated hoppers, but they may also be of other uniform colours and although green pigmentation is common, it need not be regarded as an essential phase characteristic. Moreover, this colour is due not to a single chemical substance, but to mixtures of different bile and carotenoid pigments, the biochemistry of which is imperfectly known (p. 50).

Rates of growth being dependent on temperature, it is to be expected that it should affect morphometric characters. Brett (1947) reared *Melanoplus sanguinipes* at a series of temperatures and humidities and found that the body size and the relative length of the tegmina were, generally speaking, increased by high temperature and low humidity; since the absolute length of the tegmen in that species has been regarded, without much justification, as a phase character, this led to a conclusion that the morphometrics of this species are not connected with density, although Faure (1933) provided experimental evidence to the contrary.

366

Husain & Mathur (1944) reared isolated *Schistocerca* hoppers at different temperatures and found that those at 27°C produced larger adults with lower E/F ratios (i.e. less gregarious than those reared at 40°C); this led them to conclude that morphometrics are determined by temperature and not by density, whereas their data merely indicated that temperature also has an effect on total growth and on some morphometric ratios.

Such sweeping conclusions from inadequate observations merely suggest the need for considering the effects of density against the background of rearing temperature. The problem has been approached by studies on morphometrics of wild populations of *Schistocerca* (Stower, Davies & Jones 1960). By using the method of discriminant functions, these authors demonstrated that wild gregarious populations bred at higher temperatures exhibited a shift in their morphometrics toward the solitarious type, a conclusion opposite to that of Husain and Mathur. However, the temperature conditions under which the hoppers of the populations studied lived were recorded only as the range of the mean maxima for the period, and the final comparisons were made between the two loosely defined categories of 'hot' and 'cool' habitats.

In future studies on the effects of temperature, attention must be paid to a possibly different effect of fluctuating temperatures on morphometrics (see below).

Some indications that humidity affects morphometrics of *Locusta* have been obtained by Gunn & Hunter-Jones (1952) and by Staal (1961), and more definite evidence was produced by Dudley (1961, 1964), who studied the combined effects of humidity and temperature on *Schistocerca* reared in uniform crowded conditions. Figure 213 shows that at the medium humidity range (50–70%) the E/F ratio in both sexes was higher at 35°C than at 30°C, that is, the insects were nearer the gregarious phase, whereas at the extreme low (30%) and high (90%) humidities, an opposite effect was obtained. As regards the F/C ratio, males reared at 35°C were, at all humidities, nearer to solitarious (higher ratio) than at 30°C, while results for females showed similar trends only at humidities above 70%; moreover the ranges of variation were large and often overlapping. These results mean that conclusions based on field data, which are almost inevitably inexact as regards the environmental conditions during the life of the sampled populations, can be misleading.

Food, which affects total growth, must also be expected to modify morphometric responses to density, but exact data are lacking.

All this suggests a need for carefully planned laboratory investigations of the effects of all environmental conditions (density, temperature, humidity, light, food) both on the total growth and on the relative growth of individual body parts. All these factors may act differently when studied singly, or in combinations, and special attention should be paid to the effects of their fluctuations. Gunn & Hunter-Jones (1952) demonstrated that *Locusta* kept crowded and subjected to sharp day and night fluctuations of temperature approached the extreme morphometrics of wild gregarious populations more closely than under constant conditions. The general failure to obtain extreme expression of phase in the laboratory (p. 332) may well be due to the established belief

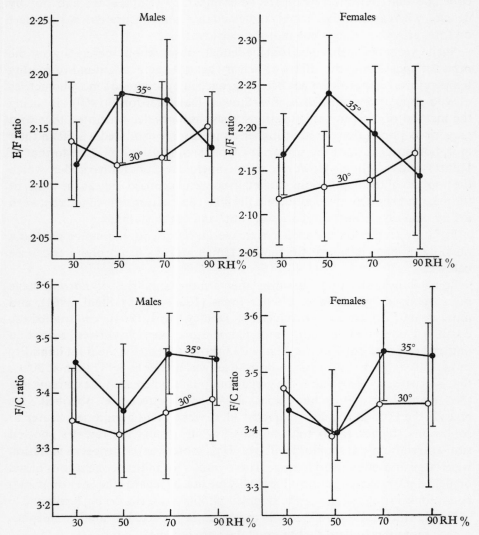

Fig. 213. *Schistocerca*, effects of rearing temperature and humidity on morphometric ratios; vertical lines show the ranges of variation (after Dudley 1964).

that constant temperature rooms are absolutely essential for all experimental work.

Field data on morphometrics can also provide valuable information, provided they refer to populations with definitely known ancestry (p. 363) and breeding conditions. These requirements are not easy to satisfy, but the value of somewhat uncertain basic data cannot be improved by their most rigorous statistical treatment.

Much more exact investigations, both in the laboratory and in the field, are needed before the relative effects of density and of other environmental conditions can be evaluated, and Rainey's (1962) conclusion, based on field evidence on *Schistocerca*, that 'direct effects of environment on the manifestation of phase, in terms both of behaviour and of morphology, are at times large compared with those of the social history of the locusts concerned', is at least premature. The present evidence, although inadequate, suggests that density effects can be substantially modified by other influences, but gives no reason to suggest that the full range of morphometric polymorphism can be obtained otherwise than by density treatment. In any case, differences induced by density alone in insects kept in otherwise identical conditions are real enough to regard it as a very important causative factor.

In addition to environmental factors, the physiological state of parent females at the time of maturation must be considered. This is suggested, particularly, by observations of Papillon (1960) that in egg-pods of crowded *Schistocerca*, which sometimes give rise to a mixture of large dark and small pale hatchlings (p. 333), the latter hatch mostly out of eggs from the lower third of the pod and some twenty hours later than the black ones. Since it is usually assumed that all ovarioles discharge their first egg simultaneously, such difference between eggs of the same pod suggests that not all ovarioles of the female produce eggs of the same size, the smaller ones coming from the ovarioles nearer the oviduct. The difference in the coloration of hatchlings suggests, moreover, a qualitative difference of the eggs. There is an obvious need for a very detailed study of ovogenesis, including its biochemical and hormonal background, in individual ovarioles.

Another effect of maternal physiology is an increase in the weight of hatchlings from successive egg-pods laid by an isolated female, which suggests an influence of ageing of the female; this was observed in *Locusta* (Albrecht, Verdier & Blackith 1959) and in *Nomadacris* (Albrecht 1959), but in *Schistocerca* the results were less clear (Papillon 1960), possibly because of the presence of two different types of eggs in each egg-pod observed by that author.

AMPLITUDES OF PHASE VARIATION

Most of the previous discussion is based on data relating to species which present the widest known amplitude of the various manifestations of phase polymorphism. Effects of density on other locusts and grasshoppers supply examples of some deviations from this complete scheme of phase polymorphism and a brief survey of them should help towards a better understanding of the phenomena involved.

A melanic pattern which is such a conspicuous feature of gregarious locust hoppers has been recorded in artificially crowded hoppers of such species as *Cyrtacanthacris tatarica* (Johnston 1932) and *Schistocerca obscura* (Duck 1944) which exhibited no other obvious density effects. On the other hand, hoppers of *Ornithacris turbida*, bred crowded for several successive generations, remained uniformly green, without black pattern (A. Antoniou, personal communication). Hoppers of *Pyrgodera armata*, a semi-desert Oedipodine grasshopper, are usually green, or buff, but in abnormally dense wild populations they develop heavy black and orange coloration and tend to aggregate (Popov 1952). Rubtzov (1935*a*) showed by both field observations and experiments, that crowded hoppers of *Chorthippus albomarginatus* developed extensive black pattern which persisted in adults; they also exhibited aggregation behaviour and the adult morphometrics reflected hopper density in the same way, though not to the same extent, as in locust phases.

In addition to the above cases of better known density effects, there are records of many species of grasshoppers which exhibit gregarious behaviour only occasionally. Some of such records are listed in table 107, which is admittedly incomplete and is merely intended to show that cases of behaviour typical of the gregarious phase are not uncommon; in most of these species, no studies of other effects of density have been made.

There is enough evidence to suggest that a tendency to respond to density in a way similar to phase polymorphism in locusts is not restricted to any taxonomic group. It appears, however, that some members of the Pyrgomorphidae exhibit gregarious habits only in the hopper stage, the adults losing it completely; here belong the African *Phymateus* spp. (Kevan 1949), *Zonocerus variegatus* (Vuillaume 1953), and the S.E. Asian *Aularches miliaris* (Hutson 1926).

Although widespread, the tendency to phase polymorphism is a specific feature. This is well shown, for example, by the case of the genus *Gastrimargus*, represented by over forty species throughout the tropics of the Old World, only one of which, the Australian *G. musicus*, exhibits phase changes in hopper coloration and behaviour, adult morphometrics and swarm flight (Common 1948). In striking contrast, a closely related and very common African species, *G. africanus*, showed no response to continuous crowded breeding in the laboratory (Hunter-Jones & Ward 1959).

A particularly illuminating case is that of geographical subspecies of *Locusta migratoria*. This species is notorious for its flights, extending for over a thousand miles (Z. Waloff 1940), and adults have been recorded from every continent and most islands of the Old World; in Europe they were known to reach as far north as Scandinavia and Scotland. Nevertheless the areas where breeding is known to occur regularly are more limited and, moreover, there must be a sufficient degree of isolation for some of them to have developed distinct geographical races. Although no detailed comparative studies of all *Locusta* subspecies have been made, no less than seven of them are known to exhibit phase polymorphism, at least in their morphometrics. In table 108, these subspecies are placed in a descending series, according to the morphological feature most characteristic (for *Locusta*) of the gregarious phase, namely the M/C ratio, which reflects the inverse variation between the minimum width of the pronotum at its constriction and the maximum width of the head (p. 347).

Table 107. *Species with less regular, or only occasional, gregarious behaviour of hoppers and adults*

	Country	Hoppers	Adults	References
CATANTOPINAE				
Melanoplus rugglesi	U.S.A.	+	+	Gurney 1949
„ *sanguinipes*	N. America	+	+	Faure 1933; Gurney & Brooks 1959
„ *bivittatus*	Canada	+	+	Criddle 1933
Dichroplus spp.	S. America		+	Carbonnel 1957
CYRTACANTHACRIDINAE				
Patanga succincta	S. Asia		+	Maxwell-Lefroy 1906; Rao 1960
Austracris guttulosa	Australia		+	Key 1938
CALLIPTAMINAE				
Calliptamus italicus	S. Europe, W. Asia	+	+	Kiritchenko 1926; Vasil'ev 1950
„ *turanicus*	C. Asia	+	+	Zimin 1934
DERICORYTHINAE				
Dericorys albidula	C. Asia		+	Enikeev 1949
HEMIACRIDINAE				
Hieroglyphus nigrorepletus	Pakistan		+	Ghouri & Ahmed 1960
OEDIPODINAE				
Oedaleus senegalensis	Africa, W. Asia	+	+	Joyce 1952; G. Popov (personal communication)
„ *australis*	Australia		+	Key 1938
Aiolopus savignyi	Africa, W. Asia		+	Joyce 1952
Camnula pellucida	Canada	+	+	R. C. Treherne & Buckell 1924; Criddle 1933
Austroicetes nullarborensis	Australia		+	Key 1954
„ *cruciata*	Australia		+	Key 1954
Dissosteira longipennis	U.S.A.	+	+	Wakeland 1958
Trimerotropis pallidipennis	U.S.A.		+	Barnes 1960
GOMPHOCERINAE				
Gomphocerus sibiricus	E. Russia, Siberia		+	Rubtzov 1935*b*
Faureia milanjica	Africa		+	Sjöstedt 1929; Uvarov 1953
Scyllinops sp.	Uruguay		+	Silveira Guido, Carbonnel *et al.* 1958
Rhammatocerus pictus	Uruguay		+	Carbonell 1957
„ *viatorius*	Venezuela		+	Guagliumi 1958

The largest head and the most constricted pronotum are found in *Locusta m. capito* which is restricted to Madagascar and the tropical African *L. m. migratorioides* is close to it. Surprisingly, the subspecies *gallica*, known only from south-western France, certainly belongs to the same group; in the solitarious phase, it is a smaller insect (compare measurements for E), and it has been known to swarm only twice in historical times (Chaboussou 1948) but the gregarious phase proved to be amply distinct morphometrically from other European subspecies; it may be conjectured that this colony was founded long ago by a stray swarm from tropical Africa. The next subspecies is again a tropical one, *L. m. manilensis* of S.E. Asia and Indonesia (Uvarov 1936), but it shows a higher M/C ratio and is much smaller (cf. E values) than *L. m. migratorioides* and *L. m. capito*. The subspecies inhabiting the basins of the Black, Caspian and Aral seas and of some lakes in Central Asia is *L. m. migratoria*, with the M/C ratio of the gregarious phase distinctly higher than in the previous group of subspecies, but in size it approaches the largest of them. Its more northern relative is *L. m. rossica*, with a similar M/C ratio, but very much smaller in size; its colonies are known in Central European Russia (Predtechenskiĭ 1928) and in several isolated localities of Central Europe (Z. Waloff 1940). Finally, the Mediterranean basin is populated by isolated colonies of *L. m. cinerascens*, which in the gregarious phase has the highest M/C ratio; this phase occurs in nature very seldom but was readily produced from a non-swarming Algerian population in the laboratory (Uvarov & Hamilton 1936).

As regards the M/C ratio of the solitarious phase, although it has not been studied in all subspecies, the table shows that in the group *capito-migratorioides-gallica* its value approaches that of the gregarious phase rather than the solitarious of other subspecies; in other words, in that group the gregarisation, as expressed by the constriction of the pronotum, starts from a level which is reached in other races only in the extreme gregarious phase. The amplitude of phase variation in all subspecies is approximately the same, but the final morphological result is very different. The subsp. *cinerascens*, with a very high M/C index in both phases, represents an extreme case, in which even the gregarious phase is but little modified.

It might be suggested that the degree of pronotal constriction and of the increase in head width is connected with the warmer habitat of the several tropical subspecies, but this argument cannot be sustained in the case of subsp. *gallica*, which is similar to them but strikingly different from subsp. *cinerascens*, living in the same climate. A climatic effect may also account for the difference between subsp. *migratoria* and subsp. *rossica*, but it is noteworthy that they differ not only in morphometrics, but also in the extent of their migratory flights, since adult individuals of *migratoria* from the Black Sea area frequently reach the British Isles, but no specimens of *rossica*, continental colonies of which are much nearer, have ever been recorded to do so; the same is true with regard to *cinerascens* (Z. Waloff 1940). This suggests that the degree of morphological gregarisation reflects the inherent biological properties of the subspecies, which may remain dormant for very many generations, as in the case of *gallica*.

It should be added that insular populations of *Locusta* (e.g. in the Azores, Canary Islands, New Zealand, Fiji, etc.) are represented by small individuals, often of dark colour, and none of them is known to swarm naturally; it would be of great interest to know whether they would exhibit a response to crowding in the laboratory. A very small subspecies *burmana* has been very inadequately

Table 108. *Morphometrics of phases of the main subspecies of Locusta migratoria*

(Some of the figures have been re-calculated from the original data)

Subspecies	Phase Sex	E S	E G	F S	F G	M S	M G	C S	C G	E/F S	E/F G	F/C S	F/C G	M/C S	M/C G	Distribution	References
capito	♂	38·5	45·5	21·5	21·9					1·79	2·07			0·82	0·70	Madagascar	Zolotarevsky 1930
	♀	51·0	48·7	28·2	22·5					1·81	2·12			0·83	0·72		
migratorioides	♂	40·02	47·97	22·61	22·96	5·48	5·84	6·16	7·75	1·79	2·09	3·67	2·96	0·89	0·75	Tropical Africa	Measurements by V. M. Dirsh
	♀	53·15	50·32	29·38	23·11	7·44	6·21	8·50	8·08	1·81	2·18	3·46	2·86	0·87	0·77		
gallica	♂	36·1	39·1	21·1	22·2	5·0	5·1	5·9	6·8	1·71	1·90	3·58	3·33	0·85	0·76	S.W. France	Remaudiére 1947; 1948
	♀	45·4	43·5	26·4	22·3	6·6	5·9	7·6	7·5	1·72	1·95	3·44	2·98	0·86	0·79		
manilensis	♂	42·0	42·6	22·5	20·8					1·73	2·12			0·91	0·81	S.E. Asia, Indonesia	Uichanco & Gines 1937; Otanes 1940
	♀	46·0	45·8	24·0	21·3					1·74	2·18			0·92	0·83		
migratoria	♂	44·4	51·0	22·2	24·4					2·00	2·09				0·85	Middle Asia, Caucasus, S. Ukraine, Rumania	Uvarov 1921
	♀	49·9	53·5	26·9	25·0					1·85	2·14				0·87		
rossica	♂	38	38	20	19					1·90	1·69				0·88	Central European Russia, Central Europe	Uvarov 1936; Z. Waloff 1940
	♀	47	41	24	23					1·97	2·05				0·86		
cinerascens	♂	39·6	40·7	22·5	21·1	5·9	6·0	6·2	6·6	1·76	1·92	3·63	3·20	0·97	0·91	Mediterranean countries	Uvarov & Hamilton 1936; Z. Waloff 1940
	♀	49·0	47·1	28·0	24·3	7·5	7·1	7·3	7·7	1·75	1·94	3·83	3·21	1·03	0·91		
burmana	♂	32·7		17·5						1·86		3·72		0·98		Upper Burma, Tibet	Ramme 1951a, p. 319; Chen Yung-lin (1963)
	♀	42·5		21·3						1·82		3·75		0·98			

described (Ramme 1951) from high altitude in Burma and specimens probably referable to it are known from 11,000–13,000 ft in Tibet; apparently the same subspecies was described, under the name *tibetensis*, by Chen Yung-lin (1963) who provided the morphometrics of its solitarious phase as shown in table 108 (no gregarious phase is known).

These facts relating to subspecies of *Locusta migratoria* indicate the exceptional interest of this species and detailed studies of them promise to be very rewarding. Such studies should embrace both field biology and ecology, as well as the comparative morphology, physiology and genetics of the different subspecies and of sufficiently isolated populations.

Another case of geographical variation in the tendency to phase polymorphism is offered by *Schistocerca gregaria*, the Desert Locust, swarms of which range over a vast area of dry south-western Asia and Africa north of the equator, extending somewhat south of it only in eastern Africa, but an isolated population of the same species lives in south-western Africa. In its main distribution region, the gregarious phase of this locust can be found almost continuously (Z. Waloff 1960), while many populations are transitional to the solitarious phase, which also occurs in many parts of the region; in fact the whole population is in a state of flux, and long-range migrations extending throughout the region prevent permanent isolation. The only effectively isolated population, that in south-western Africa, is known to produce somewhat loose swarms only very infrequently, and the adult morphometrics of such gregarious individuals are little different from those of the solitarious ones. Continuous breeding of this southern race, known as subsp. *flaviventris*, failed to change its morphometrics, the F/C ratio remaining after six crowded generations at a level well below that even of the solitarious phase of the northern subspecies (fig. 213). Hoppers, however, showed some change, acquiring black pattern resembling that of the typical gregarious phase and also developed the aggregation habit though to a lesser degree than those of the northern race (fig. 214). Crossing the two races showed that the properties of the progeny depended on the mother (P. Hunter-Jones, personal communication). This is, then, a case of an isolated geographical race with a much more limited range of response to crowding than in the main population of the species.

Figure 214 shows the results of submitting hoppers of the various locusts and grasshoppers to the aggregation tests (p. 339).

To sum up, there is a full gradation from species in which no tendency to phase polymorphism is known, or can even be detected experimentally, to those which respond to density by substantial changes in metabolism (as shown by pigmentation), morphology, reproductive potential and behaviour. The first category, presumably, includes the vast majority of acridoids, but the absence of response to density in any species should not be assumed without experimental proof. The two extreme categories are connected by a series of transitional cases, in which only some manifestations of phase variation have been either occasionally observed in nature or obtained in the laboratory.

This conclusion means that phase polymorphism is not a somewhat exceptional attribute of swarming locusts, and that some, or all, manifestations of it may be observed occasionally in many other acridoids, usually called grasshoppers. This will be more fully discussed in the second volume.

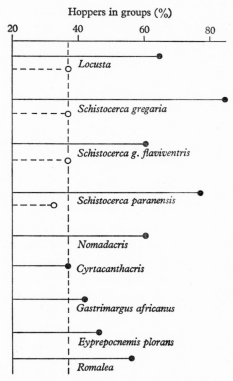

Fig. 214. Aggregation of hoppers of different locust and grasshopper species (after Ellis 1962, modified).
Solid lines, reared crowded; broken lines, reared isolated; vertical line at 38%, expected aggregation by chance.

HORMONAL CONTROL OF PHASE CHARACTERS

An early suggestion by Faure (1932) that the increased activity of crowded locust hoppers raises their metabolism and leads to the production of a hypothetical substance which he called 'locustine', may well be regarded as foreshadowing the modern approach to phase polymorphism as a result of changes in behaviour and in endocrine activity induced by mutual sensory stimulation and affecting various processes of metabolism and growth. Chauvin (1941b) suggested that Faure's locustine might be a 'hormone of gregarism', and P. Joly (1949) put forward a hypothesis of hormonal control of phase characters, providing the first experimental evidence in its favour. This approach and the stimulus from general recent advances in insect endocrinology have led to a considerable amount of experimental work. This work is progressing rapidly and a brief review of its results may be of value, although most of the conclusions are still tentative and some are contradictory.

The effects of the corpora allata secretion on coloration of *Locusta* have been reviewed by L. Joly (1960). Implantation of extra corpora allata into a gregarious hopper caused a change of blood colour from yellow to green within forty-eight hours, but the integument became green only after a moult. However, after two moults a reversion to the gregarious type of coloration was sometimes observed. The degree of response depended on the instar of the donor and even on the time within the instar, the activity of the corpora allata being, apparently, greater soon after a moult. Removal of the corpora allata from green solitarious hoppers very rapidly caused their blood to turn yellow, but the integument again changed colour only after a moult (unfortunately, the descriptions of integumental colour changes were only general, without details of pattern).

Staal's (1961) work with the same species, involving very precise surgical techniques, produced similar results. The implantation of extra corpora allata into second instar gregarious hoppers resulted in a substantial reduction of black pattern in the third instar, and its complete disappearance and general green coloration in the fourth; moreover, a subsequent removal of the implanted corpora allata resulted in the loss of green colour and the reappearance of the dark pattern. His conclusion was that the effect of corpora allata on the development of green colour in hoppers is fully comparable with that of isolation, inducing a characteristic pigmentation of the solitarious phase. On the other hand, when extra corpora allata were implanted into fifth instar hoppers, the resulting adults responded less definitely and some retained gregarious coloration, while some even assumed yellowish colour, resembling that of mature gregarious adults. This contradiction is possibly only apparent, since green has been regarded by the authors quoted above as a single pigment, while it is a mixture of yellow and blue (p. 50). It might be suggested that the corpora allata secretion affects the movement of the yellow β-carotene to the integument in both hoppers and mature adults, but it is only in hoppers that the secretion enhances also the production of the blue bilin pigment in sufficient concentration to result in green integumental colour. Nickerson (1956) suggested that two hormonal systems are involved in hopper coloration, one responsible for the pattern, another for the background colour.

The effects of the corpora allata secretion on the number of hopper instars which have been discussed elsewhere (p. 289), are under the influence of other factors, in addition to density, and definite deductions would be premature. It is to be noted that the corpora allata of the solitarious *Locusta* are larger than those of the gregarious and the South African *Schistocerca g. flaviventris* has significantly larger corpora allata, even when crowded, than the solitarious *S. g. gregaria*, which appears to agree with the lesser response of the former to density (p. 374).

The few data on changes in morphometrics due to the corpora allata activity are somewhat confused, mainly because experiments have been made on stocks with transient phase characteristics (p. 384). P. Joly (1956, 1962) claimed that the implantation of extra corpora allata into gregarious hoppers of *Locusta* resulted in adults with the solitarious, and even 'hypersolitary' morphometrics, but L. Joly (1960) in a comprehensive review makes no reference to morphometrics. Staal (1961) found that implantation of extra corpora allata into gregarious hoppers of *Locusta* produced no effect on the length of

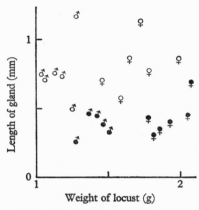

Fig. 215. *Schistocerca*, weight and the length of prothoracic gland in the solitarious (open signs) and the gregarious (black signs) adults (after Ellis & Carlisle 1961, modified).

the hind femur (F), and had an uncertain effect on the tegmen length (E) and the E/F ratio; implantation in the IInd instar caused the head width (C) to decrease, but in the Vth to increase, after a moult.

The prothoracic gland is markedly larger in isolated locusts than in crowded (fig. 215), and it is particularly large in the South African *Schistocerca g. flaviventris* (Carlisle & Ellis 1962). Partial extirpation of the gland from the third instar solitarious *Schistocerca* led to the appearance of black areas and the replacement of green background colour by yellow; the effect was less pronounced in *Locusta* (Ellis & Carlisle 1961; Carlisle & Ellis 1962). Staal (1961) obtained no effect in *Locusta*. The effects of the prothoracic gland secretion in accelerating the moults and decreasing the number of hopper instars are known (p. 289) and the implantation of an extra gland may cause a hypertrophy of the tegmen, resulting in *Locusta* adults with the E/F ratios up to 2·35, that is, much more long-winged than any normal individuals (Staal 1961; Staal & De Wilde 1962). Injection of an extract of this gland into gregarious *Schistocerca* hoppers reduced their marching (Carlisle & Ellis 1963).

The information on the relation between the corpora cardiaca and phase polymorphism is very scanty. Their extirpation from crowded *Locusta* hoppers slightly reduced the black pattern, and implantation increased it slightly (Staal 1961).

Hormonal effects on phase differences in behaviour are insufficiently known but highly probable. Haskell (1962; Haskell & Roskow, unpublished) found no difference in electrophysiological responses of two phases to identical visual, acoustic and mechanical stimuli, but suggested that this was due to the differences in their endocrine activity which affects the nervous system. Isolated hoppers of *Schistocerca* injected with haemolymph of crowded ones became more responsive and moved faster (Haskell & Moorhouse 1963), while an extraction from prothoracic gland injected into gregarious hoppers reduced their marching activity (Carlisle & Ellis 1962, 1963). These results suggest that phase polymorphism in all its aspects will ultimately be found to depend on differences in the physiology of the sensory, nervous and endocrine systems.

INHERITANCE OF PHASE CHARACTERS

The ability to respond to density changes and the amplitude of the response are properties of the genetic constitution of a species or subspecies, and attempts to influence the amplitude of the response in E/F and F/C ratios of *Locusta* by selection in several generations were not successful (Gunn & Hunter-Jones 1952; Jamieson 1955). At the same time, there is convincing evidence that changes within the hereditary limits, induced by a suitable treatment in one generation, are transmitted to the next, suggesting a non-genic type of inheritance. A possibility of concealed selection might be argued from the fact that an egg-pod of *Schistocerca* and *Locusta* may contain two types of egg, large ones producing heavy dark hatchlings, and small ones giving rise to light hatchlings (Papillon 1960; Tchelebi-Papillon 1962; Albrecht 1962*b*); Plotnikov (1915) also noted that both large and small eggs may be found in the same egg-pod of *Locusta m. migratoria*. Such effects, however, are observed in the *Schistocerca* eggs laid by females reared crowded and isolated for the first time, so that no selection could have intervened. It would appear that the inheritance of some phase characteristics is partly genetic and partly, perhaps, cytoplasmic. Additional complications in the way of analysing the inheritance mechanism arise from the instability of the characters in the progeny, caused by the immediate environmental conditions, and all these difficulties deter geneticists from work on locusts, although their help in these problems is essential. Attempts by acridologists to embark on genetic investigation of phase polymorphism have not produced anything of value. Potgieter (1929), on the basis of very few somewhat primitive experiments with *Locustana* on Medelian lines, concluded that 'green' and 'grey' individuals (presumably, corresponding to the solitarious type) when mated with 'brown' (presumably, gregarious) ones produced progeny with a 'lethal' factor. He also maintained that the crosses between two brown individuals never resulted in 'green' progeny, but did not mention whether the latter were kept isolated. The inadequacy of Potgieter's data and the unsoundness of his reasoning have been dealt with by Faure (1929, 1932). Plotnikov (1927), who was the first to observe a phase change in *Locusta m. migratoria* in laboratory, has later evolved the idea, supported by very inadequate experimental data, that the two extreme phases are genetically distinct 'races', which are able to interbreed and that each can produce, under reverse density treatment, a phenotype indistinguishable from the other; their crossing produces intermediate types. The same view was expressed, without detailed supporting evidence, by Podtiaguin (1953) with regard to *Schistocerca paranensis*, the solitarious 'race' of which, according to him, can be transformed into the gregarious only in the laboratory, but never in nature. More recently, Plotnikov (1962) again revised his views and accepted the phase theory, but suggested that the gregarious phase of *Locusta* is the normal phenotype, while the solitarious is an occasional one and unable to maintain itself for more than a few generations, unless it is crossed with the gregarious, when the vitality of the species is increased because of the heterosis. These views are entirely theoretical and find no support in facts relating to several species.

It is impossible to say whether any help in phase studies could be obtained from cytogenetics, because no comparative investigations of spermatogenesis in two extreme phases of one species have ever been carried out, except in *Locustana* for which no difference was found, but no details were given (Malan & Malan 1925). A cytogenetic study of the subspecies of *Locusta* and *Schistocerca* differing in the amplitude of phase responses (p. 374) would be of great interest.

On the whole, the problem of the mechanisms controlling the inheritance of the various phase characters remains wide open. It is to be hoped that it will attract the attention of some geneticists with the modern physiological and biochemical outlook, who would regard the difficulties inherent in the problem as a challenge rather than a deterrent; the work should be carried out in close collaboration with an acridologist fully conversant with the environmental effects on the phenotype which may be confused with manifestations of genetic variation. The phase polymorphism of locusts is not a phenomenon restricted to these insects, analogous effects being known in other groups (Uvarov 1961), which makes the problem one of wide biological interest and locusts provide particularly suitable material for its study.

THE PHASE THEORY

The conclusion that periodic swarming of locusts is correlated with changes in their coloration and morphology, which are sufficiently striking for the non-swarming individuals to have been regarded as specifically distinct, was arrived at independently (and almost simultaneously) by three entomologists in as many continents—Faure in South Africa, Plotnikov in Central Asia and myself in the Caucasus (Uvarov 1961). The fragmentary evidence then available was embodied in the original formulation of the phase theory (Uvarov 1921), later elaborated and supplemented by data referring to more species (Uvarov 1923*a*, 1923*b*, 1928; Uvarov & Zolotarevsky 1929; Zolotarevsky 1930, 1933; Faure 1932). Although the theory soon attracted the attention of many acridologists, the resulting voluminous literature was characterised mainly by inadequately supported further theorising, much of it biassed either in favour of or against the theory, while there were few objective studies of the phenomena involved (reviews by Key 1950, 1957; Kennedy 1956, 1961, 1962; Gunn 1960; Uvarov 1961; also, a series of papers and discussions concerning all aspects of phase polymorphism and its implications in the report of the recent colloquium in Paris; (see Albrecht (Ed.) 1962*a*). An emphasis in the original formulation of the theory on its importance for explaining the periodicity of locust plagues provided an incentive for its critics to concentrate on this practical issue and distracted attention from its biological aspects.

In his review of the papers published up to 1947, Key (1950) expressed surprise that they contained 'no clear and simple statement of what the Phase Theory actually is'. The above survey of the data available some fifteen years later shows that the biological background of phase changes is anything but simple and clarity could be achieved only by deliberately ignoring its complexity. Therefore, even now, only a tentative scheme can be outlined, with many gaps in our knowledge bridged by hypotheses, serving mainly to focus the attention on weak points.

A scheme of phase transformation should naturally start from the extreme solitarious individuals of a species. Such individuals, when brought into proximity, may or may not become habituated to the mutual encounters and eventually conditioned to aggregate. The outcome depends on the species, the tendency to acquire gregarious behaviour being an inherent property only of some acridoids. Pasquier (1952) has called such species, in French, *gregariapte*, and an English term *gregarisable* is suggested. Their number is restricted, but probably greater than is known at present, since evidence is accumulating of occasional manifestations of gregariousness in some normally non-swarming species. No species should be regarded as entirely unresponsive to density, until it has been studied in this respect, and even partial responses may have a definite importance in the biology of economic species. It might be suggested that all such species should be submitted to experimental studies of the density effects on their behaviour, physiology and morphology.

The first prerequisite for gregarisation is a set of conditions which bring the solitarious insects into close proximity, resulting in frequent mutual encounters. The sensory mechanisms mediating the habituation and aggregation, as stages in the gregarisation process are little known, but tactile, visual olfactory and auditory senses are known, or believed to be involved. It may be postulated that the mutual sensory stimuli, transmitted to the brain, are integrated there and transformed into impulses for muscular activity and for the neurosecretory and endocrine processes which, in their turn, affect the whole physiology of the insect, resulting in changes of metabolism, pigmentation, rates of development, activity, growth pattern, reproductive potential, vitality, etc.

A serious misconception exists with regard to the number and the density of individuals required to initiate the gregarisation process, the extreme opinion being that 'phase is almost completely dependent on numbers' (Gunn 1960). Experimental work has conclusively shown that an association of even two individuals produces deep physiological effects in gregarisable species, whereas the densest crowding of others has no effect. Furthermore, once the individuals become conditioned to aggregate, the density of a group is maintained by their own behaviour, as is well illustrated by hopper bands and, even more strikingly, by flying swarms which resist disruption by air turbulence (Z. Waloff 1958, 1962; Rainey 1958).

Direct experimental evidence on the early stages in the development of gregarious behaviour is at present available only with regard to hoppers, but other physiological effects, which in hoppers are known to follow the behaviour changes, are known to occur in adults as well; in fact, sensory stimulation of neurosecretory activity is so far known mainly for adults. This makes it reasonable to suggest that the early gregarisation stages in adults are probably the same as in hoppers, namely the habituation and conditioning to aggregation of individuals brought together by environmental factors. The greater mobility of adults favours the chances of such concentration, for example, in the areas of local rainfall, due to convergent air flow which also involves locusts (Rainey 1962), or in an environment with a patchy and unstable vegetation pattern which favours concentration of adults as well as of hoppers (Zolotarevsky 1933; Kennedy 1939; Uvarov 1957); such ecological factors of concentration will be discussed in the second volume. The profound immediate effects of aggregation on reproductive adults are known and it is also known that the resulting progeny are born already with some physiological characteristics of the gregarious phase. It has not yet been established whether such behaviour traits as the readiness for habituation and aggregation are also transmitted by crowded adults to their progeny, but it is reasonable to expect this, since both in adults and in hoppers physiological changes follow changes in behaviour. The lack of this vital information is due to the practical difficulties involved in precise quantitative studies of adult behaviour and the resulting concentration of research workers on hoppers, but these difficulties must be overcome and the attention of experimental workers drawn to adults, whose role in the initiation of phase change remains, probably, underestimated because it has not been studied.

The easily observable changes in pigmentation and morphology are now known to be a reflection of the physiological ones, and the past emphasis in phase studies on such external indices of gregarisation must be reconsidered. Changes in hopper coloration are readily induced during the life of the individuals by crowding or isolation and they are reversible. The adult morphology merely reflects the conditions which affected the relative growth of body parts during the hopper life and only the final and irreversible results of the hopper growth-pattern have been studied in the past, as adult morphometrics. In such studies, however, particular attention has been paid to the length of the tegmen (E) and of the hind femur (F) and to the E/F ratio, the inclusion of the tegmen making impossible a comparison of adults with hoppers, and it is only recently that the use of the head width (C), by itself and in relation to the femur length (F/C ratio), has avoided that difficulty (p. 338). The increase in the size of the head capsule with gregarisation is, possibly, the most significant morphological effect of crowding, when considered in relation to the behaviour. It is known that gregarious hoppers spend more time in marching than solitarious, which rest more. A hopper sitting on a plant assumes a vertical position, with the head resting on the thorax by the force of gravity; a hopper marching on a horizontal surface must support the head in position by muscular effort, which would be particularly great in a gregarious hopper with its relatively large head. The muscles supporting the head originate on the inner surface of the prothorax and thus exert a pull on the integument of the hopper and may be accountable for the pronotal constriction characteristic of the gregarious adult. This idea was put forward long ago (Uvarov & Thomas 1942) but has not attracted the attention it deserves as a means of investigating the mechanism of a morphological change during the individual life of hoppers.

Once a locust becomes adult, its morphology can no longer change, but external factors may effect a change in behaviour; for example when a swarm settles in dense vegetation interfering with the mutual contacts of the locusts, they may lose the aggregation habit and behave as solitaries, but with the morphometrics of the gregarious phase. Similarly, cases are known of gregariously-behaving swarms composed of locusts with morphometrics of the solitarious phase; their origin is supposed to be the result of a concentration of solitarious adults due to convergent air currents (Rainey 1962). These two kinds of situations have been regarded by critics of the phase theory as evidence that morphometrics have no relation to behaviour. On the other hand, overzealous protagonists of the theory have tended to regard adult morphometrics being so closely linked to behaviour as to be indicators not only of the history of a population, but also of its future swarming potentialities. Both these extreme views, although quite opposite, are based on the erroneous assumption that the phase theory demands a simultaneous change in all characters of an insect in response to a change in density. In this connection, supporters of the theory have probably done more harm to it than its critics by excessive attention to morphometric studies. This has resulted in a vast literature, largely of doubtful biological value, mainly because morphometric methods came to be used on a wide scale before their value was critically assessed and also because they were usually applied to material with inadequately known, or even quite unknown, biological background. There is a need for a new approach to morphometric research, with an emphasis not on the refinements of statistical treatment, but on the kind and the quality of the basic information and on the methods of obtaining it (p. 350).

The gradual nature of changes in the various characteristics of a species, correlated with population density, which was first noticed with regard to the external features alone, was the reason for the choice of the term 'phase', with a remark that locust phases are only a special kind of morphs (p. 395). The term, of course, has many uses in entirely different spheres and it has been applied in insects to, for example, unstable colour forms (green and yellow forms of grasshoppers), seasonal forms, or, in the recent Russian practice, even to stages in development (larval, pupal, imaginal phase). In an attempt to introduce a qualifying term for locust phases, Key & Day (1954a; Key 1957) proposed to call them 'kentromorphic phases', but this was not a happy choice. In the first place, phase being a morph, the term is tautological. Secondly, the prefix was derived from the Greek word *kentron*, meaning a goad or stimulus, and the whole combination was intended to emphasise 'that the phase of Uvarov is a physical *form*, typically a function of *stimulation*'. This reflects Key's (1950) view that phases must be defined only by morphological criteria, which is in direct contradiction to my early statement that 'the main and principal difference between the phases lies in their bionomics, while their morphology is only the apparent result of some deep physiological differences' (Uvarov 1928). When that view was expressed, it was based on intuition rather than evidence which has become abundant since then, and Key's narrow morphological conception of phase found no favour amongst acridologists. The term 'phase' is admittedly a general one, but no one yet has thought of introducing qualifying terms for phases of the moon, liquid and gaseous phases of chemical substances, and so on. When used by acridologists, the term has a special meaning, understood by them, and there is no need for a cumbersome term which, moreover, distorts the current conception of the phenomena.

All changes in the various phase manifestations being gradual, the complete picture is that of a continuous series. In this respect phase polymorphism is distinct from that exhibited in, for example, the castes of social insects, wing polymorphs of aphids, or seasonal forms of Lepidoptera, which all present a number of discrete polymorphs (Kennedy 1961). In locusts, a polymorphic series culminates in the extreme types, which were given formal names of phase *solitaria* and phase *gregaria*. Later the intermediate series of polymorphs was admitted as a distinct phase *transiens*; as the latter can be a product of a change from the solitarious to the gregarious condition or the reverse, the self-explanatory terms *congregans* and *dissocians* were introduced (Uvarov & Zolotarevsky 1929). Even if the morphological characters of adults alone were taken into account, the separation of the three main categories could be achieved only by adopting certain morphometric values as arbitrary limits of the two extreme phases, leaving a much longer series in the transient phase. More recent studies have increased greatly the number of phase attributes, many of which are real enough but not yet amenable to quantitative evaluation, and there is a need for a scheme of phase categories which would take into account the continuous and dynamic nature of phase polymorphism. The following tentative scheme will, it is hoped, be both useful for practical purposes and justified by the present knowledge of the problem. Since the original Latinised terms implied some rigidity of their contents, it is best to replace them by the English equivalents, as has been done throughout this work.

Solitarious phase. To be defined by the mean values and their standard deviations of all characters amenable to quantitative estimation (e.g. morphological, chromatic, biochemical, behavioural), obtained from a series of non-gregarious populations, all definitely known not to have exhibited even incipient gregarious behaviour for at least two preceding generations.

Gregarious phase. To be defined by the mean values and their standard deviations of the same kinds of characters, obtained from a series of swarming populations, all definitely known to be derived from at least two successive swarming generations.

The degree of precision with which the extreme phases of a species, or subspecies, can be defined depends on the state of information available in each case, and one may have to be content with a somewhat incomplete set of characters, while endeavouring to obtain other indices. It has been, in fact, an almost complete lack of quantitative data on any aspects except morphology that has induced acridologists to judge the phase status by morphometrics, though none of them went as far as to accept Key's (1950) ultra-formalistic proposal that phases must be defined by morphological characters alone and regarded as taxas of infraspecific rank. It should be made quite clear that even the Latinised names of phases *solitaria* and *gregaria* were not formal taxonomic designations, but terms of the same kind as forma *brachyptera* or *macroptera*, or those employed by Key for the pattern morphs of *Chortoicetes* (p. 39).

Transient phase. The conception of this phase belongs to Zolotarevsky (1929) and the name was to be applied to the populations 'occurring in a given locality when the species is on the increase and its individuals are beginning to form loose aggregations, or on the decrease, and the swarms are becoming loose and tend to scatter either in the hopper stage or shortly after becoming adult' (Uvarov & Zolotarevsky 1929). It was further proposed to distinguish the two kinds of the transient phase, by the names phase *congregans* and phase *dissocians*. Zolotarevsky (1930, 1933) and Stower (1959) provided evidence that some features of the coloration of transient adults reflected the sequence in its development, depending on the direction of the density change (i.e. on the history of the population). Key (1950) regarded the terms *transiens*, *congregans* and *dissocians* not as categories comparable to *solitaria* and *gregaria*, but as indications of the biological state of a population. This view is reasonable and these formal Latin terms should be replaced by their respective English equivalents, *transient*, *congregating* and *segregating* (the last term is preferable to 'dissociating'); such terms would merely denote populations which are intermediate between the extreme phases in, at least, one of the standard attributes of the latter.

This scheme, then, results in two reasonably definable extreme phases, separated by a more or less long continuous series of transient forms. Most of the experimental work on phases has been really conducted within the limits of this transitional series, since the extreme phases as known in the field have hardly ever been produced in the laboratory (p. 332). Also, most of the field data used in morphometric studies fail to satisfy the criterion that the history of at least two preceding generations should be known. As a result, most of such data probably refer to transient populations; this is particularly true with regard to *Schistocerca*, characterised by exceptional mobility, as well as by the heterogeneity of individuals produced by the same female (Albrecht 1962*b*) (p. 333). It may be suggested that, during a swarming period of a species, most of its populations are in a state of flux, some being nearer the gregarious phase in certain respects than others, and only some qualifying for the full status of that phase. This important problem will have to be more fully discussed in the next volume, but the pre-eminence of the transient series in the population dynamics of locusts should be borne in mind in all future studies, whether in the laboratory or in the field. The greater extent of that series in comparison with the well established extreme phases makes it essential to devise means of assessing the deviations of transient populations from the extremes. This can be done, when the quantitative limits of the latter have been established, by indicating the position of a transient population within the interval separating the extremes, as a percentage deviation from the index of the solitarious phase. The particular index or indices to be used will depend on the knowledge of a species or a subspecies; there may be an advantage in estimating the degree of phase transformation for each index separately, at any rate while investigating their relative discriminating value and the sequence of changes in them. In practice, however, colour criteria for hoppers, and morphometric ones for adults (as well as hoppers in the case of the F/C ratio), will have to be used, although complications will arise when a population classified according to them as one of the extreme phases does not exhibit the characteristic behaviour (p. 382). Pasquier (1952) suggested a perfectly logical solution, by adding special suffixes to the phase names. Thus, a solitarious

385

population may be 'solitaricolor', 'transiticolor' or even 'gregaricolor', as regards the coloration; it may be 'solitariform', and so on, as regards morphology; and 'solitarigeste' and so on, as regards behaviour. The same suffixes may be added to the root of the term gregarious. Apart from being cumbersome, however, the scheme has a serious disadvantage in leaving it to the observer to record by a definite term his subjective impression, which would be particularly unreliable as regards the behavioural characteristics. There is a need for qualifying information such as would be provided by the percentage changes in such phase indices established for the particular species as was, for example, proposed by Dirsh (1953) for some morphometric ratios. This latter procedure needs elaboration but it is offered here as a possible objective means of assessing the phase status of a population.

To conclude, the existence of a fluid and continuous density-dependent polymorphism has now been firmly established for locusts. Similar phenomena, though on a lesser scale and less frequently, are already known for some grasshoppers and may be expected in many more, particularly in the abundant economic species. It is right to say that no real understanding of the biology of these insects can be attained without taking phase polymorphism into account. It is also clear that these phenomena are of decisive importance in field work on them, and a full discussion of their implications for ecology, population dynamics and rational control policies will be offered in the second volume of this work.

It is noteworthy that the ideas behind the phase theory are being followed by workers on other insects, in which closely similar manifestations of density-dependent continuous polymorphism have been found (Chopard 1949, Tettigoniidae; Key 1957, Phasmatidae; Long 1953 and Iwao 1962, Lepidoptera; Uvarov 1961, general review). This means that the problem becomes one of wide interest and acridologists can be justifiably proud in bringing it to the notice of general biologists.

INTRODUCTION TO TAXONOMY

It is unfortunate that some specialist research workers (physiologists, biochemists and others) tend to attach little importance to exact identification of the insect studied, and it is not infrequent to find reports on some substance or process, meticulous in every other respect, but studied in 'a grasshopper' or 'a locust', without a scientific name. We have seen in earlier chapters how unsafe it is to generalise, on almost any point, from the data obtained from a single species, and any observations on unknown ones are of even less value. It is therefore necessary to urge all research workers to indicate not only the exact specific name, but also the source of the material studied, that is whether from a certain laboratory, or from a wild population; in the latter case full data as to where and when the material was collected are also essential.

A brief outline of the principles of classification may be of value as an introduction to a list of families and subfamilies at present recognised and mentioned repeatedly throughout this book.

TAXONOMIC CHARACTERS

Until very recently the classification of acridoids was partly based on the general shape of the body. Thus the group Oedipodinae was characterised by a short rounded head with vertical face, while that of Acridinae was separated from it by a more acute head, with the face oblique. Such features, however, occur in entirely unrelated groups, being a result of adaptation to environment, as will be discussed in connection with ecology. Recent detailed studies of external morphology and of anatomy, particularly of the male phallic complex (p. 141), made it possible to arrive at a more reasonable grouping, which may require further modifications in the future, when the rich tropical faunas, still very inadequately explored, are better known. Also, comparative anatomical studies of other systems and organs may indicate relationships between groups which are not apparent at present.

The general morphology of these insects is on the whole rather uniform and there are few features which provide exclusive characters for any taxonomic categories. In most cases, the categories are characterised by combinations of characters. Nevertheless, some structures are more useful than others in practical taxonomic work and these are briefly reviewed below.

Genitalia

The external parts of the male copulatory organs—epiproct, cercus and subgenital plate—present in some groups very stable and reliable taxonomic characters. Some sub-families, for example Calliptaminae and Euryphyminae, can be recognised by their cerci alone (p. 19). At the generic and specific levels these features are also of great value in these and some other groups, but in others (e.g. Oedipodinae, Acridinae and Gomphocerinae) they are usually very uniform and offer less help to a taxonomist.

The *phallic complex*, or concealed parts of the male copulatory apparatus, recently came to be considered the most decisive and reliable taxonomic criterion (Baranov 1925; Roberts 1941; Dirsh 1956*a*, 1961; Barnum 1959). It is often suggested that the phallic complex is less subject to environmental conditions because it is not directly exposed to them, but adaptive changes even of external morphological characters can hardly be ascribed to a direct impact of the environment, which affects the organism as a whole through its physiology and there is no reason to expect that the consequent morphological changes would be restricted to external features.

The phallic complex provides valuable characters for separating families; in fact, Dirsh (*t.c.*) found it possible to suggest a family classification almost on it alone. Some of its features, for example the ephiphallus (p. 142), provide also very reliable family and subfamily characters. It appears to be less useful at the generic level, but within many genera it provides good specific characters, with the usual caution that some individual variation may be expected and identification of single specimens can be unreliable.

Wing venation

While wing venation is accepted as a reliable basis of major classification of insect orders and of orthopteroid sub-orders (Ragge 1955), it is too uniform throughout Acridoidea to be of diagnostic value at the family level. Moreover, practically all families include a proportion of brachypterous or apterous forms and two families are characterised by apterism, and this limits the usefulness of this character. However, details of venation, particularly of the tegmina, are of great diagnostic value at the species level, particularly in the subfamily Gomphocerinae.

Sound-producing mechanisms

The great variation in these has already been discussed (p. 176) and their outstanding biological importance as means of communication is reflected in the fact that their different types are of definite diagnostic value for some families and, particularly, subfamilies. In Gomphocerinae they provide valuable, though still neglected, specific characters (p. 177).

Head

A great range of variation in the shape and structure of the head (p. 114) is connected with the habits of particular species, regardless of taxonomic relationship. A general feature of value for major classification is the fastigial furrow (p. 6), which is as characteristic of several families as its absence is of others. It is, however, not always clearly developed, or even absent, and can be considered only as a subsidiary diagnostic character.

Antenna

The mean number of antennal segments is, to some extent, related to major groupings (p. 9), but the ranges of variation overlap and this reduces the value of this character. One family, Lathiceridae, however, can be recognised by its antennae alone (p. 402). The structure of the antennae is variable (p. 10) but more in relation to habits than to taxonomy.

Legs

The only general feature of the legs which is of value at family level is the shape of the base of the posterior femur (p. 26).

Coloration

Integumental colours and patterns are so closely dependent on environmental factors that they can be expected to help mainly with regard to the lower taxonomic units, such as subspecies, ecological races, phases and populations. Their value for distinguishing species has often been exaggerated in the past, but it would be wrong to reject them altogether. As in every other case the value of a character must be judged mainly on its stability within the particular taxonomic unit.

Chromosomes

The generally recognised role of chromosomes in heredity naturally led to a hope that studies of chromosome numbers, patterns and behaviour would be particularly helpful for the evaluation of taxonomic relationships.

It is fortunate that orthopteroid insects generally, and the acridoids in particular, have proved to be exceptionally suitable for cytological studies of chromosomes. Such studies have been conducted in the University of Philadelphia by McClung and Helwig since the beginning of this century, and by now a vast literature on the subject is available (the more general publications are by McClung 1914; W. R. B. Robertson 1916; Helwig 1958; M. White 1951, 1954 and 1957).

It is an accepted technique in comparative studies to investigate chromosomes in the metaphase of the spermatogonial divisions in the testis. The typical number of chromosomes has now been established for a considerable number of species and a relatively recent catalogue (Makino 1951) lists about 200 species (though some are synonyms). Since then, additional information has become available on 24 species from India (Manna 1954; Dutt 1955), nine from Japan (Kavamura 1957), some 100 from S. America (Saez 1956*a*; Mesa 1956; Silveira Guido, Carbonell *et al.* 1958) and twenty-six from Tasmania (Sharman 1952), apart from a number of papers on individual species.

Thus, chromosome numbers are known for some 350 species, which is, of course, a very small percentage of the world fauna. Nevertheless, chromosome numbers are known for representatives of all the families except two (Chari-laidae and Lathiceridae). Most of the families are characterised by twenty-three somatic chromosomes, but Pyrgomorphidae and Pamphagidae have only nineteen. This is, however, merely a typical number, and within each group there are genera and species in which the number is reduced, while on the other hand supernumerary chromosomes occur not infrequently (up to four in *Locusta*—Itoh 1934; Hsiang Wei 1958; Rees & Jamieson 1954; one to three in *Pyrgomorpha kraussi*, Lewis & John 1959; one to two in *Myrmeleotettix*, Barker 1960; etc.). It has been suggested (Lewis & John, *t.c.*) that their occur-rence in a laboratory stock was due to inbreeding, but M. White (1954) gives a long list of species where supernumerary chromosomes were found in wild insects; thus, in several populations of *Circotettix rabula* the percentage of individuals with extra chromosomes varied from 4·79 to 27·03; and in the Tasmanian *Cryptobothrus chrysophorus* most individuals had up to four supernumerary chromosomes (Sharman 1952).

The cases of a reduction in the number of chromosomes are many. Thus, in the group of genera allied to *Chorthippus* the typical number of twenty-three is reduced to seventeen. An extreme case of reduction is that of the South American genus *Dichroplus* in which the typical number is twenty-three, but two species have eighteen, and one species only eight chromosomes (Saez 1956*b*, 1957).

Without going into further details it is clear that the number of chromo-somes can mainly serve for subsidiary characterisation of major groups, and rarely of species in a genus. On the other hand, the number and structure and, to some extent, the dimensions (Powers 1942; Helwig 1958) of homologous chromosomes may provide valuable indications of difference between geo-graphical or ecological populations of the same species. For example, four local races of *Trimerotropis sparsa* have been recognised on chromosome characters (M. White 1951*b*) and supernumerary chromosomes were more frequent in southern British populations of *Myrmeleotettix maculatus* than in northern (Barker 1960).

This brief review can best be concluded by two quotations from works of a leading cytotaxonomist: 'No instance of a direct correlation between a chromosomal rearrangement and externally visible character is known and, although further work on this point is needed, it seems probable that where chromosomal polymorphism coexists with genic polymorphism determining externally conspicuous characters, these are largely independent adaptive systems' (White 1951*a*); and: 'Cytology is certainly a tool that deserves more attention by animal taxonomists than it has received in the past, but it is not a magic key that will unlock all taxonomic problems as some have supposed' (White 1957).

Morphometrics

Measurements of different parts of the body and its appendages are always given in taxonomic descriptions of species. The usual measurements are the length of body (from apex of head to tip of abdomen), antenna, pronotum, tegmen and hind femur. Sexual dimorphism in size and in the relative dimensions of, for example, the tegmina, makes it essential to provide measurements of the two sexes separately. When series of specimens are available, the ranges of variation of each measurement are also given.

While this practice is sound in principle, since the size and the proportions of body parts serve to characterise an insect, the five standard measurements listed above are sometimes inadequate for the purpose; for example, in species with strongly elongated head its relative length supplies another valuable character. It is therefore advisable that all measurable features which from inspection appear to distinguish one species from another should be recorded quantitatively, but this is seldom done.

The value of absolute measurements for taxonomy is limited mainly to discrimination between geographical sub-species and between populations. For example, a comparative statistical study of two populations of *Oedipoda caerulescens*, one from the plains and another from 1500 metres above sea level in Jugoslavia, revealed that the lowland specimens were smaller, particularly as regards the tegmen length, than the mountain ones (Adamovich 1950). Geographical variation in absolute size and particularly in the relative tegmen length, is frequently recorded, but the measurements are seldom analysed statistically. Graphical representation of geographical variation in size of parts is also useful (Hubbell 1960).

Two species of European grasshoppers, *Chorthippus brunneus* and *C. mollis* have caused endless difficulties to taxonomists, as they often occur together and their separation has been based entirely on the relative width of certain areas of the tegmen. Perdeck (1958), in his meticulous study of these two species (as well as *C. biguttulus* and of their hybrids), used absolute measurements of the tegmen and its areas, as well as the number of femoral stridulatory pegs. As shown by Perdeck, the number of pegs alone differentiates *C. brunneus* and *C. mollis* so clearly (see also p. 178, table 42) that there is no need for the metric characters (which, however, proved valuable for the study of hybrids).

A useful method of morphometric comparison between closely related forms is using the *ratios* between measurements of two body parts. This method has been used mainly in the study of locust phases (p. 344), but attempts have been made to apply it to species taxonomy. Again, *C. brunneus* and *C. mollis* were chosen by La Greca (1955) to test the method, but no such clear discrimination was achieved as could be obtained from the number of the femoral pegs. Both the absolute measurements and several ratios were used by Yoshimeki (1952) to compare *Oxya velox* and *O. japonica*, which, however, can be separated by unambiguous characters of the external genitalia.

The most recent statistical method of analysing morphometric data for taxonomic purposes is that of discriminant functions and generalised distances. It is increasingly used in locust phase studies (p. 348), and it has been tested by Bigelow Reimer (1954) for separating two closely related species of *Arphia* by making five very precise measurements on thirty-six specimens of each species, followed by complicated statistical computations to obtain the critical values of the resultant discriminant functions for the two species and to apply them to a large mixed series of specimens. The result was that only 1·74 per cent were wrongly identified; this must have been verified by the examination of wing colour, which apparently is a sufficient criterion, causing one to question the authors' claim that the method of discriminant functions 'may serve a useful purpose in insect taxonomy by increasing the speed and accuracy of determinations by inexperienced workers'. One might add that the two species in question have not been compared critically and in detail as regards their morphology, including internal genitalia; such studies may well provide better characters which can be examined directly and certainly more speedily, even by inexperienced workers. The claim for the superior value of higher statistics over exact morphological methods has not yet been substantiated, at any rate as far as taxonomy at the species level is concerned. When differences, for example between sub-species, phases, and so on, are entirely metrical, and detailed morphological studies fail to separate them, there is of course no argument that the most exact statistical methods are essential.

Internal anatomy

As we have seen, differences have been found between species belonging to certain families and other groups in the structure of the alimentary system (p. 73), air-sacs (p. 126), testes (p. 81), ovaries (p. 144), spermatheca (p. 147), and so on. It is probable that some such differences may prove of considerable taxonomic significance, but the present evidence rests almost on single, or very few, representatives of each group. Systematic studies of the comparative anatomy of a wide range of species are obviously needed before useful conclusions can be drawn.

Early stages

Little attention has been paid so far to the study of the morphological and other characters of hoppers from the taxonomic point of view, although some practical keys for the identification of hoppers exist (p. 283). It is feasible that such studies may throw light on the interrelations of closely allied species and genera, but no more can be said in the absence of reliable evidence and the subject is mentioned here in the hope of attracting research workers to it.

As regards eggs, which often have characteristic chorionic sculpturing (p. 240), this is valuable for practical purposes at the species level, but its probable adaptive value makes it unlikely that wider studies would help the purposes of general classification.

TAXONOMIC CATEGORIES

It is not intended to discuss here the whole range of taxonomic categories (or *taxa*, singular *taxon*, as they are more conveniently called), but it may be useful to give an outline of those used by practical taxonomists.

The largest taxon within the Acridoidea is the *family*. As suggested by Dirsh (1961), a family should comprise a group of genera possessing a single character, or a combination of several characters, which does not occur in other families, and there should be no genera intermediate between families. A family may be divided into *subfamilies*, which are distinguished from each other by a conspicuous character, or a combination of characters, which does not normally occur in other subfamilies, but is not exclusive, so that two subfamilies may be connected by intermediate genera. A list of families and subfamilies, with their brief characteristics, is given below (p. 397).

A *genus* is more difficult to define. It is usually a somewhat subjective grouping of species which have in common certain characters considered of diagnostic value. Such groupings are easier to achieve when only a few species with these characters are known; genera with numerous species tend to become less definite and it is often necessary for a practising taxonomist to decide on dividing a large genus into several. Some authors prefer dividing a genus into *subgenera*, but this only leads to cumbersome names.

A *species* has been considered in the past as a basic and stable taxonomic unit, but this view is no longer tenable and it is noteworthy that studies of acridoid insects have contributed much to a comprehension of a species as consisting of a number of populations, sometimes very heterogeneous. The usual theoretical criterion of a species is its reproductive isolation, that is, the inability to produce fertile progeny when crossed with another, closely similar, species. Such a criterion can be fully satisfied only by experimental work, which is outside normal taxonomic practice. In exceptional cases two or more species may differ only in minor morphological characters but occur together, without any transitional forms; this is evidence of the absence of effective hybridisation and they can be accorded specific status. An excellent example of this, studied by Perdeck (1958), is three species of *Chorthippus* which are so difficult to distinguish that they have often been regarded as one variable species; careful analysis of their characters, however, made it clear that they are separate, and experimental work has shown that, although they can hybridise, the hybrids are very rare in nature because the three species have very different song-patterns by which the sexes of the same species are brought together.

When two closely similar species are separated geographically it is impossible to decide without experiment whether they would interbreed if they occurred together, and the decision whether to accord them specific status depends, in practice, on the personal judgment of the taxonomist, in which the degree of his experience in dealing with species of this particular genus is important. The subject of *geographical variation* has been very succinctly reviewed, largely on the evidence from acridoid insects, by Hubbell (1956). He has pointed out that the problem can be approached at different levels. An entomologist who finds that populations of the same species from different geographical areas consistently differ in some minor morphological details may assume that such variation has no biological meaning and a single blanket name for the species will suffice. Alternatively, he may ask himself whether the observed external differences, which may conceivably be accompanied by physiological differentiation, are correlated with different environments; since definite evidence on this point is not easily obtainable, it would be a wise precaution to regard such populations as geographical races which are designated by the name of the genus, species and *subspecies*.

Geographical variation, however, can be of different kinds. Perhaps the simplest case is that of insular subspecies. An example is the large forest species *Valanga nigricornis*, which occurs in Malaya, Korea, the Philippines, and through the Indonesian islands and New Guinea, being represented in different islands by forms differing mainly in coloration and minor morphological features; about a dozen of such geographical races have been given subspecific names. In this case the subspecies are separated by sea, but similar cases of the 'insular' type of distribution are found on continents. The simplest example is that of mountain species, such as *Gomphocerus sibiricus* whose main and continuous area of distribution covers north-eastern Europe and Siberia as far as Manchuria, but isolated populations of which are found on most European mountains and are characterised by minor morphological features (e.g. the antennae); it is obviously useful to distinguish them by subspecific names.

In the case of the Migratory Locust there is no such clear evidence of spatial isolation, but the species, *Locusta migratoria*, is divisible on morphometric characters into eight subspecies: *L. m. migratoria* (basins of the Black, Caspian and Aral seas and central Asia as far as northern China), *L. m. rossica* (most of central western Europe and European Russia), *L. m. gallica* (S. W. France), *L. m. cinerascens* (Mediterranean lands), *L. m. manilensis* (eastern and southern China, Japan, Philippines, Celebes, Borneo, Malaya), *L. m. migratorioides* (tropical Africa), *L. m. capito* (Madagascar) and *L. m. burmana* (upper Burma, Tibet); the races of this species occurring in India, northern Australia, New Zealand and many islands of the eastern hemisphere may also be different, but have not been studied. Some of the subspecies of *Locusta* may overlap in their distribution (partly because of long-range migrations), but such intermediate populations have not been investigated; in any case, since their morphological characteristics make it possible to distinguish them (p. 372), it is sound practice to give them distinct names, because they differ also in a very important biological respect, their tendency to swarm. Examples, on a smaller scale, are known in many flightless grasshoppers with special ecological requirements. Thus, *Melanoplus puer*, occurring in the Florida peninsula in sandy areas separated by marshland, is divisible into three subspecies differing in measurements, coloration and details of the phallic structures (Hubbell 1932, 1956). In some cases a geographical race may have a well-defined main distribution area which may overlap with the area of another race, and populations in the overlap area are of intermediate characteristics. As long as the characters of each race are reasonably constant within its main area, it is advisable to regard them as subspecies, designating specimens from the transition zone as intermediate.

A somewhat different type of geographical variation is a *cline*. In some species occurring over a large area there is a gradual change in one or more characters, the extreme limits of the range being very different but connected by an uninterrupted series of transitional forms. For example, the wings of the large Pamphagine grasshopper *Eremopeza gibbera* are entirely black in Syria, grading to broadly black-banded with a blue base in northern Iraq, then narrowly black-banded with a greenish-blue base in southern Iraq and greenish-yellow, with very narrow dark band, in southern Iran. This is clearly a cline, the specimens from different sectors of the distribution area being distinguishable, but without a break; in such a case one can merely regard the whole series as one species, but there is a practical advantage in dividing the series conventionally into named subspecies, since this helps to define the type of population occurring in a certain locality. It should be clear from the above that a cline is not a taxonomic unit but a series of intergrades.

It is possible to distinguish taxa below the level of geographical subspecies. Populations of the same subspecies occurring in somewhat different ecological environments may differ more or less consistently. For such ecological forms the term *morpha* was long ago proposed by Semenov-Tian-Shansky (1910) and again more recently by Huxley (1955). An illustration is provided by such semi-desert grasshoppers as *Oedipoda* and *Sphingonotus* living on bare ground, whose local populations are coloured in harmony with the colour of the soil, ranging from very light grey to almost black, reddish-brown, and so on (excellent colour photographs will be found in Ramme 1951 *a*, p. 126, plates *XI–XVI*). Such adaptive colours may be acquired by individuals during their life (p.52), but it is possible that they may be at least partly inheritable. There are also some small differences between populations in size, length of tegmina, and so on, and when they are linked with distinct habitats or habits they should be regarded as morphs, which are not designated by formal Latin names, but by descriptive ones.

Individual variations are more numerous in some species and populations than in others. Thus many grass-living species are either green or coloured like dry grass; although this may be due to the immediate effect of the background (p. 52), it is useful to be able to designate them by descriptive names (e.g. *forma viridis, forma straminea*, etc.). Again, patterns vary a great deal (p. 39) and forms with different types of patterns may be unequally represented in populations; it is more convenient to designate them by conventional formulae than by names. Such designations might be regarded as superfluous by taxonomists, but a population ecologist has in them the means of distinguishing between populations.

Moreover, as stressed by Hubbell (1956), it is probable that so-called 'uniform' populations are only a taxonomic simplification and individuals in a population are not identical in every respect. Apparently trivial external differences between individuals may reflect physiological differences which would never be looked for unless suspected on such external evidence. A special illustration of this principle is offered by locust phases, which are essentially morphs, but sufficiently important and well studied to be discussed fully in a special chapter (p. 332).

AN OUTLINE OF THE CLASSIFICATION OF ACRIDOIDEA

The higher classification of Acridoidea has recently undergone several changes, and further substantial modifications must be expected when the world fauna is better explored and more information is available on the morphology and the anatomy of a wider range of species representing different taxonomic groups.

The latest comprehensive treatment of the families and subfamilies of Acridoidea by Dirsh (1961) is adopted here, with some alterations. The main change is that the scope of the superfamily Acridoidea (considered by Dirsh as a suborder) is restricted by excluding the families Eumastacidae, Proscopiidae, Tanaoceridae and Pneumoridae, all of which may be regarded as distinct superfamilies.

The following outline of the families and subfamilies of the restricted Acridoidea should not be regarded as a means for identification of the insects, which requires much more detailed studies. Also, while typical representatives of each group are figured, it should be remembered that there is a wide variation within the groups as regards the general appearance of the insect so that completely unrelated genera often look very much alike, while related ones may be very dissimilar.

For the convenience of non-taxonomists, all genera and species mentioned in the book are listed under each family and subfamily in alphabetical order; their full scientific names are given in order to avoid doing so repeatedly in the text. Also, the commoner synonyms are given in brackets, since in the text the latest valid names have been substituted for those used in the original papers. It will be realised that the lists contain only a fraction of the genera and species belonging to each group.

Family XYRONOTIDAE

Small, apterous, without a tympanum. Head conical, with fastigial furrow. Femoro-abdominal stridulatory mechanism. Epiphallus shield-like.

The only species, *Xyronotus aztecus* I. Bolivar from Mexico must be given family rank, because of the highly peculiar stridulatory mechanism and the primitive phallic complex.

Family TRIGONOPTERYGIDAE. Fig. 216

Body strongly compressed laterally; head conical, with fastigial furrow. Elytra widened towards apex, often leaf-like. No stridulatory mechanism; no tympanum. Phallic complex reversed, with the penis directed forwards and the epiphallus on the ventral side.

A few genera known from Malaya, Indonesia and New Guinea.

Systella rafflesii (Westwood)

Family CHARILAIDAE. Fig. 217

Head conical, with fastigial furrow. Pronotum with the median carina double. Tegmino-alar stridulatory mechanism; tympanum present. Epiphallus shield-like.

Three genera in Southern Africa.

Charilaus carinatus Stål

Family PAMPHAGIDAE

Generally rather large insects, of greatly varying body shape; many brachypterous or apterous. Head with fastigial furrow. Tympanum present, reduced or absent (in some correlation with wing development). Lower basal lobe of the hind femur longer than the upper. Krauss's organ normally present. Epiphallus shield-like.

The family is divided into four subfamilies:

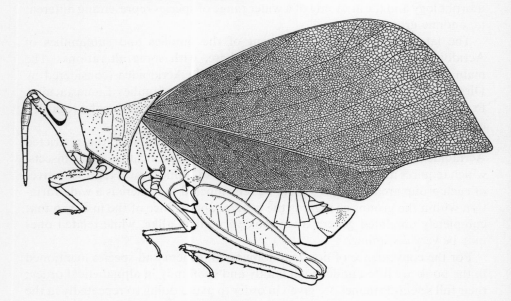

Fig. 216. *Systella rafflesii* (Westwood), male. × 3.

Subfamily Echinotropinae. Fig. 218

Body elongated, cylindrical, rugose or spinose. Krauss's organ absent. No stridulatory mechanism known.

Three South African genera.

Echinotropis horrida (Saussure)

Subfamily Porthetinae. Fig. 219

Large, rugose. Prosternal process of variable shape. Female usually apterous; tegmina of the winged males with specially modified stridulatory area. Hind femur usually spined.

From South and East Africa to the Red Sea area.

Lamarckiana
Pagopedilum bradyana (Saussure)
Porthetis carinata (Linnaeus.)
Xiphoceriana atrox (Gerstaecker) (= *Saussurea stuhlmanniana* Karsch)
    „   *brunneriana* Saussure

398

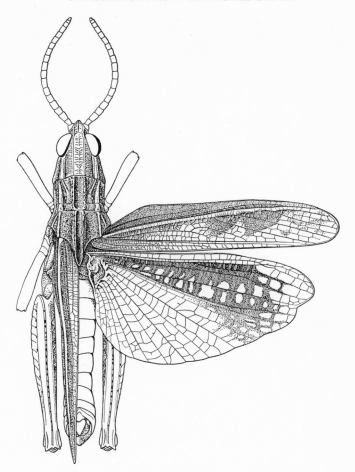

Fig. 217. *Charilaus carinatus* Stål, male, × 4.

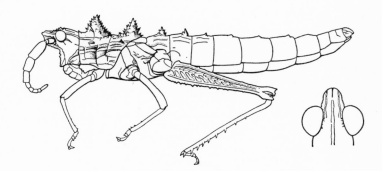

Fig. 218. *Echinotropis horrida* (Saussure), female, × 1·5

399

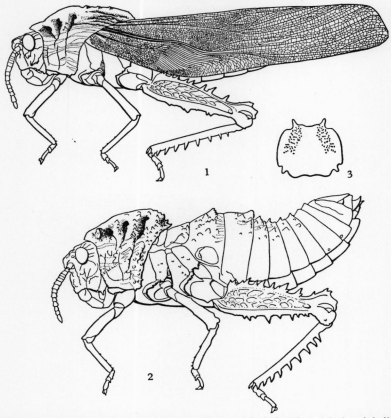

Fig. 219. *Porthetis carinata* (Linnaeus). 1, Male, × 1·3; 2, female × 1·3; 3, epiphallus.

Subfamily Akicerinae. Fig. 220

Characterised by tibio-alar stridulatory mechanism (p. 182) of the winged species.

A number of genera in southern and northern Africa, south-eastern Europe and south-western Asia.

 Adephagus cristatus (Burmeister)
 Akicera fusca (Thunberg)
 Asiotmethis muricatus (Pallas)
 Eremopeza gibbera (Stål)
 Glyphotmethis escherichi (Krauss)
 Haplotropis
 Prionotropis flexuosa (Serville)
 Tmethis cisti (Fabricius)
  ,, *pulchripennis* (Serville)

Subfamily Pamphaginae. Fig. 221

Size and shape variable, the integument generally rugose, rarely smooth. Brachypterous, micropterous or apterous.

 Some thirty genera in semi-arid parts of northern Africa, southern Europe and Asia.

 Acinipe
 Nocaracris
 Ocneridia
 Pamphagus elephas (Linnaeus)
 Prionosthenus galericulatus (Stål)
 Tropidauchen marginatum I. Bolivar
  ,,   *nizwai* Dirsh

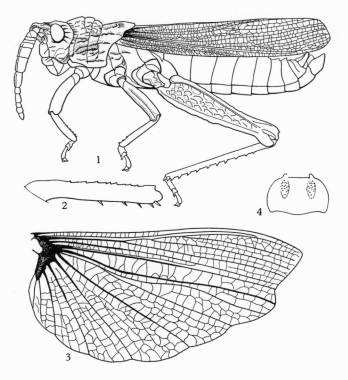

Fig. 220. *Akicera fusca* (Thunberg). 1, male, × 3·1; 2, middle tibia, with the stridulatory file; 3, hind wing, × 2·6; 4, epiphallus.

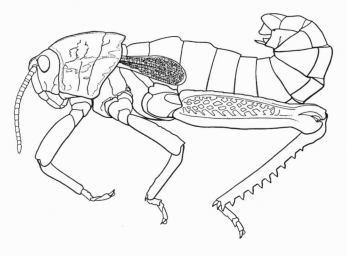

Fig. 221. *Pamphagus elephas* (Linnaeus), male, × 1·6

401

Family LATHICERIDAE. Fig. 222

Robust, depressed, rugose. Head almost prognathous. Antennae very short, fitting into the deep grooves of the frons. No ocelli, wings, stridulatory mechanism or tympanum.

Four genera in S.W. Africa.

Batrachidacris tuberculata (Rehn)
Crypsiceracris
Lathicerus cimex Saussure

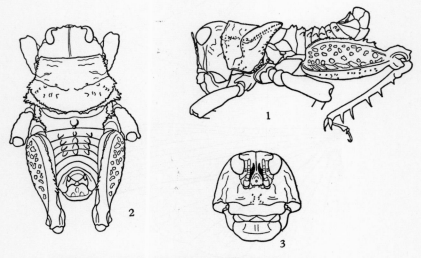

Fig. 222. *Batrachidacris tuberculata* (Rehn), male, × 2·5; 3, face.

Family PYRGOMORPHIDAE. Fig. 223

Size and shape variable. Head conical with fastigial furrow. Tegmina and the wings present, reduced or absent. Lower femoral lobe longer than the upper. No stridulatory mechanism. Tympanum normally present. Epiphallus bridge-shaped, with dorso-lateral appendages.

A large number of genera in the tropics and subtropics.

Atractomorpha bedeli I. Bolivar
    ,,   *crenulata* (Fabricius)
Aularches miliaris (Linnaeus)
    ,,   *punctatus* (Drury)
Chrotogonus homalodemus (Blanchard)
    ,,   *trachypterus* Blanchard
Colemania sphenarioides I. Bolivar
Dictyophorus
Maura
Phymateus viridipes Stål
Physemophorus socotranus (Burr)
Poekilocerus bufonius (Klug)
    ,,   *hieroglyphicus* (Klug)
    ,,   *pictus* (Fabricius)
Pyrgomorpha kraussi Uvarov
    ,,   *cognata* Krauss
Pyrgomorphella
Sphenarium mexicanum Saussure
Stibarosterna serrata Uvarov
Taphronota calliparea (Schaum)
Zonocerus elegans (Thunberg)
    ,,   *variegatus* (Linnaeus)

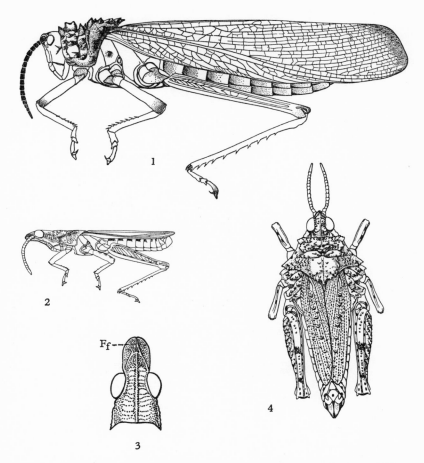

Fig. 223. 1, *Phymateus viridipes* Stål, male, × 1·8; 2, *Pyrgomorpha kraussi* Uvarov, male, × 1·8; 3, *Pyrgomorphella*, head showing the fastigial furrow (Ff); 4, *Chrotogonus*, female, × 3.

Family OMMEXECHIDAE. Fig. 224

Size medium. Shape variable. Head with fastigial furrow. Wing development variable. Valves of the penis undivided; epiphallus bridge-shaped, with the lateral plates joined by membrane.
Five genera in South America.
Graea horrida Philippi
Ommexecha servillei Blanchard

Family PAULINIIDAE. Fig. 225

Medium size. No fastigial furrow. No prosternal process. Hind tibia expanded for swimming. Valve of the penis divided; epiphallus bridge-shaped, the lateral plates joined by membrane.
Two semi-aquatic South American genera.
Marellia remipes Uvarov
Paulinia acuminata (De Geer)

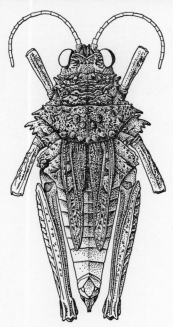

Fig. 224. *Ommexecha servillei* Blanchard, female, × 3·5.

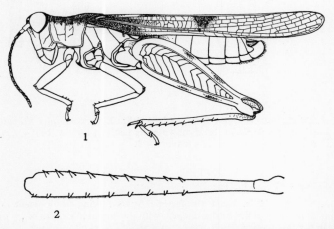

Fig. 225. *Paulinia acuminata* (De Geer). 1, male, × 3·4; 2, hind tibia expanded for swimming.

Family LENTULIDAE. Fig. 226

A highly retrogressive family. All species are apterous, have no trace of tympanum and look like hoppers. External appearance is highly variable, but excellent characters are found in the phallic complex, especially in the strongly developed capsule-like cingulum.

About twenty genera in southern and eastern Africa.

Lentula callani Dirsh
    ,,   *obtusifrons* Stål
Shelfordites

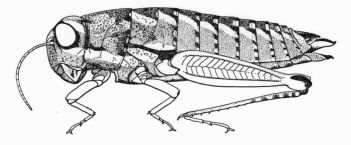

Fig. 226. *Lentula callani* Dirsh, female, × 3.

Family ACRIDIDAE.

This is the largest family and it includes many sub-divisions of unequal value, nineteen of which are recognised as subfamilies.

Subfamily Dericorythinae. Fig. 227

Size and wing development variable. No fastigial furrow. Pronotum with a crest, or hump, in the prozona only. Hind femur with basal lobes equal in length. Hind tibia curved. Epiphallus bridge-shaped.

Five genera in northern Africa and arid S.W. Asia.

Dericorys albidula Serville

Subfamily Chilacridinae. Fig. 228

Size medium; integument rugose. Wing development variable. Lower basal lobe of the hind femur as long as the upper, or slightly longer. Endophallus strongly sclerotised.

Five South American genera.

Chilacris maculipennis Liebermann

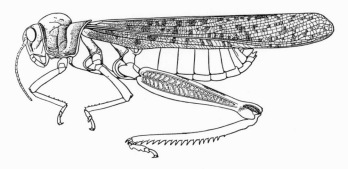

Fig, 227. *Dericorys albidula* Serville, female, × 1·2.

Subfamily Romaleinae. Fig. 229

Mostly large to medium size. Shape extremely variable, some genera resembling Pamphagidae, others Cyrtacanthacridinae, and so on. Lower basal lobe of the hind femur equal to the upper. Differs from all other subfamilies in the unique tegmino-alar stridulatory mechanism (p. 182), observable even in species with reduced wings.

405

Most of the genera occur in South and Central America and southernmost North America, and several in S.W. Asia and Somalia.

Brachystola magna (Girard)
Colpolopha obsoleta Serville
Romalea microptera (Beauvois)
Taeniopoda auricornis (Walker)
Teratodes monticollis (Gray)
Tropidacris dux (Drury)
    „   *latreillei* (Perty)
Zoniopoda cruentata (Blanchard)

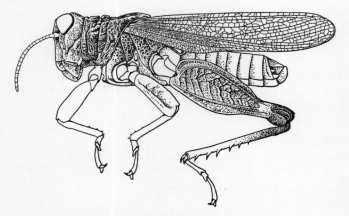

Fig. 228. *Chilacris maculipennis* Liebermann, male, × 2.

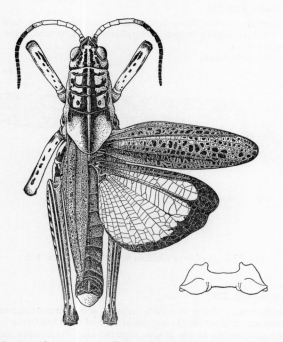

Fig. 229. *Romalea microptera* (Beauvois), male (× 1·5) and its epiphallus.

Subfamily Lithidiinae. Fig. 230

Size medium to very small. Body sturdy, depressed, rugose, usually apterous. Tympanum absent, even in winged species. Vertex very broad.

Four genera in South Africa.

Lithidium bushmanicum Dirsh
    ,,   *pusillum* Uvarov

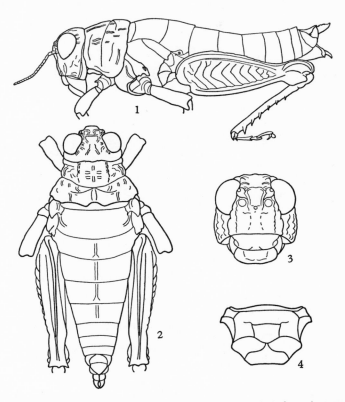

Fig. 230. *Lithidium bushmanicum* Dirsh. 1, 2, female, × 2·5; 3, face; 4, sternum.

Subfamily Hemiacridinae. Fig. 231

Extremely variable in shape. All winged species characterised by dense stridulatory veinlets in the radial area of the tegmen. Valves of the penis divided.

About forty genera occurring in the tropics and subtropics of the eastern hemisphere; two genera in South America.

Acanthoxia gladiator (Westwood)
Hemiacris fervens Walker
Hieroglyphus annulicornis (Shiraki)
    ,,   *banian* (Fabricius)
    ,,   *nigrorepletus* I. Bolivar
Leptacris hova Karsch
Parahieroglyphus bilineatus (I. Bolivar)
Spathosternum prasiniferum (Walker)
Sudanacris pallida (Burmeister)

407

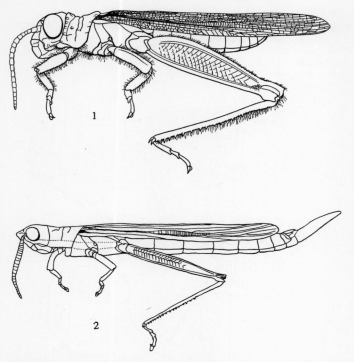

Fig. 231. 1, *Hemiacris fervens* Walker, male, × 3; 2, *Leptacris hova* Karsch, male, × 1·5.

Subfamily Tropidopolinae. Fig. 232

Body cylindrical, elongated, usually smooth. Head mostly conical. Prosternal process well developed. Mesosternal lobes contiguous.

About a dozen genera in Africa and subtropical Asia; one reaches southern Europe.

Afroxyrrhepes acuticerca Dirsh
       ,,   *procera* (Burmeister)
Mesopsilla roseoviridis Ramme
Oxyrrhepes cantonensis Tinkham
Tristria pallida Karny
Tropidopola

Subfamily Oxyinae. Fig. 233

Medium to small size; often green in colour. Cylindrical, usually elongated, body with smooth integument. Pronotum without lateral carinae. Tympanum normally present. No stridulatory mechanism. Lower knee-lobe of the hind femur spine-like. Hind tibia usually expanded (adaptation for swimming). Ovipositor valves usually serrate or spined. Epiphallus with divided bridge.

About twenty genera in humid tropical habitats of eastern hemisphere.

Oxya hyla Serville
  ,,   *japonica* Willemse
  ,,   *velox* (Fabricius)
  ,,   *vicina* Brunner-Wattenwyl

Subfamily Coptacridinae. Fig. 234

Size medium to small. Integument usually somewhat rough. Coloration usually not green, sometimes with striking dark and light spotted pattern. Occiput separated from the vertex by a ridge. Tympanum present. No stridulatory mechanism. Male cercus laterally compressed, down-curved, sometimes with an apical projection. Valves of the penis flexured. Epiphallus bridge-shaped, divided.

A number of genera in the tropics of Africa and Asia, mostly in forests.

Cyphocerastis laeta Karsch

Parepistaurus

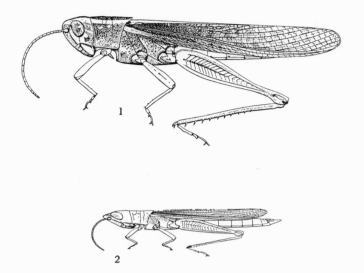

Fig. 232. 1, *Afroxyrrhepes acuticerca* Dirsh, male, × 1·5; 2, *Tropidopola*, male, × 1·6.

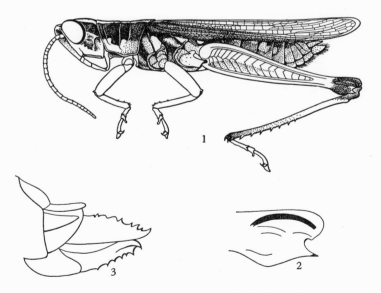

Fig. 233. *Oxya hyla* Serville. 1, male, × 3·6; 2, hind knee; 3, ovipositor.

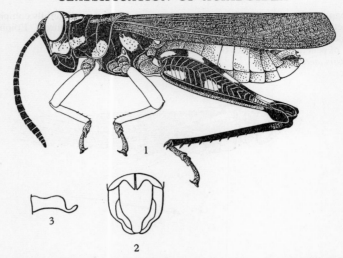

Fig. 234. *Cyphocerastis laeta* Karsch. 1, male, × 3·4; 2, end of male abdomen from above; 3, male cercus, lateral view.

Subfamily Calliptaminae. Fig. 235

Size medium to small. Head subglobular, without fastigial furrow. Pronotum usually with lateral carinae. Tympanum present. No stridulatory mechanism. Hind femur usually thick. Last tergite of the male inflated; cerci large, laterally compressed, forceps-like, with small apical lobes. Epiphallus plate-like, trapezoidal.

About a dozen genera in Africa, India and warmer parts of Europe.

Calliptamus barbarus (Costa)
    ,,   *coelesyriensis* Giglio-Tos
    ,,   *italicus* (Linnaeus)
    ,,   *palaestinensis*
    ,,   *turanicus* Ramme
Sphodromerus

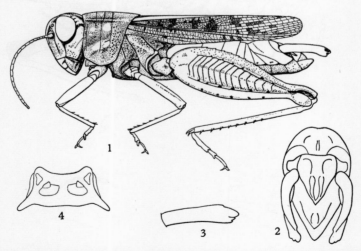

Fig. 235. *Calliptamus italicus* (Linnaeus). 1, male, × 3; 2, end of male abdomen from above; 3, male cercus, lateral view; 4, epiphallus.

Subfamily Euryphyminae. Fig. 236

Size medium to small; of sturdy build. Head sub-globular; frons vertical or slightly oblique. Pronotum with lateral carinae. Wing development variable. Tympanum present. No stridulatory mechanism. Hind margin of the last tergite of the male raised, sometimes serrate; epiproct often with sclerotised tubercles and ridges. Cercus of complicated structure, often upcurved; always with the basal articulation expanded. Epiphallus bridge-shaped, divided, with strong lophi.

Approximately twenty genera in semi-arid southern and eastern Africa.

Acrophymus cuspidatus (Karsch)
Anabibia thoracica Dirsh
Aneuryphymus rhodesianus Uvarov
Euryphymus haematopus (Linnaeus)
Platacanthoides bituberculatus Uvarov
Plegmapteropsis gracilis Dirsh
Plegmapterus splendens Dirsh

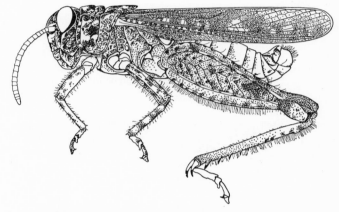

Fig. 236. *Euryphymus haematopus* (Linnaeus), male, × 2·4.

Subfamily Eyprepocnemidinae. Fig. 237

Size medium to large. Integument smooth. Head sub-globular. Pronotum usually with lateral carinae. Tympanum present. No stridulatory mechanism. Male cercus laterally compressed, down-curved. Epiphallus bridge-shaped.

Some thirty genera in the tropics and subtropics of Africa, Asia and Australia; a few species in southern Europe.

Cataloipus oberthüri (I. Bolivar)
Choroedocus capensis (Thunberg)
Eyprepocnemis hokutensis Shiraki
    ,,   *plorans meridionalis* Uvarov
    ,,   ,, *ornatipes* (Walker)
    ,,   *roseus* Uvarov
Heteracris (= *Thisoicetrus*)
    ,,   *adspersa* (Redtenbacher)
    ,,   *coerulescens* (Stål)
    ,,   *pulchripes* (Schaum)
Macrotona
Pareuprepocnemis syriaca Giglio-Tos
Phyllocercus bicoloripes Uvarov
Taramassus
Thisoecetrinus pterostichnus (Fischer-Waldheim)
(*Thisoicetrus*), see *Heteracris*
Tropidiopsis haasi I. Bolivar
Tylotropidius speciosus (Walker)

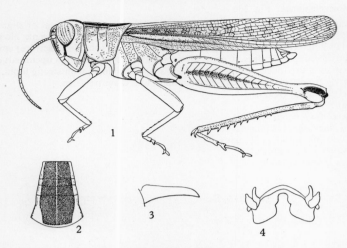

Fig. 237. *Eyprepocnemis plorans ornatipes* (Charpentier). 1, male, × 2·6; 2, dorsal view of pronotum; 3, cercus; 4, epiphallus.

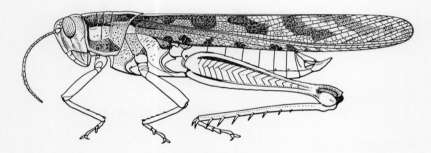

Fig. 238. *Cyrtacanthacris tatarica* (Linnaeus), male, × 1·8.

Subfamily Cyrtacanthacridinae. Fig. 238

Size large to medium. Head sub-globular; frons vertical. Pronotum without lateral carinae. Mesosternal lobes rectangular (fig. 145, C). Tegmina and wings rarely reduced. Tympanum present. No specialised stridulatory mechanism. Epiphallus robust, bridge-shaped. Comstock-Kellogg glands of the female present.

About thirty genera, confined to the tropics and the subtropics of both hemispheres.

Acanthacris ruficornis (Fabricius)

(*Acridium*), see *Anacridium*

Anacridium (= *Acridium*) *aegyptium* (Linnaeus). Referred to in the text by the generic name only.

  ,, *melanorhodon* (Walker)

  ,, *moestum* (Serville)

  ,, *wernerellum* (Karny)

Austracris guttulosa (Walker)

Cyrtacanthacris tatarica (Linnaeus)

Nomadacris septemfasciata (Serville). Referred to in the text by the generic name only.

Ornithacris turbida (Walker)

Orthacanthacris humilicrus Karsch

Patanga succincta (Linnaeus)

Schistocerca americana (Fabricius)

,,   (*cancellata*) (Serville), see *paranensis*

,,   *flavofasciata* (De Geer)

,,   *gregaria* (Forskål) (= *peregrina* Olivier). Referred to in the text by the generic
         name only.

,,   *gregaria flaviventris* (Burmeister)

,,   *lineata* Scudder

,,   *melanocera* Scudder

,,   *obscura* (Fabricius)

,,   *pallens* (Thunberg)

,,   *paranensis* (Burmeister) (? = *cancellata* Serville). The nomenclature of this species
         is not clear. Ogloblin (1955) suggested that the solitarious phase of *S. paranensis*
         is *S. cancellata*, without comparing it with the type of the latter; until this is done,
         Burmeister's name (definitely applicable to the swarming phase), is preferable.

,,   (*peregrina*), see *gregaria*

,,   *shoshone* (Thomas)

Valanga nigricornis (Burmeister)

Subfamily Catantopinae. Fig. 239

Size medium to large. Pronotum usually without any carinae. Wing development variable. Mesosternal lobes rounded. Tympanum present. No stridulatory mechanism. Epiphallus bridge-shaped. Comstock-Kellogg glands of the female present.

This is a very large group, including a great variety of forms. Until recently it comprised also the above mentioned subfamilies now separated from it, but the residue of several hundred genera distributed over the whole world is still very heterogeneous and further studies will undoubtedly result in dividing it into several subfamilies.

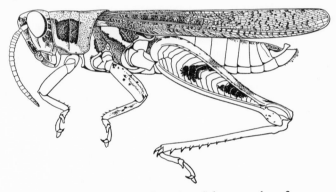

Fig. 239. *Catantops melanostictus* Schaum, male, × 3.

Anischnansis burtti (Uvarov)
Appalachia
Atrachelacris unicolor (Giglio-Tos)
Catantops axillaris (Thunberg)
     ,,   *melanostictus* Schaum
Conophyma comtulum Mistshenko
Cornops aquaticum Bruner
Crobylostenus indecisus (I. Bolivar)
Dendrotettix quercus Riley
Dichroplus
Diexis chivensis Mistshenko
Eirenephilus longipennis (Shiraki)
Hesperotettix
Kingdonella
Kosciuscicola tristis Sjöstedt
Leiotettix viridis Bruner
Leptysma marginicollis (Serville)

Mecostibus mopanei Uvarov
Mesambria
Mesopsera filum (I. Bolivar)
Melanoplus adelogyrus Hubbell
,,   (*atlanis*), see *sanguinipes*
,,   (*bilituratus*), see *sanguinipes* (Gurney 1962)
,,   *bivittatus* Say
,,   *devastator* Scudder
,,   *differentialis* Uhler. Referred to in the text by the generic name only.
,,   *femur-rubrum* (De Geer)
,,   *flavidus* Scudder
,,   *foedus* Scudder
,,   *gladstoni* Scudder
,,   *luridus* Dodge
,,   *mancus* Smith
,,   *marginatus* Scudder
,,   (*mexicanus*), see *sanguinipes*
,,   *packardi* Scudder
,,   *ponderosus* Scudder
,,   *puer* Scudder
,,   *rugglesi* Gurney
,,   *sanguinipes* (Fabricius) (= *bilituratus* Walker; *atlanis* Riley; *mexicanus* Saussure)
,,   *scudderi* Uhler
,,   *walshii* Scudder
Miramella alpina (Koller)
Odontopodisma decipiens Ramme
Oedaleonotus
Opshomala vitreipennis (Marshal)
Paraidemona mimica Scudder
Parapodisma sapporensis (Shiraki)
Paroxya atlantica (Scudder)
,,   ,,   *paroxyoides* (Scudder)
Pezocatantops impotens (Johnston)
Pezotettix giornae (Rossi)
Phaulacridium nanum Sjöstedt
,,   *vittatum* Sjöstedt
Podisma pedestris (Linnaeus)
Sauracris
Scotussa cliens (Stål)
Trybliophorus modestus Liebermann

Subfamily Egnatiinae. Fig. 240

Small. Head sub-globular. Integument rugulose. Mesosternal furcal suture curved backwards (fig. 14, E). Tegmina and wings rarely reduced. Tympanum present. Femoro-abdominal strudilatory mechanism present. Epiphallus bridge-shaped. Comstock-Kellogg glands of the female present.

A few genera in arid northern Africa and south-western Asia.
Charora pentagrammica I. Bolivar
Egnatius apicalis Stål

Subfamily Acridinae. Fig. 241

Size small to large. Body mostly very slender, compressed laterally. Head usually acute, sometimes obtusely conical; frons oblique. Tegmina and the wings usually present; medial area of the tegmen without a false vein, or the vein is weak, irregular and not serrated, even in the male, so that proper stridulatory mechanism absent. Typanum present. Epiphallus bridge-shaped.

Dirsh (1961) united this sub-family with Oedipodinae (see below), the main difference between them being the presence of stridulatory specialisation in the latter, which in my view is sufficient for their separation. An additional reason is a difference in the more acute angle of the frons and general slender shape of body of Acridinae. Most Acridinae are climbers on grass, while most Oedipodinae are ground-living.

A substantial number of genera, mainly in the tropics and subtropics, with only a few extending to the temperate regions.

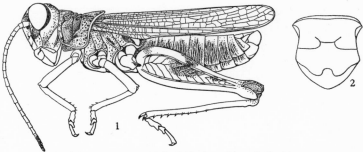

Fig. 240. *Egnatius apicalis* Stål. 1, male, × 4; 2, sternum.

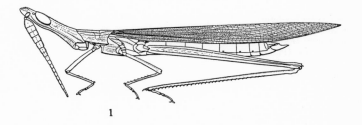

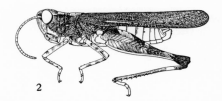

Fig. 241. 1, *Acrida turrita* (Linnaeus), male, × 1·6. 2, *Gymnobothrus temporalis* (Stål), male × 1·8.,

Acrida anatolica Dirsh
  ,,   *bicolor* (Thunberg)
  ,,   *exaltata* (Walker)
  ,,   *pellucida* (Klug)
  ,,   *turrita* (Linnaeus) (An African species; European records refer to *A. bicolor*).
Amphicremna
Cryptobothrus chrysophorus Sjöstedt
Duronia tricolor Stål
Eutryxalis
Gymnobothrus temporalis (Stål)
Machaeridia conspezsa (1. Bolivar)
Panzia
Parga
Phlaeoba
Rhadinotatum

Subfamily Oedipodinae. Fig. 242

Size medium to small; rarely large. Rather sturdy; frons usually vertical or nearly so. Integument mostly rugulose. Wing development varies; hindwings often brightly coloured. Tegminal inter-calary vein, at least in the male, well developed, serrate, forming the file of the stridulatory mechanism. Tympanum present. Epiphallus bridge-shaped.

A large number of genera in all parts of the world, but mainly in warmer drier climates.

415

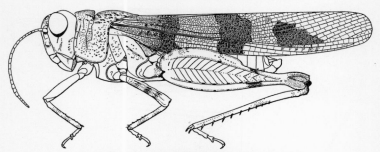

Fig. 242. *Oedipoda miniata* (Pallas), male, × 3·5.

Acrotylus angulatus Stål
    ,,   *insubricus* (Scopoli)
Aiolopus savignyi (Krauss)
    ,,   *thalassinus* (Fabricius)
Angaracris barabensis (Pallas)
Arphia sulphurea (Fabricius)
    ,,   *xanthoptera* (Burmeister)
Austroicetes cruciata (Saussure)
    ,,   *nullarborensis* Key
    ,,   *pusilla* (Walker)
Bryodema tuberculatum (Fabricius)
Camnula pellucida (Scudder)
Celes skalozubovi Adelung
    ,,   *variabilis* (Pallas)
Chortoicetes terminifera (Walker)
Chortophaga viridifasciata (De Geer)
Circotettix rabula Rehn & Hebard
    ,,   *verruculata* (Kirby)
Dissosteira carolina (Linnaeus)
    ,,   *longipennis* (Thomas)
Encoptolophus sordidus (Burmeister)
Epacromius coerulipes (Ivanov)
    ,,   *tergestinus* (Charpentier)
Froggattia
Gastrimargus africanus (Saussure)
    ,,   *musicus* (Fabricius)
    ,,   *nigericus* Uvarov
    ,,   *transversus* (Thunberg)
Helioscirtus
Heteropternis
Hippiscus apiculatus (Harris)
    ,,   *rugosus* (Scudder)
Humbe tenuicornis (Schaum)
Locusta (=*Pachytylus*) *migratoria burmana* Ramme (=*tibetensis* Chen-Yung-lin)
    ,,   *migratoria capito* Saussure
    ,,   ,,   *cinerascens* (Fabricius)
    ,,   ,,   *gallica* Remaudière
    ,,   ,,   *manilensis* (Mayne)
    ,,   ,,   *migratoria* (Linnaeus)
    ,,   ,,   *migratorioides* (Reiche & Fairmaire). Referred to in the text by the generic
                    name only.
    ,,   ,,   *rossica* Uvarov & Zolotarevsky
    ,,   ,,   (*tibetensis*), see *burmana*
Locustana pardalina (Walker). Referred to in the text by the generic name only.
Mecostethus gracilis Scudder
    ,,   *grossus* (Linnaeus)
Morphacris

416

Oedaleus australis Saussure
,,   *decorus* (Germar)
,,   *infernalis* Saussure
,,   *nigrofasciatus* (*De Geer*)
,,   *senegalensis* Krauss
Oedipoda aurea Uvarov
,,   *caerulescens* (Linnaeus)
,,   *germanica* (Latreille)
,,   *miniata* (Pallas) (= *gratiosa* Serville)
,,   *schochi* Saussure
(*Pachytylus*), see *Locusta*
Paracinema tricolor (Thunberg)
Parapleurus alliaceus (Germar)
Pardalophera phoenicoptera (Burmeister)
Psophus stridulus (Linnaeus)
Pyrgodera armata (Fischer-Waldheim)
Spharagemon bolli Scudder
Sphingonotus caerulans (Linnaeus)
,,   *carinatus* Saussure
,,   *coerulipes* Uvarov
,,   *savignyi* Saussure
Trilophidia conturbata (Walker)
Trimerotropis citrina Scudder
,,   *maritima* (Harris)
,,   *pallidipennis* (Burmeister)
,,   *sparsa* (Thomas)
Xanthippus corallipes (Haldeman)

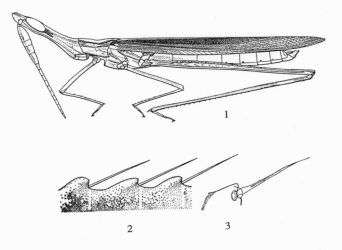

Fig. 243. 1, *Truxalis grandis* Klug, male, × 1·9; 2, Stridulatory file seen from outside; 3, ditto, from inside.

Subfamily Truxalinae. Fig. 243

Size large to medium. Body very slender, laterally compressed. Antenna flattened, ensiform. Head acute in profile; eyes nearer to its apex than to its base; frons strongly oblique. Prosternum without process. Tegmen narrow, with acute apex, without the medial vein. Hind femur long and narrow; its stridulatory file represented by closely-set rigid tubercles and articulated bristles; hind knee with acute lobes. Tympanum present. Epiphallus bridge-shaped.

This subfamily is treated here in a much more restricted sense than suggested by Dirsh (1961),

27   4I7

who included in it also the next (Gomphocerinae), which has a differently specialised stridulatory file (p. 178).

As understood here, the subfamily includes only a few genera occurring mainly in the tropical and subtropical grasslands of Africa; a few species of *Truxalis* penetrate to southern Europe and S.W. Asia.

Truxalis nasuta (Linnaeus)
  ,, *grandis* Klug

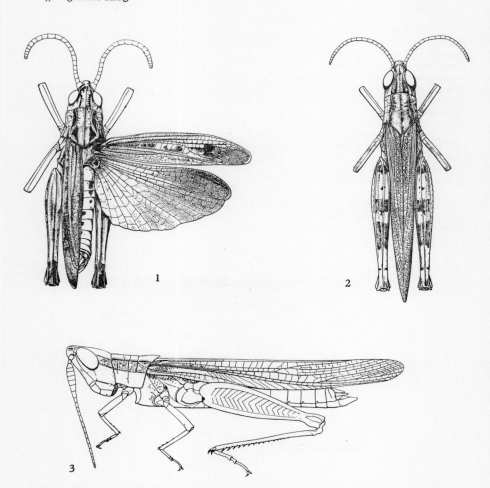

Fig. 244. 1, *Stenobothrus palpalis* Uvarov, male, × 3; 2, *Phorenula dorsata* (I. Bolivar), male, × 3; 3, *Ochrilidia geniculata* (I. Bolivar), male, × 3·2.

Subfamily Gomphocerinae. Fig. 244

Size mostly small to medium. Body usually moderately slender, laterally compressed. Antennae normally filiform, but tend to be compressed and ensiform in species with elongated body. Head in profile from subacute to acute; eyes not nearer to its apex than to the base. Prosternum without process. Tegmen with expanded (tympanate) areas; no medial vein. Hind femur never extremely narrow; its stridulatory file with articulated pegs. Tympanum present. Epiphallus bridge-shaped.

A very large subfamily, represented in all regions of the world except Madagascar and Australia.

Aeropedellus variegatus (Fischer-Waldheim)
„   *Clavatus* (Thomas)
Arcyptera fusca (Pallas)
Aulocara elliotti (Thomas)
(*Aulacobothrus*), see *Phorenula*
Baidoceracris
Bootettix
Brachycrotaphus sjöstedti Uvarov
„   *tryxalicera* Krauss
Chorthippus (= partly *Stenobothrus* of earlier authors) *albomarginatus* (De Geer)
„   *apricarius* (Linnaeus)
„   *biguttulus* (Linnaeus)
„   *brunneus* (Thunberg) (= *bicolor* Charpentier)
„   *curtipennis* (Harris) (wrongly called *longicornis* by American authors)
„   (*longicornis*), see *curtipennis* and *parallelus*
„   *mollis* (Charpentier)
„   *montanus* (Charpentier) (wrongly called *parallelus* by some recent European authors)
„   *parallelus* (Zetterstedt) (wrongly called *longicornis* by some recent European authors)
„   *vagans* (Eversmann)
Chrysochraon dispar (Germar)
Clinocephalus
Dichromorpha viridis (Scudder)
Dociostaurus (= *Stauronotus*) *brevicollis* (Eversmann)
„   *kraussi* (Ingenetiskiĭ)
„   *maroccanus* (Thunberg). Referred to in the text by the generic name only.
„   *tartarus* (Schtelknovzev)
Dysanema
Euchorthippus pulvinatus (Fischer-Waldheim)
Euthystira brachyptera (Ocskay)
Faureia milanjica (Karsch)
Gomphocerippus rufus (Linnaeus)
Gomphocerus sibiricus (Linnaeus)
Mermiria maculipennis Bruner
Mesopsis laticornis Krauss
Myrmeleotettix maculatus (Thunberg)
Neopodismopsis abdominalis (Thomas)
Peruvia
Ochrilidia (= *Platypterna*) *geniculata* (I. Bolivar)
„   *gracilis* (Krauss)
Omocestus viridulus (Linnaeus)
„   *rufipes* (Zetterstedt)
Orphulella concinnula (Walker)
Pararcyptera microptera (Fischer-Waldheim)
Phonogaster cariniventris Henry
Phlocerus
Phorenula (= *Aulacobothrus*) *dorsata* I. Bolivar
„   „   *werneriana* (Karny)
(*Platypterna*), see *Ochrilidia*
Pseudoarcyptera palpalis (Uvarov)
Rhammatocerus pictus (Bruner)
„   *viatorius* (Saussure)
Scyllinops
Spaniacris
Stauroderus scalaris (Fischer-Waldheim)
(*Stauronotus*), see *Dociostaurus*
Stenobothrus eurasius Zubowskyi
„   *lineatus* (Panzer)
„   *maroccanus* Uvarov
„   *nigromaculatus* (Herrich-Schäffer)
„   *palpalis* Uvarov
„   *stigmaticus* (Rambur)
Syrbula

419

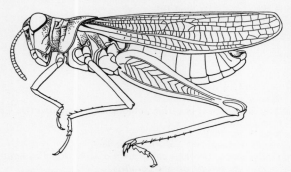

Fig. 245. *Eremogryllus hammadae* Krauss, male, × 6.

Subfamily Eremogryllinae. Fig. 245

Small. Head sub-globular. Prosternum with a convexity. Tegmen without the intercalary vein. Tympanum present. Hind femur with articulate stridulatory pegs as in Gomphocerinae. Male cerci short, thick, curved. Phallic complex small; epiphallus bridge-shaped, divided.

Only two genera in the Sahara and Israel.

Eremogryllus hammadae Krauss
Notopleura saharae Krauss

420

BIBLIOGRAPHY

The list of papers presented below is not a full bibliography of the aspects of acridology dealt with in the present volume, as it does not include preliminary communications if they were followed by a full paper which alone is quoted; also omitted are the papers which contain no substantial original information, but comprehensive reviews of special topics are, of course, included.

The bibliography comprises 1415 titles in eleven languages and is hoped to be reasonably complete up to the end of 1961; some papers published in 1962–5 and in the press have also been included, as far as possible.

Italic numbers in square brackets after each entry refer to the pages of the book where the paper is mentioned; this eliminates the need for an author index.

ADAMOVIĆ, Z. R. 1950. Quelques analyses biométriques de l'*Oedipoda coerulescens* L. (Orthoptères). (In Serbian with French summary.) *Glasn. Muz. srpsk. Zeml.* B, **3–4**: 333–42, 3 figs. [*391*].

AFIFI, A. M. 1959. On a sexual dimorphism in the olfactory lobe of the Migratory Locust, *Locusta migratoria migratorioides* (R. & F.) (Orthoptera: Acrididae). *Bull. Soc. ent. Égypte*, **43**: 315–17, 1 fig. [*151*, *152*].

—— 1960. Über die postembryonale Entwicklung des Zentralnervensystems (ZNS) bei der Wanderheuschrecke *Locusta migratoria migratorioides* (R. & F.) (Orthoptera—Acrididae). *Zool. Jb.* (Anat.), **78**: 1–38, 30 figs. [*34*, *151*, *152*, *282*].

AGARWALA, S. B. D. 1952–4. A comparative study of the ovipositor in Acrididae. *Indian J. Ent.* **13** (1951): 147–81, 35 figs.; **14**: 61–75, 26 figs.; **15**: 53–69, 32 figs.; **15** (1953): 299–318, 25 figs. [*17*, *20*, *148*, *175*, *282*, *322*, *324*].

AGRAWAL, N. S. 1955. Bionomics of *Atractomorpha crenulata* Fab. (Orthoptera: Acrididae). *Indian J. Ent.* **17**: 230–40, 7 figs. [*321*].

AHMAD, T. 1936. The influence of constant and alternating temperatures on the development of certain stages of insects. *Proc. nat. Inst. Sci. India*, **2**: 67–91, 7 figs. [*253*].

ALBRECHT, F. O. 1953a. *The Anatomy of the Migratory Locust*. London [*1*, *5*, *17*, *59*, *60*, *71*, *73*, *105*, *106*, *118*, *124*, *127*, *138*, *140*, *146*, *151*, *157*].

—— 1953b. The breeding of the Red Locust in captivity. *Bull. ent. Res.* **44**: 1–4 [*310*].

—— 1955. La densité des populations et la croissance chez *Schistocerca gregaria* (Forsk.) et *Nomadacris septemfasciata* (Serv.); la mue d'ajustement. *J. Agric. trop. Bot. appl.* **2**: 109–92, 24 figs. [*278*, *282*, *337*, *338*].

—— 1956. The anatomy of the Red Locust (*Nomadacris septemfasciata* Serville). *Anti-Locust Bull.* no. 23: 9 pp., 97 figs. [*1*, *8*, *12*, *13*, *17*, *21*, *23*, *59*, *60*, *62–4*, *73*, *105*, *124*, *125*, *126*, *127*, *148*, *151*, *152*, *153*, *157*].

—— 1959. Facteurs internes et fluctuations des effectifs chez *Nomadacris septemfasciata* (Serv.). *Bull. biol.* **93**: 414–61, 8 figs. [*333*, *355*, *362*, *369*].

—— [Ed.] 1962a. Physiologie, comportement et écologie des acridiens en rapport avec la phase. *Colloq. int. Cent. nat. Rech. sci.* no. 114: 342 pp., figs. [*380*].

—— 1962b. Some physiological and ecological aspects of locust phases. *Trans. R. ent. Soc. Lond.* **114**: 335–75, 10 figs. [*227*, *333*, *334*, *378*, *385*].

ALBRECHT, F. O. & BLACKITH, R. E. 1957. Phase and moulting polymorphism in locusts. *Evolution*, **11**: 166–77, 5 figs. [*348*].

—— 1960. Poids et délai de survie des larves nouveau-nées chez les acridiens migrateurs. Données physiologiques. *C. R. Acad. Sci., Paris*, **250**: 3388–90, 1 fig. [*234*, *334*].

ALBRECHT, F. O. & VERDIER, M. 1956. Le poids et le nombre d'ovarioles chez les larves nouveau-nées de *Locusta migratoria migratorioides* R. et F. *C. R. Acad. Sci., Paris*, **243**: 203–5, 2 figs. [*282*].

ALBRECHT, F. O., VERDIER, M. & BLACKITH, R. E. 1959. Détermination de la fertilité par l'effet de groupe chez le criquet migrateur (*Locusta migratoria migratorioides* R. & F.). *Bull. biol.* **92** (1958): 349–427, 20 figs. [*327*, *333*, *353*, *355*, *356*, *362*, *365*, *369*].

ALBRECHT, G. 1961. Untersuchungen über die chemische Zusammensetzung einiger Insektenfette. *Z. vergl. Physiol.* **44**: 487–508, 6 figs. [*101*, *102*].

ALEXANDER, R. D. 1960. Communicative mandible-snapping in Acrididae (Orthoptera). *Science*, **132**: 152–3. [*184*].

BIBLIOGRAPHY

ALICATA, P. 1962a. Morfologia comparata ed evoluzione della regione del collo negli Ortotteri. *Boll. Zool.* **29**: 49–72, 16 figs. [*60*].

—— 1962b. Muscolatura e sistema nervoso del torace di *Eyprepocnemis plorans* (Charp.) e considerazioni sul sistema nervoso cervico-toracico degli insetti. *Arch. Zool. ital.* **47**: 263–337, 24 figs. [*155*].

ALLEN, T. H. 1940. Enzymes in ontogenesis (Orthoptera). XI. Cytochrome oxidase in relation to respiratory activity and growth of the grasshopper egg. *J. cell. comp. Physiol.* **16**: 149–63, 8 figs. [*251*].

ALLEN, T. H., BOYD, G. E. & BODINE, J. H. 1942. Enzymes in ontogenesis (Orthoptera). XXI. Unimolecular films and fractions of protyrosinase activators from grasshopper egg oil. *J. biol. Chem.* **143**: 785–93, 4 figs. [*267*].

AMOROSO, C. 1936. Sugli spiracoli tracheali degli Ortotteri. *Boll. Zool.* **7**: 127–36, 4 figs. [*124*].

ANDERSEN, S. O. 1963. Characterization of a new type of cross-linkage in resilin, a rubber-like protein. *Biochim. biophys. Acta*, **69**: 249–62, 13 figs. [*32, 35*].

ANDREWARTHA, H. G. 1943. Diapause in the eggs of *Austroicetes cruciata* Sauss. (Acrididae) with particular reference to the influence of temperature on the elimination of diapause. *Bull. ent. Res.* **34**: 1–17 [*260, 261, 263*].

—— 1944. The influence of temperature on the elimination of diapause from the eggs of the race of *Austroicetes cruciata* Sauss. (Acrididae) occurring in Western Australia. *Aust. J. exp. Biol. med. Sci.* **22**: 17–20, 1 fig. [*260, 261, 263*].

—— 1952. Diapause in relation to the ecology of insects. *Biol. Rev.* **27**: 50–107, 5 figs. [*258, 260, 261, 263*].

ANDREWARTHA, H. G. & BIRCH, L. C. 1954. *The Distribution and Abundance of Animals*. Chicago [*261*].

ANTONIOU, A. & HUNTER-JONES, P. 1956. The life history of *Eyprepocnemis capitata* Miller (Orth., Acrididae) in the laboratory. *Ent. mon. Mag.* **92**: 364–8, 1 fig. [*286, 321, 328*].

ARORA, G. L. & SINGH, A. 1958. The external morphology of *Chrotogonus trachypterus* Blanch. (Orthoptera, Acrididae, Pyrgomorphinae). *Res. Bull. Panjab Univ.* (Zool.), no. 149: 149–74, 35 figs. [*1*].

ASHALL, C. & ELLIS, P. E. 1962. Studies on numbers and mortality in field populations of the Desert Locust (*Schistocerca gregaria* Forskål). *Anti-Locust Bull.* no. 38: 59 pp., 17 figs. [*356*].

ASHHURST, D. E. 1959. The connective tissue sheath of the locust nervous system: a histochemical study. *Quart. J. micr. Sci.* **100**: 401–12, 2 figs. [*69, 154, 155*].

ASHHURST, D. E. & CHAPMAN, J. A. 1961. The connective-tissue sheath of the nervous system of *Locusta migratoria*: an electron microscope study. *Quart. J. micr. Sci.* **102**: 463–7, 2 figs. [*69, 154*].

ATZINGER, L. 1957. Vergleichende Untersuchungen über die Beziehungen zwischen Ausbildung der Flügel, der Flugmuskulatur und des Flugvermögens bei Feldheuschrecken. *Zool. Jb.* (Anat.), **76**: 199–222, 14 figs. [*15, 30, 31, 62*].

AUGER, D. & FESSARD, A. 1928. Observations sur l'excitabilité de l'organe tympanique du criquet. *C. R. Soc. Biol., Paris*, **99**: 400–1 [*190*].

AUTRUM, H. & SCHNEIDER, W. 1948. Vergleichende Untersuchungen über den Erschütterungssinn der Insekten. *Z. vergl. Physiol.* **31**: 77–88, 3 figs. [*170*].

AUTRUM, H., SCHWARTZKOPFF, J. & SWOBODA, H. 1961. Der Einfluss der Schallrichtung auf die Tympanal-Potentiale von *Locusta migratoria* L. *Biol. Zbl.* **80**: 385–402, 9 figs. [*193*].

AZIZ, S. A. 1958. Probable hygroreceptors in the Desert Locust, *Schistocerca gregaria* Forsk. (Orthoptera: Acrididae). *Indian J. Ent.* **19** (1957): 164–70, 5 figs. [*165, 171, 173*].

BACCETTI, B. 1954. Su un caso di ginandromorfismo in *Podisma pedestris* L. (Orth. Catant.). *Redia*, **39**: 401–11, 6 figs. [*149*].

—— 1955a. Ricerche sulla fine struttura del perilemma nel sistema nervoso degli insetti. *Redia*, **40**: 197–212, 2 pls., 1 fig. [*69, 154*].

—— 1955b. Sulla presenza e struttura di una tunica involgente i corpi grassi degli insetti. *Redia*, **40**: 269–79, 2 pls. [*69, 96*].

—— 1956a. Ricerche preliminari sui connettivi e sulle membrane basali degli insetti. *Redia*, **41**: 75–104, 5 pls. [*32, 59, 69*].

—— 1956b. Lo stroma di sostegno di organi degli insetti esaminato a luce polarizzata. *Redia*, **41**: 259–76, 1 pl., 6 figs. [*32, 69, 73*].

—— 1957. Observations by polarized light on the supporting stroma of some organs in insects. *Exp. Cell Res.* **13**: 158–60, 1 fig. [*69*].

—— 1960. Ricerche sull'ultrastruttura dell'intestino degli insetti. I. L'ileo di un ortottero adulto. *Redia*, **45**: 263–78, 10 pls., 1 fig. [*73, 74*].

—— 1961a. Primi reperti sulla struttura submicroscopica dello stroma di sostegno di alcuni organi degli insetti. *Atti Accad. Torino*, **95**: 343–50, 10 pls. [*69*].

—— 1961b. Indagini comparative sull'ultrastruttura della fibrilla collagene nei diversi ordini degli insetti. *Redia*, **46**: 1–7, 2 pls. [*69*].

—— 1961c. Ricerche sull'ultrastruttura dell'intestino degli insetti. II. La cellula epiteliale del mesentero in un ortottero, un coleottero e un dittero adulti. *Redia*, **46**: 157–65, 7 pls. [*72, 73*].

—— 1961d. Il problema della secrezione della ooteca negli ortotteroidei alla luce delle pui recenti acquisizioni. *R. C. Accad. ital. Ent.* **8** (1960): 112–36, 3 pls., 3 figs. [*146*].

BIBLIOGRAPHY

BACCETTÍ, B. 1962. Ricerche sull'ultrastruttura dell'intestino degli insetti. IV. Le papille rettali in un ortottero adulto. *Redia*, **47**: 105–18, 11 pls., 1 fig. [*73, 74*].

BADEN, V. 1936. Embryology of the nervous system in the grasshopper, *Melanoplus differentialis* (Acrididae; Orthoptera). *J. Morph.* **60**: 159–88, 4 pls. [*246*].

——1938. Origin and fate of the median cord in the grasshopper, *Melanoplus differentialis* (Acrididae; Orthoptera). *J. Morph.* **63**: 219–27, 2 pls., 1 fig. [*246*].

BAILEY, K. & WEIS-FOGH, T. 1961. Amino acid composition of a new rubber-like protein, resilin *Biochim. biophys. Acta*, **48**: 452–9 [*35, 67*].

BARANOV, N. 1925. Material for a new classification of Acridoidea. (In Serbian.) *Polyoprivred. Ogledna Kontrol Sta. Topchider Phyto-Ent. Odesk Beograd*, no. 3: 28 pp., 14 figs. [*344, 388*].

BARAUD, J. 1955. Les pigments des insectes. *Rev. Zool. agric.* **54**: 20–8, 61–5 [*42*].

BARKER, J. F. 1960. Variation of chiasma frequency in and between natural populations of Acrididae. *Heredity*, **14**: 211–14, 1 fig. [*390*].

BARNES, O. L. 1955. Effect of food plants on the lesser migratory grasshopper. *J. econ. Ent.* **48**: 119–24, 2 figs. [*82, 83, 328, 329*].

—— 1960. Observations on the desert grasshopper, *Trimerotropis pallidipennis pallidipennis*, in Arizona. *J. econ. Ent.* **53**: 721–4 [*371*].

—— 1963. Food-plant tests with the differential grasshopper. *J. econ. Ent.* **56**: 396–9 [*83*].

BARNUM, A. H. 1959. *The phallic complex in the Oedipodinae (Orthoptera: Acrididae)*. Ph.D. thesis, Iowa State College [*143, 147, 388*].

BARSA, M. C. 1954. The behaviour of isolated hearts of the grasshopper, *Chortophaga viridifasciata*, and the moth, *Samia walkeri*, in solutions with different concentrations of sodium, potassium, calcium, and magnesium. *J. gen. Physiol.* **38**: 79–92 [*110, 113*].

BASSO STAJANO, C. & ESCALANTE ROSSI, B. 1947. Contribución al conocimiento del valor bromatológico de la langosta común (*Schistocerca cancellata*) y de sus huevos. *Rev. Fac. Agron. Montevideo*, no. 44 (1946): 229–37 [*90, 101*].

BATTAGLIA, B. 1950. Ricerche sul metabolismo degli acidi nucleici nella spermatogenesi degli Ortotteri (Acrididae). *Riv. Biol.* **42**: 27–43, 1 pl., 2 figs. [*304*].

BATTAGLIA, B. & SARÀ, M. 1951. Sulla degenerazione di cellule nella spermatogenesi di alcuni insetti. *Sci. genet.* **4**: 36–40 [*304*].

BEAMENT, J. W. L. 1959. The waterproofing mechanism of arthropods. I. The effect of temperature on cuticle permeability in terrestrial insects and ticks. *J. exp. Biol.* **36**: 391–422, 17 figs. [*231, 232*].

—— 1961. The water relations of insect cuticle. *Biol. Rev.* **36**: 281–320, 7 figs. [*32*].

BEAMS, H. W. & ANDERSON, E. 1957. Light and electron microscope studies on the striated border of the intestinal epithelial cells of insects. *J. Morph.* **100**: 601–19, 5 pls. [*72*].

BEAMS, H. W., TAHMISIAN, T. M. & DEVINE, R. L. 1955. Electron microscope studies on the cells of the Malpighian tubules of the grasshopper (Orthoptera, Acrididae). *J. biophys. biochem. Cytol.* **1**: 197–202, 6 pls. [*119*].

BECKER, E. 1942. Über Eigenschaften, Verbreitung und die genetischentwicklungsphysiologische Bedeutung der Pigmente der Ommatin- und Ommingruppe (Ommochrome) bei den Arthropoden. *Z. indukt. Abstamm.- u. Vererblehre*, **80**: 157–204, 11 figs. [*44, 199*].

BEI-BIENKO, G. YA. 1928. Synopsis of the larvae of the West Siberian locusts (Orthoptera, Acrididae). (In Russian with English summary.) *Trud. Siber. Inst. Agric. For.* **9**: 39 pp., 11 figs. [*260, 283, 287*].

BEINGOLEA GUERRERO, O. 1958. Estudios morfométricos de fases de la langosta migratoria sudamericàna en el Perú (*Schistocerca cancellata* Serv.—*S. paranensis* Burm.) *10th Int. Congr. Ent.*, Montreal 1956, vol. 2: 1037–51, 5 figs. [*347*].

BELLAMY, D. 1958. The structure and metabolic properties of tissue preparations from *Schistocerca gregaria* (Desert Locust). *Biochem. J.* **70**: 580–9 [*44, 45, 47, 68, 102*].

BENASSI, C. A., COLOMBO, G. & ALLEGRI, G. 1961. Free amino-acids of the haemolymph of *Schistocerca gregaria* Forsk. *Biochem. J.* **80**: 332–6 [*112*].

BENASSI, C. A., COLOMBO, G. & PERETTI, G. 1959. Free amino-acids of the haemolymph of *Anacridium aegyptium* L. (Orthoptera). *Experientia*, **15**: 457–8 [*112*].

BENNETT, H. S. 1953. Tracheae and sarcosomes in grasshopper leg muscle. (Abs.) *Anat. Rec.* **115**: 282–3 [*59, 126*].

BEREZHKOV, R. P. 1956. *Acrididae of Western Siberia*. (In Russian.) Tomsk [*287*].

BERGERARD, J. & SEUGÉ, J. 1959. La parthénogenèse accidentelle chez *Locusta migratoria* L. *Bull. biol.* **93**: 16–37, 1 pl., 4 figs. [*319, 320*].

BERLESE, A. 1909. *Gli Insetti. Volume Primo: Embriologia e Morfologia*. Milan [*59*].

BERNARD, F. 1937. Recherches sur la morphogénèse des yeux composés d'arthropodes. Développement, croissance, réduction. *Bull. biol.*, (Suppl.) **23**: 162 pp., 6 pls., 20 figs. [*196, 246, 278*].

BERRETTA, L. 1935. Genesi della membrana peritrofica nell'intestino degli Ortotteri. *Boll. Ist. zool. Palermo*, **2**: 117–32, 2 pls. [*73*].

—— 1937. La membrana peritrofica negli Ortotteri osservata in toto e origine di questa membrana. *Boll. Soc. Sci. nat. econ. Palermo*, **19**: 20–25, 2 figs. [*73*].

BETHE, A. 1897. Vergleichende Untersuchungen über die Functionen des Centralnervensystems der Arthropoden. *Pflüg. Arch. ges. Physiol.* **68**: 449–502, 1 pl. [*65*].

BIGELOW, R. S. & REIMER, C. 1954. An application of the linear discriminant function to insect taxonomy. *Canad. Ent.* **86**: 69–73 [*392*].

BIBLIOGRAPHY

Birch, L. C. 1942. The influence of temperatures above the developmental zero on the development of the eggs of *Austroicetes cruciata* Sauss. (Orthoptera). *Aust. J. exp. Biol. med. Sci.* **20**: 17–25, 1 fig. [*260*].

Birch, L. C. & Andrewartha, H. G. 1942. The influence of moisture on the eggs of *Austroicetes cruciata* Sauss. (Orthoptera) with reference to their ability to survive desiccation. *Aust. J. exp. Biol. med. Sci.* **20**: 1–8, 3 figs. [*261, 263, 268*].

—— 1944. The influence of drought on the survival of eggs of *Austroicetes cruciata* Sauss. (Orthoptera) in South Australia. *Bull. ent. Res.* **35**: 243–50, 3 figs. [*263, 268*].

Bishai, F. R. & Zebe, E. 1959. Enzymverteilungsmuster und Metabolitspiegel in der Beinmuskulatur der Heuschrecken. *Zool. Anz.* (Suppl.) no. 23: 314–19, 4 figs. [*68*].

Blackith, R. E. 1957. Polymorphism in some Australian locusts and grasshoppers. *Biometrics*, **13**: 183–96, 2 figs. [*348*].

—— 1961. The water reserves of hatchling locusts. *Comp. Biochem. Physiol.* **3**: 99–107 [*227, 230, 233, 234, 271, 333*].

—— 1962. L'identité des manifestations phasaires chez les acridiens migrateurs. *Colloq. int. Cent. nat. Rech. sci.* no. 114:299–310, 2 figs. [*348*].

Blackith, R. E. & Albrecht, F. O. 1960. Poids et délai de survie des larves nouveau-nées chez les acridiens migrateurs. Données chimiques. *C. R. Acad. Sci., Paris*, **250**: 3514–5 [*334*].

—— 1961. Quelques nouvelles techniques utilisables en analyse morphométrique chez les acridiens. I. Nouveaux appareils de mesure des petites dimensions. *Bull. Soc. ent. Fr.* **65** (1960): 257–60, 6 figs. [*346*].

Blackith, R. E. & Howden, G. F. 1961. The food reserves of hatchling locusts. *Comp. Biochem. Physiol.* **3**: 108–24 [*89, 92, 97, 112, 114, 334, 336, 337*].

Blackith, R. E. & Verdier, M. 1961. Quelques nouvelles techniques utilisables en analyse morphométrique chez les acridiens. II. Utilisation du fémur antérieur pour diverses discriminations. *Bull. Soc. ent. Fr.* **65** (1960): 260–73, 2 figs. [*347*].

Blumenthal, R. A. 1927. A micro blood sugar method and the blood sugars of insects. *Science*, **65**: 617–19 [*112*].

Boche, R. D. & Buck, J. B. 1942. Studies on the hydrogen-ion concentration of insect blood and their bearing on *in vitro* cytological technique. *Physiol. Zoöl.* **15**: 293–303 [*108*].

Bodenheimer, F. S. 1934. Über die Temperaturabhängigkeiten der Insekten. IV. Über die Körpertemperatur der Insekten. *Zool. Jb.* (Syst.), **66**: 113–51, 13 figs. [*214*].

—— 1935. Ökologisch-zoogeographische Untersuchungen über die Orthopterenfauna Palästinas. 1. Teil. *Arch. Naturgesch.* (N.F.), **4**: 88–142, 10 figs. [*222*].

—— 1944. Studies on the ecology and control of the Moroccan Locust (*Dociostaurus maroccanus*) in 'Iraq. I. Results of a mission of the 'Iraq Department of Agriculture to N. 'Iraq in spring 1943. *Bull. Dir.-Gen. Agric. Iraq*, no. 29: 121 pp., 21 pls., 16 figs. [*228, 356*].

Bodenheimer, F. S. *et al.* 1929. Studien zur Epidemiologie, Ökologie und Physiologie der afrikanischen Wanderheuschrecke (*Schistocerca gregaria* Forsk.). *Z. angew. Ent.* **15**: 435–557, 55 figs. [*88, 132, 207, 208, 212, 274*].

Bodenheimer, F. S. & Shulov, A. 1951. Egg-development and diapause in the Moroccan Locust (*Dociostaurus maroccanus* Thnb.). *Bull. Res. Coun. Israel*, **1**: 59–75, 6 figs. [*244, 245, 247, 260, 261*].

Bodine, J. H. 1921. Factors influencing the water content and the rate of metabolism of certain Orthoptera. *J. exp. Zool.* **32**: 137–64, 6 figs. [*132, 137, 225, 228*].

—— 1922. The effect of light and decapitation on the rate of CO_2 output of certain Orthoptera. *J. exp. Zool.* **35**: 47–55, 3 figs. [*135*].

—— 1923. Hibernation in Orthoptera. I. Physiological changes during hibernation in certain Orthoptera. *J. exp. Zool.* **37**: 457–76, 7 figs. [*225*].

—— 1925a. I. Effect of temperature on rate of embryonic development of certain Orthoptera. *J. exp. Zool.* **42**: 91–109, 7 figs. [*255*].

—— 1925b. Physiology of the Orthoptera. Hydrogen ion concentration of the blood and alimentary tract of certain Orthoptera (grasshoppers). *Biol. Bull., Woods Hole*, **48**: 79–82 [*108*].

—— 1929. Factors influencing the rate of respiratory metabolism of a developing egg (Orthoptera). *Physiol. Zoöl.* **2**: 459–82, 14 figs. [*248*].

—— 1932. Hibernation and diapause in certain Orthoptera. II. Response to temperature during hibernation, and diapause. *Physiol. Zoöl.* **5**: 538–48, 7 figs. [*248*].

—— 1933. The effect of hypertonic solutions on the oxygen consumption of a developing egg (Orthoptera). *Physiol. Zoöl.* **6**: 150–8 [*247*].

—— 1946. Uric acid formation in the developing egg of the grasshopper, *Melanoplus differentialis*. *Physiol. Zoöl.* **19**: 54–8, 1 fig. [*250*].

Bodine, J. H. & Allen, T. H. 1941. Enzymes in ontogenesis (Orthoptera): XV. Some properties of protyrosinases. *J. cell. comp. Physiol.* **18**: 151–60, 7 figs. [*251*].

Bodine, J. H. & Boell, E. J. 1935. Enzymes in ontogenesis (Orthoptera). I. Tyrosinase. *J. cell. comp. Physiol.* **6**: 263–75, 3 figs. [*43, 251*].

Bodine, J. H. & Fitzgerald, L. R. 1947a. Riboflavin and other fluorescent compounds in a developing egg (Orthoptera). *Physiol. Zoöl.* **20**: 146–60, 9 figs. [*51, 251*].

—— 1947b. A spectrophotometric study of a developing egg (Orthoptera) with especial reference to riboflavin and its derivatives. *J. exp. Zool.* **104**: 353–63, 8 figs. [*51, 251*].

BIBLIOGRAPHY

BODINE, J. H. & FITZGERALD, L. R. 1948a. The copper content of an egg and its distribution during the development of the embryo (Orthoptera). *J. exp. Zool.* **109**: 187–95, 1 fig. [*43*].
—— 1948b. Changes in riboflavin during embryonic development as functions of the embryo. *Physiol. Zoöl.* **21**: 93–100, 2 figs. [*51, 251*].
BODINE, J. H. & WEST, W. L. 1953. Carbohydrate metabolism of the developing egg and embryo. *Biol. Bull., Woods Hole*, **104**: 1–11, 8 figs. [*250*].
BOELL, E. J. 1935. Respiratory quotients during embryonic development (Orthoptera). *J. cell. comp. Physiol.* **6**: 369–85, 4 figs. [*247, 248, 249*].
BOISTEL, J. 1960. *Caractéristiques fonctionnelles des fibres nerveuses et des récepteurs tactiles et olfactifs des insectes.* Paris [*66*].
BOLDYREV, V. F. 1915. Contributions à l'étude de la structure des spermatophores et des particularités de la copulation chez Locustodea et Gryllodea. (In Russian with French summary.) *Horae Soc. ent. ross.* **41** no. 6: 245 pp., 41 figs. [*316*].
—— 1929. Spermatophore fertilization in the Migratory Locust (*Locusta migratoria* L.) (In Russian.) *Rep. Bur. appl. Ent., Leningr.* **4** (1): 189–218, 18 figs. [*143, 314, 316–318*].
—— 1946. The process of reproduction in Acrididae. (In Russian.) *Proc. Timiryazev agric. Acad.* **4**: 170–3 [*298, 305, 306*].
BONÉ, G.-J. 1945. Le rapport sodium/potassium dans le liquide coelomique des insectes. I. Ses relations avec le régime alimentaire. *Ann. Soc. zool. Belg.* **75** (1944): 123–32, 1 fig. [*110*].
BORDAS, L. 1898. L'appareil digestif des Orthoptères. (Études morphologiques, histologiques et physiologiques de cet organe et son importance pour la classification des Orthoptères.) *Ann. Sci. nat.* (Zool.), (8) **5** (1897): 1–208, 12 pls. [*70, 73, 118*].
BOWEN, T. J. & KILBY, B. A. 1953. Electrophoresis of locust haemolymph. *Arch. int. Physiol.* **61**: 413–16, 2 figs. [*112*].
BOYD, K. & EWER, D. W. 1949. Flight responses in grasshoppers. *S. Afr. Sci.* **2**: 168–9, 1 fig. [*162*].
BRETT, C. H. 1947. Interrelated effects of food, temperature, and humidity on the development of the lesser migratory grasshopper, *Melanoplus mexicanus mexicanus* (Saussure) (Orthoptera). *Tech. Bull. Okla. agric. Exp. Sta.* no. T-26: 50 pp., 18 figs. [*83, 84, 289, 366*].
BRODSKIS, B. 1944. La valeur alimentaire des sauterelles. *C. R. Soc. Sci. nat. Maroc.*, no. 2: 9–10 [*94*].
BRODSKIS, B. & RUNGS, C. 1944. Premières recherches sur les possibilités d'une détermination chimique des âges et des phases du criquet pèlerin (*Schistocerca gregaria*, Forsk.). *C. R. Soc. Sci. nat. Maroc*, no. 2: 6–8 [*101, 252*].
BROUGHTON, W. B. 1952a. Recording of stridulation; possible responsiveness of female Acrididae (Orth.) to stridulation; stridulation of *Leptophyes punctatissima* (Bosc.) (Orth., Tettigonidae). *Ent. mon. Mag.* **88**: 47 [*186*].
—— 1952b. Gramophone studies of the stridulation of British grasshoppers. *J. S.W. Essex tech. Coll.* **3**: 170–80, 4 pls. [*186*].
—— 1955. L'analyse de l'émission acoustique des Orthoptères à partir d'un enregistrement sur disque reproduit à des vitesses ralenties. *Colloque sur l'Acoustique des Orthoptères*, Paris 1954: 82–8, 14 figs. [*185*].
BROWN, A. W. A. 1937a. Studies on the excreta of a grasshopper (*Melanoplus bivittatus* Say.). *J. exp. Biol.* **14**: 87–94 [*74, 120, 121*].
—— 1937b. A note on the utilisation of polysaccharides by a grasshopper. *Bull. ent. Res.* **28**: 333–6 [*80*].
—— 1937c. A note on the chitinous nature of the peritrophic membrane of *Melanoplus bivittatus* Say. *J. exp. Biol.* **14**: 252–3 [*73, 74*].
BROWN, E. S. 1951. The stridulation of *Eremogryllus hammadae* Krauss (Orthoptera, Acrididae). *Proc. R. ent. Soc. Lond.* A, **26**: 89–92, 2 figs. [*187*].
BRUNER, L. 1898. *The first report of the Merchants' Locust Investigation Commission of Buenos Aires.* Buenos Aires [*298, 336*].
BRUNTZ, L. 1909. Sur les néphrocytes des orthoptères et la dénomination de cellules péricardiales. *Arch. Zool. exp. gén.* (5) **2**: xvii–xix [*122*].
BRYANTSEVA, I. B. 1951. Peculiarities of structure of the foregut in Acridoidea. (In Russian.) *Sborn. Inst. prikl. Zool. Phytopat.* **1**: 23–31, 7 figs. [*70, 72*].
—— 1953. Peculiarities in the structure of the foregut in acridids of the subfamily Egnatiinae (Orthoptera, Acrididae). (In Russian.) *Rev. Ent. U.R.S.S.* **33**: 194–7, 3 figs. [*70, 72*].
—— 1955. The characteristics of structure of the gonads in females of Acridoidea. (In Russian.) *Sborn. Rab. Inst. prikl. Zool. Phytopat.* **3**: 48–52, 2 figs. [*146*].
—— 1958. Some anatomical characteristics of the reproductive system of females of the family Acrididae. (In Russian.) *Sborn. Rab. Inst. prikl. Zool. Phytopat.* **5**: 67–72 [*144*].
BÜCHER, T. H. & KLINGENBERG, M. 1958. Wege des Wasserstoffs in der lebendigen Organisation. *Angew. Chem.* **70**: 552–70, 21 figs. [*68, 102*].
BUCHTHAL, F. & WEIS-FOGH, T. 1956. Contribution of the sarcolemma to the force exerted by resting muscle of insects. *Acta physiol. scand.* **35**: 345–64, 12 figs. [*59, 65*].
BUCHTHAL, F., WEIS-FOGH, T. & ROSENFALCK, P. 1957. Twitch contractions of isolated flight muscle of locusts. *Acta physiol. scand.* **39**: 246–76, 19 figs. [*65, 67*].
BURDICK, H. C. 1937. The effects of exposure to low temperature on the developmental time of embryos of the grasshopper *Melanoplus differentialis* (Orthoptera). *Physiol. Zoöl.* **10**: 156–70, 6 figs. [*263*].

BIBLIOGRAPHY

BURGESS, L. E. 1949. A preliminary quantitative study of pterine pigment in the developing egg of the grasshopper, *Melanoplus differentialis*. *Arch. Biochem.* **20**: 347–55, 1 fig. [*51, 251*].

BURGESS, L. E., CLARK, S. S. & ROLFE, D. T. 1956. Effect of crystalline vitamin B₁₂ and of a crystalline grasshopper pigment (GHP) on experimental anemia in mice. (Abs.) *Fed. Proc.* **15**: 28 [*52*].

BURGESS, L. E. & ROLFE, D. T. 1959. The effect of vitamin B₁₂ and a crystalline grasshopper pigment on growth, kidney hemorrhage, and liver fat in rats fed purified diets. (Abs.) *Fed. Proc.* **18**: 21 [*52*].

BURKHOLDER, J. R. 1934. A quantitative study of respiratory metabolism in single developing eggs (Orthoptera). *Physiol. Zoöl.* **7**: 247–70, 9 figs. [*249*].

BURNETT, G. F. 1951. Observations on the life-history of the Red Locust, *Nomadacris septemfasciata* (Serv.) in the solitary phase. *Bull. ent. Res.* **42**: 473–90, 5 figs. [*278, 279, 282, 337*].

BURR, M. 1927–30. Field notes from Angola. *Ent. Rec.* **39**: 133–6, 151–4, 170–2; **40**: 3–4, 4–6, 24–7, 49–54, 108–113, 124–9, 145–7, 169–73; **41**: 13–17, 56–61, 118–22, 141–3; **42**: 7–9 [*11, 54*].

BURTON, J. F. 1960. Notes on Orthoptera in S.E. England in 1959. *Ent. Rec.* **72**: 68–71 [*54*].

BURTT, E. D. 1946. Observations on East African Pamphaginae (Orthoptera, Acrididae) with particular reference to stridulation. *Proc. R. ent. Soc. Lond.* A, **21**: 51–4, 1 pl., 2 figs. [*180*].

—— 1951a. The ability of adult grasshoppers to change colour on burnt ground. *Proc. R. ent. Soc. Lond.* A, **26**: 45–8, 1 pl. [*54*].

—— 1951b. Occurrence of fully-winged forms in usually brachypterous African Pyrgomorphinae (Orthoptera). *Proc. R. ent. Soc. Lond.* A, **26**: 64–6, 1 pl. [*30*].

BURTT, E. D. & UVAROV, B. P. 1944. Changes in wing pigmentation during the adult life of Acrididae (Orthoptera). *Proc. R. ent. Soc. Lond.* A, **19**: 7–8, 3 figs. [*299*].

BURTT, E. T. & CATTON, W. T. 1954. Visual perception of movement in the locust. *J. Physiol.* **125**: 566–80, 1 pl., 8 figs. [*199, 201, 202*].

—— 1956. Electrical responses to visual stimulation in the optic lobes of the locust and certain other insects. *J. Physiol.* **133**: 68–88, 12 figs. [*199, 201, 206*].

—— 1959a. Transmission of visual responses in the nervous system of the locust. *J. Physiol.* **146**: 492–515, 1 pl., 13 figs. [*198, 199*].

—— 1959b. Responses of single visual receptor units in the optic lobe of the locust. *J. Physiol.* **148**: 58P–59P [*199*].

—— 1959c. Visual acuity of the compound eyes in three species of insects. (Abs.) *15th Int. Congr. Zool.*, London 1958: 535–6 [*199*].

—— 1960a. The properties of single-unit discharges in the optic lobe of the locust. *J. Physiol.* **154**: 479–90, 6 figs. [*199*].

—— 1960b. Is the mosaic theory of insect vision true? *11th Int. Congr. Ent.*, Vienna 1960, vol. 1: 670–3, 1 fig. [*199, 201*].

—— 1961a. Diffraction images in the compound eye. *J. Physiol.* **159**: 52P [*199, 201*].

—— 1961b. Visual acuity in insects. *J. Physiol.* **159**: 64P–66P, 1 fig. [*199, 201*].

—— 1962a. A diffraction theory of insect vision. I. An experimental investigation of visual acuity and image formation in the compound eyes of three species of insects. *Proc. roy. Soc.* B, **157**: 53–82, 13 figs. [*199, 201, 202*].

—— 1962b. Resolving power of the compound eye. *Symp. Soc. exp. Biol.* **16**: 72–85, 4 figs. [*199, 202*].

—— 1962c. The potential profile of the compound eye of the locust. *J. Physiol.* **163**: 49P–51P, 1 fig. [*199*].

BUSNEL, M. C. & BURKHARDT, D. 1962. An electrophysiological study of the phonokinetic reaction in *Locusta migratoria migratorioides* (L.). *Symp. zool. Soc. Lond.* no. 7 (1961): 13–44, 21 figs. [*195*].

BUSNEL, M. C. & BUSNEL, R. G. 1956. Sur une phonocinèse de certains acridiens à des signaux acoustiques synthétiques. *C. R. Acad. Sci., Paris*, **242**: 292–3, 2 figs. [*191, 193, 195*].

BUSNEL, R. G. [Ed.] 1963. *Acoustic Behaviour of Animals*. London and Amsterdam [*176, 185*].

BUSNEL, R. G. & CHAUVIN, R. 1942. Dosage et répartition de la riboflavine (vitamine B₂) chez le criquet pèlerin; son importance au point de vue alimentaire. *Bull. Soc. zool. Fr.* **67**: 53–5 [*51, 121, 251*].

BUSNEL, R. G. & DRILHON, A. 1942. Recherches sur la répartition de la riboflavine (vitamine B₂) et de quelques autres substances fluorescentes chez les insectes. *Arch. Zool. exp. gén.* **82**: 321–356, 1 pl., 3 figs. [*51, 52, 121, 251*].

BUTENANDT, A., BIEKERT, E. & LINZEN, B. 1958. Über Ommochrome, XIV. Zur Verbreitung der Ommine im Tierreich. *Hoppe-Seyl. Z.* **313**: 251–8 [*44, 199*].

BUTLER, C. G. & INNES, J. M. 1936. A comparison of the rate of metabolic activity in the solitary and migratory phases of *Locusta migratoria*. *Proc. roy. Soc.* B, **119**: 296–304, 3 figs. [*132, 336, 337*].

BUXTON, P. A. 1924. Heat, moisture, and animal life in deserts. *Proc. roy. Soc.* B, **96**: 123–31, 3 figs. [*214*].

—— 1932. Terrestrial insects and the humidity of the environment. *Biol. Rev.* **7**: 275–320, 4 figs. [*228, 230, 256*].

BUYS, K. S. 1924. Adipose tissue in insects. *J. Morph.* **38**: 485–527, 8 pls. [*96*].

BIBLIOGRAPHY

BYRNE, O. R. 1962. *Colour pattern polymorphism in the Australian plague locust*, Chortoicetes terminifera (*Othoptera: Acrididae*). Ph.D. thesis, Adelaide [*38, 42*].

CAMERON, M. L. 1953. Secretion of an orthodiphenol in the corpus cardiacum of the insect. *Nature, Lond.* **172**: 349–50 [*119, 158*].

CAMPBELL, F. L. 1929. The detection and estimation of insect chitin; and the irrelation of 'chitinization' to hardness and pigmentation of the cuticula of the American cockroach, *Periplaneta americana* L. *Ann. ent. Soc. Amer.* **22**: 401–26, 1 fig. [*239*].

CAMPBELL, J. I. 1961. The anatomy of the nervous system of the mesothorax of *Locusta migratoria migratorioides* R. & F. *Proc. zool. Soc. Lond.* **137**: 403–32, 10 figs. [*62, 155*].

CANDY, D. J. & KILBY, B. A. 1961. The biosynthesis of trehalose in the locust fat body. *Biochem. J.* **78**: 531–6, 2 figs. [*102*].

—— 1962. Studies on chitin synthesis in the Desert Locust. *J. exp. Biol.* **39**: 129–40, 5 figs. [*91*].

CARBONELL, C. S. 1957. Vuelos en masa de Acridoideos (Orthoptera) en el Uruguay. *Rev. Soc. urug. Ent.* **2**: 73–7 [*371*].

—— 1959. The external anatomy of the South American semiaquatic grasshopper *Marellia remipes* Uvarov (Acridoidea, Pauliniidae). *Smithson. misc. Coll.* **137**: 61–97, 1 pl., 20 figs. [*1*].

CARLISLE, D. B. & ELLIS, P. E. 1959. La persistance des glandes ventrales céphaliques chez les criquets solitaires. *C. R. Acad. Sci., Paris*, **249**: 1059–60 [*159*].

—— 1962. Endocrine glands and phase in locusts. *4e Congr. Un. int. Étud. Insectes sociaux*, Pavia 1961, vol. 10: 219–24, 1 fig. [*377, 378*].

—— 1963. Prothoracic gland and gregarious behaviour in locusts. *Nature, Lond.* **200**: 603–4, 1 fig. [*160, 377, 378*].

—— 1964. Effect of 2-chloro-ethanol on maturation of locusts. *J. Endocrin.* **30**: 153–4 [*298*].

CARLSON, L. D. 1941. Enzymes in ontogenesis (Orthoptera). XVIII. Esterases in the grasshopper egg. *Biol. Bull., Woods Hole*, **81**: 375–87, 4 figs. [*251*].

CAROTHERS, E. E. 1923. Notes on the taxonomy, development and life history of certain Acrididae (Orthoptera). *Trans. Amer. ent. Soc.* **49**: 7–24, 4 pls. [*255, 260, 262, 283*].

—— 1939. A hybrid acridian gynandromorph. *Genetics*, **24**: 97 [*149*].

CARSON, H. L. 1945. A comparative study of the apical cell of the insect testis. *J. Morph.* **77**: 141–161, 3 pls. [*304*].

CASSIER, P. 1960. Le phototropisme du criquet migrateur. (Note préliminaire.) *Bull. Soc. zool. Fr.* **85**: 165–74, 4 figs. [*206*].

—— 1962. Étude de la période de latence dans la réaction phototropique de *Locusta migratoria migratorioides* (phase *gregaria*). *C. R. Acad. Sci., Paris*, **255**: 188–90 [*206*].

CASTILLO, J. del, HOYLE, G. & MACHNE, X. 1953. Neuromuscular transmission in a locust. *J. Physiol.* **121**: 539–47, 6 figs. [*65, 66, 67*].

CAVANAGH, G. G. 1963. The use of the Dadd synthetic diet as a food for adult *Schistocerca gregaria* (Forsk.) and the effects of some additions and modifications to it. *J. Insect Physiol.* **9**: 759–75, 3 figs. [*87*].

CAZAL, P. 1948. Les glandes endocrines rétro-cérébrales des insectes. (Étude morphologique.) *Bull. biol.* (Suppl.) **32**: 227 pp., 186 figs. [*156, 158, 159*].

CAZAL, P. & GUERRIER, Y. 1946. Recherches sur les glandes endocrines rétro-cerebroidiennes des insectes. I. Étude morphologique chez les Orthoptères. *Arch. Zool. exp. gén.* **84**: 303–34, 12 figs. [*156, 158*].

CHABOUSSOU, F. 1948. La pullulation du criquet migrateur (*Locusta migratoria* L.) dans les Landes de Gascogne et le problème du grégarisme. *Rev. Zool. agric.*, no. spéc.: 5–19, 8 figs. [*371*].

CHAPMAN, R. F. 1955. A laboratory study of roosting behaviour in hoppers of the African Migratory Locust (*Locusta migratoria migratorioides* R. & F.). *Anti-Locust Bull.* no. 19: 40 pp., 26 figs. [*203*].

—— 1957. Observations on the feeding of adults of the Red Locust (*Nomadacris septemfasciata* (Serville). *Brit. J. Anim. Behav.* **5**: 60–75, 14 figs. [*74*].

—— 1958. A field study of the potassium concentration in the blood of the Red Locust *Nomadacris septemfasciata* (Serv.), in relation to its activity. *Anim. Behav.* **6**: 60–67, 1 fig. [*66, 110, 111*].

—— 1961. The egg pods of some tropical African grasshoppers (Orthopt.: Acridoidea). II. Egg pods from grasshoppers collected in southern Ghana. *J. ent. Soc. S. Afr.* **24**: 259–84, 26 figs. [*240, 327*].

CHAPMAN, R. F. & ROBERTSON, I. A. D. 1958. The egg pods of some tropical African grasshoppers. [I.] *J. ent. Soc. S. Afr.* **21**: 85–112, 17 figs. [*240, 326, 328*].

CHAUVIN, R. 1938. Recherches histologiques sur les oenocytes du criquet pélerin adulte. *Bull. Soc. Hist. nat. Afr. N.* **29**: 384–7, 1 pl. [*103, 104*].

—— 1939a. Influence du régime alimentaire sur le criquet pélerin grégaire. *C. R. Soc. Biol., Paris*, **131**: 31–3 [*50*].

—— 1939b. Histologie du tégument chez le criquet pélerin. *Bull. Histol. Tech. micr.* **16**: 137–48, 5 figs. [*32, 164, 295*].

—— 1941a. Variations du phototropisme du criquet pélerin (*Schistocerca gregaria*, Forsk.) suivant différentes longueurs d'onde. *Bull. Soc. zool. Fr.* **66**: 27–32, 2 figs. [*204*].

—— 1941b. Contribution à l'étude physiologique du criquet pélerin et du déterminisme des phénomènes grégaires. *Ann. Soc. ent. Fr.* **110**: 133–272, 23 figs. [*32, 43, 44, 47, 70, 76, 81, 103, 118, 121, 122, 128, 200, 292, 295, 297, 333, 352, 365, 375*].

BIBLIOGRAPHY

CHAUVIN, R. 1942. Notes sur la physiologie comparée des Orthoptères. I. Sur le phototropisme des Orthoptères. *Bull. Soc. ent. Fr.* **46**: 150–4, 1 fig. [*204*].

—— 1946. Notes sur la physiologie comparée des Orthoptères. IV. Le coefficient d'utilisation digestive, le rythme d'excrétion et le transit intestinal. *Bull. Soc. ent. Fr.* **50**: 24–9, 1 fig. [*75, 80*].

CHEFURKA, W. & PEPPER, J. H. 1955a. Determination of the constants employed in calculating the surface area of the grasshopper *Melanoplus bivittatus* (Say) (Orthoptera: Acrididae). *Canad. Ent.* **86** (1954): 554–7, 2 figs. [*3*].

—— 1955b. Studies on the cuticle of the grasshopper *Melanoplus bivittatus* (Say) (Orthoptera: Acrididae). *Canad. Ent.* **87**: 145–71, 8 figs. [*33, 232*].

CHEN YUNG-LIN 1963. A new sub-species of *Locusta migratoria*—Tibetan Migratory Locust (*Locusta migratoria tibetensis* subsp. n.). (In Chinese with English summary.) *Acta ent. sinica*, **12**: 463–75, 16 figs. [*373, 374*].

CHESLER, J. 1938. Observations on the biology of some South African Acrididae (Orthoptera). *Trans. R. ent. Soc. Lond.* **87**: 313–51, 27 figs. [*283, 284, 286, 287*].

CHEU, S. P. 1952. Changes in the fat and protein content of the African Migratory Locust, *Locusta migratoria migratorioides* (R. & F.). *Bull. ent. Res.* **43**: 101–9, 1 fig. [*91, 97, 98, 250, 351*].

CHIN CHUN-TEH, QUO FU & CHENG CHU-YUN 1957. Food specialization and food utilization of the Oriental Migratory Locust and the influence of different food plants on its growth and fecundity. (In Chinese with English summary.) *Acta ent. sinica*, **7**: 143–66, 6 figs. [*82*].

CHOPARD, L. 1920. Recherches sur la conformation et le développement des derniers segments abdominaux chez les Orthoptères. *Insecta*, **10** (1920): 1–112, 75 figs.; **11** (1921) (published 1922): 113–352, 7 pls., 548 + xiv figs. Also as *Thès. Fac. Sci. Univ. Paris*, sér. A, no. 847 (1919): 352 pp., 7 pls., 623 + xiv figs. [Rennes, 1920.] [*141*].

—— 1938. La biologie des Orthoptères. *Encycl. ent.* A, **20**: 541 pp., 5 pls., 453 figs. [*52*].

—— 1949. L'état actuel de la question des phases chez les insectes. *Année biol.* **25**: 105–9 [*386*].

CHURCH, N. S. 1960a. Heat loss and the body temperatures of flying insects. I. Heat loss by evaporation of water from the body. *J. exp. Biol.* **37**: 171–85, 1 pl. [*217, 229, 231*].

——1960b. Heat loss and the body temperatures of flying insects. II. Heat conduction within the body and its loss by radiation and convection. *J. exp. Biol.* **37**: 186–212, 1 pl., 3 figs. [*210, 211, 217*].

CHURCH, N. S. & SALT, R. W. 1952. Some effects of temperature on development and diapause in eggs of *Melanoplus bivittatus* (Say) (Orthoptera: Acrididae). *Canad. J. Zool.* **30**: 173–84, 6 figs. [*252, 261, 263*].

CLARE, S. 1951–3. Physiological studies on tropical insects of the Pacific. Further observations and experiments on the circulation of hemolymph in the insect wing. (In 18 manuscript-papers.) Edmonton, Canada. [Unpublished] [*107*].

CLARK, E. J. 1943. Colour variation in British Acrididae (Orthopt.). *Ent. mon. Mag.* **79**: 91–104, 3 figs. [*39*].

CLARK, L. R. 1947. An ecological study of the Australian plague locust (*Chortoicetes terminifera* Walk.) in the Bogan-Macquarie outbreak area, N.S.W. *Bull. Coun. sci. industr. Res. Aust.* no. 226: 71 pp., 3 pls., 10 figs. [*356*].

CLARKE, K. U. 1957a. The relationship of oxygen consumption to age and weight during the post-embryonic growth of *Locusta migratoria* L. *J. exp. Biol.* **34**: 29–41, 9 figs. [*132, 133, 136, 137*].

—— 1957b. On the increase in linear size during growth in *Locusta migratoria* L. *Proc. R. ent. Soc. Lond.* A, **32**: 35–9, 1 fig. [*274*].

—— 1957c. On the role of the tracheal system in the post-embryonic growth of *Locusta migratoria* L. *Proc. R. ent. Soc. Lond.* A, **32**: 67–79, 3 figs. [*284*].

—— 1960. Studies on the relationships between air temperature and the internal body temperature of *Locusta migratoria*. *J. Insect Physiol.* **5**: 23–36, 7 figs. [*207, 209*].

CLARKE, K. U. & GRENVILLE, H. 1960. Nervous control of movements in the foregut of *Schistocerca gregaria* Forsk. *Nature, Lond.* **186**: 98–9, 1 fig. [*76*].

CLARKE, K. U. & LANGLEY, P. A. 1962. Factors concerned in the initiation of growth and moulting in *Locusta migratoria* L. *Nature, Lond.* **194**: 160–2, 4 figs. [*290*].

—— 1963a. Studies on the initiation of growth and moulting in *Locusta migratoria migratorioides* R. & F. I. The time and nature of the initiating stimulus. *J. Insect Physiol.* **9**: 287–92, 2 figs. [*290*].

—— 1963b. Studies on the initiation of growth and moulting in *Locusta migratoria migratorioides* R. & F. II. The role of the stomatogastric nervous system. *J. Insect Physiol.* **9**: 363–73, 3 figs. [*151, 154, 290*].

—— 1963c. Studies on the initiation of growth and moulting in *Locusta migratoria migratorioides* R. & F. III. The role of the frontal ganglion. *J. Insect Physiol.* **9**: 411–21, 5 figs. [*152, 154, 290*].

——1963d. Studies on the initiation of growth and moulting in *Locusta migratoria migratorioides* R. & F. IV. The relationship between the stomatogastric nervous system and neurosecretion. *J. Insect Physiol.* **9**: 423–30, 4 figs. [*154, 290*].

CLEMENTS, A. N. 1959. Studies on the metabolism of locust fat body. *J. exp. Biol.* **36**: 665–75 [*102*].

COLE, K. S. & JAHN, T. L. 1937. The nature and permeability of grasshopper egg membranes. IV. The alternating current impedance over a wide frequency range. *J. cell. comp. Physiol.* **10**: 265–75, 2 figs. [*257*].

BIBLIOGRAPHY

COLEMAN, L. C. 1911. The jola or Deccan grasshopper (*Colemania sphenarioides* Bol). *Bull. Dep. Agric. Mysore* (Ent.) no. 2: 43 pp., 10 pls., 8 figs. [*36, 276, 278, 286, 322, 323*].

COLEMAN, L. C. & KANNAN, K. K. 1911. The rice grasshopper (*Hieroglyphus banian*, Fabr.). *Bull. Dep. Agric. Mysore* (Ent.), no. 1: 52 pp., 5 pls., 4 figs. [*276, 278, 280, 287*].

COLLENS, A. E. 1915. The manurial value of locusts. *Bull. Dep. Agric. Trin. Tob.* **14**: 199 [*94*].

COLOMBO, G. 1953. L'oogenesi negli Ortotteri. I. Ricerche istologiche e citometriche in *Anacridium aegyptium* L. dalla schiusa all'imagine. *Acta zool., Stockh.* **34**: 191–232, 33 figs. [*304, 306, 310*].

—— 1955. L'oogenesi negli Ortotteri. II. Ricerche sull'accrescimento degli oociti di *Anacridium aegyptium* L. *Arch. zool. ital.* **40**: 235–63, 2 pls., 3 figs. [*304, 310*].

COLOMBO, G. & BASSATO, M. 1957. La differenziazione delle gonadi negli embrioni della cavallette. Ricerche istologiche su embrioni di *Anacridium aegyptium* L. (Orthoptera, Acridoidea). *Boll. Zool.* **24**: 275–85, 2 pls. [*246*].

COLOMBO, G., BENASSI, C. A., ALLEGRI, G. & LONGO, E. 1962. Free amino-acids in eggs of *Schistocerca gregaria* Forsk. (Orthoptera) during development. *Comp. Biochem. Physiol.* **5**: 83–93, 2 figs. [*250*].

COLOMBO, G. & MOCELLIN, E. 1956. Ricerche sulla biologia dell'*Anacridium aegyptium* L. (Orthoptera, Catantopidae). *Redia*, **41**: 277–313, 2 pls., 5 figs. [*255, 287, 310, 321, 327*].

COLOSI, I. DE S. 1933. L'assunzione dell'acqua per via cutanea. *Pubbl. Staz. zool. Napoli*, **13**: 12–38, 4 figs. [*228*].

COMMON, I. F. B. 1948. The yellow-winged locust, *Gastrimargus musicus* Fabr., in central Queensland. *Qd. J. agric. Sci.* **5**: 153–219, 15 figs. [*287, 336, 370*].

COMSTOCK, J. H. & NEEDHAM, J. G. 1899. The wings of insects. Chapter IV (concluded). The specialization of wings by addition. V. The tracheation of the wings of Orthoptera. *Amer. Nat.* **33**: 573–82, 8 figs. [*27*].

COOK, P. M. 1951. Observations on giant fibres of the nervous system of *Locusta migratoria*. *Quart. J. micr. Sci.* **92**: 297–305, 1 pl., 4 figs. [*153, 163*].

CORNWELL, P. B. 1955. The functions of the ocelli of *Calliphora* (Diptera) and *Locusta* (Orthoptera). *J. exp. Biol.* **32**: 217–37, 13 figs. [*201, 206*].

COUPLAND, R. E. 1957. Observations on the normal histology and histochemistry of the fat body of the locust (*Schistocerca gregaria*). *J. exp. Biol.* **34**: 290–6, 1 pl. [*96, 102, 103, 104*].

CREIGHTON, M. & ROBERTSON, W. R. B. 1941. Genetic studies on *Chorthippus longicornis*. *J. Hered.* **32**: 339–41, 1 pl. [*319*].

CRESCITELLI, F. & JAHN, T. L. 1939a. The electrical response of the dark-adapted grasshopper eye to various intensities of illumination and to different qualities of light. *J. cell. comp. Physiol.* **13**: 105–12, 3 figs. [*199, 204*].

—— 1939b. The effect of temperature on the electrical response of the grasshopper eye. *J. cell. comp. Physiol.* **14**: 13–27, 4 figs. [*199*].

—— 1942. Oscillatory electrical activity from the insect compound eye. *J. cell. comp. Physiol.* **19**: 47–66, 5 figs. [*199*].

CRIDDLE, N. 1926. Studies of the immature stages of Manitoban Orthoptera. *Trans. roy. Soc. Can.*, Sect. V, ser. 3, **20**: 505–25, 4 pls. [*283*].

—— 1930. Life-history of the cow grasshopper (*Chrysochraon abdominalis* Thom.) in Manitoba. *Canad. Ent.* **62**: 25–8, 1 fig. [*287*].

—— 1931. Grasshopper control in Canada east of the Rocky Mountains. *Bull. Dep. Agric. Can.* (N.S.), no. 143: 18 pp., 2 pls., 2 figs. [*283*].

—— 1933. Notes on the habits of injurious grasshoppers in Manitoba. *Canad. Ent.* **65**: 97–102, 1 fig. [*371*].

—— 1935. Studies in the biology of North American Acrididae. Development and habits. *Proceedings of the World's Grain Exhibition and Conference*, Regina 1933, vol. 2: 474–94 [*326, 328*].

CROMARTIE, R. I. I. 1959. Insect pigments. *Annu. Rev. Ent.* **4**: 59–76 [*42*].

CROS, A. 1929. Entomologie et agriculture. Conférence faite au Grand Casino d'Oran, le 16 Mars 1929. Oran. 44 pp. [*327*].

CROUZEL, I. S. DE 1960. *Schistocerca cancellata* (Serv.): estudio hemocitario. *Act. 1° Congr. sudamer. Zool.*, La Plata 1959, vol. 5: 101–25 [*114, 117*].

CROZIER, W. J. & STIER, T. B. 1925. Critical thermal increments for rhythmic respiratory movements of insects. *J. gen. Physiol.* **7**: 429–47, 11 figs. [*129*].

CUÉNOT, L. 1895. Études physiologiques sur les Orthoptères. *Arch. Biol.* **14**: 293–341 [*73, 115, 117, 122*].

DADD, R. H. 1960a. Some effects of dietary ascorbic acid on locusts. *Proc. roy. Soc. B*, **153**: 128–43, 3 figs. [*43, 49, 85–87*].

—— 1960b. The nutritional requirements of locusts—I. Development of synthetic diets and lipid requirements. *J. Insect Physiol.* **4**: 319–47 [*85–87*].

—— 1960c. The nutritional requirements of locusts—II. Utilization of sterols. *J. Insect Physiol.* **5**: 161–8, 1 fig. [*85–87*].

—— 1960d. The nutritional requirements of locusts—III. Carbohydrate requirements and utilization. *J. Insect Physiol.* **5**: 301–16, 5 figs. [*85–87*].

—— 1960e. Observations on the palatability and utilisation of food by locusts, with particular reference to the interpretation of performances in growth trials using synthetic diets. *Ent. exp. appl.* **3**: 283–304, 1 fig. [*80, 85–87*].

BIBLIOGRAPHY

DADD, R. H. 1961a. The nutritional requirements of locusts—IV. Requirements for vitamins of the B complex. *J. Insect Physiol.* **6**: 1–12, 3 figs. [*43, 49, 85–87*].
—— 1961b. The nutritional requirements of locusts—V. Observations on essential fatty acids, chlorophyll, nutritional salt mixtures, and the protein or amino acid components of synthetic diets. *J. Insect Physiol.* **6**: 126–45 [*85–87*].
—— 1961c. Observations on the effects of carotene on the growth and pigmentation of locusts. *Bull. ent. Res.* **52**: 63–81, 3 figs. [*45, 47, 49, 50, 85*].
—— 1963. Feeding behaviour and nutrition in grasshoppers and locusts. *Advanc. Insect Physiol.* **1**: 47–109 [*43, 47, 49, 85–87*].
DAS, S. 1945. Locust as food and manure. *Indian Fmg*, **6**: 412 [*90, 94*].
DAVEY, P. M. 1954. Quantities of food eaten by the Desert Locust, *Schistocerca gregaria* (Forsk.), in relation to growth. *Bull. ent. Res.* **45**: 539–51, 7 figs. [*80, 274, 275*].
DAVIDSON, J. 1936. On the ecology of the black-tipped locust (*Chortoicetes terminifera* Walk.) in South Australia. *Trans. roy. Soc. S. Aust.* **60**: 137–52, 4 figs. [*255*].
DAVIS, H. S. 1908. Spermatogenesis in Acrididae and Locustidae. *Bull. Mus. comp. Zool. Harv.* **53**: 59–158, 9 pls., 32 figs. [*303*].
DAY, M. F. 1949. The distribution of alkaline phosphatase in insects. *Aust. J. sci. Res.* B, **2**: 31–41, 3 pls. [*73, 76*].
DEBAISIEUX, P. 1938. Organes scolopidiaux des pattes d'insectes. II. *Cellule*, **47**: 79–202, 12 pls., 28 figs. [*170*].
DEBAUCHE, H. 1938. Étude cytologique et comparée de l'organe de Johnston des insectes. III. Les principaux organes sensoriels de l'antenne chez *Schistocerca gregaria* Forsk. *5th Int. Locust Conf.*, Brussels 1938: 417–33, 4 pls. [*168*].
DEL CARRIL, L. M. 1938. Rapport sur la situation acridienne et l'organisation antiacridienne en Argentine. *5th Int. Locust Conf.*, Brussels 1938: 85–96, 5 figs. [*319*].
DE LERMA, B. 1937. Osservazioni sul sistema endocrino degli insetti (corpora allata e corpi faringei). *Arch. zool. ital.* **24**: 339–68, 17 figs. [*158*].
—— 1949. Sulla presenza e significato della riboflavina e di altre sostanze fluorescenti contenute nei tubi Malpighiani di Ortotteri, rivelate col metodo della spettrografia di fluorescenza. *Annu. Ist. Zool. Univ. Napoli*, **1**: 32 pp., 3 pls., 2 figs. [*121*].
—— 1950a. Ricerche sulla fluorescenza del sangue degli Ortotteri. Identificazione spettrografica dell'isoxantopterina. *Boll. Soc. ital. Biol. sper.* **26**: 528–30 [*51*].
—— 1950b. Endocrinologia degli insetti. *Boll. Zool.* (Suppl.) **17**: 67–192, 1 pl., 17 figs. [*158*].
—— 1951a. Spettrofotometria quantitativa e significato delle fluorescenze che si osservano nelle uova di Ortotteri. *Boll. Soc. ital. Biol. sper.* **27**: 230–2, 1 pl. [*51, 251*].
—— 1951b. Ricerche istochimiche sui 'corpi lutei' di Ortotteri con l'applicazione del test di Schultz per le sostanze colesteroliche. *Boll. Zool.* **18**: 5–6, 1 fig. [*306*].
—— 1952. Biochimica e sviluppo embrionale degli insetti. II. Sulla natura e significato delle sostanze fluorescenti delle uova di *Locusta migratoria* L. *Arch. zool. ital.* **37**: 81–92, 1 pl., 2 figs. [*51, 251*].
DE LOTTO, G. 1950. Sulla presenza di una ghiandola ripugnatoria in due Ortotteri del genere *Phymateus*. *Boll. Soc. ital. Med., Sez. Eritrea*, **10**: 195–201, 4 figs. [*50*].
—— 1951. Osservazioni sulla biologia del *Phymateus viridipes* St. (Orth. Acrididae). *Riv. Agric. subtrop.* **45**: 8–18, 9 figs. [*286*].
DELPHIN, F. 1963a. *Studies on neurosecretion in* Schistocerca gregaria *Forskål* (*Orthoptera: Acrididae*). Ph.D. thesis, London [*151, 153, 154, 157, 227, 311, 314*].
—— 1963b. Histology and possible functions of neurosecretory cells in the ventral ganglia of *Schistocerca gregaria* Forsk. *Nature, Lond.* **200**: 913–15, 1 fig. [*157, 227, 311, 314*].
DENNELL, R. 1958. The hardening of insect cuticles. *Biol. Rev.* **33**: 178–96, 3 figs. [*32*].
DEPDOLLA, P. 1917. Die Keimzellenbildung und die Befruchtung bei den Insekten. In Schröder, C. [Ed.], *Handbuch der Entomologie*. Band I: 825–1116 [*303*].
DESCAMPS, M. 1961. Comportement du criquet migrateur africain (*Locusta migratoria migratorioides* Rch. & Frm.) en 1957 dans la partie septentrionale de son aire de grégarisation sur le Niger région de Niafunké. *Locusta*, no. 8: 280 pp., 3 maps, 47 figs. [*183*].
DESCAMPS, M. & WINTREBERT, D. 1962. Quelques remarques et recherches préliminaires à propos des critères de maturité sexuelle et de ponte chez les femelles d'Acridiens migrateurs. *Rev. Path. vég.* **40**: 131–43, 3 figs. [*305*].
DETHIER, V. G. 1963. *The Physiology of Insect Senses*. London [*161*].
DIGBY, P. S. B. 1955. Factors affecting the temperature excess of insects in sunshine. *J. exp. Biol.* **32**: 279–98, 8 figs. [*212, 217, 219*].
DIRSH, V. M. 1950. A practical table for the determination of sexes of nymphs of *Locusta migratoria migratorioides* (R. & F.) (Orthoptera: Acrididae). *Proc. R. ent. Soc. Lond.* B, **19**: 136–8, 2 figs. [*281*].
—— 1951. A new biometrical phase character in locusts. *Nature, Lond.* **167**: 281–2, 3 figs. [*346*].
—— 1953. Morphometrical studies on phases of the Desert Locust (*Schistocerca gregaria* Forskål). *Anti-Locust Bull.*, no. 16: 34 pp., 31 figs. [*342, 344–347, 386*].
—— 1956a. The phallic complex in Acridoidea (Orthoptera) in relation to taxonomy. *Trans. R. ent. Soc. Lond.* **108**: 223–356, 66 pls. [*141, 143, 388*].

BIBLIOGRAPHY

DIRSH, V. M. 1956b. Orthoptera Acridoidea. In Hanström, B., Brinck, P. & Rudebeck, G. [Eds.], *South African Animal Life. Results of the Lund University Expedition in 1950–1951*, vol. III: 121–272, 2 pls., 42 figs. [*4*].
—— 1957a. The spermatheca as a taxonomic character in Acridoidea (Orthoptera). *Proc. R. ent. Soc. Lond.* A, **32**: 107–14, 28 figs. [*147, 148*].
—— 1957b. Two cases of gynandromorphism in Acrididae (Orthoptera). *Ent. mon. Mag.* **93**: 193–194, 3 figs. [*149*].
—— 1959. The early stages of *Gastrimargus nigericus* Uvarov 1926 (Acridoidea, Orthoptera). *Locusta*, no. 6: 65–72, 10 figs. [*284, 287*].
—— 1961. A preliminary revision of the families and sub-families of Acridoidea (Orthoptera, Insecta). *Bull. Brit. Mus. (nat. Hist.)* (Ent.), **10**: 351–419, 34 figs. [*143, 182, 388, 393, 397, 414, 417*].
DIRSH, V. M. & UVAROV, B. P. 1953. Tree locusts of the genus *Anacridium* (Orthoptera, Acrididae). *Eos, Madr.* **29**: 7–69, 66 figs. [*143*].
DOVNAR-ZAPOL'SKIĬ, D. P. 1926. On the larvae of Acrididae. (In Russian.) *Bull. N. Caucas. Pl. Prot. Sta.*, no. 2: 153–72 [*278, 283, 284, 287*].
DRAKE, C. J., DECKER, G. C. & TAUBER, O. E. 1945. Observations on oviposition and adult survival of some grasshoppers of economic importance. *Iowa St. Coll. J. Sci.* **19**: 207–23, 7 figs. [*327, 328*].
DRILHON, A. & BUSNEL, R. G. 1945a. Recherches sur les phosphatases d'insectes et en particulier des tubes de Malpighi et du tube digestif. *Bull. Soc. zool. Fr.* **70**: 40–7 [*76, 121*].
—— 1945b. Recherches sur les phosphatases d'insectes. *Bull. Soc. Chim. biol., Paris*, **27**: 415–18 [*76*].
DUARTE, A. J. 1938. Problems of growth of the African Migratory Locust. *Bull. ent. Res.* **29**: 425–456, 12 figs. [*274, 275, 338*].
—— 1939. On ecdysis in the African Migratory Locust. *Agron. lusit.* **1**: 22–40, 10 figs. [*103, 104, 284, 285*].
DUBOIS, R. 1893. Sur l'huile d'oeufs de la sauterelle d'Algérie, ou criquet pèlerin (*Acridium peregrinum*). *C. R. Acad. Sci., Paris*, **116**: 1393–4 [*101*].
DU BUISSON, M. 1924. Observations sur la ventilation trachéenne des insectes. Première note: La ventilation trachéenne chez un acridien. *Bull. Acad. Belg. Cl. Sci.* (5) **10**: 373–91, 6 figs. [*124, 126*].
—— 1925. Observations sur le mécanisme de la ventilation trachéenne chez les insectes. (Deuxième note). *Bull. Acad. Belg. Cl. Sci.* (5) **10** (1924): 635–56, 6 figs. [*128*].
DUCHÂTEAU, G. & FLORKIN, M. 1958. A survey of aminoacidemias with special reference to the high concentration of free aminoacids in insect hemolymph. *Arch. int. Physiol. Biochim.* **66**: 573–91, 3 figs. [*112*].
DUCHÂTEAU, G., FLORKIN, M. & SARLET, H. 1952. Sur les acides aminés, libres ou combinés sous forme non protéinique, du plasma sanguin et divers insectes. (*Locusta migratoria* L., *migratorioides* R. & F., chenilles d'*Amathes xantographa* Schiff., chenilles et chrysalides d'*Euproctis chrysorrhoea* L.). *Arch. int. Physiol.* **60**: 539–40 [*112*].
DUCK, L. G. 1944. The bionomics of *Schistocerca obscura* (Fabr.). *J. Kans. ent. Soc.* **17**: 105–19 [*237, 255, 287, 366, 370*].
DUDLEY, B. A. C. 1961. *Studies on the biology of locusts when reared under controlled conditions*. Ph.D. thesis, Cardiff [*226, 291, 292, 302, 307, 366, 367, 368*].
—— 1964. The effects of temperature and humidity upon certain morphometric and colour characters of the Desert Locust (*Schistocerca gregaria* Forskål) reared under controlled conditions. *Trans. R. ent. Soc. Lond.* **116**: 115–29, 8 figs. [*366, 367, 368*].
DUFOUR, L. 1841. Recherches anatomiques et physiologiques sur les Orthoptères, les Hyménoptères et les Névroptères. *Mém. Acad. Sci. Paris*, **7**: 265–647, 13 pls. [*73, 305*].
DUNCAN, C. D. 1924. Spiracles as sound producing organs. *Pan-Pacif. Ent.* **1**: 42–3 [*184*].
DUNHAM, J. 1962. Infrared transmission of fenestrae and ordinary cuticle of the grasshopper. *Physiol. Zoöl.* **35**: 297–303, 3 figs. [*220*].
DU PLESSIS, C. 1939. The incipient outbreaks of the Brown Locust in 1937–38, with special reference to biometrical analysis. *Sci. Bull. Dep. Agric. S. Afr.*, no. 209: 69 pp., 8 figs. [*348*].
DUTT, M. K. 1955. On the chromosome complement and meiosis in nine species of Indian grasshoppers. *Proc. zool. Soc. Calcutta*, **8**: 111–29, 8 figs. [*389*].
EADES, D. C. 1961. The terminology of phallic structures in the Cyrtacanthacridinae (Orthoptera, Acrididae). *Ent. News*, **72**: 141–9, 1 fig. [*141*].
EDER, R. 1940. Die kutikuläre Transpiration der Insekten und ihre Abhängigkeit vom Aufbau des Integumentes. *Zool. Jb.* (Physiol), **60**: 203–40, 8 figs. [*231*].
EDNEY, E. B. 1957. *The Water Relations of Terrestrial Arthropods*. London [*230*].
EGGERS, F. 1928. Die stiftführenden Sinnesorgane. Morphologie und Physiologie der chordotonalen und der tympanalen Sinnesapparate der Insekten. *Zool. Baust.* **2**: 354 pp., 149 figs. [*168, 188*].
EL ZOHEIRY, M. S. 1937. The life history, habits and methods of control of the Egyptian grasshopper *Anacridium aegyptium* L. *4th Int. Locust Conf.*, Cairo 1936, App. 41: 10 pp. [*321*].
ELLIS, P. E. 1951. The marching behaviour of hoppers of the African Migratory Locust (*Locusta migratoria migratorioides* R. & F.) in the laboratory. *Anti-Locust Bull.* no. 7: 46 pp., 32 figs. [*339, 340, 361*].

BIBLIOGRAPHY

ELLIS, P. E. 1953. Social aggregation and gregarious behaviour in hoppers of *Locusta migratoria migratorioides* (R. & F.). *Behaviour*, **5**: 225–60, 10 figs. [*339*].
—— 1956. Differences in social aggregation in two species of locust. *Nature, Lond.* **178**: 1007 [*339*, *359*].
—— 1959a. Learning and social aggregation in locust hoppers. *Anim. Behav.* **7**: 91–106, 7 figs. [*339*].
—— 1959b. Some factors influencing phase characters in the nymphs of the locust, *Locusta migratoria migratorioides* (R. and F.). *Insectes sociaux*, **6**: 21–39, 1 fig. [*363*, *364*].
—— 1962. The behaviour of locusts in relation to phases and species. *Colloq. int. Cent. nat. Rech. sci.* no. 114: 123–43, 12 figs. [*339*, *361*, *364*, *375*].
—— 1963a. The influence of some environmental factors on learning and aggregation in locust hoppers. *Anim. Behav.* **11**: 142–51, 3 figs. [*339*, *360*, *361*].
—— 1963b. Changes in the social aggregation of locust hoppers with changes in rearing conditions. *Anim. Behav.* **11**: 152–60, 6 figs. [*339*, *360*].
—— 1964a. Marching and colour in locust hoppers in relation to social factors. *Behaviour*, **23**: 177–92, 8 figs. [*340*, *361*].
—— 1964b. Changes in marching of locusts with rearing conditions. *Behaviour*, **23**: 193–202, 3 figs. [*340*, *360*].
ELLIS, P. E. & CARLISLE, D. B. 1961. The prothoracic gland and colour change in locusts. *Nature, Lond.* **190**: 368–9, 1 fig. [*377*].
ELLIS, P. E. & HOYLE, G. 1954. A physiological interpretation of the marching of hoppers of the African Migratory Locust (*Locusta migratoria migratorioides* R. & F.). *J. exp. Biol.* **31**: 271–9, 2 figs. [*110*].
ELLIS, P. E. & PEARCE, A. 1962. Innate and learned behaviour patterns that lead to group formation in locust hoppers. *Anim. Behav.* **10**: 305–18, 6 figs. [*341*, *360*].
ELSE, F. L. 1934. The developmental anatomy of male genitalia in *Melanoplus differentialis* (Locustidae, (Acrididae), Orthoptera). *J. Morph.* **55**: 577–609, 4 pls., 1 fig. [*281*].
ENIKEEV, I. F. 1949. The saxaul locust, *Dericorys albidula* Serv. in Turkmenistan. (In Russian.) *Izv. turkmensk. Fil. Akad. Nauk SSSR*, **1**: 61–3 [*371*].
ERGENE, S. 1950. Untersuchungen über Farbanpassung und Farbwechesel bei *Acrida turrita*. *Z. vergl. Physiol.* **32**: 530–51, 4 figs. [*54*, *55*, *204*].
—— 1952a. Farbanpassung entsprechend der jeweiligen Substratfärbung bei *Acrida turrita*. *Z. vergl. Physiol.* **34**: 69–74, 1 fig. [*53*].
—— 1952b. Erkennen homochrome Heuschrecken die Farbe oder die Graustufe ihrer Umgebung? *Rev. Fac. Sci. Univ. Istanbul* B, **17**: 305–14 [*204*].
—— 1953a. Bevorzugung homochromen Milieus durch *Oedipoda*-Larven. *Rev. Fac. Sci. Univ. Istanbul* B, **18**: 63–6 [*204*].
—— 1953b. Homochromer Farbwechsel ohne Häutung bei Heuschrecken auf schwarzen Untergrund. *Zool. Jb.* (Syst.), **81**: 604–9, 1 fig. [*54*, *56*].
—— 1954a. Weitere Untersuchungen über Schwarzanpassung bei Imagines von Heuschrecken. *Mitt. zool. Mus. Berl.* **30**: 107–10 [*54*].
—— 1954b. Über den angeblichen Einfluss von frischem grünem Futter auf den Farbwechsel von *Acrida turrita*. *Z. vergl. Physiol.* **36**: 235–7 [*54*].
—— 1954c. Das Verhalten der Hämolymphe im Verlauf des Farbwechsels. *Z. vergl. Physiol.* **36**: 238–40 [*54*].
—— 1955a. Über die Faktoren die Grünfärbung bei *Acrida* bedingen. *Z. vergl. Physiol.* **37**: 221–5 [*54*].
—— 1955b. Weitere Untersuchungen über Farbanpassung bei *Oedaleus decorus*. *Z. vergl. Physiol.* **37**: 226–9 [*54*].
—— 1955c. Über die Bevorzugung eines homochromen Milieus bei Heuschrecken und Gottesanbeterin. *Zool. Jb.* (Syst.), **83**: 318–22 [*204*].
—— 1957. Homochromie und Dressierbarkeit nach Versuchen mit *Oedipoda coerulescens* Imagines. *Zool. Anz.* **158**: 38–44 [*204*].
EVANS, E. J. 1952. The stridulation noise of locusts. *Proc. R. ent. Soc. Lond.* A, **27**: 39–42, 2 pls., 1 fig. [*185*].
EWER, D. W. 1953. The anatomy of the nervous system of the tree locust, *Acanthacris ruficornis* (Fab.). I. The adult metathorax. *Ann. Natal Mus.* **12**: 367–81, 13 figs. [*60*, *62*, *64*, *154*].
—— 1954a. The anatomy of the nervous system of the tree locust, *Acanthacris ruficornis* (Fab.). II. The adult mesothorax. *J. ent. Soc. S. Afr.* **17**: 27–37, 6 figs. [*60*, *62*, *64*, *154*].
—— 1954b. On the nymphal musculature of the pterothorax of certain Acrididae (Orthoptera). *Ann. Natal Mus.* **13**: 79–89, 7 figs. [*60*, *62*, *64*, *282*].
—— 1954c. The anatomy of the nervous system of the tree locust, *Acanthacris ruficornis* (Fabr.). III. The innervation of the nymphal muscles of the pterothorax and first abdominal segment. *J. ent. Soc. S. Afr.* **17**: 232–6, 2 figs. [*60*, *62*, *64*, *154*, *282*].
—— 1954d. A note on the comparative anatomy of the pterothorax of macropterous and brachypterous forms of the grasshopper, *Zonocerus elegans* Thunb. *J. ent. Soc. S. Afr.* **17**: 237–40, 1 fig. [*30*, *60*, *62*, *64*].
—— 1955. Notes on acridid anatomy. I. The prothoracic musculature of certain acridids. *J. ent. Soc. S. Afr.* **18**: 42–7, 1 fig. [*60*, *62*, *64*].

BIBLIOGRAPHY

EWER, D. W. 1957a. The anatomy of the nervous system of the tree locust *Acanthacris ruficornis* (Fab.). IV. The prothorax. V. The homologies of the thoracic musculature. *J. ent. Soc. S. Afr.* **20**: 195–216, 7 figs. [60, 62, 64, 154].

—— 1957b. Notes on acridid anatomy. II. A sexual dimorphism in the thorax of certain acridids. III. Twitch and tonic muscles in the thorax of *Locusta. J. ent. Soc. S. Afr.* **20**: 229–33, 1 fig. [60, 62, 64].

—— 1957c. Notes on acridid anatomy. IV. The anterior abdominal musculature of certain acridids. *J. ent. Soc. S. Afr.* **20**: 260–79, 8 figs. [36, 60, 64, 282].

—— 1958. Notes on acridid anatomy. V. The pterothoracic musculature of *Lentula callani* Dirsh. *J. ent. Soc. S. Afr.* **21**: 132–8, 5 figs. [14, 30, 60, 62, 64].

EWER, D. W. & RIPLEY, S. H. 1953. On certain properties of the flight muscles of the Orthoptera. *J. exp. Biol.* **30**: 170–7, 1 pl., 3 figs. [65].

FABER, A. 1929. Die Lautäusserungen der Orthopteren. (Lauterzeugung, Lautabwandlung und deren biologische Bedeutung sowie Tonapparat der Geradflügler.) Vergleichende Untersuchungen I. *Z. Morph. Ökol. Tiere*, **13**: 745–803, 13 figs. [176, 187].

—— 1932. Die Lautäusserungen der Orthopteren II. (Untersuchungen über die biozönotischen, tierpsychologischen und vergleichend-physiologischen Probleme der Orthopterenstridulation. Methodik der Bearbeitung und Auswertung von Stridulationsbeobachtungen. Einzeldarstellungen.) *Z. Morph. Ökol. Tiere*, **26**: 1–93, 10 figs. [176].

—— 1936. Die Laut- und Bewegungsäusserungen der Oedipodinen. Biologisch, tierpsychologisch und vergleichend-funktionell beschrieben; mit einem Erstnachweis von tonhaften Lauten bei Acridiiden und mehrfachen Lautformen bei Weibchen. Allgemeines zur Biologie der Paarungseinleitung und Paarung. *Z. wiss. Zool.* **149**: 1–85, 4 figs. [176, 184].

—— 1949. Eine bisher unbekannte Art der Lauterzeugung europäischer Orthopteren: Mandibellaut von *Calliptamus italicus* L. *Z. Naturf.* 4b:367–9 [184].

—— 1953. Laut- und Gebärdensprache bei Insekten. Orthoptera (Geradflügler). Teil I. Vergleichende Darstellung von Ausdrucksformen als Zeitgestalten und ihren Funktionen. *Mitt. Mus. Naturk. Stuttgart*, no. 287: 198 pp., 7 pls., 4 figs. [176, 178, 182].

—— 1957. Über den Aufbau von Gesangsformen in der Gattung *Chorthippus* Fieb. (Orthoptera) und über phylogenetische Gemeinsamkeiten bei Stridulations- und anderen Bewegungsformen. *Stuttgart. Beitr. Naturk.* no. 1: 28 pp., 51 figs. [182].

FAURE, J. C. 1923. The life-history of the Brown Locust (*Locustana pardalina* (Walker)). *Bull. Fac. Agric. Transv. Univ. Coll.* no. 4: 30 pp., 1 pl., 3 figs. [299, 319, 336].

—— 1929. The biology of the Brown Swarm Locust. [Discussion on Potgieter's paper.] *Proc. Pan-Afr. (agric.) vet. Conf.*, Pretoria 1929: 113–27 [379].

—— 1932. The phases of locusts in South Africa. *Bull. ent. Res.* **23**: 293–405, 25 pls. [46, 52, 53, 332, 336, 358, 375, 379, 380].

—— 1933. The phases of the Rocky Mountain Locust *Melanoplus mexicanus* (Saussure). *J. econ. Ent.* **26**: 706–18, 1 pl. [336, 366].

FAUSSEK, V. 1887. Beiträge zur Histologie des Darmkanals der Insekten. *Z. wiss. Zool.* **46**: 694–712 [118].

FEDOROV, S. M. 1927. Studies in the copulation and oviposition of *Anacridium aegyptium*, L. (Orthoptera, Acrididae). *Trans. ent. Soc. Lond.* **75**: 53–60, 4 pls. [140, 314, 316, 318, 322].

FÉNARD, A. 1896. Recherches sur les organes complémentaires internes de l'appareil génital des Orthoptères. *Bull. sci. Fr. Belg.* **29**: 390–532, 4 pls. [140, 147].

FERNÁNDEZ-MORAN, H. 1958. Fine structure of the light receptors in the compound eyes of insects. *Exp. Cell Res.* (Suppl.), no. 5: 586–644, 28 pls., 1 fig. [197, 200].

FICKENDEY, E. 1918. Die Organisation der Bekämpfung und deren Ergebnisse in den Jahren 1916 und 1917. D. Die Verwertbarkeit der gesammelten Heuschreckeneier und Heuschrecken. *Monogr. angew. Ent.* no. 3: 151–6 [267].

FINGERMAN, M., LAGO, A. D. & LOWE, M. E. 1958. Rhythms of locomotor activity and O$_2$-consumption of the grasshopper *Romalea microptera*. *Amer. Midl. Nat.* **59**: 58–66, 9 figs. [135].

FISHELSON, L. 1960. The biology and behaviour of *Poecilocerus bufonius* Klug, with special reference to the repellent gland (Orth. Acrididae). *Eos, Madr.* **36**: 41–62, 7 figs. [36, 286].

FITZGERALD, L. R. 1949. The alkaline phosphatase of the developing grasshopper egg. *J. exp. Zool.* **110**: 461–87, 11 figs. [251].

FODOR, P. J. 1949. The multiplicity of lipolytic enzyme systems. *Experientia*, **5**: 334–5 [251].

FORD, N. 1923. A comparative study of the abdominal musculature of orthopteroid insects. *Trans. R. Canad. Inst.* **14**: 207–319, 17 pls. [64].

FOX, H. M. & VEVERS, G. 1960. *The Nature of Animal Colours*, London [38, 42, 44, 47].

FRAENKEL, G. 1932a. Beiträge zur Physiologie der Atmung der Insekten. *Arch. zool. ital.* **16**: 905–921, 9 figs. [128, 130].

—— 1932b. Untersuchungen über die Koordination von Reflexen und automatisch-nervösen Rhythmen bei Insekten. I. Die Flugreflexe der Insekten und ihre Koordination. *Z. vergl. Physiol.* **16**: 371–93 [130].

—— 1932c. Untersuchungen über die Koordination von Reflexen und automatisch-nervösen Rhythmen bei Insekten. III. Das Problem des gerichteten Atemstromes in den Tracheen der Insekten. *Z. vergl. Physiol.* **16**: 418–43, 11 figs. [128, 130].

BIBLIOGRAPHY

FRAENKEL, G. 1932d. Untersuchungen über die Koordination von Reflexen und automatisch-nervösen Rhythmen bei Insekten. IV. Über die nervösen Zentren der Atmung und die Koordination ihrer Tätigkeit. *Z. vergl. Physiol.* **16**: 444–62 [*130, 131*].

—— 1959. The chemistry of host specificity of phytophagous insects. *4th Int. Congr. Biochem.*, Vienna 1958, vol. 12: 1–14 [*82*].

FRANZ, H. 1930. Untersuchungen über den Wärmehaushalt der Poikilothermen. *Biol. Zbl.* **50**: 158–82, 7 figs. [*211, 215*].

FRAPPA, M. C. 1938. Recherches sur l'action de la température et de l'humidité sur le comportement du criquet migrateur (*Locusta migratoria capito* Sauss.) à Madagascar. *Rev. Path. vég.* **25**: 46–58 [*255*].

FRIAUF, J. J. 1947. Notes on two orthopteran gynandromorphs. *Occ. Pap. Mus. Zool. Univ. Mich.* no. 501: 1–4, 2 pls. [*149*].

FRIEDRICH, H. 1929. Vergleichende Untersuchungen über die tibialen Scolopalorgane einiger Orthopteren. *Z. wiss. Zool.* **134**: 84–148, 29 figs. [*169*].

FRINGS, H. & FRINGS, M. 1958. Uses of sounds by insects. *Annu. Rev. Ent.* **3**: 87–106 [*176*].

FRINGS, M. & FRINGS, H. 1960. *Sound Production and Sound Reception by Insects. A Bibliography.* University Park, Pa. [*176, 185*].

FRIZA, F. 1929. Zur Frage der Färbung und Zeichnung des facettierten Insektenauges. *Z. vergl. Physiol.* **8**: 289–336, 25 figs. [*197, 200*].

FU, Y.-Y. 1957. Changes in distribution of sulfur-containing amino acids in developing grasshopper egg (*Melanoplus differentialis*). *Physiol. Zoöl.* **30**: 1–12, 8 figs. [*250*].

FUDALEWICZ-NIEMCZYK, W. 1958. Analysis of the wing venation on the background of their innervation in *Stauroderus biguttulus* (L.) and *Tettigonia cantans* (Fuessl.) (Saltatoria, Latreille) and in *Phyllodromia germanica* (L.) (Dictyoptera, Leach). (In Polish with English summary.) *Bull. ent. Pologne,* **28**(4): 59–89, 11 figs. [*27*].

FUZEAU-BRAESCH, S. 1960. Étude biologique et biochimique de la pigmentation d'un insecte, *Gryllus bimaculatus* de Geer (gryllide, orthoptère). *Bull. biol.* **94**: 525–627, 3 pls., 17 figs. [*43, 45*].

GANGWERE, S. K. 1960a. The use of the mouthparts of Orthoptera during feeding. *Ent. News,* **71**: 193–206, 4 figs. [*7*].

—— 1960b. Notes on drinking and the need for water in Orthoptera. *Canad. Ent.* **92**: 911–15 [*227*].

—— 1961. A monograph on food selection in Orthoptera. *Trans. Amer. ent. Soc.* **87**: 67–230 [*7*].

—— 1962. A study of the feculae of Orthoptera, their specificity, and the role which the insects' mouthparts, alimentary canal, and food-habits play in their formation. *Eos, Madr.* **38**: 247–262, 19 figs. [*120*].

GARDINER, B. G. 1958. Some observations on the respiration of young nymphs of *Schistocerca gregaria* (Forskål) in relation to phase and rearing density. *Proc. R. ent. Soc. Lond.* A, **33**: 159–66, 3 figs. [*132, 337*].

GATENBY, J. B. & TAHMISIAN, T. N. 1959. Centriole adjunct, centrioles, mitochondria, and ergastoplasm in orthopteran spermatogenesis. An electron microscope study. *Cellule,* **60**: 103–34, 1 pl., 21 figs. [*304*].

GEIST, R. M. 1928. The heat sensitive areas of certain grasshoppers. *Ann. ent. Soc. Amer.* **21**: 614–618 [*220*].

GEORGE, J. C. & EAPEN, J. 1959a. Histochemical demonstration of lipase and alkaline phosphatase activity in the fat body of the Desert Locust. *Nature, Lond.* **183**: 268, 2 figs. [*102*].

—— 1959b. Lipase activity in the fat body of the Desert Locust *Schistocerca gregaria. J. cell. comp. Physiol.* **54**: 293–5 [*102*].

GEORGE, J. C. & HEGDEKAR, B. M. 1961. Histochemical demonstration of succinic dehydrogenase in the fat body of the Desert Locust and some grasshoppers. *J. Histochem. Cytochem.* **9**: 157–160, 3 figs. [*102*].

GEORGE, J. C., VALLYATHAN, N. V. & SCARIA, K. S. 1958. Lipase activity in insect flight muscle. *Experientia,* **14**: 250–1, 2 figs. [*68, 102*].

GERD, A. 1961. Untersuchungen über die chemische Zusammensetzung einiger Insektenfette. *Z. vergl. Physiol.* **44**: 487–508 [*102*].

GETTRUP, E. 1962. Thoracic proprioceptors in the flight system of locusts. *Nature, Lond.* **193**: 498–499, 1 fig. [*170*].

GHOURI, A. S. K. & AHMED, H. 1960. Swarming of *Hieroglyphus nigrorepletus. FAO Pl. Prot. Bull.* **8**: 135–6 [*371*].

GIARDINA, A. 1901. Funzionamento dell'armatura genitale femminile e considerazioni intorno alle ooteche degli Acridii. *G. Sci. nat. econ. Palermo,* **23**: 54–61, 8 figs. [*322*].

GILMOUR, D. 1941. Repayment of the anerobic oxygen debt in grasshopper skeletal muscle. *Biol. Bull., Woods Hole,* **80**: 45–9 [*68, 137*].

—— 1953. The biochemistry of muscle. In Roeder, K. D. [Ed.], *Insect Physiology,* pp. 404–22, 3 figs. New York & London [*68*].

—— 1961. *The Biochemistry of Insects.* New York & London [*42, 43, 44, 46, 47, 68, 91, 295*].

GILMOUR, D. & CALABY, J. H. 1952. The magnesium-activated apyrase of insect muscle. *Arch. Biochem. Biophys.* **41**: 83–103, 10 figs. [*68*].

—— 1953a. Physical and enzymic properties of actomyosins from the femoral and thoracic muscles of an insect. *Enzymologia,* **16**: 23–33, 5 figs. [*68*].

434

BIBLIOGRAPHY

GILMOUR, D. & CALABY, J. H. 1953b. Myokinase and pyrgophosphatase of insect muscle. *Enzymologia*, **16**: 34–40 [*68*].

GIRAL, F. 1941. Sobre aceites de insectos. I. *Taeniopoda auricornis*. *Rev. Soc. mex. Hist. nat.* **2**: 243–50 [*94*, *101*].

—— 1946. Fats of insects. V. *Sphenarium purpurascens* Charpentier. *J. biol. Chem.* **162**: 61–3 [*94*, *101*].

—— 1954. Aceites de insectos. VI. Distribución filogenética del azufre tóxico. *Ciencia, Méx.* **14**: 163–4 [*94*, *101*].

GIRAL, J., GIRAL, F. & GIRAL, M. L. 1943. Sobre aceites de insectos. II. *Melanoplus* sp. *Ciencia, Méx.* **4**: 155–6 [*94*, *101*, *102*].

—— 1944. Sobre aceites de insectos. III. Nuevos datos sobre *Taeniopoda auricornis* Walker. *Ciencia, Méx.* **4**: 215–16 [*94*, *101*, *102*].

—— 1946. Fats of insects. IV. Composition of the fat of *Melanoplus atlanis* Riley. *J. biol. Chem.* **162**: 55–9 [*94*, *101*, *102*].

GOLDING, F. D. 1934. On the ecology of Acrididae near Lake Chad. *Bull. ent. Res.* **25**: 263–303, 5 figs. [*180*].

GONÇALVES, C. R. 1957. Dados sobre a biologia do gafanhoto no nordeste do Brasil. *Com. interamer. perm. antiacrid., B. Aires*, **1957**: 10 pp. [*255*].

GONZALES, S. S. 1932. Further studies of the biology of the Migratory Locust (*Pachytylus migratorioides* Reiche and Fairm.), Locustidae Orthoptera. *Philipp. J. Agric.* **3**: 1–38, 7 pls. [*255*].

GOODHUE, D. 1958. The radiographic examination of small objects. *Radiography*, **24**: 263–4, 3 figs. [*74*].

—— 1962. *The effects of stomach poisons on the Desert Locust*. Ph.D. thesis, London [*74*, *75*, *76*].

—— 1963. Some differences in the passage of food through the intestines of the Desert and Migratory Locusts. *Nature, Lond.* **200**: 288–9, 2 figs. [*74*].

GOODMAN, L. J. 1959. Hair plates on the first cervical sclerites of the Orthoptera. *Nature, Lond.* **183**: 1106–7, 2 figs. [*10*, *163*].

GOODWIN, T. W. 1949. The biochemistry of locusts. 2. Carotenoid distribution in solitary and gregarious phases of the African Migratory Locust (*Locusta migratoria migratorioides* R. & F.) and the Desert Locust (*Schistocerca gregaria* Forsk.). *Biochem. J.* **45**: 472–9, 4 figs. [*47*, *48*, *49*].

—— 1950a. Carotenoids and reproduction. *Biol. Rev.* **25**: 391–413 [*47*, *48*].

—— 1950b. Biochemistry of locusts. 4. Insectorubin metabolism in the Desert Locust (*Schistocerca gregaria* Forsk.) and the African Migratory Locust (*Locusta migratoria migratorioides* R. and F.). *Biochem. J.* **47**: 554–62, 2 figs. [*44*, *45*, *46*, *49*].

—— 1951. Biochemistry of locusts. 7. A note on the effect of breeding temperature on the carotenoid content of locusts (the African Migratory Locust, *Locusta migratoria migratorioides* R. & F. and the Desert Locust, *Schistocerca gregaria* Forsk.). *Biochem. J.* **49**: 86–8 [*47*, *49*].

—— 1952a. The biochemistry of locust pigmentation. *Biol. Rev.* **27**: 439–60, 2 pls. [*42*, *43*, *44*, *45*, *47*, *49*, *50*, *199*, *295*, *335*].

—— 1952b. *The Comparative Biochemistry of the Carotenoids*. London [*47*, *49*].

GOODWIN, T. W. & SRISUKH, S. 1949. The biochemistry of locusts. 1. The carotenoids of the integument of two locust species (*Locusta migratoria migratorioides* R. & F. and *Schistocerca gregaria* Forsk.). *Biochem. J.* **45**: 263–8, 2 figs. [*47*, *49*, *251*].

—— 1950. Biochemistry of locusts. 3. Insectorubin: the redox pigment present in the integument and eyes of the Desert Locust (*Schistocerca gregaria* Forsk.), the African Migratory Locust (*Locusta migratoria migratorioides* R. and F.) and other insects. *Biochem. J.* **47**: 549–54, 5 figs. [*44*, *51*, *199*].

—— 1951a. Biochemistry of locusts. 5. The green pigment of the haemolymph and integument of solitary locusts (*Locusta migratoria migratorioides* R. & F. and *Schistocerca gregaria* Forsk.). *Biochem. J.* **48**: 199–203, 3 figs. [*50*].

—— 1951b. Biochemistry of locusts. 6. The occurrence of a flavin in the eggs and of a pterin in the eyes of the African Migratory Locust (*Locusta migratoria migratorioides* R. & F.) and the Desert Locust (*Schistocerca gregaria* Forsk.). *Biochem. J.* **49**: 84–6, 2 figs. [*51*, *199*, *251*].

GRABER, V. 1871. Ueber den Ursprung und Bau der Ton-Apparate bei den Akridiern. *Verh. zool.-bot. Ges. Wien*, **21**: 1097–1102, 1 pl. [*178*].

—— 1876. Die tympanalen Sinnesapparate der Orthopteren. *Denkschr. Akad. Wiss. Wien*, **36**: 1–140, 10 pls. [*188*].

GRADOJEVIČ, Z. 1960. Some laboratory experiments on phases in the Moroccan Locust (*Dociostaurus maroccanus* Thunb.). (In Serbian with English summary.) *Zasht. Bilja*, no. 57–8: 129–142 [*338*].

GRANT, G. R. M. 1949. The sensory pits of insects considered as dielectric wave guides and resonators to infra-red rays. *Proc. roy. Soc. Qd.* **60**: 89–98, 3 figs. [*166*].

GRASSÉ, P. P. 1922. Étude biologique sur le criquet égyptien *Orthacanthacris aegyptia* (L.). *Bull. biol.* **56**: 545–78, 7 figs. [*318*, *322*, *324*].

—— 1937. L'hémaphrorrhée rejet-réflexe de sang et d'air par les acridiens phymatéides. *C. R. Acad. Sci., Paris*, **204**: 65–7 [*36*].

GRAY, E. G. 1959. Electron microscopy of collagen-like connective tissue fibrils of an insect. *Proc. roy. Soc.* B, **150**: 233–9, 2 pls., 2 figs. [*69*].

—— 1960. The fine structure of the insect ear. *Phil. Trans.* B, **243**: 75–94, 12 pls., 5 figs. [*189*].

BIBLIOGRAPHY

GRAYSON, J. M. 1951. Acidity-alkalinity in the alimentary canal of twenty insect species. *Virginia J. Sci.* (N.S.) **2**: 46–59, 2 figs. [*79*].

GRAYSON, J. M. & TAUBER, O. E. 1943. Carotin—the principal pigment responsible for variations in coloration of the adult grasshopper, *Melanoplus bivittatus* Say. *Iowa St. Coll. J. Sci.* **17**: 191–6, 1 fig. [*49*].

GRÉGOIRE, C. 1955. Blood coagulation in arthropods. V. Studies on hemolymph coagulation in 420 species of insects. *Arch. Biol.* **66**: 103–48, 10 pls. [*115*].

—— 1957. Studies by phase-contrast microscopy on distribution of patterns of hemolymph coagulation in insects. *Smithson. misc. Coll.* **134**(6): 35 pp., 1 pl., 4 figs. [*115*].

—— 1959. Further observations on distribution of patterns of coagulation of the hemolymph in neotropical insects. *Smithson. misc. Coll.* **139**(3): 23 pp. [*115*].

GRÉGOIRE, C. & JOLIVET, P. 1957. Coagulation du sang chez les arthropodes. VIII. Réactions du sang et de l'hémolymphe *in vitro*, étudiées au microscope à contraste de phase, chez 210 espèces d'arthropodes africains. *Explor. Parc nat. Albert*, (2) no. 4: 45 pp., 9 pls. [*115*].

GREGORY, G. E. 1965a. The formation and fate of the spermatophore in the African Migratory Locust, *Locusta, migratoria, migratorioides* Reiche and Fairmaire. *Trans. R. ent. Soc. Lond.*, **117**: 33-66, 5 pls., 30 figs. [*140, 146, 147, 316, 317*]

—— 1965b. On the initiation of spermatophore formation in the African Migratory Locust, *Locusta migratoria migratorioides* Reiche and Fairmaire. *J. exp. Biol.*, **42**: 423-435. [*316-319*]

GUAGLIUMI, P. 1958. Una nueva langosta que esta invadiendo las sabanas de Apure. *Agron. trop., Maracay*, **8**: 27–31, 2 figs. [*371*].

GUARINO, L. 1935. Osservazioni sull'armatura genitale degli Acrididi. *Arch. zool. ital.* **21**: 427–45, 2 pls., 5 figs. [*64*].

GUEUTAL, J. 1941. Études physiologiques sur les Orthoptères. La teneur en graisses du criquet pélerin. *Bull. biol.* **75**: 88–98 [*101, 228*].

GUIGNON, G. 1936. Étude de la circulation sanguine des ailes chez les Coléoptères et les Orthoptères au moyen de la nicotine. *C. R. Acad. Sci., Paris*, **202**: 2105–6 [*106*].

GUNN, D. L. 1942. Body temperature in poikilothermal animals. *Biol. Rev.* **17**: 293–314, 4 figs. [*22.1*]

—— 1960. The biological background of locust control. *Annu. Rev. Ent.* **5**: 279–300 [*380, 381*].

GUNN, D. L. & HUNTER-JONES, P. 1952. Laboratory experiments on phase differences in locusts. *Anti-Locust Bull.* no. 12: 1–29, 3 figs. [*332, 358, 361, 367, 378*].

GUNN, D. L., PERRY, F. C. *et al.* 1948. Behaviour of the Desert Locust (*Schistocerca gregaria* Forskål) in Kenya in relation to aircraft spraying. *Anti-Locust Bull.* no. 3: 70 pp., 8 pls., 21 figs. [*207, 215*].

GUPTA, B. L., GUPTA, R. K. & NATH, V. 1960. Histochemistry of spermatogenesis in *Chrotogonus trachypterus* Blanch. (Orthoptera-Acrididae). *Res. Bull. Panjab Univ.* **11**: 105–12, 22 figs. [*304*].

GURNEY, A. B. 1949. *Melanoplus rugglesi*, a migratory grasshopper from the Great Basin of North America. *Proc. ent. Soc. Wash.* **51**: 267–72 [*371*].

—— 1962. On the name of the migratory grasshopper of the United States and Canada, *Melanoplus sanguinipes* (F.) (Orthoptera, Acrididae). *Proc. biol. Soc. Wash.* **75**: 189–92 [*414*].

GURNEY, A. B. & BROOKS, A. R. 1959. Grasshoppers of the *mexicanus* group, genus *Melanoplus* (Orthoptera: Acrididae). *Proc. U.S. nat. Mus.* **110**: 1–93, 5 pls., 18 figs. [*371*].

GUTHRIE, D. M. 1964. Observations on the nervous system of the flight apparatus in the locust *Schistocerca gregaria*. *Quart. J. micr. Sci.* **105**: 183–201, 11 figs. [*155*].

HACKMAN, R. H. 1959. Biochemistry of the insect cuticle. *4th Int. Congr. Biochem.*, Vienna 1958, vol. 12: 48–62, 4 figs. [*32*].

HAFEZ, M. & IBRAHIM, M. M. 1958. Studies on the egg and nymphal stages of *Acrida pellucida* Klug, in Egypt [Orthoptera: Acrididae]. *Bull. Soc. ent. Égypte*, **42**: 183–98, 2 figs. [*236, 255, 284, 287, 322, 324*].

—— 1959. Histology of the alimentary canal of *Acrida pellucida* Klug (Orthoptera: Acrididae). *Bull. Soc. ent. Égypte*, **43**: 115–31, 21 figs. [*72, 73*].

—— 1960. Anatomical studies on *Acrida pellucida* Klug. *Bull. Soc. ent. Égypte*, **44**: 451–76, 18 figs. [*118, 126, 138*].

HAGIWARA, S. & WATANABE, A. 1953. Action potential of insect muscle examined with intra-cellular electrode. *Jap. J. Physiol.* **4**: 65–78, 9 figs. [*65*].

HAMILTON, A. G. 1936. The relation of humidity and temperature to the development of three species of African locusts—*Locusta migratoria migratorioides* (R. & F.), *Schistocerca gregaria* (Forsk.), *Nomadacris septemfasciata* (Serv.). *Trans. R. ent. Soc. Lond.* **85**: 1–60, 2 pls., 26 figs. [*256, 291, 293, 306, 307, 309*].

—— 1937. The mechanism of respiration of locusts and its bearing on the problem of inhalation of poison dusts. *Bull. ent. Res.* **28**: 53–68, 2 figs. [124, 128].

—— 1950. Further studies on the relation of humidity and temperature to the development of two species of African locusts—*Locusta migratoria migratorioides* (R. & F.) and *Schistocerca gregaria* (Forsk.) *Trans. R. ent. Soc. Lond.* **101**: 1–58, 34 figs. [*291, 293, 294, 307, 308, 329*].

—— 1955. Parthenogenesis in the Desert Locust (*Schistocerca gregaria* Forsk.) and its possible effect on the maintenance of the species. *Proc. R. ent. Soc. Lond.* A, **30**: 103–14, 1 pl. [*319, 320, 331*].

—— 1958. Variations in the metabolic rate in male Desert Locusts (*Schistocerca gregaria* Forsk.). *10th Int. Congr. Ent.*, Montreal 1956, vol. 2: 343–7, 2 figs. [*132, 133*].

BIBLIOGRAPHY

HAMILTON, A. G. 1959. The infra-red gas analyser as a means of measuring the carbon dioxide output of individual insects. *Nature, Lond.* **184**: 367–9, 4 figs. [*132, 137*].
—— 1961. The relationship between the output of carbon dioxide and sexual maturation in two species of locusts (*Schistocerca gregaria* Forsk. and *Nomadacris septemfasciata* Serv.) as shown by the infra red gas analyser. *11th Int. Congr. Ent.*, Vienna 1960, vol. 1: 701–6, 2 figs. [*132–134*].
—— 1964. The occurrence of periodic or continuous discharge of carbon dioxide by male Desert Locusts (*Schistocerca gregaria* Forskål) measured by an infra-red gas analyser. *Proc. roy. Soc.* B, **160**: 373–95, 29 figs. [*132*].
HAMILTON, H. L. 1939. The action of acetylcholine, atropine and nicotine on the heart of the grasshopper (*Melanoplus differentialis*). *J. cell. comp. Physiol.* **13**: 91–103, 2 figs. [*108*].
HAMORI, J. 1961. Innervation of insect leg muscle. *Acta. biol. hung.* **12**: 219–30, 20 figs. [*65*].
HANDFORD, R. H. 1946. The identification of nymphs of the genus *Melanoplus* of Manitoba and adjacent areas. *Sci. Agric.* **26**: 147–80, 12 pls., 1 fig. [*198, 283*].
HANSTRÖM, B. 1940. Inkretorische Organe, Sinnesorgane und Nervensystem des Kopfes einiger niederer Insektenordnungen. *K. svenska VetenskAkad. Handl.* (3) **18**: 266 pp., 239 figs. [*151, 157*].
HARLOW, P. A. 1958. The action of drugs on the nervous system of the locust (*Locusta migratoria*). *Ann. appl. Biol.* **46**: 55–73, 5 figs. [*220*].
HARTLEY, J. C. 1961. The shell of acridid eggs. *Quart. J. micr. Sci.* **102**: 249–55, 2 figs. [*237, 239, 242, 258*].
HARTLINE, H. K. 1928. A quantitative and descriptive study of the electric response to illumination of the arthropod eye. *Amer. J. Physiol.* **83**: 466–83, 4 figs. [*199*].
HASKELL, P. T. 1956a. Hearing in certain Orthoptera. I. Physiology of sound receptors. *J. exp. Biol.* **33**: 756–66, 4 figs. [*191, 193, 195*].
—— 1956b. Hearing in certain Orthoptera. II. The nature of the response of certain receptors to natural and imitation stridulation. *J. exp. Biol.* **33**: 767–76, 3 figs. [*194*].
—— 1957a. The influence of flight noise on behaviour in the Desert Locust *Schistocerca gregaria* (Forsk.). *J. Insect Physiol.* **1**: 52–75, 2 pls., 2 figs. [*183, 188, 191*].
—— 1957b. Stridulation and associated behaviour in certain Orthoptera. 1. Analysis of the stridulation of, and behaviour between, males. *Brit. J. Anim. Behav.* **5**: 139–48, 2 pls., 2 figs. [*187*].
—— 1959a. Function of certain prothoracic hair receptors in the Desert Locust. *Nature, Lond.* **183**: 1107, 1 fig. [*163*].
—— 1959b. Physiology of some wind-sensitive receptors of the Desert Locust (*Schistocerca gregaria*). (Abs.) *15th Int. Congr. Zool.*, London 1958: 960–1 [*163*].
—— 1960. The sensory equipment of the migratory locust. *Symp. zool. Soc. Lond.* no. 3: 1–23, 1 pl., 7 figs. [*163*].
—— 1961. *Insect Sounds*. London [*185, 192, 193*].
—— 1962. Sensory factors influencing phase change in locusts. *Colloq. int. Cent. nat. Rech. sci.* no. 114: 145–63 [*313, 352, 378*].
HASKELL, P. T. & MOORHOUSE, J. E. 1963. A blood-borne factor influencing the activity of the central nervous system of the Desert Locust. *Nature, Lond.* **197**: 56–8, 1 fig. [*378*].
HASKELL, P. T., PASKIN, M. W. J. & MOORHOUSE, J. E. 1962. Laboratory observations on factors affecting the movements of hoppers of the Desert Locust. *J. Insect Physiol.* **8**: 53–78, 4 figs. [*207, 218, 219*].
HASTINGS, E. & PEPPER, J. H. 1943. Studies on body fluids of seven orthopterans, their pH, buffering capacity, and effect on solubility of fractionated insecticides. *J. econ. Ent.* **36**: 857–64, 4 figs. [*108, 109, 117*].
HAUSER, G. 1880. Physiologische und histologische Untersuchungen über das Geruchsorgan der Insekten. *Z. wiss. Zool.* **34**: 367–403, 3 pls. [*171*].
HEARFIELD, D. A. H. & KILBY, B. A. 1958. Enzymes of the tricarboxylic acid cycle and cytochrome oxidase in the fat body of the Desert Locust. *Nature, Lond.* **181**: 546–7 [*102*].
HEBARD, M. 1937. Studies in Orthoptera which occur in North America north of the Mexican boundary. VII–IX. *Trans. Amer. ent. Soc.* **43**: 347–79, 3 pls. [*315*].
HELWIG, E. R. 1958. Cytology and taxonomy. *Bios, Mount Vernon, Iowa*, **29**: 59–72, 19 figs. [*389, 390*].
HENRY, G. M. 1942. Three remarkable stridulatory mechanisms in Acrididae (Orthoptera). *Proc. R. ent. Soc. Lond.* A, **17**, 59–62, 2 figs. [*181, 184*].
HENRY, L. M. 1958. Musculature of the cervical region in insects. *Microentomology*, **23**: 95–105, 6 figs. [*11, 60, 163*].
HERBER, E. C. & SLIFER, E. H. 1928. The regularity of respiratory movements of Locustidae. *Physiol. Zoöl.* **1**: 593–602, 9 figs. [*129*].
HERS, J. 1938. Organe tympanal du *Schistocerca gregaria* Forsk. *5th Int. Locust Conf.*, Brussels 1938: 434–45, 2 pls. [*188*].
HERTZ, M. & IMMS, A. D. 1937. On the responses of the African Migratory Locust to different types of background. *Proc. roy. Soc.* B, **122**: 281–97, 3 figs. [*52, 53*].
HESS, R., SCARPELLI, D. G. & PEARSE, A. G. E. 1958. Cytochemical localization of pyridine nucleotide-linked dehydrogenase. *Nature, Lond.* **181**: 1531–2, 2 figs. [*102*].
HIGHNAM, K. C. 1961. The histology of the neurosecretory system of the adult female Desert Locust, *Schistocerca gregaria*. *Quart. J. micr. Sci.* **102**: 27–38, 1 pl., 2 figs. [*157, 311*].

437

BIBLIOGRAPHY

HIGHNAM, K. C. 1962a. Neurosecretory control of ovarian development in the Desert Locust. In Heller, H. & Clark, R. B. (Eds.), *Neurosecretion*, pp. 379–90, 5 figs. London [*112, 311, 312*].

—— 1962b. Neurosecretory control of ovarian development in *Schistocerca gregaria*, and its relation to phase differences. *Colloq. int. Cent. nat. Rech. sci.* no. 114: 107–22, 18 figs. [*311*].

—— 1962c. Neurosecretory control of ovarian development in *Schistocerca gregaria*. *Quart. J. micr. Sci.* **103**: 57–72, 5 figs. [*311, 312*].

—— 1964. Endocrine relationships in insect reproduction. *2nd Symp. R. ent. Soc. Lond.*, London 1963: 26–42 [*311*].

HIGHNAM, K. C. & HASKELL, P. T. 1964. The endocrine systems of isolated and crowded *Locusta* and *Schistocerca* in relation to oöcyte growth, and the effects of flying upon maturation. *J. Insect Physiol.* **10**: 849–64, 10 figs. [*311, 313*].

HIGHNAM, K. C. & LUSIS, O. 1962. The influence of mature males on the neurosecretory control of ovarian development in the Desert Locust. *Quart. J. micr. Sci.* **103**: 73–83, 4 figs. [*311, 313*].

HIGHNAM, K. C., LUSIS, O. & HILL, L. 1963a. The role of the corpora allata during oöcyte growth in the Desert Locust, *Schistocerca gregaria* Forsk. *J. Insect Physiol.* **9**: 587–96, 10 figs. [*311*].

—— 1963b. Factors affecting oöcyte resorption in the Desert Locust, *Schistocerca gregaria* (Forskål). *J. Insect Physiol.* **9**: 827–37, 2 figs. [*313*].

HILL, D. L. 1945. Carbohydrate metabolism during embryonic development (Orthoptera). *J. cell. comp. Physiol.* **25**: 205–16, 3 figs. [*249*].

HILL, L. 1962. Neurosecretory control of haemolymph protein concentration during ovarian development in the Desert Locust. *J. Insect Physiol.* **8**: 609–19, 4 figs. [*112, 114, 311*].

—— 1963. *The endocrine control of oocyte development in the Desert Locust*, Schistocerca gregaria Forskål. Ph.D. thesis, Sheffield [*112, 114, 311*].

HILL, L. & TAYLOR, H. J. 1933. Locusts in sunlight. *Nature, Lond.* **132**: 276 [*214*].

HILLIARD, J. R. 1959. *The specificity of acridian egg pods and eggs, with biological notes.* Ph.D. thesis, Texas [*240, 326*].

HINTON, H. E. 1954. Insect blood. *Sci. Progr., Lond.* **42**: 684–96 [*115*].

—— 1957. Some aspects of diapause. *Sci. Progr., Lond.* **45**: 307–20 [*258*].

—— 1962. Respiratory systems of insect egg-shells. *Sci. Progr., Lond.* **50**: 96–113, 1 pl., 20 figs. [*248*].

HOCHRAINER, H. 1942. Der Wassergehalt bei Insekten und die Faktoren, die denselben bestimmen. *Zool. Jb.* (Physiol.), **60**: 387–436, 14 figs. [*92, 225*].

HODGE, C. 1933. Growth and nutrition of *Melanoplus differentialis* Thomas (Orthoptera: Acrididae). I. Growth on a satisfactory mixed diet and on diets of single food plants. *Physiol. Zoöl.* **6**: 306–28, 8 figs. [*82, 274*].

—— 1936. The anatomy and histology of the alimentary tract of the grasshopper, *Melanoplus differentialis* Thomas. *J. Morph.* **59**: 423–34, 2 pls. [*72, 73, 74*].

—— 1937. Some effects of diet on the gastric epithelial cells of the grasshopper, *Melanoplus differentialis* Thomas. *Biol. Bull., Woods Hole,* **72**: 203–11 [*73, 74*].

—— 1939. The anatomy and histology of the alimentary tract of *Locusta migratoria* L. (Orthoptera: Acrididae). *J. Morph.* **64**: 375–400, 4 pls. [*72, 73*].

—— 1940. The anatomy and histology of the alimentary tract of *Radenotatum carinatum* var. *peninsulare* Rehn and Hebard (Orthoptera: Acrididae). *J. Morph.* **66**: 581–604, 4 pls. [*72, 73, 118*].

—— 1943. The internal anatomy of *Leptysma marginicollis* (Serv.) and of *Opshomala vitreipennis* (Marsch.) (Orthoptera: Acrididae). *J. Morph.* **72**: 87–124, 4 pls. [*73, 118, 138, 140*].

HODSON, A. C. & AL RAWY, M. A. 1958. Temperature in relation to developmental thresholds of insects. *10th Int. Congr. Ent.*, Montreal 1956, vol. 2: 61–5, 4 figs. [*254*].

HOLDGATE, M. W. 1955. The wetting of insect cuticles by water. *J. exp. Biol.* **32**: 591–617, 8 figs. [*37*].

HOLLANDE, A. C. 1922. La cellule péricardiale des insectes (cytologie, histo-chimie, rôle physiologique). *Arch. Anat. micr.* **18**: 85–307, 4 pls., 31 figs. [*122*].

—— 1926. La signification de l'autohémorrhée des insectes. *Arch. Anat. micr.* **22**: 374–412, 16 figs. [*35*].

HORRIDGE, G. A. 1961. Pitch discrimination in locusts. *Proc. roy. Soc.* B, **155**, 218-31, 2 pls., 1 fig. [*191, 193*].

HOUSE, H. L. & STEPHENS, J. M. 1958. Note on specific gravity of haemolymph of *Melanoplus bivittatus* (Say) and *Melanoplus mexicanus* (Sauss.) (Orthoptera: Locustidae). *Canad. Ent.* **90**: 463 [*114*].

HOWDEN, G. F. 1957. *A biochemical investigation of the haemolymph of the locust.* Ph.D. thesis, Leeds [*112*].

HOWDEN, G. F. & HUNTER-JONES, P. 1958. An artificial diet for the laboratory rearing of locusts. *Nature, Lond.* **182**: 1527–8, 2 figs. [*87, 227*].

HOWDEN, G. F. & KILBY, B. A. 1956. Trehalose and trehalase in the locust. *Chem. & Ind.*, Dec. 8th: 1453–4 [*112*].

—— 1960. Biochemical studies on insect haemolymph—I. Variations in reducing power with age and the effect of diet. *J. Insect Physiol.* **4**: 258–69, 13 figs. [*112, 113, 114*].

—— 1961. Biochemical studies on insect haemolymph—II. The nature of the reducing material present. *J. Insect Physiol.* **6**: 85–95, 2 figs. [*112, 113*].

438

BIBLIOGRAPHY

HOYLE, G. 1953. Potassium ions and insect nerve muscle. *J. exp. Biol.* **30**: 121–35, 6 figs. [*65, 66, 155*].

—— 1954. Changes in the blood potassium concentration of the African Migratory Locust (*Locusta migratoria migratorioides* R. & F.) during food deprivation, and the effect on neuromuscular activity. *J. exp. Biol.* **31**: 260–70, 3 figs. [*110, 111, 155*].

—— 1955a. The anatomy and innervation of locust skeletal muscle. *Proc. roy. Soc.* B, **143**: 281–92, 2 pls., 5 figs. [*62*].

—— 1955b. Neuromuscular mechanisms of a locust skeletal muscle. *Proc. roy. Soc.* B, **143**: 343–367, 17 figs. [*65*].

—— 1955c. Functioning of the insect ocellar nerve. *J. exp. Biol.* **32**: 397–407, 11 figs. [*206*].

——1956. Sodium and potassium changes occurring in the haemolymph of insects at the time of moulting and their physiological consequences. *Nature, Lond.* **178**: 1236–7, 1 fig. [110, 286].

—— 1957. Nervous control of insect muscles. In Scheer, B. T. [Ed.], *Recent Advances in Invertebrate Physiology. A Symposium*, pp. 73–98, 6 figs. Eugene, Oreg. [*59, 62, 65, 66*].

—— 1958. The leap of the grasshopper. *Sci. Amer.* **198**: 30–5, 9 figs. [*65, 163*].

—— 1959. The neuromuscular mechanism of an insect spiracular muscle. *J. Insect Physiol.* **3**: 378–394, 12 figs. [*64, 124*].

—— 1960. The action of carbon dioxide gas on an insect spiracular muscle. *J. Insect Physiol.* **4**: 63–79, 8 figs. [*131*].

—— 1961. Functional contracture in a spiracular muscle. *J. Insect Physiol.* **7**: 305–14, 5 figs. [*131*].

HSIANG WEI 1958. Cytological studies on Migratory Locust hybrid, *Locusta migratoria migratoria* L. × *Locusta migratoria manilensis* Meyen. (In Chinese with English summary.) *Acta zool. sinica,* **10**: 53–9, 9 figs. [*390*].

HSÜ, FONTZOU; LIU, WI-TEH & SHEN, LIE-MEI 1952. The abdominal tympanal organs of some Acrididae. (In Chinese with English summary.) *Acta ent. sinica,* **2**: 19–37, 14 figs. [*188*].

HUBBARD, S. J. 1959. Femoral mechanoreceptors in the locust. *J. Physiol.* **147**: 8P–10P, 1 fig. [*170*].

HUBBELL, T. H. 1932. A revision of the puer group of the North American genus *Melanoplus*, with remarks on the taxonomic value of the concealed male genitalia in the Cyrtacanthacrinae (Orthoptera, Acrididae). *Misc. Publ. Mus. Zool. Univ. Mich.* no. 23: 64 pp., 4 pls. [*143, 149, 395*].

—— 1956. Some aspects of geographic variation in insects. *Annu. Rev. Ent.* **1**: 71–88, 1 fig. [*394, 395, 396*].

—— 1960. The sibling species of the *alutacea* group of the bird-locust genus *Schistocerca* (Orthoptera, Acrididae, Cyrtacanthacridinae). *Misc. Publ. Mus. Zool. Univ. Mich.* no. 116: 136 pp., 23 pls., 9 figs. [*391*].

HUBBELL, T. H. & CANTRALL, I. J. 1938. A new species of *Appalachia* from Michigan (Orthoptera, Acrididae, Cyrtacanthacrinae). *Occ. Pap. Mus. Zool. Univ. Mich.* no. 389: 22 pp., 1 pl., 1 fig. [*148*].

HUBER, F. 1955. Über die Funktion der Pilzkörper (Corpora pedunculata) beim Gesang der Keulenheuschrecke *Gomphocerus rufus* L. (Acrididae). *Naturwissenschaften,* **42**: 566–7 [151].

HUKUSÍMA, S. 1955. On the thermal reaction of the long-winged vegetable grasshopper, *Eirenephilus longipennis* Shiraki and some considerations of the cause of increase in populations in 1951. (Activity fluctuation in insects and environmental condition, 16). *Bull. Fac. Agric. Hirosaki Univ.* no. 1: 45–53, 3 figs. [*222*].

HUMPHREY, G. F. & SIGGINS, L. 1949. Glycolysis in the wing muscle of the grasshopper, *Locusta migratoria*. *Aust. J. exp. Biol. med. Sci.* **27**: 353–9 [68].

HUNTER-JONES, P. 1957. An albino strain of the Desert Locust. *Nature, Lond.* **180**: 236–7 [46].

—— 1958. Laboratory studies on the inheritance of phase characters in locusts. *Anti-Locust Bull.* no. 29: 32 pp., 6 figs. [*320, 333, 362, 363*].

—— 1960. Fertilization of eggs of the Desert Locust by spermatozoa from successive copulations. *Nature, Lond.* **185**: 336 [*318*].

—— 1961. *Rearing and Breeding Locusts in the Laboratory.* London [vii].

—— 1964. Egg development in the Desert Locust (*Schistocerca gregaria* Forsk.) in relation to the availability of water. *Proc. R. ent. Soc. Lond.* A, **39**: 25–33, 3 figs. [*247, 257, 268*].

HUNTER-JONES, P. & LAMBERT, J. G. 1961. Egg development of *Humbe tenuicornis* Schaum (Orthoptera: Acrididae) in relation to availability of water. *Proc. R. ent. Soc. Lond.* A, **36**: 75–80, 3 figs. [*255, 262, 263*].

HUNTER-JONES, P. & WARD, V. K. 1959. The life-history of *Gastrimargus africanus* Saussure (Orth., Acrididae) in the laboratory. *Ent. mon. Mag.* **95**: 169–72 [*255, 287, 370*].

HUSAIN, M. A. & AHMAD T. 1936a. Studies on *Schistocerca gregaria* Forsk. II. The biology of the Desert Locust with special relation to temperature. *Indian J. agric. Sci.* **6**: 188–262, 6 figs. [*264*].

—— 1936b. Studies on *Schistocerca gregaria* Forsk. VI. Influence of temperature on the intensity and extent of black pattern in the Desert Locust hoppers bred crowded. *Indian J. agric. Sci.* **6**: 624–64, 5 pls. [*44, 366*].

HUSAIN, M. A., AHMAD, T. & MATHUR, C. B. 1941. Studies on *Schistocerca gregaria* Forsk. X. Role of water in the bionomics of the Desert Locust. *Indian J. agric. Sci.* **10** (1940): 927–44 [*256, 273, 292*].

HUSAIN, M. A. & BHATIA, D. R. 1936. Studies on *Schistocerca gregaria* Forsk. VII. Factors determining the movement of the vermiform larvae. *Indian J. agric. Sci.* **6**: 665–71, 4 figs. [*272*].

439

BIBLIOGRAPHY

HUSAIN, M. A. & MATHUR, C. B. 1936. Studies on *Schistocerca gregaria* Forsk. VIII. Influence of carbon dioxide on development of black pigmentation in *Schistocerca gregaria* Forsk. *Indian J. agric. Sci.* **6**: 1005–30, 3 pls. [*44*].

—— 1944. Studies on *Schistocerca gregaria* Forsk. XI. The influence of temperature on the growth in weight and size of the hoppers. *Indian J. Ent.* **5**:107–15, 1 fig. [367].

—— 1946. Studies on *Schistocerca gregaria* Forsk. XIII. Sexual life. *Indian J. Ent.* **7** (1945): 89–101[[*319*].

HUSAIN, M. A. & ROONWAL, M. L. 1933. Studies on *Schistocerca gregaria* Forsk. I. The micropyle in *Schistocerca gregaria* Forsk. and some other Acrididae. *Indian J. agric. Sci.* **3**: 639–45, 1 pl. [*242*].

HUSSEIN, M. 1937. The effect of temperature on locust activity. *Bull. Minist. Agric. Egypt*, no. 184: 55 pp., 25 figs. [*221, 222*].

HUTSON, J. C. 1926. The spotted locust, *Aularches miliaris* L. *Yearb. Dep. Agric. Ceylon*, **1926**: 36–44, 1 pl. [*370*].

HUXLEY, J. 1955. Morphism and evolution. *Heredity*, **9**: 1–52 [*395*].

HWANG GUAN-HUEI & LONG CHING-CHENG 1962. The change of body temperature of the Oriental Migratory Locust (*Locusta migratoria manilensis* Meyen) during flight. (In Chinese with English title.) *Acta ent. sinica*, **11**: 419–21, 4 figs. [*217*].

IBRAHIM, M. M. 1959. *Comparative studies on the ecology and behaviour of two species of grasshoppers in Egypt,* Aiolopus thalassinus *F. and* Sphingonotus carinatus *Sauss.* (Acrididae, Orthoptera). Ph.D. thesis, Cairo [*171*].

—— 1963. Anatomical and histological studies on the digestive tract of *Chrotogonus lugubris* Blanchard (Orthoptera: Acrididae). *Bull. Soc. ent. Égypte*, **46** (1962): 419–27, 11 figs. [*73*].

ICHÍKAWA, C. 1936. Biochemical studies on the locust (1st note). (In Japanese.) *J. agric. chem. Soc. Japan*, **12**: 408–11 [*90*].

—— 1937. Biochemical studies on the locust (3rd note). Differences on the chemical constituents between two sexes. (In Japanese.) *J. agric. chem. Soc. Japan*, **13**: 710–12 [*94*].

ICHIKAWA, C. 1938. Biochemical studies on the locust (4th note). Differences on the proteins between two sexes. (In Japanese.) *J. agric. chem. Soc. Japan*, **14**: 43–4 [*91*].

IL'ENKO, M. I. 1930. The development and metamorphosis of the Siberian grasshopper (*Gomphocerus sibiricus* L.). (In Russian.) *Bull. Irkutsk Pl. Prot. Sta.* no. 2: 87–103, 18 figs. [*287*].

INTERNATIONAL, 1937. *Proceedings of the 4th International Locust Conference, Cairo, April 22, 1936.* Cairo [*344*].

ISELY, F. B. 1936. Flight-stridulation in American acridians (Orthop: Acrididae). *Ent. News*, **47**: 199–205 [*183*].

—— 1938. The relations of Texas Acrididae to plants and soils. *Ecol. Monogr.* **8**: 551–604, 7 figs. [*88*].

—— 1944. Correlation between mandibular morphology and food specificity in grasshoppers. *Ann. ent. Soc. Amer.* **37**: 47–67, 4 figs. [*6, 7*].

ITO, H. 1924. Contribution histologique et physiologique à l'étude des annexes des organes génitaux des Orthoptères. (Tubes glandulaires ou glandes annexe, spermathèques, vésicules séminales, glandes prostatiques). *Arch. Anat. micr.* **20**: 343–460, 6 pls., 17 figs. [*140*].

ITOH, H. 1934. Chromosomal variations in the spermatogenesis of a grasshopper, *Locusta danica* Linnaeus (Orthoptera). (In Japanese with English summary.) *Jap. J. Genet.* **10**: 115–34, 6 figs. [*390*].

IVANOVA, S. A. 1925. Zur Frage über die Spermatophorbefruchtung bei den Acridoidea (*Locusta migratoria* L.). *Zool. Anz.* **65**: 75–86, 10 figs. [*316, 318*].

—— 1926. Structure of the reproductive organs of the male of *Locusta migratoria* L. (In Russian.) *Uchen. Zap. Kazan. Univ.* **86**: 50–6, 5 figs. [*140, 316, 318*].

IVANOVA, T. S. 1947. Development of the wing base in *Calliptamus italicus* L. (In Russian.) *Dokl. Akad. Nauk SSSR*, **56**: 885–7, 3 figs. [*279*].

—— 1952. Anatomy of the peripheral nervous system of the abdominal segments of the Asiatic Locust (*Locusta migratoria* L.). (In Russian.) *Ent. Obozr.* **32**: 148–59, 6 figs. [*154, 155*].

—— 1956. Innervation of skeleton muscles by the system of unpaired ventral nerve in *Locusta migratoria* L. (Orthoptera, Acrididae). (In Russian with English summary.) *Ent. Obozr.* **35**: 782–8, 6 figs. [*154, 155*].

IWANOFF, P. P. & MESTSCHERSKAYA, K. A. 1935. Die physiologischen Besonderheiten der geschlechtlich unreifen Insektenovarien und die zyklischen Veränderungen ihrer Eigenschaften. *Zool. Jb.* (Physiol.), **55**: 281–348, 8 figs. [*160, 313*].

IWAO, S. 1962. Studies on the phase variation and related phenomena in some lepidopterous insects. *Mem. Coll. Agric. Kyoto*, no. 84: 80 pp., 3 pls., 42 figs. [*386*].

JACOBS, W. 1953. Verhaltensbiologische Studien an Feldheuschrecken. *Z. Tierpsychol.* (Beih.), no. 1: 228 pp., 83 figs. [*154, 176, 177, 178, 179, 180*].

JAHN, T. L. 1935a. The nature and permeability of the grasshopper egg membranes. I. The EMF across membranes during early diapause. *J. cell. comp. Physiol.* **7**: 23–46, 7 figs. [*257*].

—— 1935b. Nature and permeability of grasshopper egg membranes. II. Chemical composition of membranes. *Proc. Soc. exp. Biol.*, *N.Y.* **33**: 159–63 [*239, 257*].

—— 1936. Studies on the nature and permeability of the grasshopper egg membranes. III. Changes in electrical properties of the membranes during development. *J. cell. comp. Physiol.* **8**: 289–300, 4 figs. [*257*].

BIBLIOGRAPHY

JAHN, T. L. & CRESCITELLI, F. 1938. The electrical response of the grasshopper eye under conditions of light and dark adaptation. *J. cell. comp. Physiol.* **12**: 39–55, 5 figs. [*199*].

—— 1940. Diurnal changes in the electrical response of the compound eye. *Biol. Bull., Woods Hole*, **78**: 42–52, 3 figs. [*199*].

JAHN, T. L. & KOEL, B. S. 1948. The effect of temperature on the frequency of beat of the grasshopper heart. *Ann. ent. Soc. Amer.* **41**: 258–66, 4 figs. [*107, 108*].

JAHN, T. L. & WULFF, V. J. 1942a. The effect of temperature on the retinal action potential. *Anat. Rec.* **84**: 535 [*199*].

—— 1942b. Allocation of electrical responses from the compound eye of grasshoppers. *J. gen. Physiol.* **26**: 75–88 [*199*].

JAKOVLEV, V. 1957. Wasserdampfabgabe der Acrididen und Mikroklima ihrer Biotope. *Verh. dtsch. zool. Ges.* **1956**: 136–42, 4 figs. [*230, 232*].

—— 1959. Der Ort der Transpiration bei *Locusta migratoria* R. & F. (Orth., Ins.). *Zool. Anz.* (Suppl.), no. 22: 111–14, 3 figs. [*231, 232*].

JAKOVLEV, V. & KRÜGER, F. 1953. Vergleichende Untersuchungen zur Physiologie der Transpiration der Orthopteren. *Zool. Jb.* (Physiol.), **64**: 391–428, 18 figs. [*228, 229*].

JAMIESON, A. 1955. *The genetical basis of response to environment.* Ph.D. thesis, Birmingham [*378*].

JANNONE, G. 1937. Importanza dell'organo copulatore maschile nella speciografia del gen. *Calliptamus* Serv. e ridescrizione del *C. okbaensis* Kheil (Orth. Acrididae) dell'Africa settentrionale. *Ann. Mus. Stor. nat. Genova*, **59**: 479–93, 5 figs. [*143*].

—— 1938. Osservazioni sulla presenza, struttura e funzione d'una vescicola ghiandolare confinata nel protorace delle specie mediterranee del gen. *Acrotylus* Fieb., con particolare riguardo all'*A. insubricus* (Scop.) (Orthoptera, Acridoidea). *Boll. Lab. Zool. Portici*, **31**: 41–62, 6 figs. [*35, 36*].

—— 1939a. Sulla diffusione della vescicola ghiandolare protoracica negli Ortotteri della subfam. Oedipodinae. *Boll. Zool.* **10**: 1–3 [*35*].

—— 1939b. Studio morfologico, anatomico e istologico del *Dociostaurus maroccanus* (Thunb.) nelle sue fasi *transiens congregans, gregaria e solitaria.* (Terzo contributo): *Boll. Lab. Ent. agr. Portici*, **4**: 1–443, 150 figs. [*1, 7, 9, 10, 14, 15, 16, 18, 20, 24, 25, 27, 28, 29, 32, 37, 60, 70, 73, 105, 107, 118, 124, 126, 140, 151, 163, 164, 165, 166, 168, 173, 175, 177, 179, 236, 242, 243, 245, 282, 344*].

—— 1950. Osservazioni sull'organo di Brunner in dieci specie di Ortotteri Acridioidei (Insecta). *Riv. Biol.* (N.S.), **42**: 81–92, 3 figs. [*166*].

JAWLOWSKI, H. 1954. Über die Struktur des Gehirnes bei Saltatoria. *Ann. Univ. M. Curie-Sklodowska* C, **8**: 403–34, 10 pls., 17 figs. [*152*].

JENSEN, M. & WEIS-FOGH, T. 1962. Biology and physics of locust flight. V. Strength and elasticity of locust cuticle. *Phil. Trans.* B, **245**: 137–69, 25 figs. [*32, 35, 67*].

JHINGRAN, V. G. 1944. An unusual mode of copulation in *Heteracris capensis* Thunb. Acrididae. *Indian J. Ent.* **5** (1943): 243–4 [*315*].

—— 1949. Early embryology of the Desert Locust, *Schistocerca gregaria* (Forskål) (Orthoptera, Acrididae). *Rec. Indian Mus.* **45** (1947): 181–200, 4 pls., 3 figs. [*245*].

JOHNSON, C. G. 1942. Insect survival in relation to the rate of water loss. *Biol. Rev.* **17**: 151–77, 12 figs. [*256*].

JOHNSTON, H. B. 1932. Notes on two locusts of minor economic importance in the Sudan. *Bull. ent. Res.* **23**: 49–64 [*370*].

JOLY, L. 1955. Analyse du fonctionnement des corpora allata chez la larve de *Locusta migratoria* L. *C. R. Soc. Biol., Paris*, **149**: 584–7 [*289, 313*].

—— 1958. Comparaison des divers types d'adultoïdes chez *Locusta migratoria* L. *Insectes sociaux*, **5**: 373–8, 6 figs. [*289*].

—— 1960. *Fonctions des Corpora Allata chez* Locusta migratoria (L.). Strasbourg [*103, 158, 289, 290, 304, 313, 366, 376, 377*].

JOLY, P. 1949. Le système endocrine retrocérébral chez les acridiens migrateurs. *Ann. Sci. nat.* (Zool.), (11) **11**: 255–62, 11 figs. [*156, 375*].

—— 1951. Rôle de l'organe de Brunner chez *Locusta migratoria* (L.). *C. R. Soc. Biol., Paris*, **145**: 1354–7 [*167*].

—— 1952. Déterminisme de la pigmentation chez *Acrida turrita* L. (Insecte orthoptéroïde). *C. R. Acad. Sci., Paris*, **235**: 1054–6 [*58*].

—— 1956. Croissance et indices de grégarisation chez *Locusta migratoria* (L.). *Insectes sociaux*, **3**: 17–24, 7 figs. [*377*].

—— 1958. Les corrélations humorales chez les acridiens. *Année biol.* **34**: 97–118, 15 figs. [*159, 289*].

—— 1960. Un cas de gynandromorphisme chez *Locusta migratoria* L. *Bull. Soc. zool. Fr.* **84** (1959): 407–10, 1 pl., 1 fig. [*149*].

—— 1962. Rôle joué par les corpora allata dans la réalisation du polymorphisme de phase chez *Locusta migratoria* L. *Colloq. int. Cent. nat. Rech. sci.* no. 114: 77–88 [*377*].

JONES, B. M. 1956a. Endocrine activity during insect embryogenesis. Function of the ventral head glands in locust embryos (*Locustana pardalina* and *Locusta migratoria*, Orthoptera). *J. exp. Biol.* **33**: 174–85, 1 pl., 3 figs. [*43, 246, 251, 264, 269*].

—— 1956b. Endocrine activity during insect embryogenesis. Control of events in development following the embryonic moult (*Locusta migratoria* and *Locustana pardalina*, Orthoptera). *J. exp. Biol.* **33**: 685–96, 1 pl., 2 figs. [*246, 264, 269*].

441

BIBLIOGRAPHY

JONES, B. M. 1958. Enzymatic oxidation of protein as a rate-determining step in the formation of highly stable surface membranes. *Proc. roy. Soc.* B, **148**: 263–77, 13 figs. [*243*].

JONES, B. M. & SINCLAIR, W. 1958. Induction of melanin patterns and of hardening as separate processes in the cuticle of albino locusts with internally absorbed phenol substrates. *Nature, Lond.* **181**: 926–7 [*43, 295*].

JÖRSCHKE, H. 1914. Die Facettenaugen der Orthopteren und Termiten. *Z. wiss. Zool.* **111**: 153–280, 1 pl., 57 figs. [*197*].

JOVANČIĆ, L. 1953. Genèse des pigments tégumentaires de la mante religieuse et d'autres animaux. Leur rôle biologique et physiologique. *Bull. biol.* **87**: 92–104 [*54*].

—— 1960. Genèse des pigments tégumentaires et leur rôle physiologique chez la mante religieuse et chez d'autres espèces animales. (Doctoral thesis.) (In French with Russian summary.) *Posebna Izd. prir. Muz.*, no. 29: 114 pp., 9 figs. [*54*].

JOYCE, V. 1952. The ecology of grasshoppers in East Central Sudan. *Anti-Locust Bull.* no. 11: 97 pp., 34 figs. [*371*].

JUDD, W. W. 1948. A comparative study of the proventriculus of orthopteroid insects with reference to its use in taxonomy. *Canad. J. Res.* D, **26**: 93–161, 97 figs. [*73*].

JUNGE, H. 1941. Über grüne Insektenfarbstoffe. *Hoppe-Seyl. Z.* **268**: 179–86, 1 fig. [*50*].

KADZEVICH, I. S. 1935. Biological observations on *Chorthippus albomarginatus* De Geer in the Kuznetsk steppe. (In Russian.) *Bull. W. Sib. Pl. Prot. Sta.* no. 1 (9): 119–36 [*287*].

KARAMAN, M. 1959. Sur un *Chorthippus longicornis* Latr. (Orthop. Acrididae) hermaphrodite. *Bull. Soc. ent. Mulhouse*, **1959** (Jul.–Sep.): 51–3, 5 figs. [*149*].

KARANDIKAR, K. R. 1939. External structures of the Desert Locust (*Schistocerca gregaria*, Forsk.). *J. Univ. Bombay* B, **7** (5): 56 pp., 52 figs. [*1, 70, 125*].

—— 1942. External structures of the Desert Locust (*Schistocerca gregaria*, Forsk.). *J. Univ. Bombay* B, **11** (3): 29 pp., 52 figs. [*1, 20, 246, 282*].

—— 1945. Studies on the post-embryonic development and tracheation of wings in *Schistocerca gregaria* Forsk. *J. Univ. Bombay* B, **13** (5): 5 pp., 11 figs. [*27, 278*].

KARELINA, R. I. 1957. The problem of the biology of the white-striped grasshopper in the Central Yakutia. (In Russian.) *Uchen. Zap. Yakutsk. Gosud. Univ.* **1**: 99–119, 7 figs. [*287*].

—— 1960. The problem of feeding of *Chorthippus albomarginatus* in the conditions of Yakutia. (In Russian.) *Uchen. Zap. Yakutsk. Gosud. Univ.* **8**: 93–107 [*329, 330*].

KARLSON, P. & SCHLOSSBERGER-RAECKE, I. 1962. Zum Tyrosinstoffwechsel der Insekten—VIII. Die Sklerotisierung der Cuticula bei der Wildform und der Albinomutante von *Schistocerca gregaria* Forsk. *J. Insect Physiol.* **8**: 441–52, 2 figs. [*43, 47*].

KARNY, H. 1908. Ueber das Schnarren der Heuschrecken. *Stettin. ent. Ztg* **69**: 112–19, 9 figs. [*183*].

—— 1912. Über die Reduktion der Flugorgane bei den Orthopteren. Ein Beitrag zu Dollo's Irreversibilitätsgesetz. *Zool. Jb.* (Physiol.), **33**: 27–40, 2 pls. [*29*].

KATIYAR, K. N. 1952. A new mode of copulation in the short-horned grasshoppers (Orthoptera, Acridiidae). *Z. angew. Ent.* **34**: 284–90, 1 pl., 2 figs. [*315*].

—— 1953. Variation and post-embryonic growth in the number of antennal segments in three species of Indian short-horned grasshoppers (Orthoptera, Acridoidea), together with observations on the number of segments in adult Acrididae based on the collections at the Forest Research Institute, Dehra Dun. *Agra Univ. J. Res.* (Sci.), **2**: 331–55, 3 figs. [*9, 276, 278, 286, 287*].

—— 1955. The life-history and ecology of the northern spotted grasshopper, *Aularches punctatus* Drury (Orthoptera: Acrididae). *Agra Univ. J. Res.* (Sci.), **4**: 397–413, 7 figs. [*286, 327*].

—— 1956a. On variation in the spermathecae of some Indian grasshoppers (Orthoptera: Acrididae) *J. zool. Soc. India*, **8**: 35–42, 3 figs. [*147*].

—— 1956b. Modes of copulation in short-horned grasshoppers (Orthoptera: Acrididae). *J. Bom.-bay nat. Hist. Soc.* **53**: 664–8, 1 pl. [*315*].

—— 1960. Ecology of oviposition and the structure of egg-pods and eggs in some Indian Acrididae. *Rec. Indian Mus.* **55** (1957): 29–68, 19 figs. [*240, 327*].

KATSUKI, Y. & SUGA, N. 1960. Neural mechanism of hearing in insects. *J. exp. Biol.* **37**: 279–90, 5 figs. [*191, 193–195*].

KAUFMANN, T. 1959. Ecological and anatomical studies on nutrition in Acrididae (1956–1958). [Unpublished.] [*72, 80, 144*].

KAWAMURA, K. 1957. Studies on mitotic apparatus and cytokinesis of spermatocytes of nine species of grasshopper. *Cytologia, Tokyo*, **22**: 337–46, 53 figs. [*389*].

KENNEDY, J. S. 1939. The behaviour of the Desert Locust (*Schistocerca gregaria* (Forsk.)) (Orthopt.) in an outbreak centre. *Trans. R. ent. Soc. Lond.* **89**: 385–542, 9 pls., 37 figs. [*211, 261, 361, 381*].

—— 1956. Phase transformation in locust biology. *Biol. Rev.* **31**: 349–70 [*332, 380*].

—— 1961. Continuous polymorphism in locusts. *1st Symp. R. ent. Soc. Lond.*, London 1961: 80–90 [*332, 380, 383*].

—— 1962. La division du travail entre les phases acridiennes. *Colloq. int. Cent. nat. Rech. sci.* no. 114: 269–97 [*380*].

KEPPEN, T. 1870. On the locust and other injurious Orthoptera of the family Acridiodea, particularly in relation to Russia. (In Russian.) *Horae Soc. ent. ross.* **5**: viii+1–352, 1 map [*332*].

KERLY, M. & LEABACK, D. H. 1957. The characteristics of hexokinase from *Locusta migratoria* muscle. *Biochem. J.* **67**: 245–50, 2 figs. [*68*].

BIBLIOGRAPHY

KERMACK, W. O. & STEIN, J. M. 1959. Nitrogenous constituents of the thoracic muscle of the African Migratory Locust (*Locusta migratoria migratorioides*). *Biochem. J.* **71**: 648–54 [*68*].

KESSEL, R. G. 1960. Electron microscope and cytochemical studies on the oenocytes of the grasshopper, *Melanoplus differentialis differentialis* Thomas. (Abs.) *Anat. Rec.* **137**: 371 [*104, 122*].

—— 1961. Electron microscope observations on the submicroscopic vesicular component of the subesophageal body and pericardial cells of the grasshopper, *Melanoplus differentialis differentialis* (Thomas). *Exp. Cell Res.* **22**: 108–19, 10 figs. [*122, 123, 152, 246*].

KEVAN, D. K. McE. 1943. An account of *Schistocerca flavofasciata* (De Geer 1773) in Trinidad (Orthoptera: Acrididae). *Bull. ent. Res.* **34**: 291–310, 13 figs. [*287, 319*].

—— 1949. Notes on East African bush locusts with special reference to *Phymateus aegrotus* (Gerstaecker 1869) (Orth., Acrid., Pyrgomorphinae). *Bull. ent. Res.* **40**: 359–69 [*370*].

—— 1955. Méthodes inhabituelles de production de son chez les Orthoptères. *Colloque sur l'Acoustique des Orthoptères*, Paris 1954: 103–41, 23 figs. [*176*].

—— 1959. A study of the genus *Chrotogonus* Audinet-Serville, 1839 (Orthoptera: Acridoidea: Pyrgomorphidae). V. A revisional monograph of the Chrotogonini. VI. The history and biogeography of the Chrotogonini. *Publ. cult. Cia Diamant. Angola*, no. 43: 1–246, 151 figs. [*30*].

KEY, K. H. L. 1936. Observations on rate of growth, coloration, and the abnormal six-instar life-cycle in *Locusta migratoria migratorioides* R. & F. *Bull. ent. Res.* **27**: 77–85, 4 figs. [*274*].

—— 1938. The regional and seasonal incidence of grasshopper plagues in Australia. *Bull. Coun. sci. industr. Res. Aust.* no. 117: 87 pp., 3 maps, 14 figs. [*30, 371*].

—— 1950. A critique on the phase theory of locusts. *Quart. Rev. Biol.* **25**: 363–407, 1 fig. [*380, 383, 384*].

—— 1954. *The Taxonomy, Phases, and Distribution of the Genera* Chortoicetes *Brunn. and* Austroicetes *Uv.* (*Orthoptera: Acrididae*). Canberra [*39, 40, 299, 356, 371*].

—— 1957. Kentromorphic phases in three species of Phasmatodea. *Aust. J. Zool.* **5**: 247–84, 3 pls., 4 figs. [*380, 383, 386*].

KEY, K. H. L. & DAY, M. F. 1954a. A temperature-controlled physiological colour response in the grasshopper *Kosciuscola tristis* Sjöst. (Orthoptera: Acrididae). *Aust. J. Zool.* **2**: 309–39, 2 pls., 2 figs. [*56, 57, 383*].

—— 1954b. The physiological mechanism of colour change in the grasshopper *Kosciuscola tristis* Sjöst. (Orthoptera: Acrididae). *Aust. J. Zool.* **2**: 340–63, 7 figs. [*56, 57*].

KEY, K. H. L. & EDNEY, E. B. 1936. Precocious adults resulting from the omission of the fifth instar in *Locusta migratoria migratorioides* (R. & F.). *Proc. R. ent. Soc. Lond.* A, **11**: 55–8, 2 figs. [*289*].

KHALIFA, A. 1957. The development of eggs of some Egyptian species of grasshoppers, with a special reference to the incidence of diapause in the eggs of *Euprepocnemis plorans* Charp. (Orthoptera: Acrididae). *Bull. Soc. ent. Égypte*, **41**: 299–330, 7 figs. [*255*].

KHAN, M. A. 1961. *Studies on the secretion of some digestive enzymes in certain insects with special reference to feeding.* Ph.D. thesis, London [*72, 73, 74, 76, 78*].

—— 1962. The distribution of dipeptidase activity in the digestive system of *Locusta migratoria* L. and *Dysdercus fasciatus* Dallus. *Comp. Biochem. Physiol.* **6**: 169–70 [*76*].

—— 1963a. The secretory cycle of invertase in the midgut and caeca tissue of *Locusta migratoria* L. in relation to moulting. *Curr. Sci.* **32**: 169, 1 fig. [*76, 78*].

—— 1963b. The distribution of proteinase, invertase and amylase activity in various parts of alimentary canal of *Locusta migratoria* L. *Indian J. Ent.* **25**: 200–3 [*76, 78*].

—— 1963c. Studies on the secretion of digestive enzymes in *Locusta migratoria* L. I. Proteinase activity. *Ent. exp. appl.* **6**: 181–93, 4 figs. [*76, 78*].

—— 1964. Studies on the secretion of digestive enzymes in *Locusta migratoria* L. II. Invertase activity. *Ent. exp. appl.* **7**: 125–30, 3 figs. [*76, 78*].

KIKAL, T. & SMITH, J. N. 1959. Comparative detoxication. 6. The metabolism of 6-amino-4-nitro-*o*-cresol and 4:6-dinitro-*o*-cresol in locusts. *Biochem. J.* **71**: 48–54, 1 fig. [*76*].

KILBY, B. A. 1963. The biochemistry of the insect fat body. *Advanc. Insect Physiol.* **1**: 111–74, 6 figs. [*102*].

KILBY, B. A. & NEVILLE, E. 1957. Amino-acid metabolism in locust tissues. *J. exp. Biol.* **34**: 276–289, 5 figs. [*102*].

KING, R. L. & SLIFER, E. H. 1934. Insect development. VIII. Maturation and early development of unfertilized grasshopper eggs. *J. Morph.* **56**: 603–19, 2 pls. [*319, 320*].

KIRICHENKO, A. 1926. A study of the ecology and biology of *Calliptamus italicus* L. in the steppe zone of the Ukraine. (In Russian.) *Odessa Reg. Agric. Exp. Stat.* **1**: 47 pp., 2 pls. [*371*].

KLEIN, M. S. 1955. Ionophone ou haut-parleur ionique. *Colloque sur l'Acoustique des Orthoptères*, Paris 1954: 46–9, 1 fig. [*186*].

KLEINMAN, L. W. 1934. The effect of temperature upon the respiratory quotients of nymphs of the grasshopper, *Chortophaga viridifasciata* De Geer, and larvae of the Japanese beetle, *Popillia japonica* Newman, with reference to changes during hibernation. *J. cell. comp. Physiol.* **4**: 221–235, 1 fig. [*136*].

KNETSCH, H. 1939. Die Korrelation in der Ausbildung der Tympanalorgane, der Flügel, der Stridulationsapparate und anderer Organsysteme bei den Orthopteren. *Arch. Naturgesch.* (N.F.), **8**: 1–69, 62 figs. [*189*].

443

BIBLIOGRAPHY

KNIPLING, E. B. & SULLIVAN, W. N. 1957. Insect mortality at low temperatures. *J. econ. Ent.* **50**: 368–9 [*223*].

—— 1958. The thermal death points of several species of insects. *J. econ. Ent.* **51**: 344–6 [*221, 222*].

KOIDSUMI, K. 1934–1935. Experimentelle Studien über die Transpiration und den Wärmehaushalt bei Insekten. *Mem. Fac. Sci. Agric. Taihoku*, **12**: 1–19, 2 figs.; 21–40; 41–79, 6 figs.; 81–107, 6 figs.; 109–24, 8 figs.; 125–36, 1 fig.; 137–79, 24 figs.; 281–315, 3 figs.; 317–37, 2 figs.; 339–49; 351–72, 3 figs.; 373–80, 3 figs. [*207, 208, 210, 220, 221, 228, 230, 231*].

KOLLER, G. 1955. Zur Frage der hormonalen Steuerung bei rhythmischen Eingeweidebewegungen von Insekten. *Verh. dtsch. zool. Ges.* **1954**: 417–22, 3 figs. [*119, 158*].

KORIGAWA, K. 1934. Chemical studies on the locust (1st report). General analysis and protein. (In Japanese.) *Zyozagaku Zassi*, **12** (5): 361–5, 1 fig. [*90, 91, 92*].

KOWALEVSKY, A. 1892. Sur les organes excréteurs chez les arthropodes terrestres. *2nd Int. Congr. Zool.*, Moscow 1892, pt. 1: 187–235, 4 pls. [*115, 122*].

—— 1894a. Études sur le coeur de quelques Orthoptères. (Communication préliminaire.) *Arch. Zool. exp. gén.* (3) **2**: 485–90 [*106, 117, 118, 122*].

—— 1894b. Études expérimentales sur les glandes lymphatiques des invertebrés. (Communication préliminaire.) *Bull. Acad. Sci. St-Pétersb.* (4) **36**: 273–95 [*106, 115, 117, 122*].

KOZHANCHIKOV, I. V. 1950. Fundamental features of food specialisation in the Asiatic Locust. (In Russian.) *Izv. Akad. Nauk SSSR* (Biol.), no. 4: 73–86, 4 figs. [*82, 83, 329*].

KOZHANTSCHIKOW, I. W. 1934. Zur Frage nach dem Temperaturoptimum des Lebens. II. Über die Temperaturabhängigkeit einzelner physiologischer Prozesse und ihre Beziehung auf das Lebensoptimum des Organismus. *Z. angew. Ent.* **20**: 590–610, 4 figs. [*129*].

KREASKY, J. B. 1960. Extended diapause in eggs of high-altitude species of grasshoppers, and a note on food-plant preferences of *Melanoplus bruneri*. *Ann. ent. Soc. Amer.* **53**: 436–8 [*261*].

—— 1962. A growth factor in romaine lettuce for the grasshoppers *Melanoplus sanguinipes* (F.) and *M. bivittatus* (Say). *J. Insect Physiol.* **8**: 493–504, 1 fig. [*87*].

KREPS, E. M. & CHENYKAEVA, E. J. 1942. On the respiratory function of the blood of insects. *C. R. Acad. Sci. U.R.S.S.* **34**: 142–5 [*117*].

KROGH, A. 1913. On the composition of the air in the tracheal system of some insects. *Skand. Arch. Physiol.* **29**: 29–36, 1 fig. [*68, 131, 137*].

KROGH, A. & WEIS-FOGH, T. 1951. The respiratory exchange of the Desert Locust (*Schistocerca gregaria*) before, during and after flight. *J. exp. Biol.* **28**: 344–57, 4 figs. [*68, 133, 135*].

KRÜGER, F. & BISHAI, F. R. 1957. Zur Frage der experimentellen Umfärbung bei der Wanderheuschrecke *Locusta migratoria migratorioides* (R. u. F.). *Naturwissenschaften*, **44**: 337 [*337*].

KRÜGER, P. 1931. Weitere Beiträge über die Faktoren des Wärmehaushaltes der Poikilothermen. *Z. Morph. Ökol. Tiere*, **22**: 759–73, 3 figs. [*211*].

KRÜGER, P. & DUSPIVA, F. 1933. Der Einfluss der Sonnenstrahlung auf die Lebensvorgänge der Poikilothermen. *Biol. gen.* **9**: 168–88, 7 figs. [*211*].

KUBIŠTA, V. 1956. The resting oxygen consumption of insect muscles. *Mém. Soc. zool. tchécosl.* **20**: 188–92 [*68*].

—— 1958. Anaerobe Glykolyse in den Insektenmuskeln. *Biochem. Z.* **330**: 315–23, 1 fig. [*68*].

—— 1959. Stoffwechsel der isolierten Insektenmuskulatur. *S. B. Ges. ges. Naturw.* **81**: 17–31, 3 figs. [*68*].

KUBIŠTA, V. & BARTOŠ, Z. 1960. Free and fixed glycogen in insect muscle. *Physiol. bohemoslov.* **9**: 235–9 [*68*].

KULAGIN, N. M. 1923. On the development of certain varieties of Acrididae. (In Russian.) *Bull. Soc. ent. Moscou*, **2** (2): 1–11 [*246, 269*].

—— 1932. De l'enveloppe des oeufs des sauterelles migratoires. (In Russian with French summary.) *Zool. Zh.* **11**: 124–32, 7 figs. [*237, 238*].

KUMASHIRO, S. 1935. On some experiments and observations concerning *Oxya*. (In Japanese.) *Nogaku Kenkyu*, **25**: 195–220, 1 pl. [*255, 287*].

KUNASHEVA, K. 1932. Détermination du carbone dans certaines espèces des Acrididae. (In Russian with French summary.) *Trav. Lab. Biogéochim. U.R.S.S.* **2**: 27–30 [*93*].

KÜNCKEL D'HERCULAIS, J. 1890a. Mécanisme physiologique de l'éclosion, des mues et de la métamorphose chez les insectes Orthoptères de la famille des Acridides. *C. R. Acad. Sci.*, Paris, **110**: 657–9 [*270, 315, 322, 336*].

—— 1890b. Du rôle de l'air dans le mécanisme physiologique de l'éclosion, des mues et de la métamorphose chez les insectes Orthoptères de la famille des Acridides. *C. R. Acad. Sci.*, Paris, **110**: 807–9 [*270*].

—— 1893–1905. *Invasions des Acridiens vulgo Sauterelles en Algérie.* Algiers [*270, 271,272,297,336*].

KYL, G. 1938. A study of copulation and the formation of spermatophores in *Melanoplus differentialis*. *Proc. Iowa Acad. Sci.* **45**: 299–308, 2 pls. [*314*].

LA BAUME, W. 1918. Biologie der marokkanischen Wanderheuschrecke (*Stauronotus maroccanus* Thunb.) Beobachtungen aus Kleinasien in den Jahren 1916 u. 1917. *Monogr. angew. Ent.* no. 3: 157–274, 11 pls., 15 figs. [*271, 299*].

LA GRECA, M. 1947. Morfologia funzionale dell'articolazione alare degli Ortotteri. *Arch. zool. ital.* **32**: 271–327, 28 figs. [*14, 47*].

—— 1948. Su una particolare maniera di deambulazione di un Acridide: *Tropidopola cylindrica* (Marsch.). *Boll. Zool.* **14**: 83–104, 5 figs. [*164*].

BIBLIOGRAPHY

LA GRECA, M. 1949. I nervi motori e sensori degli organi di volo degli Acrididi. *R. C. Accad. Napoli*, **15** (1948): 121–30, 6 figs. [*62, 63, 154*].
—— 1950. Sulla presenza di un organo dermale nei cerci dei maschi di *Calliptamus italicus* (L.) (Orthoptera, Acrididae). *Boll. Zool.* **17**: 75–80, 3 figs. [*19*].
—— 1954. Riduzione e scomparsa delle ali negli insetti pterigoti. *Arch. zool. ital.* **39**: 361–440, 25 figs. [*29*].
—— 1955. Studio biometrico di popolazioni italiane di *Chorthippus brunneus* (Thunb.) e di *Chorthippus mollis* (Charp.) (Orthoptera, Acrididae). *Arch. zool. ital.* **40**: 183–204, 4 figs. [*391*].
LAIRD, A. K. 1943. A study of the types of male gonads found in the Acrididae (Orthoptera). *J. Morph.* **72**: 477–90, 4 figs. [*138, 139*].
LAL, R. & PARSHAD, B. 1961. Studies on the male genitalia of some Indian Acridinae (Acrididae–Orthoptera). *Indian J. Ent.* **21** (1959): 167–83, 6 pls. [*143*].
LANDOIS, H. 1867. Die Ton- und Stimmapparate der Insecten in anatomisch-physiologischer und akustischer Beziehung. *Z. wiss. Zool.* **17**: 105–86, 2 pls. [*178*].
LAPP, C. & ROHMER, J. 1937. Composition et valeur alimentaire du criquet pélerin. *Bull. Soc. Chim. biol.*, **19**: 321–4, 2 figs. [*94, 95, 101*].
LATIF, A. & HAQ, A. 1951. Bionomics of *Chrotogonus robertsi* Kirby with special reference to temperature and food. (Abs.) *Proc. 3rd Pakist. Sci. Conf.*, Dacca 1951, pt. III: 48–9 [*286*].
LATIF, A., HAQUE, K. A. & KHAN, M. R. 1959. The external anatomy of *Poecilocerus pictus* (Fb.). *Biologia, Lahore*, **5**: 143–98, 45 figs. [*1*].
LEA, A. 1962. The nature and significance of phase variation in the Brown Locust, *Locustana pardalina* (Walk.). *Colloq. int. Cent. nat. Rech. sci.* no. 114: 241–58, 4 figs. [*361*].
LAUB-DROST, I. 1959. Verhaltensbiologie, besonders Ausdrucksäusserungen (einschliesslich Lautäusserungen) einiger Wanderheuschrecken und anderer Orthopteren (Orthopt., Acrid.: Catantopinae und Oedipodinae). *Stuttgart. Beitr. Naturk.* no. 30: 27 pp., 11 figs. [*148, 182, 184*].
—— 1960. Verhaltensweisen im Zustand niederer Aktivität bei einigen Wanderheuschrecken und anderen Acridiern (Orthopt.). *Z. Tierpsychol.* **17**: 614–26, 3 figs. [*180, 182*].
LEBEDEVA, E. A. 1925. Contributions au diagnostic des phases chez les larves des acridiens. (In Russian.) *Pl. Prot., Leningr.* **2**: 309–11 [*276*].
LE BERRE, J.-R. 1953. Contribution à l'étude biologique du criquet migrateur des Landes (*Locusta migratoria gallica* Remaudière). *Bull. biol.* **87**: 227–73, 9 figs. [*254, 255, 261*].
LEDERER, E. 1935. Les caroténoïdes des animaux. *Actualités sci. industr.* no. 238: 62 pp. [*47*].
—— 1938. Sur les caroténoïdes des invertébrés. *Bull. Soc. Chim. biol.* **20**: 567–610 [*49*].
LEE, M. O. 1925. On the mechanism of respiration in certain Orthoptera. *J. exp. Zool.* **41**: 125–54, 2 figs. [*128, 137*].
LEE, R. M. 1961. The variation of blood volume with age in the Desert Locust (*Schistocerca gregaria* Forsk.). *J. Insect Physiol.* **6**: 36–51, 6 figs. [*108, 109, 227, 282*].
LEES, A. D. 1955. *The Physiology of Diapause in Arthropods*. London [*103, 262*].
LEMCHE, H. 1935. The primitive colour-pattern on the wings of insects and its relation to the venation. Preliminary notice. *Vidensk. Medd. dansk naturh. Foren. Kbh.* **99**: 45–64, 14 figs. [*42*].
LEO TSU-YÜ & QUO FU 1962. Studies on the reproduction of the Oriental Migratory Locust: the physiological effect of the pairing action. (In Chinese with English summary.) *Acta ent. sinica*, **11**: 217–22 [*319*].
LEONE, C. A. 1947. Systematic serology among certain insect species. *Biol. Bull., Woods Hole*, **93**: 64–71, 3 figs. [*114*].
LEPESME, P. 1938. Note préliminaire sur la cytologie du sang des acridiens. *Bull. Soc. Hist. nat. Afr. N.* **29**: 241–8, 5 pls. [*114*].
LEVENBOOK, L. & CLARK, A. M. 1950. The physiology of carbon dioxide transport in insect blood. Part II. The effect of insect blood on the rate of hydration of CO_2. *J. exp. Biol.* **27**: 175–83, 6 figs. [*117*].
LEWIS, K. R. & JOHN, B. 1959. Breakdown and restoration of chromosome stability following inbreeding in a locust. *Chromosoma, Berl.* **10**: 589–618, 47 figs. [*390*].
LICHTENSTEIN, N., BODENHEIMER, F. S. & SHULOV, A. 1949. Proteolytic enzymes of insects. II. Proteases of the eggs of the Moroccan Locust (*Dociostaurus maroccanus* Thnbg.). *Enzymologia*, **13**: 276–80 [*251*].
LIEBERMANN, J. 1951. Sobre una nueva forma de oviposicion en un acridio sudamericano *Scotussa cliens* (Stäl) Lieb. (Orth. Acrid. Cyrtacanth.). *Rev. Invest. agric., B. Aires*, **5**: 235–80, 1 map, 6 pls., 5 figs. [*287*].
—— 1953. El alotipo hembra de *Trybliophorus modestus* Bruner (Orth. Acrid. Trybliophorini) con la descripcion de un organo desconocido en su septimo esternito abdominal. *An. Soc. cient. argent.* **156**: 34–49, 5 figs. [*35, 38*].
LIN, S., HODSON, A. C. & EICHARDS, A. G. 1954. An analysis of threshold temperatures for the development of *Oncopeltus* and *Tribolium* eggs. *Physiol. Zoöl.* **27**: 287–311, 11 figs. [*252, 254*].
LINK, E. 1909. Über die Stirnaugen der hemimetabolen Insecten. *Zool. Jb.* (Anat.), **27**: 281–376, 4 pls., 14 figs. [*205*].
LINZEN, B. 1959. Über Ommochrome aus Heuschrecken. *17th Int. Congr. Chem.*, Munich 1959: 6 pp. [Unpublished.] [*44, 46*].

445

BIBLIOGRAPHY

LISON, L. 1937. Etudes histophysiologiques sur le tube de Malpighi des insectes. I. Elimination des colorants acides par le tube de Malpighi chez les Orthoptères. *Arch. Biol.* **48**: 321–60 [*121*].

—— 1938. Les phénomènes d'athrocytose dans le tube de Malpighi chez les insectes. *Ann. Soc. zool. Belg.* **68**: 41–8 [*121*].

LIU, Y. S., LEE, P. C. & LEO, P. L. 1960. On the anatomy and histology of the circulatory system and the organs of elimination of the Asiatic Migratory Locust, *Locusta migratoria manilensis* Meyen. (In Chinese with English summary.) *Acta ent. sinica*, **10**: 129–41, 21 figs. [*105*].

LIU, Y. S. & LEO, P. L. 1955. On the anatomy and histology of the digestive system of the Asiatic Migratory Locust, *Locusta migratoria manilensis* Meyen. (In Chinese with English summary.) *Acta ent. sinica*, **5**: 245–60, 7 pls. [*71, 73*].

—— 1959. On the anatomy and histology of the reproductive system of the Oriental Migratory Locust, *Locusta migratoria manilensis* Meyen (Acrididae, Orthoptera). (In Chinese with English summary.) *Acta. ent. sinica*, **9**: 1–11, 8 pls. [*139, 145, 304*].

LIU WEI-TEH 1952. Über die Morphologie und Entwicklung des abdominalen Tympanalorgans der Heuschrecke (*Locusta migratoria manilensis* Meyen). (In Chinese with German summary.) *Acta ent. sinica*, **2**: 155–65, 22 figs. [*188, 282*].

LOHER, W. 1957. Untersuchungen über den Aufbau und die Entstehung der Gesänge einiger Feld-heuschreckenarten und den Einfluss von Lautzeichen auf das akustische Verhalten. *Z. vergl. Physiol.* **39**: 313–56, 19 figs. [*185*].

—— 1959. Contributions to the study of the sexual behaviour of *Schistocerca gregaria* Forskål (Orthoptera: Acrididae). *Proc. R. ent. Soc. Lond.* A, **34**: 49–56, 1 pl. [*182, 184*].

—— 1960. The chemical acceleration of the maturation process and its hormonal control in the male of the Desert Locust. *Proc. roy. Soc.* B, **153**: 380–97, 9 figs. [*35, 49, 295, 298, 299, 311*].

—— 1961. Die Beschleunigung der Reife durch ein Pheromon des Männchens der Wüsten-heuschrecke und die Funktion der Corpora allata. *Naturwissenschaften*, **48**: 657–61, 4 figs. [*35, 49, 295, 311*].

LOHER, W. & BROUGHTON, W. B. 1955. Études sur le comportement acoustique de *Chorthippus bi-color* (Charp.) avec quelques notes comparatives sur des espèces voisines (Acrididae). *Colloque sur l'Acoustique des Orthoptères*, Paris 1954: 248–77, 39 figs. [*185*].

LONG, D. B. 1953. Effects of population density on larvae of Lepidoptera. *Trans. R. ent. Soc. Lond.* **104**: 543–85, 6 pls., 14 figs. [*386*].

LOUNSBURY, C. P. 1915. Some phases of the locust problem. *S. Afr. J. Sci.* **12**: 33–45 [*261*].

LOWER, H. F. 1959. The insect epicuticle and its terminology. *Ann. ent. Soc. Amer.* **52**: 381–5 [*32*].

LOZINA-LOZINSKIĬ, L. K. & SOKOLOV, S. S. 1938. A contribution on the frost resistance of the eggs of *Locusta migratoria*. (In Russian with English summary.) *Zool. Zh.* **17**: 91–101, 4 figs. [*258, 262, 266*].

LU KIAO-HUNG & BODINE, J. H. 1953. Changes in the distribution of phosphorous in the developing grasshopper (*Melanoplus differentialis*) embryo. *Physiol. Zoöl.* **26**: 242–54, 7 figs. [*251*].

LUDWIG, D. 1937. The effect of different relative humidities on respiratory metabolism and survival of the grasshopper *Chortophaga viridifasciata* De Geer. *Physiol. Zoöl.* **10**: 342–51, 2 figs. [*226, 228, 230, 234, 235*].

—— 1950a. The metabolism of starved nymphs of the grasshopper, *Chortophaga viridifasciata* De Geer. *Physiol. Zoöl.* **23**: 41–7 [*89*].

—— 1950b. Changes in the distribution of nitrogen during starvation in the grasshopper, *Chortophaga viridifasciata* De Geer. *Physiol. Zoöl.* **23**: 208–13 [*89*].

LUH CHIN-JEN & YU PEI-YU 1957. The skeleto-muscular system of the Asiatic Migratory Locust. *Locusta migratoria manilensis* (Meyen). I. The head region. (In Chinese with English summary.) *Acta ent. sinica*, **7**: 1–19, 19 figs. [*60*].

LŪSIS, O. 1963. The histology and histochemistry of development and resorption in the terminal oocytes of the Desert Locust, *Schistocerca gregaria*. *Quart. J. micr. Sci.* **104**: 57–68, 1 pl., 2 figs. [*304, 305, 306, 311, 314*].

LUTZ, F. E. 1924. Insect sounds. *Bull. Amer. Mus. nat. Hist.* **50**: 333–72 [*184*].

McARTHUR, J. M. 1929. An experimental study of the functions of the different spiracles in certain Orthoptera. *J. exp. Zool.* **53**: 117–28 [*128*].

McCLUNG, C. E. 1914. A comparative study of the chromosomes in orthopteran spermatogenesis. *J. Morph.* **25**: 651–749, 10 pls. [*389*].

—— 1939. The apical cell of the insect testis—a possible function. *Trav. Sta. zool. Wimereux*, **13**: 437–48, 2 pls. [*304*].

McCUTCHEON, F. H. 1940. The respiratory mechanism in the grasshopper. *Ann. ent. Soc. Amer.* **33**: 35–55, 7 figs. [*128, 129, 130*].

McFARLANE, J. E. 1953. The morphology of the chordotonal organs of the antenna, mouthparts and legs of the lesser migratory grasshopper, *Melanoplus mexicanus mexicanus* (Saussure). *Canad. Ent.* **85**: 81–103, 33 figs. [*168, 169, 170*].

McGOVRAN, E. R. 1931. A method of measuring tracheal ventilation in insects and some results obtained with grasshoppers. *Ann. ent. Soc. Amer.* **24**: 751–61, 2 figs. [*128, 131, 132*].

—— 1932. The effect of some gases on the tracheal ventilation of grasshoppers. *J. econ. Ent.* **25**: 271–6 [*131*].

McHARGUE, J. S. 1917. A study of the proteins of certain insects with reference to their value as food for poultry. *J. agric. Res.* **10**: 633–7 [*90, 91, 94*].

446

McINDOO, N. E. 1920. The olfactory sense of Orthoptera. *J. comp. Neurol.* **31**: 405–27, 92 figs. [*165, 166*].

McNABB, J. W. 1928. A study of the chromosomes in meiosis, fertilization, and cleavage in the grasshopper egg (Orthoptera). *J. Morph.* **45**: 47–93, 9 pls. [*237*].

MAKHOTIN, A. A. 1953. Phylogenetic interrelations of the main groups of Orthoptera Saltatoria and the morphology of their ovipositor. (In Russian.) *Trud. Inst. Morf. Zhiv.* **8**: 5–62, 30 figs. [*20*].

MAKI, T. 1938. Studies on the thoracic musculature of insects. *Mem. Fac. Sci. Agric. Taihoku*, **24**: 1–344, 17 pls. [*60*].

MAKINGS, P. 1964. Slifer's patches and the thermal sense in Acrididae (Orthoptera). *J. exp. Biol.* **41**: 473–97, 2 figs. [*220*].

MAKINO, S. 1951. *An Atlas of the Chromosome Numbers in Animals.* Ames, Iowa [*389*].

MALAN, D. J. & MALAN, D. E. 1925. The spermatogenesis of *Locustana pardalina* (Walker) (the brown trek locust). *Trans. roy. Soc. S. Afr.* **13**: 1–22, 2 pls., 1 fig. [*303, 379*].

MALEK, S. R. A. 1957. Sclerotization and melanization: two independent processes in the cuticle of the Desert Locust. *Nature, Lond.* **180**: 237, 2 figs. [*32, 47, 295*].

—— 1958a. The origin and nature of the ecdysial membrane in *Schistocerca gregaria* (Forskål). *J. Insect Physiol.* **2**: 298–312, 3 pls., 1 fig. [*32, 284*].

—— 1958b. The appearance and histological structure of the cuticle of the Desert Locust, *Schistocerca gregaria* (Forskål). *Proc. roy. Soc. B*, **149**: 557–70, 2 pls., 4 figs. [*32, 33, 35, 284, 285, 295, 323*].

—— 1961. Polyphenols and their quinone derivatives in the cuticle of the Desert Locust, *Schistocerca gregaria* (Forskål). *Comp. Biochem. Physiol.* **2**: 35–50, 1 fig. [*32, 295*].

MANNA, G. K. 1954. A study of chromosomes during meiosis in fifteen species of Indian grasshoppers. *Proc. zool. Soc. Beng.* **7**: 39–58, 6 figs. [*389*].

MARCUZZI, G. 1960. Osservazioni sui grassi degli insetti. *R. C. Accad. Lincei*, (8) **28**: 497–501 [*101*].

MARIKOVSKII, P. I. 1955. Some particulars of the stridulatory apparatus in Acrididae. (In Russian.) *Trud. Inst. Zool. Parasit.* **3**: 139–46, 9 figs. [*178, 187*].

MARSHALL, W. S. 1945. The rectal sac of the red-legged grasshopper, *Melanoplus femur-rubrum* De Geer. *Ann. ent. Soc. Amer.* **38**: 461–71 [*73*].

MARTOJA, R. 1959. Données cytologiques et histochimiques sur les tubes de Malpighi et leurs sécrétions muqueuses chez *Locusta migratoria* R. et F. (Orthoptère, Acridien). *Acta histochem.* **6**: 185–217, 1 pl., 12 figs. [*119*].

—— 1961. Caractéristiques histologiques du segment muqueux de l'appareil excréteur des Orthoptères. *C. R. Acad. Sci., Paris*, **253**: 3063–5 [*119*].

MASON, J. B. 1954. Number of antennal segments in adult Acrididae (Orthoptera). *Proc. R. ent. Soc. Lond. B*, **23**: 228–38, 4 figs. [*9*].

—— 1959. Presence of elytra in supposedly apterous genera of the family Pamphagidae (Acridoidea, Orthoptera). *Proc. R. ent. Soc. Lond. A*, **34**: 73–5, 8 figs. [*30*].

MASSIEU, H., CRAVIOTO, R. O., CRAVIOTO, O. Y. & FIGUEROA, F. DE M. 1959. Nuevos datos sobre el valor nutritivo de algunos insectos comestibles mexicanos. *An. Soc. Biol. Pernambuco*, **16**: 91–104 [*90, 91, 94*].

MATHUR, C. B. & SONI, B. N. 1937. Studies on *Schistocerca gregaria* Forsk. IX. Some observations on the histology of the blood of the Desert Locust. *Indian J. agric. Sci.* **7**: 317–25, 2 pls. [*114, 115*].

MATHUR, R. S. 1960. Studies on the normal and x-irradiated spermatogenesis of *Stenobothrus viridulus* and *Schistocerca gregaria* (Orthoptera). *Cellule*, **61**: 171–90, 36 figs. [*304*].

MATTHÉE, J. J. 1945. Biochemical differences between the solitary and gregarious phases of locusts and noctuids. *Bull. ent. Res.* **36**: 343–71 [*97, 101, 112, 257, 258, 261, 262, 268, 337, 357*].

—— 1951. The structure and physiology of the egg of *Locustana pardalina* (Walk.). *Sci. Bull. Dep. Agric. S. Afr.* no. 316: 83 pp., 19 figs. [*237, 239, 242, 245, 255, 257–9, 261–2, 268*].

MAXWELL-LEFROY, H. 1906. The Bombay locust (*Acridium succinctum* Linn.). A report on the investigations of 1903–1904. *Mem. Dep. Agric. India, Ent.* **1**: 1–112, 13 pls. [*299, 371*].

MAZEK-FIALLA, K. 1941. Die Körpertemperatur poikilothermer Tiere in Abhängigkeit vom Kleinklima. *Z. wiss. Zool.* **154** (1940): 170–246, 26 figs. [*113*].

MAZOUÉ, H., BUSNEL, M.-C. & CHAUCHARD, P. 1957. Les modifications réflexes de l'excitabilité nerveuse par les sons et les ultrasons chez divers Orthoptères. *C. R. Acad. Sci., Paris*, **244**: 666–8 [*193*].

MAZZI, V. & BACCETTI, B. 1957. Prime ricerche istochimiche comparative sui tubi Malpighiani degli insetti. *Redia*, **42**: 383–91, 1 pl., 1 fig. [*119*].

MÉDIONI, J. 1961. Le problème de l'existence d'un sens dermatoptique chez les insectes. L'état actuel de la question. *Psychol. franç.* **6**: 11–20 [*196*].

MELIS, G. 1961. Ricerche sulla fine struttura dei gangli dell'apparato nervoso stomatogastrico negli Ortotteri. *Redia*, **46**: 183–98, 4 pls., 1 fig. [*154, 155*].

MELVIN, R. 1931. A quantitative study of copper in insects. *Ann. ent. Soc. Amer.* **24**: 485–8 [*94, 95*].

MENDES, M. V. 1948. Histology of the corpora allata of *Melanoplus differentialis* (Orthoptera: Saltatoria). *Biol. Bull., Woods Hole*, **94**: 194–207, 10 figs. [*103, 158*].

MERCER, E. H. & DAY, M. F. 1952. The fine structure of the peritrophic membranes of certain insects. *Biol. Bull., Woods Hole*, **103**: 384–94, 8 figs. [*73*].

BIBLIOGRAPHY

MERTON, L. F. H. 1959. Studies in the ecology of the Moroccan Locust (*Dociostaurus maroccanus* Thunberg) in Cyprus. *Anti-Locust Bull.* no. 34: 123 pp., 44 figs. [*299, 356*].

MESA, A. 1956. Los cromosomas de algunos Acridoideos Uruguayos (Orthoptera, Caelifera, Acridoidea). *Agros, Montevideo*, no. 141: 32–45, 4 pls. [*389*].

MESTSCHERSKAYA, K. 1931. Experimentelle Untersuchungen über die Permeabilität der wachsenden Oocyten in Insektenovarien. *Z. Zellforsch.* **13**: 109–60, 12 figs. [*313*].

MEYER, H., PREISS, B. & BAUER, S. 1960. The oxidation of fatty acids by a particulate fraction from Desert Locust (*Schistocerca gregaria*) thorax tissues. *Biochem. J.* **76**: 27–35, 11 figs. [*102, 103*].

MICHELMORE, A. P. G. & ALLAN, W. 1934. Observations on phases of the red-winged locust in Northern Rhodesia. *Bull. ent. Res.* **25**: 101–28, 5 figs. [*278, 299*].

MIDDLEKAUFF, W. W. 1964. Effects of photoperiod upon oögenesis in *Melanoplus devastator* Scudder (Orthoptera: Acrididae). *J. Kans. ent. Soc.* **37**: 163–8, 2 figs. [*311*].

MIKA, G. 1959. Über das Paarungsverhalten der Wanderheuschrecke *Locusta migratoria* R. und F. und deren Abhängigkeit vom Zustand der inneren Geschlechtsorgane. *Zool. Beitr., Berl.* (N.F.), **4**: 153–203, 15 figs. [*140*].

MIKHEL'SON, J. 1922. Observations sur les acridiens migrateurs. (In Russian.) *Bull. Soc. ent. Moscou*, **2**: 7–67, 7 figs. [*88, 270, 272*].

MILLARA, P. 1947. Contribution à l'étude cytologique et physiologique des leucocytes d'insectes. *Bull. biol.* **81**: 129–53, 4 pls. [*114*].

MILLER, P. L. 1960. Respiration in the Desert Locust. I. The control of ventilation; II. The control of the spiracles; III. Ventilation and the spiracles during flight. *J. exp. Biol.* **37**: 224–36, 6 figs.; 237–63, 17 figs; 264–78, 9 figs. [*124, 128, 130, 131*].

MILLOT, J. & FONTAINE, M. 1937. Études physiologiques sur les Orthoptères. I. La teneur en eau du criquet pèlerin adulte. *Bull. Soc. Hist. nat. Afr. N.* **28**: 412–18 [*92, 226, 228, 235*].

—— 1938. Le taux de chitine chez *Schistocerca gregaria*. *Bull. Soc. zool. Fr.* **63**: 123–4 [*92*].

MISRA, S. D. 1946. Studies on the somatic musculature of the Desert Locust, *Schistocerca gregaria* (Forskål). Part I. The head. *Indian J. Ent.* **7** (1945): 103–38, 11 figs. [*9, 60, 70*].

—— 1947. Studies on the somatic musculature of the Desert Locust, *Schistocerca gregaria* (Forskål). Part II. The neck and the prothorax. *Indian J. Ent.* **8** (1946): 1–29, 7 figs. [*10, 60, 128*].

—— 1950. Studies on the somatic musculature of the Desert Locust, *Schistocerca gregaria* (Forskål) phase *gregaria*. Part III. The pterothorax. *Indian J. Ent.* **9** (1947): 19–72, 10 figs. [*60, 63*].

—— 1962. Nutritional ecology of the clear-winged grasshopper *Camnula pellucida* (Scudder) (Orthoptera: Acrididae). *Mem. Indian Mus.* **14**: 87–172, 1 pl., 28 figs. [*80*].

MISRA, S. D., NAIR, K. R. & ROONWAL, M. L. 1952. Studies in intra-specific variation. Part VI. Dynamics of variability in respect of eye-stripe characters, sex-ratios and body-size of Desert Locust populations during the initial years (1949–1950) of a new swarming cycle in India, together with a statistical note on Roonwal's hypotheses on prediction of swarming. *Indian J. Ent.* **14**: 95–152, 3 figs. [*348*].

MOORE, H. W. 1948. Variations in fall embryological development in three grasshopper species. *Canad. Ent.* **80**: 83–8 [*245, 260*].

MORALES AGACINO, E. 1957. The abdominal morphology of a gynandromorph of *Schistocerca paranensis* (Burm.) (Orthoptera: Acrididae). *Proc. R. ent. Soc. Lond.* A, **32**: 169–70, 1 fig. [*149*].

MOSSOP, M. C. 1933. Description of hopper instars of the Red Locust, *Nomadacris septemfasciata* Serv. phase *gregaria*, and some changes in adult coloration. *Proc. Rhod. sci. Ass.* **32**: 113–18 [*337*].

MOUSSA, T. A. & BANHAWY, M. 1960. On a possible relation between vitamin C and the Golgi dictyosomes of insect neurones. *J. R. micr. Soc.* **78** (1958): 111–13, 1 pl. [*86*].

MOXON, A. L. 1939. The selenium content of grasshoppers found feeding on seleniferous vegetation. *Proc. S. Dak. Akad. Sci.* **19**: 69–70 [*94, 95*].

MUKERJI, S. & BATRA, R. N. 1938. A note on the post-embryonic development of eye stripes and their correlation with the number of larval instars and the antennal segments in the life-cycle of *Schistocerca gregaria* Forsk. *5th Int. Locust Conf.*, Brussels 1938: 410–16 [*84, 278*].

MUKERJI, S. & CHATTERJEE, S. N. 1953. Permeability of insect cuticle to aqueous stains and vulnerability to insecticides. *Nature, Lond.* **171**: 119–20 [*25*].

—— 1956. An additional phase character in specimens of *Locusta migratoria* Linnaeus collected from South India. *Indian J. Ent.* **18**: 161–4, 2 figs. [*343*].

MUNSELL BOOK OF COLOR, 1929–1942. Pocket edition. Baltimore [*41*].

MUTTKOWSKI, R. A. 1921. Studies on the respiration of insects. I. The gases and respiratory proteins of insect blood. *Ann. ent. Soc. Amer.* **14**: 150–6, 1 fig. [*110*].

NAGY, B. 1952. Food consumption of *Dociostaurus crucigerus brevicollis* Eversm. and *Oedipoda coerulescens* L. (Orth. Acrididae). *Acta biol. Budapest*, **3** (1951): 41–52, 2 figs. [*80*].

NAIR, K. R. 1953. A biometric study of the Desert Locust. *Bull. int. statist. Inst.* **33**: 349–58 [*348, 350*].

NATORI, B. 1931. On an ovo-testis found in a larva of locust *Podisma sapporense* Shiraki. *Trans. Sapporo nat. Hist. Soc.* **12**: 1–5, 1 pl. [*149*].

NAYAR, K. K. 1954. The structure of the corpus cardiacum of *Locusta migratoria*. *Quart. J. micr. Sci.* **95**: 245–50, 1 pl. [*158*].

BIBLIOGRAPHY

NEL, R. I. 1929. Studies on the development of the genitalia and the genital ducts in insects. I. Female of Orthoptera and Dermaptera. *Quart. J. micr. Sci.* 73: 25–85, 3 pls., 5 figs. [*148, 246, 282*].

NELSEN, O. E. 1931a. The development of the ovary in the grasshopper, *Melanoplus differentialis.* (Abs.) *Anat. Rec.* (Suppl.), 51: 76 [*246, 282*].

—— 1931b. Life cycle, sex differentiation, and testis development in *Melanoplus differentialis* (Acrididae, Orthoptera). *J. Morph.* 51: 467–525, 5 pls., 2 figs. [*245, 246, 281, 282*].

—— 1934. The development of the ovary in the grasshopper, *Melanoplus differentialis* (Acrididae: Orthoptera). *J. Morph.* 55: 515–43, 6 pls. [*246*].

NENYUKOV, D. V. & PARFENT'EV, I. A. 1929. Digestive process and structure of intestine in the Migratory Locust. (In Russian.) *Pl. Prot., Leningr.* 6: 21–37, 12 figs. [*72, 73, 75, 76*].

NEVILLE, A. C. 1963a. Motor unit distribution of the dorsal longitudinal flight muscles in locusts. *J. exp. Biol.*, 40: 123–36, 1 pl., 10 figs. [*65*].

—— 1963b. Daily growth layers in locust rubber-like cuticle influenced by an external rhythm. *J. Insect Physiol.* 9: 177–86, 1 pl. [*32, 35, 276*].

—— 1963c. Growth and deposition of resilin and chitin in locust rubber-like cuticle. *J. Insect Physiol.* 9: 265–78, 8 figs. [*32, 35, 276*].

—— 1963d. Daily growth layers for determining the age of grasshopper populations. *Oikos*, 14: 1–8, 16 figs. [*32, 276*].

NEVILLE, A. C. & WEIS-FOGH, T. 1963. The effect of temperature on locust flight muscle. *J. exp. Biol.* 40: 111–21, 8 figs. [*65*].

NEWELL, G. E. & BAXTER, E. W. 1936. On the nature of the free cell-border of certain mid-gut epithelia. *Quart. J. micr. Sci.* 79: 123–50, 1 pl., 7 figs. [*72*].

NICKERSON, B. 1956. Pigmentation of hoppers of the Desert Locust (*Schistocerca gregaria* Forskål) in relation to phase coloration. *Anti-Locust Bull.* no. 24: 34 pp. 7 figs. [*44, 160, 358, 376*].

NIKOL'SKIĬ, V. V. 1918. Causes of the migration of larvae of the Asiatic Locust. (In Russian.) *Turkest. sel. Khoz.* 13 (3–4): 1–12 [*222, 228*].

—— 1925. The Asiatic Locust *Locusta migratoria* L. (In Russian.) *Trud. Otd. prikl. Ent.* 12: 332 pp., 36 figs. [*35, 270*].

NOLTE, D. J. 1939. A comparative study of seven species of Transvaal Acrididae, with special reference to the chromosome complex. *J. ent. Soc. S. Afr.* 2: 196–260, 144 figs. [*138*].

NORRIS, M. J. 1950. Reproduction in the African Migratory Locust (*Locusta migratoria migratorioides* R. & F.) in relation to density and phase. *Anti-Locust Bull.* no. 6: 48 pp., 7 figs. [*327 331, 352, 353, 355, 362, 363*].

—— 1952. Reproduction in the Desert Locust (*Schistocerca gregaria* Forsk.) in relation to density and phase. *Anti-Locust Bull.* no. 13: 49 pp., 8 figs. [*311, 327, 331, 352, 353, 355, 362*].

—— 1954. Sexual maturation in the Desert Locust (*Schistocerca gregaria* Forskål) with special reference to the effects of grouping. *Anti-Locust Bull.* no. 18: 44 pp., 2 figs. [*132, 297, 298, 300, 311, 313, 318, 319, 352*].

—— 1957. Factors affecting the rate of sexual maturation of the Desert Locust (*Schistocerca gregaria* Forskål) in the laboratory. *Anti-Locust Bull.* no. 28: 26 pp., 2 figs. [*310*].

—— 1959a. Reproduction in the Red Locust (*Nomadacris septemfasciata* Serville) in the laboratory. *Anti-Locust Bull.* no. 36: 46 pp., 3 figs. [*301, 309, 321, 352, 353, 355*].

—— 1959b. The influence of day-length on imaginal diapause in the Red Locust, *Nomadacris septemfasciata* (Serv.). *Ent. exp. appl.* 2: 154–68, 1 fig. [*309*].

—— 1961. Group effects on feeding in adult males of the Desert Locust, *Schistocerca gregaria* (Forsk.) in relation to sexual maturation. *Bull. ent. Res.* 51: 731–53, 3 figs. [*80, 351, 352*].

—— 1962a. The effects of density and grouping on sexual maturation, feeding and activity in caged *Schistocerca gregaria. Colloq. int. Cent. nat. Rech. sci.* no. 114: 23–35 [*351*].

—— 1962b. Group effects on the activity and behaviour of adult males of the Desert Locust (*Schistocerca gregaria* Forsk.) in relation to sexual maturation. *Anim. Behav.* 10: 275–91 [*351*].

—— 1962c. Diapause induced by photoperiod in a tropical locust, *Nomadacris septemfasciata* (Serv.). *Ann. appl. Biol.* 50: 600–3, 2 figs. [*309*].

—— 1963. Laboratory experiments on gregarious behaviour in ovipositing females of the Desert Locust (*Schistocerca gregaria* (Forsk.)). *Ent. exp. appl.* 6: 279–303 [*351*].

—— 1964a. Reproduction of the grasshopper *Anacridium aegyptium* L. in the laboratory. *Proc. R. ent. Soc. Lond.* In press [*309, 310*].

—— 1964b. Environmental control of sexual maturation in insects. *2nd Symp. R. ent. Soc. Lond.,* London 1963: 56–65 [*309, 351*].

—— 1964c. Accelerating and inhibiting effects of crowding on sexual maturation in two species of locusts. *Nature, Lond.* 203: 784–5 [*298, 352*].

NUTTING, W. L. 1951. A comparative anatomical study of the heart and accessory structures of the orthopteroid insects. *J. Morph.* 89: 501–97, 21 pls. [*105, 106, 115, 122*].

OBOLENSKY, G. 1955. Étude statistique des valeurs du nombre des dents de la rape de *Locusta, migratoria gallica* Rem. *Colloque sur l'Acoustique des Orthoptères*, Paris 1954: 97–101 [*343*].

ÖGEL, S. 1955. A contribution to the study of blood-cells in Orthoptera. *Commun. Fac. Sci. Ankara,* C, 4: 15–41, 2 pls., 10 figs. [*114, 115*].

—— 1959. Observations on a probable blood-forming (leucopoietic) tissue in *Locusta migratoria* phase *danica* (Orthoptera, Acrididae). *Rev. Fac. Sci. Univ. Istanbul*, B, 24: 55–72, 1 pl., 15 figs. [*116, 117, 122*].

29

OGLOBLIN, A. 1947. Las glandulas odoriferas de la langosta *Schistocerca cancellata* (Serville) (Orthopt., Acridoidea). *Arthropoda*, **1**: 54–77, 17 figs. [*35*].

—— 1950. Los organos reproductores de la langosta voladora *Schistocerca cancellata* (Serv.). (Comunicación preliminar.) In *Reunion Anual del C.I.P.A.* (*Comité Interamericano Permanente Antiacridiano*) *en Asunción del Paraguay 8 a 11 de mayo de 1950*, pp. 116–29, 1 pl., 3 figs. Buenos Aires [*144*].

—— 1955. Nota sobre el polimorfismo de la langosta. *Rev. Invest. agríc.*, *B. Aires*, **9**: 23–36, 2 figs. [*413*].

OKAY, S. 1945. Pigmentation of Orthoptera. *Nature, Lond.* **155**: 635 [*49*].

—— 1947. Sur les pigments des ailes postérieures bleues, rouges et jaunes des acridiens. *Rev. Fac. Sci. Univ. Istanbul*, B, **12**: 1–8 [*49*].

—— 1948. Sur le pigment brun des Orthoptères. *Commun. Fac. Sci. Ankara*, **1**: 178–86 [*45*].

—— 1949. Sur les pigments des ailes postérieures rouges, bleues et jaunes des Acrididae. II. *Bull. Soc. zool. Fr.* **74**: 11–15 [*49*].

—— 1953. Formation of green pigment and colour changes in Orthoptera. *Bull. ent. Res.* **44**: 299–315, 1 fig. [*50, 53, 96*].

—— 1954. Further investigations on colour change in Orthoptera. *Commun. Fac. Sci. Ankara*, C, **4**: 31–43, 1 pl., 2 figs. [*45*].

—— 1956. The effect of temperature and humidity on the formation of green pigment in *Acrida bicolor* (Thunb.). *Arch. int. Physiol. Biochim.* **64**: 80–91, 1 fig. [*53*].

ONSAGER, J. A. & MULKERN, G. B. 1963. Identification of eggs and egg-pods of North Dakota grasshoppers (Orthoptera: Acrididae). *Tech. Bull. N. Dak. agric. Exp. Sta.* no. 446: 48 pp., 7 pls. [*240*].

OSMAN, M. F. H. & SCHMIDT, G. H. 1961. Analyse der Körperfette von imaginalen Wanderheuschrecken der Art *Locusta migratoria migratorioides* L. (Orth.). *Biochem. Z.* **334**: 441–50, 1 fig. [*97, 102*].

OTANES, F. Q. 1940. Notes on the Oriental Migratory Locust (*Locusta migratoria manilensis* Meyen) with special reference to its solitary phase and breeding place or outbreak area. *Philipp. J. Agric.* **11**: 331–53, 1 map, 4 pls. [*373*].

ÖZBAŞ, S. 1957a. Morphological and histological studies on the corpora allata and cardiaca in Orthoptera. *Commun. Fac. Sci. Ankara*, C, **8**: 19–44, 13 figs. [*157, 158, 159*].

—— 1957b. Two kinds of secretions in corpora cardiaca of *Locusta migratoria* (L) ph. *solitaria* (Orthoptera: Acrididae). *Commun. Fac. Sci. Ankara*, C, **8**: 45–57, 3 pls., 7 figs. [*157, 158*].

PABST, H. & SCHWARTZKOPFF, J. 1962. Zur Leistung der Flügelgelenk-Rezeptoren von *Locusta migratoria*. *Z. vergl. Physiol.* **45**: 396–404, 4 figs. [*170*].

PAGDEN, H. T. 1959. *Patanga succincta* (L.), the 'Bombay Locust', in Malaya. *Bull. Dep. Agric. Malaya*, no. 106: 39 pp., 2 maps, 10 pls., 2 figs. [*255, 287*].

PALM, N.-B. 1946. Studies on the peristalsis of the Malpighian tubes in insects. *Acta Univ. lund.* (N.F.), **42** (11): 39 pp., 17 figs. [*119*].

—— 1949a. Sexual differences in size and structure of the corpora allata in some insects. *K. svenska VetenskAkad. Handl.* (4) **1** (6): 24 pp., 17 figs. [*159*].

—— 1949b. The rectal papillae in insects. *Acta Univ. lund.* (N.F.), **45** (8): 30 pp., 8 figs. [*73*].

—— 1952. Storage and excretion of vital dyes in insects with special regard to trypan blue. *Ark. Zool.* (2) **3**: 195–272, 76 figs. [*121, 122*].

PANOV, A. A. 1962. Distribution of neurosecretory cells in the abdominal portion of the neural chain in Orthoptera. (In Russian.) *Dokl. Akad. Nauk SSSR*, **145** (6): 1409–12, 1 pl., 1 fig. [*157*].

PANTEL, J. 1886. Contribution à l'orthoptérologie de l'Espagne centrale. *An. Soc. esp. Hist. nat.* **15**: 237–87, 1 pl., 3 figs. [*182*].

PAOLI, G. 1937a. Osservazioni su alcune particolarità di struttura e funzione dell'apparato genitale femminile di *Dociostaurus maroccanus* Thunb. (Orthopt. Acrididae). *Redia*, **23**: 17–26, 8 figs. [*322, 325*].

—— 1937b. Studi sulle cavallette di Foggia (*Dociostaurus maroccanus* Thunb.) e sui loro oofagi (Ditteri Bombiliidi e Coleotteri Meloidi) ed Acari ectofagi (Eritreidi e Trombidiidi). *Redia*, **23**: 27–206, 3 pls., 99 figs. [*276, 322, 325*].

PAPILLON, M. 1960. Étude préliminaire de la répercussion du groupement des parents sur les larves nouveau-nées de *Schistocerca gregaria* Forsk. *Bull. biol.* **93**: 203–63, 16 figs. [*327, 333, 354, 355, 369, 378*].

PARKER, J. R. 1924. Observations on the clear-winged grasshopper (*Camnula pellucida* Scudder). *Bull. Minn. agric. Exp. Sta.* no. 214: 44 pp., 6 figs. [*222, 223*].

—— 1930. Some effects of temperature and moisture upon *Melanoplus mexicanus mexicanus* Saussure and *Camnula pellucida* Scudder (Orthoptera). *Bull. Mont. agric. Exp. Sta.* no. 223: 132 pp., 25 figs. [*221, 222, 256, 261, 263, 264, 265, 291, 294*].

PARRY, D. A. 1947. The function of the insect ocellus. *J. exp. Biol.* **24**: 211–19, 3 figs. [*206*].

—— 1951. Factors determining the temperature of terrestrial arthropods in sunlight. *J. exp. Biol.* **28**: 445–62, 8 figs. [*217*].

PASQUIER, R. 1934. Contribution à l'étude du criquet marocain, *Dociostaurus maroccanus* Thnb., en Afrique mineure. (1re note.) *Bull. Soc. Hist. nat. Afr. N.* **25**: 167–200, 4 pls., 8 figs. [*336*].

—— 1946. Les étapes de la vie de la Sauterelle pèlerine. *Bull. Off. nat. anti-acrid., Algér.* no. 1 (1945): 7–13 [*297*].

BIBLIOGRAPHY

PASQUIER, R. 1952. Quelques propositions de terminologie acridologique. Première note. Terminologie concernant le comportement et l'aspect des Acrididae gregariaptes. *Ann. Inst. agric. Algér.* **6** (6): 16 pp. [*380, 385*].

PASQUINELLY, F. 1955. Technique de la prise de son objective et son application à l'acoustique animale. *Colloque sur l'Acoustique des Orthoptères*, Paris 1954: 50–63, 2 figs. [*185*].

PASQUINELLY, F. & BUSNEL, M.-C. 1955. Études préliminaires sur les mécanismes de la production des sons par les Orthoptères. *Colloque sur l'Acoustique des Orthoptères*, Paris 1954: 145–53, 2 pls., 4 figs. [*185*].

PAULY, L. K. 1956. Serological relationships among orthopteroid insects as determined by their whole 'blood'. *J. N.Y. ent. Soc.* **63** (1955): 83–93, 1 fig. [*114*].

PAVLOVA, M. I. 1895. On the structure of the circulatory and sympathetic nervous system of insects, particularly of the Orthoptera. (In Russian.) *Rab. Lab. zool. Kab.*, *Varshava*, **1895**: 96 pp., 6 pls., 1 fig. [*105, 106, 107, 157*].

PAVLOWSKY, E. 1916. On the anatomy of *Phymateus hildebrandti* (Orthoptera, Phymateidea) in connection with the peculiarities of its dermal secretion. (In Russian with English summary.) In Dogiel, V. & Sokolov, I. [Eds.], *Scientific Results of the Zoological Expedition to British East Africa and Uganda in the year 1914*, vol. I (3): 28 pp., 12 figs. [*36*].

PAYNE, D. W. 1961. *Digestion in locusts*. Ph.D. thesis, London [*76, 78, 79*].

PAYNE, M. A. 1933. The structure of the testis and movement of sperms in *Chortophaga viridifasciata* as demonstrated by intravitam technique. *J. Morph.* **54**: 321–45, 2 pls., 3 figs. [*140*].

PENER, M. P. 1963. *Studies on phase differences in the Desert Locust* (Schistocerca gregaria *Forskål*), *reared under crowded and isolated conditions, with special reference to the oxygen consumption.* (In Hebrew with English summary.) Ph.D. thesis, Jerusalem [*47, 336, 337*].

——— 1964. Two gynandromorphs of *Schistocerca gregaria* Forskål (Orthoptera: Acridoidea): morphology and behaviour. *Proc. R. ent. Soc. Lond.* A, **39**: 89–100, 6 figs. [*150*].

PENER, M. P. & SHULOV, A. 1960. The biology of *Calliptamus palaestinensis* Bdhmr, with special reference to the development of its eggs. *Bull. Res. Coun. Israel* (Zool.), **9**: 131–56, 5 figs. [*245, 260*].

PEPPER, J. H. & HASTINGS, E. 1952. The effects of solar radiation on grasshopper temperatures and activities. *Ecology*, **33**: 96–103 [*214, 217*].

PERDECK, A. C. 1958. The isolating value of specific song patterns in two sibling species of grasshoppers (*Chorthippus brunneus* Thunb. and *C. biguttulus* L.). *Behaviour*, **12**: 1–75, 2 pls., 7 figs. [*177, 391, 393*].

PÉREZ-GONZÁLEZ, M. D. & EDWARDS, G. A. 1954. Metabolic differences among several specialized insect muscles. *Bol. Fac. Filos. Ciênc. S. Paulo* (Zool.), no. 19: 373–89 [*68*].

PETERSEN, B. & WEBER, R. 1949. A comparison between growth ratio and geographic variation of allometry in *Omocestus viridulus* L. ♀ (Orthoptera). *Zool. Bidr. Uppsala*, **29**: 39–43, 5 figs. [*276*].

PETROV, S. 1905. Matériaux sur l'histoire naturelle des criquets. (In Russian.) *Ann. Inst. agron. Moscou*, **1905**: 114–218, 13 pls. [*7*].

PETRUNKEWITSCH, A. & GUAITA, G. VON 1901. Ueber den geschlechtlichen Dimorphismus bei den Tonapparaten der Orthopteren. *Zool. Jb.* (Syst.), **14**: 291–310, 4 pls. [*178*].

PFADT, R. E. 1949. Food plants as factors in the ecology of the lesser migratory grasshopper, *Melanoplus mexicanus* (Sauss.). *Bull. Wyo. agric. Exp. Sta.* no. 290: 51 pp., 11 figs. [*82, 83, 329*].

PFLUGFELDER, O. 1947. Über die Ventraldrüsen und einige andere inkretorische Organe des Insektenkopfes. *Biol. Zbl.* **66**: 211–35, 32 figs. [*159*].

——— 1958. *Entwicklungsphysiologie der Insekten*. 2nd ed. Leipzig [*159*].

PHILLIPS, J. E. 1964. Rectal absorption in the Desert Locust, *Schistocerca gregaria* Forskål. I. Water; II. Sodium, potassium and chloride; III. The nature of the excretory process. *J. exp. Biol.* **41**: 15–38, 8 figs.; 39–67, 7 figs.; 69–80, 1 fig. [*73, 74, 110, 227, 228*].

PHIPPS, J. 1949. The structure and maturation of the ovaries in British Acrididae (Orthoptera). *Trans. R. ent. Soc. Lond.* **100**: 233–47, 7 figs. [*304, 305*].

——— 1950. The maturation of the ovaries and the relation between weight and maturity in *Locusta migratoria migratorioides* (R. & F.). *Bull. ent. Res.* **40**: 539–57, 15 figs. [*96, 226, 301, 303, 304, 305*].

PHIPPS, J. 1959. Studies on East African Acridoidea (Orthoptera), with special reference to egg-production, habitats and seasonal cycles. *Trans. R. ent. Soc. Lond.* **111**: 27–56, 1 fig. [*144, 237*].

——— 1962. The ovaries of some Sierra Leone Acridoidea (Orthoptera) with some comparisons between East and West African forms. *Proc. R. ent. Soc. Lond.* A, **37**: 13–21 [*144, 145*].

PICHLER, F. 1952. Vergleichende funktionsanatomische Untersuchungen an dem Männchen-Abdomen einiger Feldheuschrecken. *Zool. Jb.* (Anat.), **72**: 560–76, 12 figs. [*19, 64, 297*].

——— 1953. Beitrag zur Kenntnis der tympanalen Muskulatur der Feldheuschrecken. *Zool. Anz.* **150**: 12–15, 2 figs. [*64*].

——— 1956. Zur postembryonalen Entwicklung der Feldheuschrecken. *Öst. zool. Z.* **6**: 513–31, 10 figs. [*282, 283, 287*].

——— 1957. Zur postembryonalen Entwicklung einiger Feldheuschrecken aus der Gattung *Podisma* Latr. *Zool. Anz.* **159**: 291–303, 11 figs. [*282, 283, 287*].

PICKFORD, R. 1958. Observations on the reproductive potential of *Melanoplus bilituratus* (Wlk.) (Orthoptera: Acrididae) reared on different food plants in the laboratory. *Canad. Ent.* **90**: 483–5 [*329, 330*].

BIBLIOGRAPHY

PIERCE, G. W. 1948. *The songs of Insects with Related Material on the Production, Propagation, Detection, and Measurement of Sonic and Supersonic Vibrations.* Cambridge, Mass. & London [*183, 188*].

PILAT, M. 1935a. Histological researches into the action of insecticides on the intestinal tube of insects. *Bull. ent. Res.* **26**: 165–72, 4 pls. [*72, 76*].

—— 1935b. The effects of intestinal poisoning on the blood of locusts (*Locusta migratoria*). *Bull. ent. Res.* **26**: 283–8, 2 pls. [*117*].

PIMONOV, L. 1955. Analyseur de fréquence et décibelmètre pour ultrasons. *Colloque sur l'Acoustique des Orthoptères*, Paris 1954: 38–45, 2 figs. [*185*].

PLOTNIKOV, V. 1912. Observations on the hatching of eggs of the Moroccan Locust under artificial conditions and probable conclusions. (In Russian.) *Turkest. sel. Khoz.* no. 1: 15 pp. [*255, 262*].

—— 1915. *Report of the activities of the Turkestan Entomological Station for 1912, 1913, 1914 and part of 1915.* (In Russian.) Tashkent [*378*].

—— 1921. Parthenogenesis in Acrididae. (In Russian.) *Byull. 3go vseross. ent.-fit. Sov.*, Petrograd 1921, no. 7: 9 [*319*].

—— 1926. *Insects Injurious to Agricultural Plants in Central Asia.* (In Russian.) Tashkent [*287*].

—— 1927. *Locusta* (*Pachytylus*) *migratoria* L. and *L. danica* as independent forms and their derivatives. (In Russian with German summary.) *Uzbekist. op. Stants. Zashch. Rast.* **1927**: 33 pp., 16 figs. [*262, 344, 357, 379*].

—— 1962. Heterosis—one of the possible reasons for mass multiplication of locusts. (In Russian.) *Trud. Inst. Zool. Akad. Nauk Kazakh SSR*, **18**: 201–4 [*379*].

PODTIAGUIN, B. 1953. Sintesis de los estudios y observaciones llevadas a cabo en el Chaco Boreal Paraguayo, sobre la langosta *Schistocerca cancellata* (Serv.) 1839, por el entomologo Dr. Boris Podtiaguin, comisionado por el servicio tecnico de lucha contra la langosta. Parte II. In *Reunion Anual del C.I.P.A.* (*Comite Interamericano Permanente Antiacridiano*) *en Porto Alegre* (*Brasil*) *15 a 20 de septiembre de 1952*, pp. 84–92. Buenos Aires [*379*].

POPOV, G. [B.] 1952. Apparent tendency to phase variation in an Iranian grasshopper, *Pyrgodera armata* (F.W.) (Orthoptera, Acrididae). *Eos, Madr.* **28**: 277–83, 2 pls., 1 fig. [*370*].

—— 1954. Notes on the behaviour of swarms of the Desert Locust (*Schistocerca gregaria* Forskål) during oviposition in Iran. *Trans. R. ent. Soc. Lond.* **105**: 65–77, 5 pls., 3 figs. [*321*].

—— 1958. Ecological studies on oviposition by swarms of the Desert Locust (*Schistocerca gregaria* Forskål) in eastern Africa. *Anti-Locust Bull.* no. 31: 70 pp., 14 pls., 17 figs. [*315*].

—— 1959. A revision of the genera *Allaga* Karsch and *Sauracris* Burr (Orthoptera: Acrididae). *Trans. R. ent. Soc. Lond.* **111**: 1–26, 2 pls., 19 figs. [*237*].

PORCHINSKIĬ, I. [A.] 1886. Several new and little-known Orthoptera. (With biological notes.) (In Russian.) *Horae Soc. ent. ross.* **20**: 111–27, 1 pl. [*11*].

POSPELOV, V. P. 1926a. The influence of temperature on the maturation and general health of *Locusta migratoria* L. *Bull. ent. Res.* **16**: 363–7, 3 pls. [*96, 102, 307*].

—— 1926b. Théorie physiologique des migrations de la sauterelle. (In Russian.) *Pl. Prot., Leningr.* **2** (1925): 423–35 [*96*].

POTGIETER, J. T. 1929. A contribution to the biology of the Brown Swarm Locust *Locustana pardalina* (Wlk.) and its natural enemies. *Sci. Bull. Dep. Agric. S. Afr.* no. 82: 48 pp., 7 pls. [*319, 378*].

POTTER, E. 1940. A gynandromorph specimen of *Anacridium moestum* (Serv.) Orthoptera, Acrididae. *Proc. R. ent. Soc. Lond.* A, **15**: 41–6, 15 figs. [*149*].

POULTON, E. B. 1926. Protective resemblance borne by certain African insects to the blackened areas caused by grass fires. *3rd Int. Congr. Ent.*, Zurich 1925, vol. 2: 433–51, 1 pl. [*54*].

POWERS, P. B. A. 1942. Metrical studies on spermatogonial chromosomes of Acrididae (Orthoptera). *J. Morph.* **71**: 523–76, 1 fig. [*390*].

POWNING, R. F., DAY, M. F. & IRZYKIEWICZ, H. 1951. Studies on the digestion of wool by insects. II. The properties of some insect proteinases. *Aust. J. sci. Res.* B, **4**: 49–63, 6 figs. [*76*].

PRADHAN, S. & BINDRA, O. S. 1956. Studies on resistance to contact toxicity of *gamma*–BHC suspensions by successive instars of *Schistocerca gregaria* Forsk. and certain associated factors. *Indian J. Ent.* **18**: 93–111, 3 figs. [*33, 232, 274*].

PRAT, H. 1954. Analyse micro-calorimétrique des variations de la thermogenèse chez divers insectes. *Canad. J. Zool.* **32**: 172–97, 1 pl., 31 figs. [*215, 216*].

PRECHT, H., CHRISTOPHERSEN, J. & HENSEL, H. 1955. *Temperatur und Leben.* Berlin [*224*].

PREDTECHENSKIĬ, S. A. 1928. *Locusta migratoria* L. in central Russia. (In Russian with English summary.) *Rep. Bur. appl. Ent., Leningr.* **3**: 113–99, 4 figs. [*372*].

—— 1935. Studies on the Desert Locust (*Schistocerca gregaria* Forsk.) in Central Asia and Trans-caucasus in 1929–1930. (In Russian with English summary). *Bull. Pl. Prot., Leningr.* (Ent.), no. 11: 92 pp., 6 figs. [*75, 340*].

PRINGLE, J. W. S. 1957. *Insect Flight.* London [*166*].

PRUTHI, H. S. & NIGAM, L. N. 1939. The bionomics, life-history and control of the grasshopper, *Poecilocerus pictus* (Fab.)—a new pest of cultivated crops in North India. *Indian J. agric. Sci.* **9**: 629–41, 2 pls. [*286, 319*].

PUMPHREY, R. J. 1940. Hearing in insects. *Biol. Rev.* **15**: 107–32, 10 figs. [*193*].

PUMPHREY, R. J. & RAWDON-SMITH, A. F. 1936. Sensitivity of insects to sound. *Nature, Lond.* **137**: 990, 1 fig. [*163, 191, 193*].

452

BIBLIOGRAPHY

Puschnig, R. 1914. Bemerkungen zur Arbeit H. Karny's: Über die Reduktion der Flugorgane bei den Orthopteren. *Zool. Jb.* (Zool.), **34**: 515–42 [*29*].

Putnam, L. G. 1958. Albinism in the migratory grasshopper, *Melanoplus bilituratus* (Wlk.). *Nature, Lond.* **182**: 1529 [*46*].

Putnam, L. G. & Handford, R. H. 1958. Two-year and one-year life cycles in *Melanoplus bivittatus* (Say) (Orthoptera: Acrididae) in western Canada. *10th Int. Congr. Ent.*, Montreal 1956, vol. 2: 651–6 [*261*].

Putnam, L. G. & Peters, E. G. 1960. The growth characteristics, in terms of live weight, of some grasshoppers (Orthoptera: Acrididae) of western Canada. *Canad. Ent.* **92**: 908–10 [*274*].

Qadri, M. A. H. 1940. On the development of the genitalia and their ducts of orthopteroid insects. *Trans. R. ent. Soc. Lond.* **90**: 121–75, 7 pls., 17 figs. [*246*].

Quo Fu 1956. Biological observations on the reproduction of the Oriental Migratory Locust, *Locusta migratoria manilensis* Meyen (Orthoptera, Acrididae). (In Chinese with English summary.) *Acta ent. sinica*, **6**: 145–67, 2 figs. [*304, 319*].

Ragge, D. R. 1955. *The Wing-venation of the Orthoptera Saltatoria, with notes on Dictyopteran wing-venation.* London [*27, 279, 388*].

Rainey, R. C. 1958. Some observations on flying locusts and atmosphere turbulence in eastern Africa. *Quart. J. R. met. Soc.* **84**: 334–54, 2 pls., 6 figs. [*202, 381*].

—— 1962. Some effects of environmental factors on movements and phase-change of locust populations in the field. *Colloq. int. Cent. nat. Rech. sci.* no. 114: 175–199, 1 fig. [*369, 381, 382*].

Rainey, R. C., Waloff, Z. & Burnett, G. F. 1957. The behaviour of the Red Locust (*Nomadacris septemfasciata* Serville) in relation to the topography, meteorology and vegetation of the Rukwa Rift Valley, Tanganyika. *Anti-Locust Bull.* no. 26: 96 pp., 5 pls., 14 figs. [*217, 220, 221, 346*].

Ramme, W. 1951a. Zur Systematik, Faunistik und Biologie der Orthopteren von Südost-Europa und Vorderasien. *Mitt. zool. Mus. Berl.* 27 (1950): 1–431, 39 pls., 134 figs. [*29, 39, 373, 374, 395*].

—— 1951b. Die parallele Färbungsvariation ('Parallelochromie') der Acrididae; ihre genetische und phylogenetische Bedeutung (Orthopt.). *Eos, Madr.*, tomo extra-ord. (1950): 249–66, 1 pl., 1 fig. [*39*].

Ramsay, J. A. 1953. Active transport of potassium by the Malpighian tubules of insects. *J. exp. Biol.* **30**: 358–69, 1 fig. [*110, 121, 230*].

Randell, R. L. 1963. On the presence of concealed genitalic structures in female Caelifera (Insecta: Orthoptera). *Trans. Amer. ent. Soc.* **88**: 247–60, 9 pls., 1 fig. [*20, 314*].

Rao, Y. R. 1937. A report on the work done by the research staff under the locust research entomologist to the Imperial Council of Agricultural Research at Karachi during the year 1936. Simla [*337*].

—— 1960. *The Desert Locust in India.* New Delhi [*58, 337, 371*].

Rao, Y. R. & Gupta, R. L. 1939. Some notes on eye-stripes in Acrididae. *Indian J. agric. Sci.* **9**: 727–9 [*198*].

Razet, P. 1961. Recherches sur l'uricolyse chez les insectes. *Bull. Soc. sci. Bretagne*, **36**: 3–206, 32 figs. [*121*].

Rees, H. & Jamieson, A. 1954. A supernumerary chromosome in *Locusta. Nature, Lond.* **173**: 43–44, 1 fig. [*390*].

Rees, K. R. 1954. Aerobic metabolism of the muscle of *Locusta migratoria. Biochem. J.* **58**: 196–202 [*68*].

Rehn, J. A. G. 1952. On attempts to correlate the presence of Brunner's organ in grasshoppers with habits or habitats (Orthoptera: Acridoidea). *Ent. News*, **63**: 3–10 [*167*].

Rehn, J. A. G. & Grant, H. J. jr. 1961. A monograph of the Orthoptera of North America (north of Mexico). Volume I: Acridoidea in part, covering the Tetrigidae, Eumastacidae, Tanaoceridae, and Romaleinae of the Acrididae. *Monogr. Acad. nat. Sci. Philad.* no. 12: 257 pp., 36 maps, 8 pls., 403 figs. [*184*].

Rehn, J. A. G. & Rehn, J. W. H. 1938. The post-oak locust (*Dendrotettix quercus*) in the eastern United States, with notes on macropterism in the species (Orthoptera: Acrididae). *Trans. Amer. ent. Soc.* **64**: 79–95, 2 pls. [*30*].

Remaudière, G. 1947. Sur l'existence en France d'une nouvelle sous-espèce de *Locusta migratoria* L. *C. R. Acad. Sci., Paris*, **225**: 1025–6 [*373*].

—— 1948. Contribution à l'étude des *Locusta migratoria* L. phase *solitaria* de la région de Palavas (Hérault). (1re partie.) *Rev. Path. vég.* **27**: 147–63, 5 figs. [*373*].

—— 1954. Étude écologique de *Locusta migratoria migratorioides* Rch. et Frm. (Orth. Acrididae) dans la zone d'inondation du Niger en 1950. *Locusta*, no. 2: 248 pp., 24 pls., 64 figs. [*272, 276, 279*].

Reng, G. 1961. Untersuchungen über Verdauungsfermente bei Insekten. *Zool. Jb.* (Zool.), **69**: 285–316, 22 figs. [*76*].

Richards, A. G. 1951. *The Integument of Arthropods. The chemical components and their properties, the anatomy and development, and the permeability.* Minneapolis & London [*32, 35, 38, 42, 91, 104, 105, 106*].

—— 1963. The ventral diaphragm of insects. *J. Morph.* **113**: 17–47, 6 pls., 14 figs. [*105, 106*].

Richards, A. G. & Korda, F. H. 1950. Studies on arthropod cuticle. IV. An electron microscope survey of the intima of arthropod tracheae. *Ann. ent. Soc. Amer.* **43**: 49–71, 3 pls., 1 fig. [*124, 126*].

BIBLIOGRAPHY

RICHARDS, O. W. & WALOFF, N. 1954. Studies on the biology and population dynamics of British grasshoppers. *Anti-Locust Bull*. no. 17: 182 pp., 4 pls., 59 figs. [*39, 41, 146, 263, 276, 283, 287, 299, 300, 301, 303, 320, 326, 327*].

RIEDEL, F. A. 1941. Visceral anatomy of two American lubber grasshoppers, with special reference to digestive and respiratory systems. *Univ. Colo. Stud*. A, **26**: 128–9 [*118*].

—— 1946. Connective tissue pattern in the ventriculus of certain lubber grasshoppers. *Ann. ent. Soc. Amer*. **39**: 296–303, 2 pls. [*69*].

RIEGERT, P. W. 1960. The humidity reactions of *Melanoplus bivittatus* (Say) (Orthoptera, Acrididae): antennal sensilla and hygro-reception. *Canad. Ent*. **92**: 561–70, 13 figs. [*161, 162, 164, 171, 173, 174*].

—— 1961. Embryological development of a nondiapause form of *Melanoplus bilituratus* Walker (Orthoptera: Acrididae). *Canad. J. Zool*. **39**: 491–4, 17 figs. [*245, 255, 261*].

RIPLEY, S. H. & EWER, D. W. 1953. Neuro-muscular facilitation in the locust. *S. Afr. J. Sci*. **49**: 320–2, 2 figs. [*65*].

ROBERTS, H. R. 1941. A comparative study of the subfamilies of the Acrididae (Orthoptera) primarily on the basis of their phallic structures. *Proc. Acad. nat. Sci. Philad*. **93**: 201–46, 90 figs. [*143, 388*].

ROBERTSON, I. A. D. 1954. The numbers of eggs in pods of the Red Locust, *Nomadacris septemfasciata* (Serville) (Orth., Acrididae). *Ent. mon. Mag*. **90**: 254–5 [*356*].

ROBERTSON, I. A. D. & CHAPMAN, R. F. 1962. Notes on the biology of some grasshoppers (Orthoptera, Acrididae) from the Rukwa Valley, S.W. Tanganyika (Orth. Acrididae). *Eos, Madr*. **38**: 51–114, 2 figs. [*144, 326*].

ROBERTSON, W. R. B. 1916. Chromosome studies. I. Taxonomic relationships shown in the chromosomes of Tetrigidae and Acrididae: V-shaped chromosomes and their significance in Acrididae, Locustidae, and Gryllidae; chromosomes and variation. *J. Morph*. **27**: 179–279, 26 pls. [*389*].

ROBINSON, D. 1956. The fluorimetric determination of β-glucosidase: its occurrence in the tissues of animals including insects. *Biochem. J*. **63**: 39–44, 1 fig. [*76*].

ROBINSON, D., SMITH, J. N. & WILLIAMS, R. T. 1953. Studies in detoxication. 45. β-glucuronidase and arylsulphatase in the crop fluid of locusts. *Biochem. J*. **53**: 125–9, 1 fig. [*76*].

ROEDER, K. D. 1939. Synchronized activity in the optic and protocerebral ganglia of the grasshopper, *Melanoplus femur-rubrum*. *J. cell. comp. Physiol*. **14**: 299–307, 3 figs. [*199*].

—— 1940. The origin of visual rhythms in the grasshopper, *Melanoplus femur-rubrum*. *J. cell. comp. Physiol*. **16**: 399–401 [*199*].

—— 1953. *Insect Physiology*. New York & London [*74, 206*].

ROEHRICH, R. & MOUTOUS, G. 1955. La structure de la pars stridens alaire du criquet migrateur des Landes de Gascogne (*Locusta migratoria gallica* Rem.): influence de la phase et comparaison avec *L.m. migratoria* L. de l'Herault. *Colloque sur l'Acoustique des Orthoptères*, Paris 1954: 91–6, 5 figs. [*343*].

RÖHLER, E. 1906. Beiträge zur Kenntnis der Sinnesorgane der Insecten. *Zool. Jb*. (Anat.), **22**: 225–288, 2 pls., 1 fig. [*164, 173, 174*].

ROONWAL, M. L. 1936a. The growth-changes and structure of the egg of the African Migratory Locust, *Locusta migratoria migratorioides* R. & F. (Orthoptera, Acrididae). *Bull. ent. Res*. **27**: 1–14, 5 figs. [*237, 246*].

—— 1936b. Studies on the embryology of the African Migratory Locust, *Locusta migratoria migratorioides* R. and F. I. The early development, with a new theory of multi-phased gastrulation among insects. *Phil. Trans*. B, **226**: 391–421, 3 pls., 16 figs. [*245, 246, 247*].

—— 1937. Studies on the embryology of the African Migratory Locust, *Locusta migratoria migratorioides* Reiche and Frm. (Orthoptera, Acrididae). II. Organogeny. *Phil. Trans*. B, **227**: 175–244, 7 pls., 15 figs. [*245, 246, 270, 271*].

—— 1946. Studies in intraspecific variation. II. New rules governing the correlation between normal- and extra-moulting and directional reversal of the elytron-wing complex in the Desert Locust and other Acrididae (Orthoptera). *Indian J. Ent*. **7** (1945): 77–84 [*286*].

—— 1947a. Variation and structure of the eyes in the Desert Locust, *Schistocerca gregaria* (Forskål). *Proc. roy. Soc*. B, **134**: 245–72, 3 pls., 4 figs. [*196, 197, 200, 278, 352*].

—— 1947b. On variation in the number of hind-tibial spines in the Desert Locust, *Schistocerca gregaria* (Forskål) (Orthoptera, Acrididae). *Indian J. Ent*. **8** (1946): 71–7, 1 fig. [*343*].

—— 1947c. On variation in the number of ovarioles and its probable origin in the Desert Locust, *Schistocerca gregaria* (Forskål) (Orthoptera, Acrididae). *Rec. Indian Mus*. **44** (1946): 375–84, 1 fig. [*144, 146*].

—— 1949. On reddish pigments in eggs, ovarioles, embryonic eyes, etc., in the Desert Locust, *Schistocerca gregaria* (Forskål) (Orthoptera, Acrididae). *Indian J. Ent*. **8** (1946): 186–194, 2 figs. [*305*]

—— 1952a. Further observations on directional changes in locusts and other short-horned grasshoppers (Insecta: Orthoptera: Acrididae), and the importance of the third instar. *Proc. nat. Inst. Sci. India*, **18**: 207–15, 1 fig. [*280*].

—— 1952b. Variation and post-embryonic growth in the number of antennal segments in the *phadka* grasshopper (*Hieroglyphus nigrorepletus* Bolivar), with remarks on the Desert Locust and other Acrididae (Insecta: Orthoptera). *Proc. nat. Inst. Sci. India*, **18**: 217–32, 2 figs. [*276, 278, 286, 287*].

454

ROONWAL, M. L. 1954a. The egg-wall of the African Migratory Locust, *Locusta migratoria migratorioides* Reiche and Frm. (Orthoptera, Acrididae). *Proc. nat. Inst. Sci. India*, **20**: 361–70, 2 pls., 2 figs. [*237, 242, 243*].
—— 1954b. Size, sculpturing, weight and moisture content of the developing eggs of the Desert Locust, *Schistocerca gregaria* (Forskål) (Orthoptera, Acrididae). *Proc. nat. Inst. Sci. India*, **20**: 388–98, 2 pls., 3 figs. [*237, 242, 247*].
ROONWAL, M. L. & BHANOTAR, R. K. 1959. Femoral spines as a phase character in the Desert Locust. *Curr. Sci.* **28**: 33–4 [*343*].
ROSCOW, J. M. 1961. *The structure, development and variation of the stridulatory apparatus of the species* Stenobothrus lineatus (*Panzer*), *Acrididae*. Undergraduate thesis, Imperial College, London [*166, 167, 178, 297*].
—— 1963. The structure, development and variation of the stridulatory file of *Stenobothrus lineatus* (Panzer) (Orthoptera: Acrididae). *Proc. R. ent. Soc. Lond.* A, **38**: 194–9, 5 figs. [*178, 296, 297*].
ROSEDALE, J. L. 1945. Some aspects of insect metabolism. *J. S. Afr. chem. Inst.* **28**: 3–9 [*90, 92, 101*].
ROTHMAN, M. N. 1929. Contributions to the study of the chitin of the Migratory Locust in its different stages and phases. (In Russian.) *Bull. Inst. Zool. appl., Leningr.* **5**: 10 pp. [*92*].
ROUBAUD, E. 1953. Diapauses secondaires et diapauses substitutives dans l'évolution de certains insectes. *C. R. Acad. Sci., Paris*, **236**: 2457–9 [*286*].
ROUSCHAL, W. 1940. Osmotische Werte wirbelloser Landtiere und ihre ökologische Bedeutung. *Z. wiss. Zool.* **153**: 196–218, 2 figs. [*113*].
ROWELL, C. H. F. 1961. The structure and function of the prothoracic spine of the Desert Locust, *Schistocerca gregaria* Forskål. *J. exp. Biol.* **38**: 457–69, 1 pl., 8 figs. [*164*].
RUBTZOV, I. A. 1932. *Key to larvae of Acrididae of Eastern Siberia.* (In Russian.) Moscow [*283*].
—— 1934. Fertility and climatic adaptations in Siberian grasshoppers. *Bull. ent. Res.* **25**: 339–48 [*144, 145, 326*].
—— 1935a. Phase variation in non-swarming grasshoppers. *Bull. ent. Res.* **26**: 499–524, 2 pls., 2 figs. [*39, 370*].
—— 1935b. Regularities in the development and behaviour of Siberian Acrididae in connection with climatic factors. (In Russian with German summary.) *Bull. Acad. Sci. U.R.S.S.* **1935**: 789–824, 3 figs. [*222, 223, 264, 265, 371*].
RUCK, P. 1954. Electrical responses of insect dorsal ocelli. *J. cell. comp. Physiol.* **44**: 527–33, 1 pl. [*206*].
—— 1957. The electrical responses of dorsal ocelli in cockroaches and grasshoppers. *J. Insect Physiol.* **1**: 109–23, 2 pls., 2 figs. [*206*].
RUDALL, K. M. 1963. The chitin/protein complexes of insect cuticles. *Advanc. Insect Physiol.* **1**: 257–313, 24 figs. [*32*].
RUNGS, C. 1933. Observations préliminaires sur la résistance au froid de *Schistocerca gregaria* Forsk. *Rev. Path. vég.* **20**: 314–22 [*223*].
SACHAROV, N. L. 1930. Studies in cold resistance of insects. *Ecology*, **11**: 505–17 [*223, 265*].
SACKTOR, B. 1961. The role of mitochondria in respiratory metabolism of flight muscle. *Annu. Rev. Ent.* **6**: 103–30, 2 figs. [*68*].
SÁEZ, F. A. 1956a. Estudios citogenéticos en ortópteros sudamericanos. *Biológica, Santiago*, fasc. 22: 21–6 [*389*].
—— 1956b. Caso extraordinario de un ortóptero acridido con ocho cromosomas diploides y mecanismo sexual XY. *Biológica, Santiago*, fasc. 22: 27–30, 4 figs. [*390*].
—— 1957. An extreme karyotype in an orthopteran insect. *Amer. Nat.* **91**: 259–64, 18 figs. [*390*].
SALFI, M. 1935. Ipognatismo ed oxycefalia negli Ortotteri. *Boll. Zool.* **6**: 311–15, 3 figs. [*4*].
SALT, R. W. 1949a. A key to the embryological development of *Melanoplus bivittatus* (Say), *M. mexicanus mexicanus* (Sauss.), and *M. packardii* Scudder. *Canad. J. Res.* D, **27**: 233–5 [*245, 261*].
—— 1949b. Water uptake in eggs of *Melanoplus bivittatus* (Say). *Canad. J. Res.* D, **27**: 236–42, 2 figs. [*256, 258, 261*].
—— 1950. Time as a factor in the freezing of undercooled insects. *Canad. J. Res.* D, **28**: 285–91, 2 figs. [*224, 266*].
—— 1952. Some aspects of moisture absorption and loss in eggs of *Melanoplus bivittatus* (Say). *Canad. J. Zool.* **30**: 55–82, 1 fig. [*237, 256, 258, 268*].
—— 1958. Cold-hardiness of insects. *10th Int. Congr. Ent.*, Montreal 1956, vol. 2: 73–7 [*224*].
—— 1962. Intracellular freezing in insects. *Nature, Lond.* **193**: 1207–8 [*224, 267*].
SALZEN, E. A. 1960. The growth of the locust embryo. *J. Embryol. exp. Morph.* **8**: 139–62, 11 figs. [*247, 249*].
SANDERSON, M. W. 1939. Crop replacement in relation to grasshopper abundance. *J. econ. Ent.* **32**: 484–6 [*321, 329*].
SATIJA, R. C. 1957. Studies on the course and functions of the giant nerve fibres from the eye and the tegumentary nerve to the ventral nerve cord in *Locusta migratoria. Res. Bull. Panjab Univ.* (Zool.), **71**: 511–19, 2 pls. [*152, 153, 198*].
—— 1958. A histological and experimental study of nervous pathways in the brain and thoracic nerve cord of *Locusta migratoria migratorioides* (R. & F.). *Res. Bull. Panjab Univ.* (Zool.), **72**: 13–32, 8 pls., 2 figs. [*152, 153, 198*].

BIBLIOGRAPHY

SAVAGE, A. A. 1956. The development of the Malpighian tubules of *Schistocerca gregaria* (Orthoptera). *Quart. J. micr. Sci.* **97**: 599–615, 5 figs. [*118, 119, 246, 282*].

SCHARRER, E. & SCHARRER, B. 1963. *Neuroendocrinology.* New York. [*156*].

SCHLOTTKE, E. 1937. Untersuchungen über die Verdauungsfermente von Insekten. II. Die Fermente der Laub- und Feldheuschrecken und ihre Abhängigkeit von der Lebensweise. *Z. vergl. Physiol.* **24**: 422–50, 4 figs. [*74, 76*].

SCHMITT, J. B. 1955. The nervous system of the pregenital abdominal segments of some Orthoptera. *Ann. ent. Soc. Amer.* **47** (1954): 677–82, 3 pls. [*155*].

—— 1959. The cervicothoracic nervous system of a grasshopper. *Smithson. misc. Coll.* **137**: 307–29, 5 figs. [*152, 153, 155*].

—— 1962. The comparative anatomy of the insect nervous system. *Annu. Rev. Ent.* **7**: 137–56, 1 fig. [*155*].

SCHNEIDERMAN, H. A. 1957. Onset and termination of insect diapause. In Bullock, T. H. [Ed.], *Physiological Triggers and Discontinuous Rate Processes*, pp. 46–59, 1 fig. Washington [*264*].

SCHROEDER, J. 1909. Versuche zur Bekämpfung der Wanderheuschrecke mit chemischen Produkten. *Z. Pflkrankh.* **19**: 1–13, 4 figs. [*94*].

SCHWABE, J. 1906. Beiträge zur Morphologie und Histologie der tympanalen Sinnesapparate der Orthopteren. *Zoologica, Stuttgart*, no. 50: 154 pp., 5 pls., 7 figs. [*188*].

SELLIER, R. 1955. Recherches sur la morphogenèse et le polymorphisme alaires chez les Orthoptères Gryllides. *Ann. Sci. nat.* (Zool.), (11) **16** (1954): 595–739, 2 pls., 66 figs. [*31*].

SEMENOV-TIAN-SHANSKY, A. D. 1910. *Die taxonomischen Grenzen der Art und ihrer Unterabteilungen.* Berlin [*395*].

SEMICHON, L. 1924. L'articulation fémoro-tibiale des criquets (Orth.). *Bull. Soc. ent. Fr.* **1924**: 162–164, 1 fig. [*25*].

SEVERIN, H. C. 1943. A study of a gynandromorph of *Melanoplus mexicanus mexicanus* (Sauss.) (Orthoptera). *J. N. Y. ent. Soc.* **51**: 179–82, 1 pl. [*149*].

—— 1955. A gynandromorph of *Melanoplus mexicanus mexicanus* (Saussure) extreme migratory phase (Orthoptera: Acrididae). *Psyche, Camb., Mass.* **62**: 104–7, 1 pl. [*149*].

SHAFIQ, S. A. 1954. Cytological studies of the neurones of *Locusta migratoria*. Part II. Cytoplasmic inclusions during the differentiation and growth of the nerve cells. *Quart. J. micr. Sci.* **95**: 305–14, 1 pl., 1 fig. [*246*].

—— 1955. The lipochondria in the developing nerve-cells of the locust. *J. R. micr. Soc.* **74** (1954): 207–8 [*246*].

SHAPINSKII, D. V. 1923. Biological observations on the Acrididae of the Chelyabinsk district, Orenburg, in 1916. (In Russian.) *Bull. Soc. ent. Moscou*, **2** (2): xxvi–ix [*272*].

SHARAN, R. K. 1958. The embryonic cuticle of *Locustana pardalina* (Walker). *Ann. Zool.* **3**: 1–8, 2 figs. [*238, 270*].

SHARMAN, G. B. 1952. The cytology of Tasmanian short-horned grasshoppers (Orthoptera: Acridoidea). *Pap. roy. Soc. Tasm.* **86**: 107–22, 1 pl., 57 figs. [*389, 390*].

SHAW, E. I. 1955. Amino compounds and ethanolamine phosphoric acid of the grasshopper egg. *Exp. Cell Res.* **9**: 489–501, 2 figs. [*250*].

SHAW, J. & STOBBART, R. H. 1963. Osmotic and ionic regulation in insects. *Advanc. Insect Physiol.* **1**: 315–99, 16 figs. [*74, 110*].

SHINOZAKI, J. 1957. The specific heat of insects. *J. Fac. Sci. Hokkaido Univ.* (Zool.), **13**: 470–4, 1 fig. [*210*].

SHOTWELL, R. L. 1930. A study of the lesser migratory grasshopper. *Tech. Bull. U.S. Dep. Agric.* no. 190: 34 pp., 13 figs. [*283*].

—— 1941. Life histories and habits of some grasshoppers of economic importance on the Great Plains. *Tech. Bull. U.S. Dep. Agric.* no. 774: 47 pp., 10 pls., 12 figs. [*282, 287, 288*].

SHPET, G. 1930. Entwicklung der sekundären Geschlechtsmerkmale in der Ontogenese des *Chorthippus parallelus* Zett. (Orthoptera). *Roux Arch. EntwMech. Organ.* **122**: 593–628, 9 figs. [*282, 287*].

—— 1931. Entwicklung der Artunterschiede in der postembryonalen Ontogenese zweier Arten der Gattung *Chorthippus* (Orthoptera). *Roux Arch. EntwMech. Organ.* **124**: 241–72, 8 figs. [*287*].

—— 1934. On the problem of insect growth. (In Russian with English summary.) *Zool. Zh.* **13**: 195–206 [*274, 276, 277*].

—— 1935. Zur Phänogenetik der systematischen Unterschiede bei Geradflüglern. (In Russian with German summary.) *Zool. Zh.* **14**: 674–700 [*287*].

SHULOV, A. 1952a. Studies on Krauss' organ of *Tmethis pulchripennis asiaticus* Uvarov (Acrididae, Orthoptera). *Bull. Res. Coun. Israel*, **2**: 58–63, 15 figs. [*21, 22*].

—— 1952b. The development of eggs of *Schistocerca gregaria* (Forskål) in relation to water. *Bull. ent. Res.* **43**: 469–76 [*247, 256, 268*].

—— 1952c. Studies on Krauss' organ of *Tmethis pulchripennis asiaticus* Uvarov (Acrididae, Orthoptera). *9th Int. Congr. Ent.*, Amsterdam 1951, vol. 1: 255–8 [*21, 22*].

—— 1952d. Observations on the behaviour and the egg development of *Tmethis pulchripennis asiaticus* Uv. *Bull. Res. Coun. Israel*, **2**: 249–54, 1 fig. [*246, 247, 255, 258, 286*].

—— 1956. The role of water in the eggs of Acrididae. *14th Int. Congr. Zool.*, Copenhagen 1953, section 12: 395–401 [*247, 255, 256*].

456

BIBLIOGRAPHY

SHULOV, A. & PENER, M. P. 1959. A contribution to knowledge of the development of the egg of *Locusta migratoria migratorioides* (R. & F.). *Locusta*, no. 6: 73–88, 6 figs. [*245, 247*].

—— 1961. Environmental factors in interruption of development of Acrididae eggs. In Grossowicz, N. *et al.* [Eds.], *Cryptobiotic Stages in Biological Systems.* (*Proc. Symp. 5th Biol. Conf., Oholo, Israel, 1960*), pp. 144–53, 2 figs. Amsterdam & London [*245, 255, 256, 258, 261, 268*].

—— 1963. Studies on the development of eggs of the Desert Locust (*Schistocerca gregaria* Forskål) and its interruption under particular conditions of humidity. *Anti-Locust Bull.* no. 41: 59 pp., 11 figs. [*245, 246, 256, 258, 268, 273*].

SHULOV, A., PENER, M. P., KUK-MEIRI, S. & LICHTENSTEIN, N. 1957. Proteolytic enzymes in various embryonic stages of the eggs of *Locusta migratoria migratorioides* (R. and F.). *J. Insect Physiol.* **1**: 279–85 [*251*].

SHUMAKOV, E. M. & YAKHIMOVICH, L. A. 1950. Peculiarities of the embryonic development of the Asiatic Locust (*Locusta migratoria* L.) in certain conditions of the external environment. (In Russian.) *Zool. Zh.* **29**: 327–40, 5 figs. [*243, 245, 246, 247, 260, 262, 268*].

SHUTTS, J. H. 1949. An electron miscroscope study of the egg membranes of *Melanoplus differentialis* (Thomas). *Biol. Bull., Woods Hole*, **97**: 100–7, 14 figs. [*237*].

—— 1952. Some characteristics of the hatching enzyme in the eggs of *Melanoplus differentialis* (Thomas). *Proc. S. Dak. Acad. Sci.* **31**: 158–63 [*270*].

SIHLER, H. 1924. Die Sinnesorgane an den Cerci der Insekten. *Zool. Jb.* (Anat.), **45**: 519–80, 4 pls. [*20, 163, 165*].

SILVEIRA GUIDO, A., CARBONELL BRUHN, J. F., NÚNEZ, O. & VALDÉS, E. 1958. *Investigaciones sobre Acridoideos del Uruguay.* (*Sistemática, Morfología, Citología, Economía, Habitat, Ciclo biológico, Costumbres, Ecología, Geografía, Enemigos naturales y Control.*) *Primera contribucion.* Montevideo [*371, 389*].

SINGH, T. 1958. Ovulation and corpus luteum formation in *Locusta migratoria migratorioides* Reiche and Fairmaire and *Schistocerca gregaria* (Forskål). *Trans. R. ent. Soc. Lond.* **110**: 1–20, 22 figs. [*305, 355*].

SJÖSTEDT, Y. 1929. Acridoidea aus Zentralafrika gesammelt von R. Grauer während seiner Expedition 1909–1911. *Ark. Zool.* A, **20** (15): 41 pp., 2 pls., 3 figs. [*371*].

SKRYABINA, E. 1936. pH of the insect's intestines and blood and its modification at poisoning with arsenic and fluorine compounds. (In Russian with English summary.) *Bull. Pl. Prot., Leningr.* (3) no. 7: 9–24, 5 figs. [*79, 108*].

SLIFER, E. H. 1930. Insect development. I. Fatty acids in the grasshopper egg. *Physiol. Zoöl.* **3**: 503–18, 4 figs. [*249*].

——1931. Insect development. II. Mitotic activity in the grasshopper embryo. *J. Morph.* **51**: 613–18, 2 figs. [*245*].

—— 1932a. Insect development. III. Blastokinesis in the living grasshopper egg. *Biol. Zbl.* **52**: 223–229 [*245*].

—— 1932b. Insect development. IV. External morphology of grasshopper embryos of known age and with a known temperature history. *J. Morph.* **53**: 1–22, 4 pls., 1 fig. [*244, 245, 255*].

—— 1932c. Insect development. V. Qualitative studies on the fatty acids from grasshopper eggs. *Physiol. Zoöl.* **5**: 448–56 [*267*].

—— 1935. Morphology and development of the femoral chordotonal organs of *Melanoplus differentialis* (Orthoptera, Acrididae). *J. Morph.* **58**: 615–37, 5 pls., 5 figs. [*170, 246*].

—— 1936. The scoloparia of *Melanoplus differentialis* (Orthoptera, Acrididae). *Ent. News*, **47**: 174–80 [*169, 170*].

—— 1937. The origin and fate of the membranes surrounding the grasshopper egg; together with some experiments on the source of the hatching enzyme. *Quart. J. micr. Sci.* **79**: 493–506, 3 pls., 1 fig. [*237, 238, 269, 270*].

—— 1938a. The formation and structure of a special water absorbing area in the membranes covering the grasshopper egg. *Quart. J. micr. Sci.* **80**: 437–58, 1 pl., 5 figs. [*237, 241, 242*].

—— 1938b. A cytological study of the pleuropodia of *Melanoplus differentialis* (Orthoptera, Acrididae) which furnishes new evidence that they produce the hatching enzyme. *J. Morph.* **63**: 181–206, 4 pls., 1 fig. [*269*].

—— 1939. The internal genitalia of female Acridinae, Oedipodinae and Pauliniinae (Orthoptera, Acrididae). *J. Morph.* **65**: 437–70, 7 pls., 1 fig. [*147*].

—— 1940a. The internal genitalia of female Thrinchinae, Batrachotetriginae, Pamphaginae and Pyrgomorphinae (Orthoptera, Acrididae). *J. Morph.* **66**: 175–96, 5 pls., 2 figs. [*147*].

—— 1940b. The internal genitalia of female Ommexechinae and Cyrtacanthacridinae (Orthoptera, Acrididae). *J. Morph.* **67**: 199–239, 12 pls., 1 fig. [*147, 148*].

—— 1940c. Variations in the spermatheca of two species of grasshoppers (Orthoptera, Acrididae). *Ent. News*, **51**: 1–3, 2 pls. [*147*].

—— 1943. The internal genitalia of some previously unstudied species of female Acrididae (Orthoptera). *J. Morph.* **72**: 225–37, 3 pls. [*147*].

—— 1946. The effects of xylol and other solvents on diapause in the grasshopper egg; together with a possible explanation for the action of these agents. *J. exp. Zool.* **102**: 333–56, 3 figs. [*258, 262*].

—— 1948. Interaction of water and porous materials. Isolation of a wax-like material from the shell of the grasshopper egg. *Disc. Faraday Soc.* no. 3: 182–7 [*239*].

457

BIBLIOGRAPHY

SLIFER, E. H. 1949a. Changes in certain of the grasshopper egg coverings during development as indicated by fast green and other dyes. *J. exp. Zool.* **110**: 183–203, 4 pls., 1 fig. [*237, 242, 257*].

—— 1949b. Variations, during development, in the resistance of the grasshopper egg to a toxic substance. *Ann. ent. Soc. Amer.* **42**: 134–40, 2 figs. [*237, 257*].

—— 1950a. Vulnerable areas on the surface of the tarsus and pretarsus of the grasshopper (Acrididae, Orthoptera); with special reference to the arolium. *Ann. ent. Soc. Amer.* **43**: 173–88, 17 figs. [*25, 164, 174*].

—— 1950b. A microscopical study of the hydropyle and hydropyle cells in the developing egg of the grasshopper, *Melanoplus differentialis. J. Morph.* **87**: 239–73, 10 pls. [*242*].

—— 1951. Some unusual structures in *Locusta migratoria migratorioides* and their probable function as thermoreceptors. *Proc. roy. Soc.* B, **138**: 414–37, 21 figs. [*9, 33, 34, 220*].

—— 1952. Connective tissue in the locust. (Abs.) *Anat. Rec.* **113**: 572 [*32*].

—— 1953a. The pattern of specialized heat-sensitive areas on the surface of the body of Acrididae (Orthoptera). Part I. The males. *Trans. Amer. ent. Soc.* **79**: 37–68, 17 pls., 5 figs. [*2, 3, 33*].

—— 1953b. The pattern of specialized heat-sensitive areas on the surface of the body of Acrididae (Orthoptera). Part II. The females. *Trans. Amer. ent. Soc.* **79**: 69–97, 18 pls., 6 figs. [*2, 3, 33*].

—— 1954a. The permeability of the sensory pegs on the antennae of the grasshopper (Orthoptera, Acrididae). *Biol. Bull., Woods Hole*, **106**: 122–8, 7 figs. [*161, 171*].

—— 1954b. The variation in size and pattern of the heat-sensitive areas in *Melanoplus keeleri luridus* (Dodge) males (Orthoptera, Acrididae). *Ann. ent. Soc. Amer.* **47**: 255–64, 9 figs. [*33*].

—— 1954c. A method for calculating the surface area of the body of grasshoppers and locusts (Orthoptera, Acrididae). *Ann. ent. Soc. Amer.* **47**: 265–71, 2 figs. [*2*].

—— 1954d. The reaction of a grasshopper to an odorous material held near one of its feet (Orthoptera: Acrididae). *Proc. R. ent. Soc. Lond.* A, **29**: 177–9 [*175*].

—— 1955. The detection of odours and water vapor by grasshoppers (Orthoptera, Acrididae) and some new evidence concerning the sense organs which may be involved. *J. exp. Zool.* **130**: 301–17 [*171, 174*].

—— 1956. The response of a grasshopper, *Romalea microptera* (Beauvois), to strong odours following amputation of the metathoracic leg at different levels. *Proc. R. ent. Soc. Lond.* A, **31**: 95–8 [*175*].

—— 1957. The specialized heat-sensitive areas of the Moroccan Locust, *Dociostaurus maroccanus* (Thunberg), and of several closely-related species. *Ann. ent. Soc. Amer.* **50**: 496–9, 2 figs. [*33*].

—— 1958a. Specialized areas on the body surface of grasshoppers and locusts (Orthoptera, Acrididae). *10th Int. Congr. Ent.*, Montreal 1956, vol. 1: 531–4 [*33*].

—— 1958b. Diapause in the eggs of *Melanoplus differentialis* (Orthoptera, Acrididae). *J. exp. Zool.* **138**: 259–82, 6 figs. [*239, 258, 260*].

—— 1959. Survival of grasshopper eggs kept for long periods in mineral oil. *Nature, Lond.* **184**: 1424–5 [*258*].

—— 1960. An abnormal grasshopper with two median ocelli (Orthoptera, Acrididae). *Ann. ent. Soc. Amer.* **53**: 441–2, 3 figs. [*205*].

—— 1961. The fine structure of insect sense organs. *Int. Rev. Cytol.* **11**: 125–59, 30 figs. [*161*].

SLIFER, E. H. & FINLAYSON, L. H. 1956. Muscle receptor organs in grasshoppers and locusts (Orthoptera, Acrididae). *Quart. J. micr. Sci.* **97**: 617–20, 1 pl., 1 fig. [*170*].

SLIFER, E. H. & KING, R. L. 1933. Grasshopper eggs and the paraffin method. *Science*, **78**: 366 [*237*].

—— 1936. An internal structure in the Cyrtacanthacrinae (Orthoptera, Acrididae) of possible taxonomic value. *J. N.Y. ent. Soc.* **44**: 345–8 [*148*].

—— 1961. The inheritance of diapause in grasshopper eggs. *J. Hered.* **52**: 39–44 [*261*].

SLIFER, E. H., PRESTAGE, J. J. & BEAMS, H. W. 1957. The fine structure of the long basiconic sensory pegs of the grasshopper (Orthoptera, Acrididae) with special reference to those on the antenna. *J. Morph.* **101**: 359–97, 8 pls., 2 figs. [*171, 172*].

—— 1959. The chemoreceptors and other sense organs on the antennal flagellum of the grasshopper (Orthoptera; Acrididae). *J. Morph.* **105**: 145–91, 41 figs. [*171, 172*].

SLIFER, E. H. & SEKHON, S. S. 1963. The fine structure of the membranes which cover the egg of the grasshopper *Melanoplus differentialis*, with special reference to the hydropyle. *Quart. J. micr. Sci.* **104**: 321–34, 10 figs. [*237, 241, 258*].

SLIFER, E. H. & UVAROV, B. P. 1938. Brunner's organ; a structure found on the jumping legs of grasshoppers (Orthoptera). *Proc. R. ent. Soc. Lond.* A, **13**: 111–15, 1 pl. [*166, 167*].

SMART, J. 1953a. A note on the wing-venation of *Dissosteira carolina* (Linn.) (Insecta: Acridiidae). *Proc. zool. Soc. Lond.* **123**: 203–5, 7 figs. [*27*].

—— 1953b. The wing-venation of the Migratory Locust (*Locusta migratoria* Linn.) (Insecta: Acridiidae). *Proc. zool. Soc. Lond.* **123**: 207–17, 3 pls., 2 figs. [*27*].

SMIT, C. J. B. 1960. The behaviour of the Brown Locust in its solitary phase. (D.Sc. thesis.) *Tech. Commun. Dep. agric. tech. Serv. Pretoria*, no. 1: 132 pp., 32 figs. [*207, 214*].

SMIT, C. J. B. & REYNEKE, A. L. 1940. Do nymphs of Acrididae stridulate? *J. ent. Soc. S. Afr.* **3**: 72–5 [*184*].

SMITH, D. S. 1958. *The utilization of food plants by the grasshopper* Melanoplus mexicanus mexicanus (*Sauss.*). Ph.D. thesis, Minnesota [*81*].

BIBLIOGRAPHY

SMITH, D. S. 1959. Utilization of food plants by the migratory grasshopper, *Melanoplus bilituratus* (Walker) (Orthoptera: Acrididae), with some observations on the nutritional value of the plants. *Ann. ent. Soc. Amer.* **52**: 674–80, 3 figs. [*80, 81, 83, 84*].

—— 1960a. Effects of changing the phosphorus content of the food plant on the migratory grasshopper, *Melanoplus bilituratus* (Walker) (Orthoptera: Acrididae). *Canad. Ent.* **92**: 103–7 [*331*].

—— 1960b. Survival of unfed first-instar grasshoppers. *Canad. Ent.* **92**: 755–6, 1 fig. [*88*].

SMITH, D. S., HANDFORD, R. H. & CHEFURKA, W. 1952. Some effects of various food plants on *Melanoplus mexicanus mexicanus* (Sauss.) (Orthoptera: Acrididae). *Canad. Ent.* **84**: 113–17 [*82*].

SMITH, D. S. & NORTHCOTT, F. E. 1951. The effects on the grasshopper, *Melanoplus mexicanus mexicanus* (Sauss.) (Orthoptera: Acrididae), of varying the nitrogen content in its food plant. *Canad. J. Zool.* **29**: 297–304, 1 fig. [*86, 330*].

SMITH, R. W. 1952. Another method of rearing grasshoppers (Orthoptera) in the laboratory. *Canad. Ent.* **84**: 269–71, 2 figs. [*87*].

SNODGRASS, R. E. 1928. Morphology and evolution of the insect head and its appendages. *Smithson. misc. Coll.* **81** (3): 158 pp., 57 figs. [*60*].

—— 1929. The thoracic mechanism of a grasshopper, and its antecedents. *Smithson. misc. Coll.* **82** (2): 111 pp., 54 figs. [*23, 27, 59, 60*].

—— 1935a. The abdominal mechanisms of a grasshopper. *Smithson. misc. Coll.* **94** (6): 89 pp., 41 figs. [*20, 59, 60, 64, 122*].

—— 1935b. *Principles of Insect Morphology.* New York & London [*60, 167*].

—— 1937. The male genitalia of orthopteroid insects. *Smithson. misc. Coll.* **96** (5): 107 pp., 42 figs. [*60, 246*].

SOKOLOW, A. Y. 1926a. Zur Frage der Spermatophorbefruchtung bei der Wanderheuschrecke (*Locusta migratoria* L.). Das Weibchen. *Z. wiss. Zool.* **127**: 608–18, 4 figs. [*316*].

—— 1926b. The structure of the external female genital apparatus in the Asiatic Locust. The fate of the spermatophores. (In Russian.) *Uchen. Zap. kazan. Univ.* **86**: 57–64, 11 figs. [*316*].

SOUZA SANTOS, H. L., EDWARDS, G. A., SOUZA SANTOS, P. & SAWAYA, P. 1954. Electron microscopy of insect tracheal structures. *Ann. Acad. bras. Sci.* **26**: 309–15, 9 pls. [*124*].

SRIVASTAVA, P. D. 1957. Observations on the breeding habits of *Atractomorpha crenulata* (F.), the tobacco grasshopper (Orthoptera, Acrididae). *Ann. ent. Soc. Amer.* **50**: 15–20 [*255*].

SRIVASTAVA, U. S. & SRIVASTAVA, P. D. 1956. On the hydrogen-ion concentration in the alimentary canal of certain orthopteroid insects. *Beitr. Ent.* **6**: 493–8 [*79, 108*].

STAAL, G. B. 1961. Studies on the physiology of phase induction in *Locusta migratoria migratorioides* R. & F. (Doctoral thesis.) *Publ. Fds Landb. Expt. Bur. 1916–1918*, no. 40: 125 pp., 1 pl., 12 figs. [*156, 159, 289, 338, 348, 351, 367, 376, 377, 378*].

STAAL, G. B. & WILDE, J. DE 1962. Endocrine influences on the development of phase characters in *Locusta. Colloq. int. Cent. nat. Rech. sci.* no. 114: 89–105, 1 fig. [*377*].

STÄGER, R. 1930. Beiträge zur Biologie einiger einheimischer Heuschreckenarten. *Z. wiss. Insekt-Biol.* **25**: 36–41, 53–70 [*183*].

STAMM, M. D. 1959. Estudios sobre hormonas de invertebrados. II. Aislamiento de hormonas de la metamorfosis en el ortóptero *Dociostaurus maroccanus. An. Fis. Quim.* B, **55**: 171–8, 11 figs. [*160, 289*].

STEELE, H. V. 1941. Some observations on the embryonic development of *Austroicetes cruciata* Sauss. (Acrididae) in the field. *Trans. roy. Soc. S. Aust.* **65**: 329–32, 1 pl. [*245*].

STEFANOWSKA, M. 1890. Disposition histologique du pigment dans les yeux des arthropodes, sous l'influence de la lumière directe et de l'obscurité complète. *Rec. zool. suisse*, **5**: 151–200, 2 pls. [*57, 200*].

STEPHEN, W. P. 1961. Phylogenetic significance of blood proteins among some orthopteroid insects. *Syst. Zool.* **10**: 1–9 [*91, 112*].

STOWER, W. J. 1959. The colour patterns of hoppers of the Desert Locust (*Schistocerca gregaria* Forskål). *Anti-Locust Bull.* no. 32: 75 pp., 5 pls., 24 figs. [*41, 44, 50, 359, 366, 385*].

STOWER, W. J., DAVIES, D. E. & JONES, I. B. 1960. Morphometric studies of the Desert Locust, *Schistocerca gregaria* (Forsk.). *J. Anim. Ecol.* **29**: 309–39, 8 figs. [*346, 348, 349, 367*].

STOWER, W. J. & GRIFFITHS, J. F. 1965. The body temperature of the Desert Locust (*Schistocerca gregaria* Forsk.). *Ent. exp. appl.* In press [*207, 213, 215, 221*].

STRELNIKOV, I. D. 1932. The effect of solar radiation and wind on the temperature of the body and the behaviour of the larvae of the locust *Locusta migratoria* L. (In Russian.) *Sborn. Vizra*, **4**: 76–81, 2 figs. [*211*].

—— 1934. Light as factor in animal ecology. I. Influence of solar radiation on the body temperature of some poikilothermic animals. (In Russian with German summary.) *Bull. Inst. sci. Leshaft*, **17–18**: 313–72, 12 figs. [*211*].

—— 1935. Zur Frage über die Wärmeproduktion der Insekten infolge von Bewegungen und Sonnenbestrahlung. (In Russian with German summary.) *Bull. Inst. sci. Leshaft*, **19**: 243–55 [*211, 216, 217*].

—— 1936. Effect of solar radiation and the micro-climate upon the body temperature and the behaviour of the larvae of *Locusta migratoria* L. (In Russian with English summary.) *Trav. Inst. zool. Acad. Sci. U.R.S.S.* **2** (1935): 637–733, 16 figs. [*211, 212, 213, 214, 218, 219*].

BIBLIOGRAPHY

STRENGER, A. 1942. Funktionelle Analyse des Orthopterenkopfes, eine systematisch-funktions-anatomische Studie. *Zool. Jb.* (Syst.), **75**: 1–72, 23 figs. [*60*].

STRICH, M.-C. 1955. Étude de la glande ventrale chez *Locusta migratoria migratorioides* L. (Orth. Acridioidea). *Ann. Sci. nat.* (Zool.), (11) **16** (1954): 399–411, 9 figs. [*159, 160, 289*].

STRICH-HALBWACHS, M. C. 1958. Action de la glande ventrale sur le développement ovarien de *Locusta migratoria* L. (Orthoptera). *J. Insect Physiol.* **1**: 346–51, 1 fig. [*159, 304, 313*].

—— 1959. Contrôle de la mue chez *Locusta migratoria*. *Ann. Sci. nat.* (Zool.), (12) **1**: 483–570, 34 figs. [*159, 160, 289, 295, 313*].

STUART, R. R. 1935a. The anatomy and histology of the Malpighian tubules and the adjacent alimentary canal in *Melanoplus differentialis*. *J. Morph.* **58**: 173–88, 3 pls., 2 figs. [*118, 119*].

—— 1935b. The development of the mid intestine in *Melanoplus differentialis* (Acrididae: Orthoptera). *J. Morph.* **58**: 419–37, 2 pls. [*246*].

SUGA, N. 1960. Peripheral mechanism of hearing in locust. *Jap. J. Physiol.* **10**: 533–46, 8 figs. [*191, 193*].

SUGA, N. & KATSUKI, Y. 1961. Central mechanism of hearing in insects. *J. exp. Biol.* **38**: 545–58, 5 figs. [*193*].

SUGIYAMA, K. 1958. Observations of the endocrine organs in the head of a grasshopper, *Oxya japonica*. (In Japanese with English summary.) *Zool. Mag., Tokyo*, **67**: 80–3, 2 figs. [*158*].

SVIRIDENKO, P. A. 1924. *Biological observations on the Moroccan Locust*. (In Russian.) Petrograd. [*319*].

SWANN, M. F. & MICKEY, G. H. 1947. Parthenogenetic grasshoppers and their bearing upon polyploidy and sex-determination. *Proc. La Acad. Sci.* **10**: 73–92, 10 figs. [*319*].

SWIFT, H. & KLEINFELD, R. 1953. DNA in grasshopper spermatogenesis, oögenesis, and cleavage. *Physiol. Zoöl.* **26**: 301–11, 2 pls., 2 figs. [*306*].

SWINGLE, M. 1931. Notes on digestion in seven species of insects. *Ann. ent. Soc. Amer.* **24**: 177–80 [*76*].

TADDEI, A. 1949. Ricerche sugli elementi dell'emolinfa di *Anacridium aegyptium* L. *Monit. zool. ital.* **57**: 1–11, 1 fig. [*114*].

TAHMISIAN, T. N. 1943. Enzymes in ontogenesis: choline-esterase in developing *Melanoplus differentialis* eggs. *J. exp. Zool.* **92**: 199–213, 5 figs. [*246, 251*].

TAKAHASHI, R. 1925. Postembryonic development of *Pachytylus migratorioides* (Acrididae). (In Japanese.) *Zool. Mag., Tokyo*, **37**: 191–203, 4 figs. [*276*].

TARBINSKIĬ, S. P. 1932. On the question of the phase variability of locusts. (In Russian with English title.) *Bull. Leningr. Inst. Controll. Fm For. Pests*, no. 3: 303–20, 4 figs. [*344*].

TAREEVA, A. I. & NENYUKOV, D. V. 1931. Effect of poisons on normal digestion and the blood of *Calliptamus*. (In Russian with English summary.) *Bull. Pl. Prot., Leningr.* **3** (1): 39–49 [*76, 108, 115, 117*].

TASSONI, J. P. 1957. Studies on the nitrogen and phosphorus content of insect protein. *Physiol. Zoöl.* **30**: 128–32 [*89, 91, 93*].

TAUBER, O. E., DRAKE, C. J. & DECKER, G. C. 1945. Effects of different food plants on egg production and adult survival of the grasshopper, *Melanoplus bivittatus* (Say). *Iowa St. Coll. J. Sci.* **19**: 343–59 [*329*].

TAUBER, O. E. & YEAGER, J. F. 1935. On total hemolymph (blood) cell counts of insects. I. Orthoptera, Odonata, Hemiptera, and Homoptera. *Ann. ent. Soc. Amer.* **28**: 229–40 [*115*].

TAYLOR, I. R. & CRESCITELLI, F. 1944. The electrical changes in response to illumination of the dark- and light-adapted eye of *Dissosteira carolina*. *Physiol. Zoöl.* **17**: 193–9, 6 figs. [*199*].

TCHELEBI-PAPILLON, M. 1962. Interaction du groupement, de l'alimentation et d'un facteur saisonnier sur *Schistocerca gregaria* (Forsk.). *Colloq. int. Cent. nat. Rech. sci.* no. 114: 37–61, 2 figs. [*354, 378*].

TELENGA, N. A. 1930. Biological observations on *Schistocerca gregaria* Forsk. in Khoresm in 1929. (In Russian.) *Izv. Khoresm. sel.-khoz. Opuit. St.* **6**: 27 pp., 1 pl., 6 figs. [*83, 288, 319*].

TEPPERT, W. A. 1958. *Determination of free amino acids in the developing grasshopper egg of* Melanoplus differentialis. Ph.D. thesis, State University of Iowa [*250*].

THOMAS, J. G. 1952. A comparison of the pterothoracic skeleton and flight muscles of male and female *Lamarckiana* species (Orthoptera, Acrididae). *Proc. R. ent. Soc. Lond.* A, **27**: 1–12, 6 figs. [*30, 62*].

—— 1953. A comparison of flight muscles of Acrididae with different wing development. *Proc. R. ent. Soc. Lond.* A, **28**: 47–56, 4 figs. [*30, 31, 62*].

—— 1954a. The post-embryonic development of the flight muscles of *Lamarckiana* sp. (Orthoptera) and a brief comparison of these with those of *Saussurea stuhlmanniana* (Karsch) and *Tanita dispar* (Miller). *Proc. R. ent. Soc. Lond.* A, **29**: 23–30, 5 figs. [*30, 31, 62, 281, 286*].

—— 1954b. The post-embryonic development of the dorsal part of the pterothoracic skeleton and certain muscles of *Locusta migratoria migratorioides* (Reiche & Fairm.). *Proc. zool. Soc. Lond.* **124**: 229–38, 2 figs. [*62, 282*].

—— 1962. The mesosternal bodies of Acridoidea. *Proc. R. ent. Soc. Lond.* A, **37**: 107–13, 6 figs. [*15, 16*].

—— 1963. *Dissection of the Locust*. London [*1*].

——1965. The abdomen of the female Desert Locust (*Schistocerca gregaria* Forskål) with special reference to the sense organs. *Anti-Locust Bull.* no. 42: 20pp., 45 figs. [*20, 148, 161, 163, 165, 170, 171, 324, 326*].

460

BIBLIOGRAPHY

THOMSON, R. H. 1960. Insect pigments. *11th Int. Congr. Ent.*, Vienna 1960, vol. 3: 21–43 *[42]*.

THOMPSON, V. 1937. Effects of temperature on movements of embryos (Acrididae, Orthoptera). *Physiol. Zöol.* **10**: 21–30, 8 figs. *[246]*.

—— 1938. Action of electrolytes on lateral body wall movements of grasshopper embryos (Acrididae, Orthoptera). *J. exp. Zool.* **78**: 19–46, 16 figs. *[246]*.

THOMPSON, V. & BODINE, J. H. 1936. Oxygen consumption and rates of dehydration of grasshopper eggs (Orthoptera). *Physiol. Zöol.* **9**: 455–70, 10 figs. *[268]*.

——1938. Phosphorus distribution in the grasshopper embryo. *J. cell. comp. Physiol.* **12**: 247–54, 4 figs. *[251]*.

TIEGS, O. W. 1955. The flight muscles of insects—their anatomy and histology; with some observations on the structure of striated muscle in general. *Phil. Trans.* B, **238**: 221–348, 16 pls., 17 figs. *[59, 62]*.

TIETZ, A. 1961. Fat synthesis in cell-free preparations of the locust fat-body. *J. Lipid Res.* **2**: 182–7 1 fig. *[102, 103]*.

TIETZ, H. M. 1923. The anatomy of the digestive system of the Carolina locust (*D. carolina*, Linn.). *Ann. ent. Soc. Amer.* **16**: 256–68, 5 pls. *[118]*.

TIMON-DAVID, J. 1930. Recherches sur les matières grasses des insectes. *Ann. Fac. Sci. Marseille*, (2) **4**: 29–207, 4 pls. *[101]*.

—— 1947. Pigments des insectes. *Année biol.* **23**: 238–71 *[42]*.

TINKHAM, E. R. 1940. Taxonomic and biological studies on the Cyrtacanthacrinae of South China. *Lingnan Sci. J.* **19**: 269–382, 6 pls. *[286]*.

—— 1948. Faunistic and ecological studies on the Orthoptera of the Big Bend Region of Trans-Pecos Texas, with especial reference to the Orthopteran zones and faunae of Midwestern North America. *Amer. Midl. Nat.* **40**: 521–663, 36 figs. *[22]*.

TOBIAS, J. M. 1948. The high potassium and low sodium in the body fluid and tissues of a phytophagous insect, the silkworm *Bombyx mori* and the change before pupation. *J. cell. comp. Physiol.* **31**: 143–8 *[110]*.

TORTAJADA, J. M. 1960. Sobre la estructura del cerebro en los acrídidos. *Trab. Inst. Cajal Invest. biol.* **52**: 131–47 *[151]*.

TREHERNE, J. E. 1958a. The absorption of glucose from the alimentary canal of the locust *Schistocerca gregaria* (Forsk.). *J. exp. Biol.* **35**: 297–306, 6 figs. *[112]*.

—— 1958b. The absorption and metabolism of some sugars in the locust, *Schistocerca gregaria* (Forsk.). *J. exp. Biol.* **35**: 611–25, 7 figs. *[112]*.

—— 1959. Amino-acid absorption in the locust (*Schistocerca gregaria* Forsk.). *J. exp. Biol.* **36**: 533–45, 8 figs. *[112]*.

—— 1961. Sodium and potassium fluxes in the abdominal nerve cord of the cockroach, *Periplaneta americana* L. *J. exp. Biol.* **38**: 315–22, 4 figs. *[155]*.

TREHERNE, R. C. & BUCKELL, E. R. 1924. Grasshoppers of British Columbia. *Bull. Dep. Agric. Can.* (N.S.), no. 39: 40 pp., 3 pls., 18 figs. *[371]*.

TREVITHICK, H. P. & LEWIS, R. R. 1939. Fat from locusts. *Oil & Soap*, **16**: 128 *[101]*.

TRIVELLONI, J. C. 1960. Biosynthesis of glucosides and glycogen in the locust. *Arch. Biochem. Biophys.* **89**: 149–50 *[102]*.

TROWBRIDGE, C. & BODINE, J. H. 1940. Nitrogen content and distribution in eggs of *Melanoplus differentialis* during embryonic development. *Biol. Bull., Woods Hole* **79**: 452–8, 5 figs. *[250]*.

TSUJIMOTO, M. 1929. Research on insect oils. I. Firefly, locust and cricket oils. *J. Soc. chem. Ind. Japan*, **32**: 49B–54B *[101]*.

TSVILENEVA, V. A. 1953. On the structure of the ventral brain of the Asiatic Locust. (In Russian.) *Izv. Otdel. estest. Nauk, Akad. Nauk Tadzhik. SSR*, no. 2: 49–55, 5 figs. *[154]*.

TUCK, J. B. & SMITH, R. C. 1940. Identification of the eggs of Mid-Western grasshoppers by the chorionic sculpturing. *Tech. Bull. Kans. agric. Exp. Sta.* no. 48 (1939): 39 pp., 11 pls. *[237, 240]*.

TÜMPEL, R. 1934. Bau und Wirkungsweise der Punktaugen bei *Acridium aegypticum* L. *Z. wiss. InsektBiol.* **10**: 275–82, 5 figs. *[205, 206]*.

UCHIYAMA, H. & KATSUKI, Y. 1956. Recording of action potentials from the antennal nerve of locusts by means of micro-electrodes. *Physiol. comp.* **4**: 154–63, 5 figs. *[169]*.

UICHANCO, L. B. & GINES, R. B. 1937. A biometrical study of the adult components of Philippine locust swarms. *Philipp. Agric.* **26**: 237–89, 10 figs. *[373]*.

UNITED STATES, 1878. *First Annual Report of the United States Entomological Commission for the year 1877 relating to the Rocky Mountain Locust and the best Methods of preventing its Injuries and of guarding against its Invasions, in Pursuance of an Appropriation made by Congress for this Purpose.* Washington *[94, 118]*.

USHATINSKAYA, R. S. 1957. *Principles of Cold Resistance in Insects.* (In Russian.) Moscow *[224]*.

UVAROV, B. P. 1921. A revision of the genus *Locusta*, L. (=*Pachytylus*, Fieb.), with a new theory as to the periodicity and migrations of locusts. *Bull. ent. Res.* **12**: 135–63, 8 figs. *[332, 343, 344, 373, 380]*.

—— 1922. Rice grasshoppers of the genus *Hieroglyphus* and their nearest allies. *Bull. ent. Res.* **13**: 225–41, 3 figs. *[30]*.

—— 1923a. Notes on locusts of economic importances, with some new data on the periodicity of locust invasion. *Bull. ent. Res.* **14**: 31–9, 1 fig. *[341, 380]*.

—— 1923b. Quelques problèmes de la biologie des sauterelles. *Ann. Épiphyt.* **9**: 84–108 *[361, 380]*.

461

BIBLIOGRAPHY

UVAROV, B. P. 1928. *Locusts and Grasshoppers. A Handbook for their Study and Control.* London [*1, 238, 270, 316, 323, 357, 361, 380, 383*].
—— 1929. Contributions to a knowledge of the fauna of South West Africa. VIII. Records and descriptions of Acrididae from S.W. Africa. *Ann. S. Afr. Mus.* **29**: 41–75, 2 pls., 12 figs. [*8*].
—— 1931. Insects and climate. *Trans. ent. Soc. Lond.* **79**: 1–247, 53 figs. [*224, 252*].
—— 1932. A revision of the genus *Brachycrotaphus* Kraus. *Soc. ent. Fr.*, Livre Cent: 285–300, 8 figs. [*177*].
—— 1933. Preliminary experiments on the annual cycle of the Red Locust (*Nomadacris septemfasciata*, Serv.). *Bull. ent. Res.* **24**: 419–20 [*309*].
—— 1934. Fundamental research on the locust problem. *3rd Int. Locust Conf.*, London 1934, pp. 93–6 [*361*].
—— 1936. The Oriental Migratory Locust (*Locusta migratoria manilensis*, Meyen 1835). *Bull. ent. Res.* **27**: 91–104, 2 figs. [*372, 373*].
—— 1937. Biological and ecological basis of locust phases and their practical application. *4th Int. Locust Conf.*, Cairo 1936, Appendix 7: 16 pp. [*361*].
—— 1943. The tribe Thrinchini of the subfamily Pamphaginae, and the interrelations of the acridid subfamilies (Orthoptera). *Trans. R. ent. Soc. Lond.* **93**: 1–72, 73 figs. [*21, 182*].
—— 1948. Recent advances in acridology: anatomy and physiology of Acrididae. *Anti-Locust Bull.* no. 1: 75 pp., 21 figs. [*42, 78, 147, 164, 207, 228*].
—— 1953. Grasshoppers (Orthoptera, Acrididae) of Angola and Northern Rhodesia, collected by Dr. Malcolm Burr in 1927–1928. *Publ. cult. Cia Diamant. Angola*, no. 21: 9–217, 295 figs. [*371*].
—— 1957. The aridity factor in the ecology of locust and grasshoppers of the Old World. In *Arid Zone Research: VIII Human and Animal Ecology, Reviews of Research*, pp. 164–98. Paris [*381*].
—— 1961. Quantity and quality in insect populations. *Proc. R. ent. Soc. Lond.* C, **25**: 52–9 [*379, 380, 386*].
UVAROV, B. P. & HAMILTON, A. G. 1936. Phase variation and rate of development in the Algerian race of the Migratory Locust (*Locusta migratoria* L.). *Bull. ent. Res.* **27**: 87–90 [*372, 373*].
UVAROV, B. P. & THOMAS, J. G. 1942. The probable mechanism of phase variation in the pronotum of locusts. *Proc. R. ent. Soc. Lond.* A, **17**: 113–18, 4 figs. [*382*].
UVAROV, B. P. & ZOLOTAREVSKY, B. N. 1929. Phases of locusts and their interrelations. *Bull. ent. Res.* **20**: 261–5 [*380, 384*].
UVAROV, E. B. 1931. The ash content of insects. *Bull. ent. Res.* **22**: 453–7 [*94*].
VARDÉ, V. P. 1929. Contribution à l'étude morphologique et éthologique des Orthoptères Acrididae. *Bull. Soc. zool. Fr.* **54**: 477–83, 4 figs. [*148*].
—— 1934. The protrusible vesicles in Cyrtacanthacrinae–Acridinae (Orthoptera). *J. Univ. Bombay* (Biol. Sci.), **2**: 53–7, 5 figs. [*148*].
VARLEY, G. C. 1939. Unusual methods of stridulation in a cicada (*Clidophleps distanti* (Van D.)) and a grasshopper (*Oedaleonotus fuscipes* Scud.) in California. *Proc. R. ent. Soc. Lond.* A, **14**: 97–100, 2 figs. [*184*].
VASIL'EV, K. A. 1950. Phases in the Italian Locust (*Calliptamus italicus* L.). (In Russian.) *Dokl. Akad. Nauk SSSR*, **74**: 639–42 [*371*].
VEL'TISCHEV, P. A. 1941. New data on bio-ecology of the Asiatic Locust in the Amu-Darya delta. (In Russian.) *Priroda*, **1941**: 78–81 [*305*].
VERDIER, M. 1960. Sur la transmission du caractère diapause dans une race du criquet migrateur. *11th Int. Congr. Ent.*, Vienna 1960, vol. 1: 644–7, 2 figs. [*320*].
—— 1962. Rôle annexe de la densité sur la transmission de la diapause embryonnaire chez *Locusta migratoria* 'de Palavas'. *Colloq. int. Cent. nat. Rech. sci.* no. 114: 63–72, 1 fig. [*262*].
VIADO, G. B. 1950. Reproductive capacity of the Oriental Migratory Locust. *Philipp. Agric.* **33**: 221–38, 2 pls., 1 fig. [*354*].
VIALLANES, H. 1887. Études histologiques et organologiques sur les centres nerveux et les organes des sens des animaux articulés. *Ann. Sci. nat.* (Zool.), (7) **4**: 1–120, 6 pls., 2 figs. [*151*].
VINAL, S. C. 1919. The respiratory system of the Carolina locust (*Dissosteira carolina* Linne). *J. N.Y. ent. Soc.* **27**: 19–32, 3 pls. [*124*].
VINOGRADOV, A. & NEUSTRUEVA, M. 1930. Le manganèse dans les insectes. II. (In Russian.) *C. R. Acad. Sci. URSS*, **1930**: 127–32 [*94, 95*].
VINOKUROV, G. M. 1916. Biological observations on the Migratory Locust. (In Russian.) In Uvarov, B. P. [Ed.], *Rapport sur les travaux de Bureau Entomologique de Stavropol au Caucase pour l'année 1914*, pp. 84–101, 2 figs. Petrograd [*299*].
VISART, O. 1894. Contribuzione allo studio del tubo digerente degli Artropodi. Ricerche istologiche e fisiologiche sul tubo digerente degli Ortotteri. *Mem. Soc. tosc. Sci. nat.* **13**: 20–54, 34 figs. [*73*].
VOGELL, W., BISHAI, F. R., BÜCHER, T., KLINGENBERG, M., PETTE, D. & ZEBE, E. 1959. Über strukturelle und enzymatische Muster in Muskeln von *Locusta migratoria*. *Biochem. Z.* **332**: 81–117, 13 figs. [*59, 68*].
VOLKONSKY, M. A. 1937. Elevage et croissance larvaire du criquet égyptien (*Anacridium aegyptium* L.). *C. R. Soc. Biol.*, Paris, **125**: 739–42, 1 fig. [*255, 287, 310, 337*].
—— 1938a. Une mutation mélanique de *Schistocerca gregaria* Forsk. obtenue en élevage. *C. R. Soc. Biol.*, Paris, **127**: 254–6 [*46*].

462

BIBLIOGRAPHY

VOLKONSKY, M. A. 1938b. Possibilité de changement de phase à l'état imaginal chez le criquet pélerin (*Schistocerca gregaria* Forsk.). *C. R. Soc. Biol., Paris*, **127**: 583–5 [*362*].

—— 1938c. Stries oculaires et ages larvaires chez les acridiens. *Arch. Inst. Pasteur Algér.* **16**: 523–532, 1 fig. [*198, 287*].

—— 1939. Sur la photo-akinèse des acridiens. *Arch. Inst. Pasteur Algér.* **17**: 194–220, 1 pl., 1 fig. [*207, 211, 213*].

—— 1942. Observations sur le comportement du criquet pèlerin (*Schistocerca gregaria* Forsk.) dans le Sahara algéro-nigérien. *Arch. Inst. Pasteur Algér.* **20**: 236–48, 1 map, 1 fig. [*361*].

VOLKONSKY, M. T. 1943. Rearing locusts in captivity. *Bull. ent. Res.* **34**: 253–6 [*255, 351*].

VORONTZOVSKIĬ, P. A. 1928. On the question of homologous series of colour variation in Acrididae. (In Russian.) *Izv. orenburg. Stants. Zashch. Rast.* **1**: 27–39 [*39*].

VOSKRESENSKAYA, A. K. 1936. Poison penetration through the intestine wall of insects. (In Russian with English summary.) *Bull. Pl. Prot., Leningr.* (3) no. 7: 25–39, 8 figs. [*75, 76*].

—— 1947. Functional peculiarities of the neuro-muscular apparatus of wings in the insects. (In Russian.) *Sechenov J. Physiol.* **33**: 381–92, 13 figs. [*65*].

—— 1950. On the 'sympathetic' innervation of the skeleton muscles in insects. (In Russian.) *Sechenov J. Physiol.* **36**: 176–83, 6 figs. [*65, 154*].

—— 1959. *Functional Properties of the Neuro-Muscular Apparatus of Insects.* (In Russian.) Moscow & Leningrad [*65, 154*].

VOSSELER, J. 1902. Beiträge zur Faunistik und Biologie der Orthopteren Algeriens und Tunesiens. *Zool. Jb.* (Syst.), **16**: 337–404, 2 pls., 8 figs. [*35*].

—— 1905. Die Wanderheuschrecken in Usambara im Jahre 1903/1904, zugleich ein Beitrag zu ihrer Biologie. *Ber. Land.- u. Forstw. D.-Ostafr.* **2**: 291–374, 2 pls., 2 figs. [*270, 273, 297, 323, 324*].

VOY, A. 1949. Contribution à l'étude anatomique et histologique des organes accessoires de l'appareil génital femelle chez quelques espèces d'orthoptéroïdes. *Ann. Sci. nat.* (Zool.), (11) **11**: 269–345, 2 pls., 71 figs. [*144, 147*].

VUILLAUME, M. 1953. Biologie et comportement, en A.O.F., de *Zonocerus variegatus* avec essais de comparaison entre Acridiens grands et petits migrateurs. *Thès. Fac. Sci. Univ. Paris*, sér. A, no. 2756: 78 pp., 5 photos, 27 figs. [*370*].

—— 1954. Étude de quelques tropismes chez les *Zonocerus variegatus*. *Fruits d'outre mer*, **9**: 242–9, 5 figs. [*204*].

—— 1955. Effet de groupe chez le *Zonocerus variegatus* (Acrid., Pyrgomorphinae). *Vie et Milieu*, **6**: 161–93, 7 figs. [*97*].

WAKELAND, C. 1958. The High Plains grasshopper. A compilation of facts about its occurrence and control. *Tech. Bull. U.S. Dep. Agric.* no. 1167: 168 pp., 29 figs. [*287, 371*].

WALKER, J. F. 1935. Effect of CO_2 on the beat of the lateral body walls of the grasshopper embryo. *J. cell. comp. Physiol.* **6**: 317–34, 10 figs. [*246*].

WALLACE, G. K. 1958. Some experiments on form perception in the nymphs of the Desert Locust, *Schistocerca gregaria* Forskål. *J. exp. Biol.* **35**: 765–75, 1 fig. [*202, 203*].

—— 1959. Visual scanning in the Desert Locust *Schistocerca gregaria* Forskål. *J. exp. Biol.* **36**: 512–25, 4 figs. [*202, 203*].

WALLING, E. V. 1906. The influences of gases and temperature on the cardiac and respiratory movements in the grasshopper. *J. exp. Zool.* **3**: 621–9 [*108*].

WALOFF, N. 1954. The number and development of ovarioles of some Acridoidea (Orthoptera) in relation to climate. *Physiol. comp.* **3**: 370–90, 2 figs. [*144, 146*].

WALOFF, Z. V. 1940. The distribution and migrations of *Locusta* in Europe. *Bull. ent. Res.* **31**: 211–246, 4 figs. [*370, 372, 373*].

—— 1958. The behaviour of locusts in migrating swarms. (Abs.) *10th Int. Congr. Ent.*, Montreal 1956, vol. 2: 567–9, 1 fig. [*381*].

—— 1960. The fluctuating distributions of the Desert Locust in relation to the strategy of control. *Rep. Commonw. ent. Conf.* **7**: 132–40, 4 figs. [*374*].

—— 1961. Fat content changes in migrating Desert Locusts (*Schistocerca gregaria* Forsk.). (Abs.) *11th Int. Congr. Ent.*, Vienna 1960, vol. 1: 735 [*100*].

—— 1962. Flight activity of different phases of the Desert Locust in relation to plague dynamics. *Colloq. int. Cent. nat. Rech. sci.* no. 114: 201–16 [*381*].

—— 1963. Field studies on solitary and *transiens* Desert Locusts in the Red Sea area. *Anti-Locust Bull.* no. 40: 93 pp., 28 figs. [*215, 220*].

WATERSTON, A. R. 1951. Observations on adult locusts [*Dociostaurus maroccanus*, Cyprus, 1950]. *Anti-Locust Bull.* no. 10: 36–52 [*299, 321*].

WATTS, D. T. 1952. Intratracheal pressure in insect respiration. *Ann. ent. Soc. Amer.* **44** (1951): 527–38, 5 figs. [*128, 129, 130*].

WEBLEY, D. P. 1951. Blood-cell counts in the African Migratory Locust (*Locusta migratoria migratorioides* Reiche & Fairmaire). *Proc. R. ent. Soc. Lond.* A, **26**: 25–37, 6 figs. [*115, 116, 282*].

WEED PFEIFFER, I. 1939. Experimental study of the function of the corpora allata in the grasshopper, *Melanoplus differentialis*. *J. exp. Zool.* **82**: 439–61, 1 fig. [*312*].

—— 1945a. The influence of the corpora allata over the development of nymphal characters in the grasshopper *Melanoplus differentialis*. *Trans. Conn. Acad. Arts Sci.* **36**: 489–513, 1 pl. [*58*].

—— 1945b. Effect of the corpora allata on the metabolism of adult female grasshoppers. *J. exp. Zool.* **99**: 183–233, 6 figs. [*96, 97, 99, 103, 226, 312*].

WEIH, A. S. 1951. Untersuchungen über das Wechselsingen (Anaphonie) und über das angeborene Lautschema einiger Feldheuschrecken. *Z. Tierpsychol.* **8**: 1–41, 5 figs. [*184*].

WEIR, J. S. 1957. Preliminary investigation of thermoreception on the thin regions of the cuticle of *Locusta migratoria migratorioides*. Report to Anti-Locust Research Centre, London. Typescript. [Unpublished.] [*220*].

WEIS-FOGH, T. 1952. Fat combustion and metabolic rate of flying locusts (*Schistocerca gregaria* Forskål). *Phil. Trans.* B, **237**: 1–36, 12 figs. [*3, 68, 96, 99, 102, 134, 215, 302*].

—— 1956a. The flight of locusts. *Sci. Amer.* **194**: 116–20, 122–4, 11 figs. [*65, 217*].

—— 1956b. Biology and physics of locust flight. II. Flight performance of the Desert Locust (*Schistocerca gregaria*). *Phil. Trans.* B, **239**: 459–510, 1 pl., 26 figs. [*217*].

—— 1956c. Biology and physics of locust flight. IV. Notes on sensory mechanisms in locust flight. *Phil. Trans.* B, **239**: 553–84, 10 figs. [*162, 163*].

—— 1956d. Tetanic force and shortening in locust flight muscle. *J. exp. Biol.* **33**: 668–84, 7 figs. [*66*].

—— 1956e. The ventilatory mechanism during flight of insects in relation to the call for oxygen. *14th Int. Congr. Zool.*, Copenhagen 1953: 283–5 [*128, 130, 131*].

—— 1959. Elasticity in arthropod locomotion: a neglected subject, illustrated by the wing system of insects. (Abs.) *15th Int. Congr. Zool.*, London 1958: 393–5 [*67*].

—— 1960. A rubber-like protein in insect cuticle. *J. exp. Biol.* **37**: 889–907, 1 pl., 6 figs. [*35, 67*].

WEISS, H. B. 1944. Insect responses to colors. *J. N.Y. ent. Soc.* **52**: 267–71 [*199*].

WERMAN, R., MCCANN, F. V. & GRUNDFEST, H. 1961. Graded and all-or-none electrogenesis in arthropod muscle. I. The effects of alkali-earth cations on the neuromuscular system of *Romalea microptera. J. gen. Physiol.* **44**: 979–95, 14 figs. [*66*].

WEVER, E. G. 1935. A study of hearing in the sulfur-winged grasshopper (*Arphia sulphurea*). *J. comp. Psychol.* **20**: 17–20, 1 fig. [*191*].

WEVER, E. G. & VERNON, J. A. 1957. The auditory sensitivity of the Atlantic grasshopper. *Proc. nat. Acad. Sci., Wash.* **43**: 346–8, 1 fig. [*191*].

—— 1959. The auditory sensitivity of Orthoptera. *Proc. nat. Acad. Sci.. Wash.* **45**: 413–19, 5 figs. [*191*].

WHITE, M. J. D. 1935. The effects of X-rays on mitosis in the spermatogonial divisions of *Locusta migratoria* L. *Proc. roy. Soc.* B, **119**: 61–84, 26 figs. [*304*].

—— 1951a. Cytogenetics of orthopteroid insects. *Advanc. Genet.* **4**: 267–330, 6 figs. [*304, 389, 390*].

—— 1951b. A cytological survey of wild populations of *Trimerotropis* and *Circotettix* (Orthoptera, Acrididae). II. Racial differentiation in *T. sparsa. Genetics*, **36**: 31–53, 6 figs. [*390*].

—— 1954. *Animal Cytology and Evolution.* London [*304, 389, 390*].

—— 1955. Patterns of spermatogenesis in grasshoppers. *Aust. J. Zool.* **3**: 222–6 [*304*].

—— 1957. Cytogenetics and systematic entomology. *Annu. Rev. Ent.* **2**: 71–90 [*389, 390*].

WHITE, M. J. D. & KEY, K. H. L. 1957. A cytotaxonomic study of the *pusilla* group of species in the genus *Austroicetes* Uv. (Orthoptera: Acrididae). *Aust. J. Zool.* **5**: 56–87, 1 map, 7 figs. [*39*].

WHITTINGTON, B. 1951. The sense organs and nervous system of *Schistocerca gregaria* and *Locusta migratoria migratorioides*. Report on present state of work. [Unpublished.] [*200, 201*].

WIESEND, P. 1957. Die postembryonale Entwicklung der Thoraxmuskulatur bei einigen Feldheuschrecken mit besonderer Berücksichtigung der Flugmuskeln. *Z. Morph. Ökol. Tiere*, **46**: 529–70, 19 figs. [*30, 31, 62, 271, 276*].

WIGGLESWORTH, V. B. 1948. The insect cuticle. *Biol. Rev.* **23**: 408–51, 1 fig. [*32*].

—— 1949. Insect biochemistry. *Annu. Rev. Biochem.* **18**: 595–614 [*42*].

—— 1953. *The Principles of Insect Physiology.* London [*106, 130, 135, 200*].

—— 1954. *The Physiology of Insect Metamorphosis.* London [*289*].

—— 1957. The physiology of insect cuticle. *Annu. Rev. Ent.* **2**: 37–54 [*32*].

WIGGLESWORTH, V. B. & BEAMENT, J. W. L. 1950. The respiratory mechanisms of some insect eggs. *Quart. J. micr. Sci.* **91**: 429–52, 1 pl., 7 figs. [*243, 247*].

WILDE, J. DE & STAAL, G. B. 1955. Kleuraanpassingsvermogen bij Sprinkhanen (Orth.). *Ent. Ber., Amst.* **15**: 497–8 [*53*].

WILLIAMS, C. M. 1956. Physiology of insect diapause. X. An endocrine mechanism for the influence of temperature on the diapausing pupa of the *Cecropia* silkworm. *Biol. Bull., Woods Hole*, **110**: 201–18, 5 figs. [*264*].

—— 1958. Hormonal regulation of insect metamorphosis. In McElroy, W. D. & Glass, B. [Eds.], *A Symposium on the Chemical Basis of Development*, pp. 794–806. Baltimore [*160, 289*].

WILLIAMS, L. H. 1954. The feeding habits and food preferences of Acrididae and the factors which determine them. *Trans. R. ent. Soc. Lond.* **105**: 423–54, 25 figs. [*70, 203*].

WILLIAMS, M. E. 1936. Catalase activity during embryonic development (Acrididae, Orthoptera). *Physiol. Zoöl.* **9**: 231–7, 3 figs. [*251*].

WILSON, C. C. & KEIFER, H. H. 1941. A study of the marginate grasshopper, with notes on associ-ated congeneric species. *Bull. Dep. Agric. Calif.* **30**: 291–311, 5 pls., 2 figs. [*282, 287*].

WILSON, D. M. 1961. The central nervous control of flight in a locust. *J. exp. Biol.* **38**: 471–90, 8 figs. [*166*].

—— 1962. Bifunctional muscles in the thorax of grasshoppers. *J. exp. Biol.* **39**: 669–77, 12 figs. [*30, 62, 63, 65*].

BIBLIOGRAPHY

WILSON, D. M. 1964. Relative refractoriness and patterned discharge of locust flight motor neurones. *J. exp.Biol.* **41**: 191–205, 11 figs. [*65*].

WILSON, D. M. & WEIS-FOGH, T. 1962. Patterned activity of co-ordinated motor units, studied in flying locusts. *J. exp. Biol.* **39**: 643–67, 1 pl., 24 figs. [*62, 65*].

WOOD, D. W. 1963. The sodium and potassium composition of some insect skeletal muscle fibres in relation to their membrane potentials. *Comp. Biochem. Physiol.* **9**: 151–9, 1 fig. [*66, 68*].

WOODROW, D. F. 1963. *Egg laying behaviour in locusts*. Ph.D. thesis, London [*324*].

WOODRUFF, B. H. 1933. Studies of the epithelium lining the caeca and mid-gut in the grasshopper. *J. Morph.* **55**: 53–79, 2 pls. [*72, 74*].

WULFF, V. J., FRY, W. J. & LINDE, F. A. 1955. Retinal action potential-theory and experimental results for grasshopper eyes. *J. cell. comp. Physiol.* **45**: 247–63, 3 figs. [*199*].

WULFF, V. J. & JAHN, T. L. 1947. The electroretinogram of *Cynomya. J. N.Y. ent. Soc.* **55**: 65–83, 3 figs. [*199*].

—— 1948. Retinal-nerve interval in the grasshopper. *J. Neurophysiol.* **11**: 117–23, 2 figs. [*199*].

YAKHIMOVICH, L. A. 1952. *Development of Eggs and Maturation of the Asiatic Locust in Relation to the Conditions of its Existence*. (In Russian.) Leningrad [*255, 305*].

YOSHIMEKI, M. 1952. On the dimensional characters of the rice hoppers, *Oxya japonica* Willemse and *Oxya velox* Fabricius. (In Japanese with English summary.) *Ecol. Rev., Sendai*, **13**: 87–94, 17 figs. [*391*].

ZACWILICHOWSKI, J. 1934. Über die Innervierung und die Sinnesorgane der Flügel der Feld-heuschrecke *Stauroderus biguttulus* (L.). *Bull. int. Acad. Cracovie* B, **1934**: 187–96, 1 pl. [*27, 165*].

ZAMBIN, I. M. 1939. The theoretical basis of the distribution of harmful insects and of predictions as to their mass multiplication. VI. The resistance to cold of the eggs of the Migratory Locust (*Locusta migratoria* L.). (In Russian with English summary.) *Pl. Prot., Leningr.* no. 19: 45–55, 2 figs. [*249, 250, 265, 266, 267*].

ZEBE, E. 1958. Studies on glycolytic enzymes in insect muscle. *10th Int. Congr. Ent.*, Montreal 1956, vol. 2: 371–6, 2 figs. [*68, 99*].

—— 1960. Die Verteilung von Enzymen des Fettstoffwechsels im Heuschreckenkörper. *Zool. Anz.* (Suppl.), no. 23: 309–14, 3 figs. [*99, 103*].

—— 1962. Zur stoffwechselphysiologischen Funktion der verschiedenen Organe des Insekten-körpers. *Zool. Anz.* (Suppl.), no. 25: 344–50 [*103*].

ZEBE, E. C. & MCSHAN, W. H. 1957. Lactic and α-glycerophosphate dehydrogenases in insects. *J. gen. Physiol.* **40**: 779–90, 2 figs. [*68, 102*].

ZIEGLER-GÜNDER, I. 1956. Pterine: Pigmente und Wirkstoffe im Tierreich. *Biol. Rev.* **31**: 313–48, 1 pl., 6 figs. [*51*].

ZIMIN, L. S. 1934. On the biology and ecology of *Calliptamus turanicus* Tarb. in Central Asia. (In Russian.) In Lepeshkin, S.N. *et al.*, *Acrididae of Central Asia*, pp. 82–112. Tashkent [*371*].

—— 1938. Les pontes des acridiens. Morphologie, classification et écologie. (In Russian.) *Tabl. anal. Faune URSS*, no. 23: 83 pp., 10 pls., 6 figs. [*240, 241, 326*].

ZNOIKO, D. 1928. Zur Systematik der Acrididen der Steppenzone des europäischen Russlands, nebst einer kurzen Uebersicht der russischen *Omocestus* und *Myrmeleotettix*-Arten (Orthop-tera, Acridodea). (In Russian.) *Rev. russe Ent.* **22**: 185–201, 2 pls., 13 figs. [*143*].

ZOLESSI, L. C. DE 1958. *Bioecologia y Ontogenesis de* Scotussa cliens (Stål) *Lieb.* (*Acridoidea, Catantopidae*) *en el Uruguay*. Montevideo [*276, 282, 287*].

ZOLOTAREVSKY, B. N. 1929. Sur le comportement de *Locusta migratoria* L. subsp. *migratorioides* Rch. et Frm. phasis *transiens. C. R. Acad. Sci., Paris*, **189**: 131–3 [*380, 384*].

—— 1930. Le criquet migrateur (*Locusta migratoria capito* Sauss.) à Madagascar. *Ann. Épiphyt.* **15** (1929): 185–236, 1 map, 2 pls., 8 figs. [*373, 380, 385*].

—— 1933. Contribution à l'étude biologique du criquet migrateur (*Locusta migratoria capito* Sauss.) dans ses foyers permanents. *Ann. Épiphyt.* **19**: 47–142, 1 map, 1 pl., 13 figs. [*380, 381, 385*].

SUBJECT INDEX

Abdomen, 1, 17–22, 146, 153, 323-5
  air-sacs, 126–8
  hairs, 38
  heat sensitivity, 34, 220
  muscles, 63–64
  nerves and ganglia, 152–5
  oviposition, 322–5
  respiratory movements, 128–30
  sensilla, 326
  sound production, 181, 184
  spiracles, 1, 22, 124–7
  stretch receptors, 170
  tracheae, 126–7
  trichoid sensilla, 195
Accessory glands
  female, 146, 148, 325
  male, 140, 317
Acridioxanthin; see Ommochrome
Actomysin, 68
Adult development
  colour, 44, 45, 48, 295–300, 311, 335
  cuticle growth, 92, 98, 276, 295–6, 302
  weight, 83, 98, 300–3
Adult maturation; see also Ovary, Ovogenesis, Spermatogenesis
  colour changes, 44, 45, 48, 295–300, 311, 335
  diapause, 308–11
  effects of
    activity, 313
    food, 308
    grouping, 298, 311
    humidity, 306–8
    photoperiod, 308–11
    temperature, 307–8
  fat, 96–8, 101, 304, 313
  protein, 112
  rate, 307–310, 352
  weight changes, 226, 300–3
Adult phases; see Phase–adult
Aedeagus; see Penis
Aerodynamic organ, 153, 162
Aggregation; see Phase, hoppers and adults
Air-sacs, 126–8, 130, 164, 284, 324
  taxonomic value, 126, 392
Albinism, 43, 46, 295, 318, 336
Alimentary system, 70–3; see also Digestion; Food
  embryonic development, 246
  functions, 73–82
  hoppers, 282
Amoebocyte, see Haemocyte
Amphion, 32
Anatrepsis; see Embryo
Antenna, 9, 10
  ampulla, 10, 106, 107
  crescents, 33, 34
  growth, 276
  Johnston's organ, 168
  muscles, 9, 60

Antenna—cont.
  nerves, 9, 168
  scoloparia, 168–70
  segment number, 9–10, 276
  sensilla, 164, 165, 168–70, 173, 174, 220
  taxonomic value, 9–10, 388
Aorta, 105, 152, 157
Apical cell, 303–4
Apterism, 29
  muscles, 30
  ocelli, 206
  tympanum, 190
Arolium, 23–25
  sensilla, 164
Ascorbic acid, 43, 86, 334
Astaxanthin, 47, 48, 199
Auditory sense, 163, 188–95; see also Sound

Basement membrane, 32, 37, 57, 119, 285
Basiconic sensillum, 162, 171–4
Bile pigments, 50, 335, 376
Blastokinesis, 244
Blood; see Haemolymph
Blood cells; see Haemocytes
Body, 1–4
  shape, 1, 2
  size, 2
  surface area, 2, 3
  temperature; see Temperature, internal
  volume, 3
  weight, 3
Brachypterism, 29, 84, 289
  muscles, 30
Brain, 151–8, 198
  neurosecretory cells, 157, 290, 311, 314
Bristle; see Trichoid sensillum
Brunner's organ, 166
Brustia, 18, 163
Buccal cavity; see Preoral cavity

Campaniform sensillum, 20, 27, 165, 166, 168, 172, 173
Carbohydrates; see also Chitin, Glycogen, Sugar
  content, 90, 93
  egg, 249, 266, 267
  excreta, 121
  haemolymph, 112, 113
  nutrition, 86
Carbon, 93
Cardiac valve, 70, 71
Carotene and Carotenoids, 43, 47–50, 86, 199, 251, 306, 335–6
  eggs, 251
  phases, 48, 336 376
Cercus, 18–20
  development, 282, 297
  muscles, 64, 297
  sensilla, 163, 165, 194–5, 318
  taxonomic value, 388

TAXONOMIC INDEX

Six of the insects which are frequently referred to in the text under their generic names only are similarly listed in the index; they are *Anacridium aegyptium*, *Dociostaurus maroccanus*, *Locusta migratoria migratorioides*, *Melanoplus differentialis*, *Nomadacris septemfasciata* and *Schistocerca gregaria*.

The names in parentheses are synonyms and the corresponding full valid names will be found in the lists on pp. 397–420.